The Lesson of the Masters

The Lesson of the Masters

AN ANTHOLOGY OF
THE NOVEL FROM CERVANTES
TO HEMINGWAY

Texts with Commentaries by
MALCOLM COWLEY
and HOWARD E. HUGO

CHARLES SCRIBNER'S SONS
New York

PRINTED IN THE UNITED STATES OF AMERICA
Library of Congress Catalog Card Number 74-123859

ACKNOWLEDGMENTS

On this and the following pages, which constitute an extension of the copyright page,
acknowledgment is gratefully made to the following publishers, agents and individuals
who have permitted the use of their materials in copyright:

Bantam Books, Inc., for a selection from *Dangerous Liaisons* by Choderlos de Laclos,
translated by Lowell Bair, copyright © 1962 by Bantam Books, Inc., all rights reserved.
For a selection from *Eugénie Grandet* by Honoré de Balzac, translated by Lowell Bair,
copyright © 1959 by Bantam Books, Inc., all rights reserved. For a selection from
Fathers and Sons by Ivan Turgenev, translated by Barbara Makanowitzky, copyright ©
1959 by Bantam Books, Inc., all rights reserved.

Chatto and Windus Ltd. and George Scott Moncrieff for a selection from *The Guermantes
Way (Remembrance of Things Past)* by Marcel Proust, translated by C. K. Scott
Moncrieff.

Harcourt, Brace & World, Inc., for a selection from *Mrs. Dalloway* by Virginia Woolf,
copyright 1925 by Harcourt, Brace & World, Inc., and renewed 1953 by Leonard Woolf,
reprinted by permission of the publishers.

Harper & Row, Publishers, Inc., for a selection from *Jude the Obscure* by Thomas Hardy.

Holt, Rinehart and Winston, Inc., for a selection from *The Sorrows of Young Werther*
by Johann Wolfgang von Goethe, translated by Victor Lange, Rinehart Edition, translation copyright 1949 by Victor Lange, reprinted by permission of the publishers.

Alfred A. Knopf, Inc., for a selection from *Tonio Kröger* from *Stories of Three Decades* by
Thomas Mann, copyright 1936 and renewed 1964 by Alfred A. Knopf, Inc., reprinted
by permission.

Macmillan & Co. Ltd., the Macmillan Company of Canada Ltd. and the Trustees of the Hardy Estate for a selection from *Jude the Obscure* by Thomas Hardy.

The New American Library, Inc., for a selection from *The Red and the Black* by Stendhal, translated by Lloyd C. Parks, copyright © 1970 by Lloyd C. Parks, reprinted by arrangement with The New American Library, Inc., New York. For a selection from *War and Peace* by Leo Tolstoy, translated by Ann Dunnigan, copyright © 1968 by Ann Dunnigan, reprinted by permission of the publishers.

Penguin Books Ltd. for a selection from *The Brothers Karamazov* by Fyodor Mikhailovich Dostoevsky, translated by David Magarshack. For a selection from *Don Quixote* by Miguel de Cervantes Saavedra, translated by J. M. Cohen. For a selection from *Germinal* by Emile Zola, translated by L. W. Tancock.

Random House, Inc., for a selection from *The Guermantes Way* (*Remembrance of Things Past*) by Marcel Proust, translated by C. K. Scott Moncrieff, copyright 1925 and renewed 1953 by Random House, Inc., reprinted by permission. For a selection from *Madame Bovary* by Gustave Flaubert, translated by Francis Steegmuller, copyright © 1957 by Francis Steegmuller, reprinted by permission of Random House, Inc. For a selection from *The Sound and the Fury* by William Faulkner, copyright 1929 and renewed 1957 by William Faulkner, reprinted by permission of Random House, Inc.

Laurence Pollinger Ltd. and the Estate of the late Mrs. Frieda Lawrence for a selection from *Sons and Lovers* by D. H. Lawrence.

Charles Scribner's Sons for a selection from *For Whom the Bell Tolls*, pages 301-322, by Ernest Hemingway, copyright 1940 by Ernest Hemingway, renewal copyright © 1968 by Mary Hemingway.

The Society of Authors as the literary representative of the Estate of James Joyce for a selection from *A Portrait of the Artist as a Young Man* by James Joyce.

The Viking Press, Inc., for a selection from *A Portrait of the Artist as a Young Man* by James Joyce, copyright © 1916 by B. W. Huebsch, Inc., and renewed 1944 by Nora Joyce, copyright © 1964 by the Estate of James Joyce, all rights reserved, reprinted by permission of the publishers. For a selection from *Sons and Lovers* by D. H. Lawrence, copyright 1913 by Thomas Seltzer, Inc., all rights reserved, reprinted by permission of the publishers.

Leonard Woolf and The Hogarth Press Ltd. for a selection from *Mrs. Dalloway* by Virginia Woolf.

. . . *the Novel remains still, under the right persuasion,
the most independent, most elastic, most prodigious of
literary forms.*

Henry James, Preface to *The Ambassadors*

Contents

The Lesson of the Masters

Introduction

AN ANTHOLOGY OF THE NOVEL? AND IN ONE VOLUME? At first glance that appears to be an impossible undertaking. Any comprehensive anthology would require a whole collection of novels and would come to resemble the fiction shelves of a small college library. A single volume, on the other hand, would become a little treasury of extracts from novels and would be likely to display one or the other of two opposite faults. Either the extracts would be fragmentary and hence of interest chiefly as examples of fine writing, or else they would be stories "complete in themselves" and hence outside the proper structure of the novels from which they were taken—as if we had compiled an anthology of statues consisting only of brilliant flaws in the marble.

But wasn't there some way out of the dilemma?

We asked ourselves that question and found what I hope is a usable answer. If we gave a summary of each novel—"The Story"—readers could approach the selected passage with understanding of what has gone before and what will follow. The editors would be free to choose passages that were not episodic, but truly novelistic, being part of the author's larger scheme. Then, if we lengthened the explanatory text— if we furnished a headnote about the career of each author and an afterword that discussed his methods and their relation to the development of fiction in general—each chapter might stand for the work under discussion. No, it would not be a substitute for reading the work; that was far from our intention. On the other hand, it would be a preparation for reading the work with heightened enjoyment—and for reading many other novels, too, including those not represented in our volume.

3

The book as a whole might serve in a modest way as a history of the novel, with examples, and a conspectus of the art of writing longer fictions.

We have spent eight years on the project, though at first with many interruptions and many problems to be solved. A first problem was choosing the novels to be represented. Here we made the early decision to aim at being useful rather than original. We had no wish to vie with archaeologists in unearthing buried masterpieces: the novels we wanted were those belonging to the visible corpus of Western culture. Moreover, we hoped to represent them adequately, and this decreased the number of novels to be included. We found room for twenty-seven, all, I think, in the mainstream of fiction. Our regret is for the books we had to omit, by authors as influential as Defoe, Richardson, Sterne, Eliot, Conrad, Gide, and Kafka. Perhaps a place can be found for some of these in a latter edition.

A second problem, or group of problems, was choosing a key passage from each novel. Here again the standard was usefulness rather than originality; the more widely remembered a passage was, the better it suited our modest purposes. Sometimes the choice was obvious, as in the case of *Pride and Prejudice*, of *Madame Bovary*, of *The Ambassadors*. Almost any reader would say, "Yes, the ball at Netherfield; yes, the agricultural show; yes, the Sunday afternoon in Gloriani's garden." Each of these scenes is close to the center of an author's vision. *The Brothers Karamazov* presented a more difficult problem, for here the remembered passage, the fable of the Grand Inquisitor, is not part of the story properly speaking. After arguing back and forth, we chose a shorter passage, the scene between Alyosha and little Lise. Though merely an episode that does not affect the main action, it perfectly reflects the author's method. The choice of passages became a fascinating game: what from *Eugénie Grandet*, what from *The Red and the Black*—it might be a seduction scene—and what from *Mrs. Dalloway*? In *Vanity Fair* there was an unavoidable passage, Becky Sharp's charade, but what should we choose from *Bleak House*? In this case we settled on the first chapter, since Dickens had a special gift for setting the tone of a long novel. In other cases as well, we inclined toward passages that perform an essential function in the plot: beginnings, confrontations, tableaus, climaxes, or endings.

With novels from foreign languages, there was the special problem of finding the best translation. Most of the European classics have been retranslated in recent years, largely under the auspices of Penguin Books, Bantam Books, and the New American Library, but there are several cases in which an older version has remained standard. Examples are C. K. Scott Moncrieff's *Remembrance of Things Past,* which is a monument of English prose not always distinguished by fidelity to the original, and Mrs. H. T. Lowe-Porter's almost complete translation of Thomas Mann, and Francis Steegmuller's *Madame Bovary*; from all of these we have gratefully drawn. Other formerly standard translations, notably those of Constance Garnett for most of the Russian classics, have been replaced by one or more later versions. Often but not always, the latest is the best, since the translator has profited from the mistakes of his predecessors. We have had to compare, and we have looked for the versions that speak most clearly to the contemporary reader.

The problem of editorial text was fairly simple until we came to the afterwords. The headnotes could be lives in brief—and what remarkable lives those masters led!—with some attention paid to their background in literature and society, to the audience that each of them addressed, and to their literary production as a whole. "The Story" should make it possible to read each selection without being puzzled. But after it was read, what should we offer by way of comment? Here once again we decided to follow our custom of preferring usefulness to originality. We tried to explain the function of the selected passage in the general scheme of the novel, the method followed by the novelist (with remarks on his style and his narrative point of view), and the relation of the book to the historical development of fiction. I hope we have said what was necessary. We have made our little discoveries, as who could fail to do in that inspired company?—but I hope that we have resisted the temptation of trying to come up with another "brilliantly original reading."

We have not carried our selections beyond 1940, chiefly because the present situation of the novel seems too confused for accurate choice. There are fashions in technique and subject matter—how many changing fashions!—but which of them will persist after twenty years? There are distinguished novelists in many countries, now including Japan, but there is none revered as Joyce was by his younger contemporaries (or Proust or Thomas Mann), and none whose work marks a direction that now seems certain to be widely followed. The present anthology is devoted to the relevant past of the novel: the given, the accepted, the traditions of the craft as novelists and readers alike should know them. Those traditions might lead to prophecies about the future of the novel. For example, they suggest that Joyce and Proust and Mann, with other masters of the early twentieth century, carried some tendencies in fiction to what would seem to be their practical limits. It was as if each of them had discovered new territories and left his mark of ownership: not a lead plate inscribed with the arms of France or Britain, but simply a signed masterpiece. Others have done their best to exploit the new territories, but truly ambitious novelists of the future will prefer to make their own explorations. And in what direction? That is more than can be prophesied, but at least this anthology gives a notion of the line from which novelists must diverge, at the present edge of mapped and settled country.

We have acknowledgments to make for help and advice, and in one instance for actual writing. Since neither of the editors presumed to be an authority on Proust, we enlisted my old friend Ramon Guthrie, late of Dartmouth, who for twenty years or more gave a famous course on *Remembrance of Things Past.* It was Ramon who selected the episode of the Duchess's red shoes as truly characteristic of the novel, but he did more than that. He also made changes in the English text of the episode to bring it into agreement with the authoritative Pléiade edition, not yet available when Scott Moncrieff made his famous translation, and then he volunteered to write both the headnote and the afterword. For all this good labor, special thanks must be rendered. Passages to select from other novels were discussed with Professors Thomas Flanagan, Carl Dawson, and Peter Dale Scott, all of the Berkeley campus, University of California. Professor Edgar Johnson of the City University of New York, the biographer of Scott and Dickens, saved us from making errors in the chapter on *The Heart of Midlothian.* Professor Julia Randall Sawyer of Hollins College offered valuable suggestions about *Mrs. Dalloway.* Thanks are also owed to, among others, Professors John R. Moore and George Garrett of Hollins College and to James Harmon, our indulgent and vastly helpful editor at Scribners.

MALCOLM COWLEY

Don Quixote (Part II, 1615)

MIGUEL DE CERVANTES SAAVEDRA (1547-1616) started late in the literary world. Born a *hidalgo*, that is, a member of the lower nobility, he was barred from trade. So far as is known, he had no university education, though he did study with the Madrid humanist Juan López de Hoyos. His great moment in life came at the age of twenty-four, when he fought in the Battle of Lepanto (1571) and suffered three wounds, including a shattered left hand; hence his later sobriquet, of which he was proud, "the one-handed man of Lepanto," *el manco de Lepanto*. Captured with his brother by Barbary pirates on the voyage home, he spent five years as a galley slave in Algiers. His mother and his sister finally scraped together a ransom of five hundred ducats that permanently impoverished the family.

From the profession of arms he turned to writing. At the age of thirty-eight he published a pastoral romance, *La Galatea*, and in subsequent years he produced twenty or thirty mediocre plays; the exact number is uncertain. *La Galatea* is mentioned in Part One of *Don Quixote*, at the point where the knight returns from his first disastrous venture into the world. The priest and the barber—a nice alliance of the sacred and the profane—then burn the romances they find in his library, but they spare the *Galatea*, speaking of the author as a man "more versed in adversity than in verses"—almost as if Cervantes knew that prose, not poetry, was to become his vehicle of expression.

He was made a commissary officer in 1587; his task was to requisition supplies for the Invincible Armada, and later he became a tax collector. Both experiences helped to give him the encyclopedic knowl-

7

edge of his native country that appears in *Don Quixote*. Excommunicated temporarily by the Church on the charge of having seized ecclesiastical property, and twice jailed for debts, Cervantes also learned the extent of man's inhumanity to man, as well as the place of money in the "new" world of the seventeenth century.

In 1595 he won a prize in a poetry contest: three silver spoons. Ten years later, at the age of fifty-seven, he owned nothing tangible as a result of all his experiences except the spoons—if he had managed to keep them—and one daughter. Then, in 1605, Part One of *Don Quixote* appeared. Five pirated editions were immediately issued, and these, as well as nine legitimate editions in the author's lifetime, attest to its instantaneous popularity. The second part of the novel was long delayed, but at the end its publication (1615) was hastened by a spurious sequel to Part One by the hack writer Avellenada.

Cervantes profited little from the success of his novel. A French ambassador paid him a visit near the end of Cervantes' life and expressed surprise to find that the author was "a gentleman, a soldier, and so poor." The ambassador suggested vainly that such a man ought to be subsidized by the royal treasury. We must remember, however, that the novel was a new form, still on shaky feet, and that Cervantes, its first major practitioner in Europe, had felt it necessary to have his novel prefaced with three "approbations" by the royal censor. The first of these is worth quoting. "It does not," the censor declared, "contain anything contrary to the Faith or to good morals, but rather it offers a great deal of wholesome entertainment blended with moral philosophy."

Cervantes died on April 23, 1616: the same year and month and—except for the difference between New and Old Calendars—the same day as Shakespeare. At least Shakespeare had thrived financially and retired to his house in Stratford-on-Avon with a coat of arms. Cervantes, whose coat of arms was inherited, died as poor as he had lived, but his posthumous career has been something like Shakespeare's. By 1625 *Don Quixote* had been translated into English, French, German, and Italian, and its reputation has continued to grow. "The Bible of humanity . . . the world's best-loved book . . . the grandest and saddest book ever conceived by the genius of man . . . a real epic unto all who have thought . . . the saddest book ever written . . . the bitterest irony which man is capable of conceiving"—all these are quotations from famous nineteenth-century men of letters. With such judgments in mind, it is salutary to recall that *Don Quixote* is an intensely *funny* book. Cervantes' original purpose was to laugh chivalric romance out of existence. If he aimed at one fairly simple target and posterity claims he hit another, or several others, his dispersed but firmly embedded arrows may be one more testimonial to his genius.

THE STORY

The simplest way to present the pattern of *Don Quixote*, both parts, is as a series of three sorties. The first of these is brief and the aged quasi-chevalier goes forth alone, but in the second he is accompanied by his squire, Sancho Panza. These two sorties together compose Part One; the third and longest sortie constitutes Part Two. Here knight and squire set forth once more, and Don Quixote comes home to die in one of the most moving scenes in literature—for at last a spade is called a spade and the Don admits to being merely Alonso Quixano.

Chiefly the story consists of a series of episodes, with the sequence dictated by the wanderings of Rozinante, the knight's seedy horse. But the vagrant narrative is tightened in Part Two, where Cervantes seems to have found that the device of having characters reappear—for example, Gines de Pasamonte, a prisoner in Part One, comes back as Peter the Puppet-Master in Part Two—could make for greater formal concision. The characters fill out in body, and the romances interpolated in Part One are replaced by pithy realistic narratives.

The most important theme in Part Two—from which we have chosen Chapter XLI, the episode of Clavileño, the wooden horse—is the interaction between knight and squire. It may be that introducing Sancho Panza into the story after the knight returns from his first sortie was Cervantes' greatest stroke of genius, for by so doing he created a dialectic between idealist and realist. The two were to have a distinguished literary progeny; some of the pairs that seem to be their direct descendants are Tom Jones and Partridge, Pickwick and Sam Weller, Sherlock Holmes and Dr. Watson, Stephen Dedalus and Leopold Bloom, Bertie Wooster and Jeeves.

The contrast between master and servant is simple in Part One, and the enchanted world of Don Quixote is always set against Sancho's observations of the world as it is: windmills are not giants, flocks of sheep are not armies, and inns are not castles. In Part Two the contrast is treated more ambiguously, and this becomes especially true when knight and squire are entertained by a duke and his duchess, who subject them to a series of elaborate mystifications. The bearded Countess Trifaldi appears at the duke's court, attended by a dozen bearded duennas. She explains that an East Indian magician, the giant Malambruno, has cast a spell on her and the other ladies. They are condemned to wear beards until the famous Don Quixote rides through the air on a wooden horse, with his squire on the crupper, and engages Malambruno in single combat. In the scene that follows, it is Sancho Panza who seems deluded, not his "mad" knight; and the last two sentences suggest that we all have our dreams and that idealism and realism may not be the polar opposites we think they are.

The new translation (1950) of the Spanish text was made by J. B. Cohen for Penguin Books.

Chapter 41. Of the coming of Clavileño
   and the end of this protracted Adventure.

By this time night had come on, and with it the moment fixed for the arrival of the famous horse Clavileño, whose failure to appear troubled Don Quixote. For he thought that Malambruno's delay in sending him meant either that he was not the knight for whom that adventure was reserved, or that the giant dared not meet him in single combat. But all of a sudden there entered through the garden four savages, all dressed in green ivy, bearing a great wooden horse on their shoulders. This they put on its feet on the ground, and one of them cried: "Let the knight who has courage enough climb upon this machine."

"I shan't mount it then," said Sancho, "for I've no courage and I'm no knight."

But the savage went on to say: "Let the squire, if there is one, take the crupper and trust the valiant Malambruno, for except by his sword he will be injured by no other, nor by the malice of any other person. There is no more to do than to turn this peg upon the horse's neck, and he will bear them through the air to where Malambruno awaits them. But for fear the height and distance from the earth should cause them giddiness they must keep their eyes covered till the horse neighs, which will be a sign that they have completed their journey."

This said, they left Clavileño and retired with a graceful movement in the direction they had come from. And at the sight of the horse the Afflicted One said to Don Quixote, almost in tears: "Valiant Knight, Malambruno has kept his word. The horse is here, our beards are growing, and each one of us implores you by every hair to shave and shear us, for nothing remains to do but for you to mount with your squire and make a happy start on your strange journey."

"That I will do, lady Countess Trifaldi," said Don Quixote, "with a strong and resolute heart. I will not even wait to find a cushion or put on spurs, for fear of delay, such is my desire to see you, lady, and all these waiting-women smooth and clean."

"That I will not do," said Sancho, "neither with good nor ill will, nor in any way. And if this shaving can't be done without my climbing on the crupper, my master may look for another squire to go with him, and these ladies another way of smoothing their faces, for I'm no sorcerer to enjoy travelling through the air. And what will my islesmen say when they learn that their governor goes roaming down the winds? And another thing: it is nine thousand and odd miles from here to Candaya, and supposing the horse should tire or the giant be in a bad mood, we might be half a dozen years before we got back, and then there would be no isle or islesmen in the world to recognize me. Now since the saying is that there's danger in delay, and when they give you the calf run with the halter, with all due respect to these ladies' beards St. Peter's all right at Rome. I mean that I'm all right in this house, where they have done me such favours, and from whose master I expect the great benefit of seeing myself governor."

Upon which the Duke replied: "Sancho, my friend, the isle which I have promised you is neither movable nor fugitive. It has such deep roots struck into the abysses of the earth that it will not be tugged or budged from where it is with three pulls. And I am aware, as you must realize, that there is no kind of position of the first rank that is not gained by some sort of bribe, some more, some less. So the price I mean to exact for this governorship is that you shall go with your master Don Quixote to complete and crown this memorable adventure. For whether you return on Clavileño with the speed his swiftness promises, or adverse fortune befalls you and you return on foot like a pilgrim, from tavern to tavern and inn to inn, whenever you return you will find your isle where you left it, and your islesmen longing as they have always been to receive you as their governor. My goodwill also shall be constant. Do not doubt the truth of this, Master Sancho, for that would be grievously to misunderstand my desire to serve you."

"No more, sir," cried Sancho. "I'm a poor squire and can't

carry all these favours on my back. Let my master mount; let them bind these eyes of mine, and commend me to God; and let me be informed whether I shall be able to commend myself to our Lord or invoke the angels to favour me, when we pass through those altitudes."

To which the Trifaldi replied: "Sancho, you may safely commend yourself to God, or to whom you will; for though Malambruno is an enchanter he is a Christian, and performs his enchantments with great sagacity and caution, meddling with nobody."

"Well then," said Sancho, "God help me, and the Holy Trinity of Gaeta!"

"Since the memorable adventure of the fulling-mills," said Don Quixote, "I have never seen Sancho in such a fright as now; and if I were as superstitious as some, his pusillanimity would cause me some tremors of heart. But come here, Sancho, for with these gentlemen's permission I should like to say a word or two to you in private."

Then, leading Sancho among some of the garden trees and grasping him by both hands, he said: "Now you see, Sancho, what a long journey awaits us, and God knows when we shall return, or what opportunities or leisure our business will afford us. Therefore I would have you now retire to your room, as if you were going to look for something needed for the journey, and give yourself in a brace of shakes, say five hundred on account of the three thousand and three hundred lashes promised. They will stand to your credit, for a thing well begun is half done."

"By God," said Sancho, "but your worship must be out of your wits. You might just as well say: you see me in difficulties and ask me for a maidenhead. Now that I've to be sitting on a bare board, does your worship want me to flay my bum? Really and truly, it isn't right of you. Let's go now and shave these waiting-women, and when we get back I promise you, upon my soul, I'll be so quick to redeem my debt that your worship'll be content. I say no more."

"Well, with that promise, good Sancho," replied Don Quixote, "I am comforted; for indeed, though you are foolish you are a veracious man."

"My complexion's not verdigris but brown," said Sancho, "but even if I were a mixture I would keep my word."

With that they came back to mount Clavileño and, as he

climbed on, Don Quixote said: "Blindfold yourself, Sancho, and mount, Sancho! For whoever sends for us from such distant lands will not deceive us, seeing how little glory would redound to him from defrauding one who trusts him. But supposing everything to turn out contrary to my expectation, no malice can obscure the glory of our having undertaken this exploit."

"Let's go, sir," said Sancho, "for these ladies' beards and tears are sticking into my heart, and I shan't get any nourishment out of my food till I see them in their first smoothness. Get on, your worship, and blindfold yourself beforehand, for if I have to go on the crupper it's clear that the rider in the saddle mounts first."

"That is true," replied Don Quixote and, taking a handkerchief from his pocket, he begged the Afflicted One to cover his eyes carefully. But after they were bandaged he uncovered them again to say: "If I remember rightly, I have read in Virgil of the Trojan Palladium, which was the wooden horse the Greeks presented to the goddess Pallas, and which was pregnant with armed knights who afterwards worked the total ruin of all Troy. So first it would be well to see what Clavileño carries in his stomach."

"There is no need," said the Afflicted One. "I will answer for him, for I know that Malambruno has nothing malicious or treacherous about him. You may mount, Don Quixote, without any fear, and on my shoulders be it if any harm befalls you."

It seemed to Don Quixote that anything he might say in reply concerning his own safety would be to cast a slur on his valour. So, without further discussion, he mounted Clavileño and tried the peg, which turned easily; and as he had no stirrups and his legs hung down, he looked like nothing so much as a figure in a Flemish tapestry, painted or woven, riding in some Roman triumph. Grudgingly and slowly Sancho also managed to get up and, making himself as comfortable as he could on the crupper, found it rather hard and not at all pleasant. So he begged the Duke, if it were possible, to oblige him with a cushion or pillow, even one from his lady the Duchess's couch or from a page's bed; for the crupper of that horse felt more like marble than wood. To which the Trifaldi objected that Clavileño would suffer no sort or kind of trappings on him, but what he could do was to sit side-saddle like a woman, as he would not feel the hardness so much that way. This Sancho did and, taking his farewell, allowed them to bind his eyes, though after they were bound he uncovered them again and, looking tenderly and tearfully on everyone in the garden, begged them to aid him in his peril with a couple of Paternosters and as many Ave Marias, that God might provide someone to say the same for them when they were in a like predicament. On which Don Quixote said:

"Scoundrel, are you on the gallows, perhaps, or at your last gasp, to resort to prayers of this kind? Are you not, soulless and cowardly creature, in the same seat the fair Magalona occupied, and from which she climbed down, not to her grave but to be Queen of France, if the histories do not lie? And I, who am beside you, cannot I compare with the valiant Pierres, who rested on the same spot where now I rest? Blindfold yourself, blindfold yourself, spiritless beast, and do not let the fear which possesses you issue from your mouth, at least not in my presence."

"Let them blindfold me," replied Sancho, "but since they won't let me commend myself or be commended to God, is it surprising that I'm afraid there may be some region of devils hereabouts, who will bear us off to Peralvillo?"

They were now blindfolded, and Don Quixote, feeling that all was in order, touched the peg; and no sooner did he set his fingers on it than the waiting-women and everyone else present raised their voices and cried: "God guide you, valorous knight!" "God be with you, dauntless squire!" "Now you are in the air already, cleaving it more swiftly than an arrow." "Now you are beginning to mount and soar to the astonishment of all of us below;" "Hold on, valorous Sancho, you are swaying. Be careful not to tumble. For your fall would be worse than that rash youth's who sought to drive the chariot of his father the sun."

Sancho heard their shouts and, pressing closer to his master, with his arms around him, asked: "Sir, how can they say we're flying so high when their voices reach us here, and they seem to be speaking just beside us?"

"Pay no attention to that, Sancho. For as these matters of flights are out of the ordinary course of things, you will see and hear what you please a thousand miles away. And do not press me so tight or you will upset me. Indeed I do not know what is so troubling and frightening you, for I dare swear that never in all the days of my life have I ridden an easier-paced mount. We seem not to be moving from one spot. Banish fear, my friend; for really this business is going as it should, and we have the wind astern."

"That's true enough," replied Sancho. "On this side there's

such a breeze striking me that it might be a thousand bellows blowing."

And Sancho was right, for they were giving him air from several large bellows. Indeed so well had the Duke, the Duchess and their steward planned the adventure that no detail was lacking to make it perfect. And when he felt the wind blow on him, Don Quixote said: "There can be no doubt, Sancho, that we have come to the second region of the air, where the hail and snow are born. Thunder, lightning and thunderbolts are engendered in the third region. If we go on climbing at this rate we shall soon strike the region of fire, and I do not know how to manage this peg so as not to mount so high that we shall scorch."

Here, with some pieces of tow hanging from a stick and easily lit and quenched, they warmed the riders' faces from the distance. At which Sancho, who felt the heat, exclaimed: "May I die if we're not in the fiery place already, or very near it, for a great piece of my beard has been singed. And, sir, I'm for taking off the bandage and seeing where we are."

"Do no such thing," replied Don Quixote. "Remember the true story of Doctor Torralva, whom the devils took flying through the air riding on a broomstick, with his eyes shut. In twelve hours he reached Rome and got down at the Torre di Nona, which is a street in that city, and saw all the turmoil, and the attack and the death of Bourbon, and by morning he was back in Madrid, where he gave an account of all he had seen. He also said that, as he was going through the air, the Devil bade him open his eyes, which he did and found himself, it seemed to him, so near the body of the moon that he could have taken hold of it with his hands; and he dared not look down to the earth for fear of turning giddy. So, Sancho, there is no need for us to unbind our eyes; for he in whose charge we are will take care of us. Now perhaps we are fetching round and climbing so that we can swoop down on the kingdom of Candaya, like a hawk or a falcon on a heron, to seize it the better for mounting. And although it seems to us not half an hour since we left the garden, believe me, we must have gone a long way."

"I know nothing about that," answered Sancho Panza. "I can only say that if the lady Magallanes or Magalona was happy on this crupper her flesh couldn't have been very tender."

All this conversation between the two heroes was overheard by the Duke, the Duchess and those in the garden, and gave them extraordinary delight. But, desiring to bring this strange and well-contrived adventure to an end, they set light to Clavileño's tail with some tow, and suddenly the horse, which was stuffed with crackers, flew into the air with a tremendous bang and threw Don Quixote and Sancho Panza to the ground, half scorched.

By this time the whole troop of bearded waiting-women had disappeared from the garden, the Trifaldi and all; and those who remained lay stretched on the earth as if in a faint. Don Quixote and Sancho rose up in a sorry state and, looking in all directions, were surprised to find themselves in the same garden they had started from, and to see such a number of people lying on the ground. But their wonder grew greater when they saw a tall lance planted in one corner of the garden, and hanging from it by two green silk cords a smooth white parchment on which was written in large gold letters: *"By the mere attempting of it the illustrious Don Quixote de la Mancha has finished and achieved the adventure of the Countess Trifaldi, otherwise called the Afflicted Waiting-woman. Malambruno is completely content and satisfied. The chins of the waiting-women are now smooth and clean, and their Majesties Don Clavijo and Antonomasia are in their pristine state. Now once the squirely whipping is completed, the white dove will be free from the pestiferous goshawks which pursue her, and in the arms of her loving mate; for so it is ordained by the sage Merlin, proto-enchanter of enchanters."*

When Don Quixote read the letters on the parchment, he clearly understood that they referred to Dulcinea's disenchantment, and giving deep thanks to Heaven for the achievement of so great a deed with so little peril, and for restoring to their former bloom the faces of the venerable waiting-women, who were now nowhere to be seen, he approached the Duke and Duchess, who had not yet come to their senses and, grasping the Duke by the hand, said to him:

"Well, my good lord, courage, courage! It is all nothing. The adventure is achieved, with no harm to anyone, as the words on that parchment clearly show."

The Duke came to himself gradually, like someone waking from a heavy sleep, and so did the Duchess and all the others who were lying about the garden; and with such signs of wonder and alarm as almost to convince one that what they had learnt so well to act in jest had happened in earnest. The Duke read the scroll with his eyes half closed, and then went with open arms to embrace Don Quixote, telling him that he was the bravest knight ever seen in any age. Meanwhile Sancho went to look for the Afflicted One, to see what her face was like without her beard and whether she was as beautiful without it as her brave appearance promised. But they told him that as soon as Clavileño came down burning through the air and struck the ground, the whole troop of waiting-women, and the Trifaldi with them, had disappeared, and that they had gone shaved clean and without their bristles. The Duchess asked Sancho how he had fared in that long journey, and he replied:

"I felt, lady, that we were going, as my master said, flying through the region of fire, and I wanted to uncover my eyes a bit. But when I asked my master's leave to take off the bandage he wouldn't allow me. But as I have some sparks of curiosity in me, and want to know what is forbidden and denied me, softly and stealthily I pushed the handkerchief that covered my eyes just a little bit up up on my nose and looked down towards the earth. And the whole of it looked to me no bigger than a grain of mustard seed, and the men walking on it little bigger than hazel-nuts. So you can see how high we must have been then."

At which the Duchess remarked: "Sancho my friend, reflect what you are saying. For seemingly you did not see the earth but the men going about on it, since it is clear that if the earth appeared to you like a grain of mustard seed and each man like a hazel nut, one man alone would have covered the whole earth."

"That's true," replied Sancho, "but, all the same, I looked through one little corner and saw the whole of it."

"Mind, Sancho," said the Duchess, "for we do not see the whole of what we look at from one little corner."

"I don't understand these lookings," answered Sancho. "I only know that your ladyship would do well to realize that as we flew by enchantment, by enchantment I could see the whole earth and all men on it from wherever I looked. And if you don't believe this, your Grace won't believe that when I moved the bandage up by my eyebrows I saw myself so near the sky that there wasn't a hand's breadth and a half between me and it; and I can swear to you, my lady, it was mighty big too. We happened to be going by the place where the seven little she-goats are and, by God, as I was a goatherd in my country when I was young, as soon as I saw them I felt a longing to play with them for a bit. And if I hadn't done so I think I should have burst. So, quick as a thought, what do I do? Saying nothing to anyone or to my master either, softly and gently I got down from Clavileño and played with the kids—which are sweet as gillyflowers—for almost three-quarters of an hour, and Clavileño didn't stir from the spot nor move on."

"And while the good Sancho was playing with the goats," asked the Duchess, "how was Don Quixote amusing himself?"

To which Don Quixote replied: "As all these matters and all such happenings are out of the order of nature, it is no wonder Sancho says what he does. I can only answer for myself that I did not slip the bandage either up or down, nor did I see sky, earth, sea or sands. It is true that I felt myself passing through the regions of air, and even touching the region of fire, but that we passed beyond it I am unable to believe. The region of fire being between the atmosphere of the moon and the farthest region of air, we could not have reached the sky, where the seven kids are that Sancho speaks of, without being scorched. So, seeing that we are not burnt, either Sancho is lying or Sancho is dreaming."

"I'm neither lying nor dreaming," answered Sancho. "Just you ask me the marks on those same goats, and you will see by that whether I'm telling the truth or not."

"Tell me them, then, Sancho," said the Duchess.

"Two of them," answered Sancho, "are green, two scarlet, two blue and one mottled."

"That is a new kind of goat," said the Duke, "for in this our region of the earth such colours are not usual—I mean she-goats of such colours."

"That's clear enough," said Sancho, "for there certainly should be a difference between the she-goats of heaven and of earth."

"Tell me, Sancho," asked the Duke, "did you see any he-goats there amongst the she-goats?"

"No, sir," answered Sancho. "But I've heard tell that not one has passed the horns of the moon."

They were in no mind to ask him anything more about his journey, for Sancho seemed to be in the mood to roam through all the heavens and give an account of everything in them, although he had not stirred from the garden. In fact this was the end of the adventure of the Afflicted Waiting-woman, which gave the Duke and Duchess cause for laughter, not only at the time but for all their lives, and Sancho a subject of talk for ages, if he should live so long.

But Don Quixote went up to Sancho and whispered in his ear: "Sancho, if you want me to believe what you saw in the sky, I wish you to accept my account of what I saw in the Cave of Montesinos. I say no more."

AFTERWORD

This episode is an ingenious variation on one of the leading comic motifs in the book, namely, the frequent unhorsing of Don Quixote, a mishap that represents the reduction of chivalric ideals to the values of the "real" world. Here Rozinante, the sorry nag—in the hero's eyes the equal of any famous steed in history—is supplanted by a wooden toy. Three other literary figures come to mind, in scenes where chivalric concepts are ridiculed, in part through equine-human complications: Falstaff "uncolted" at the Gadshill robbery in *Henry IV, Part One*; the Waterloo scene in Stendhal's *The Charterhouse of Parma*, where Fabrice del Dongo loses one horse after another—most of them stolen from him—and learns that the infantryman's musket has superseded the cavalier's sword; and Lewis Carroll's dreamy White Knight, who is advised by Alice, after his repeated tumbles, to get a safer wooden horse on wheels. *Our* wooden horse reminds Don Quixote of a still more famous wooden steed, when he suggests that they examine Clavileño's stomach. Thus Cervantes neatly plays the novel as a mock-epic against the *Iliad*, a contrast which his admirer Fielding was to exploit more self-consciously.

The modern reader may find the scene naively externalized: simple actions, long speeches with small feeling for "real" dialogue (though here they seem appropriate to the formal elegance of the setting), and almost no attempt to enter into the inner life of the characters. Yet within the technical limits of the novel in its nascent form, Cervantes conveys the affection between master and servant as well as the knight's perplexing mixture of sanity and madness ("We seem not to be moving from one spot"). The slapstick humor may also seem crude to modern tastes: the exploding horse makes one think of fraternity initiations, and the bearded ladies might come out of a collegiate musical comedy. It is all effective, however, and the humor is augmented by Sancho's insistent use of proverbs, with their blend of folk wisdom and banality.

Many of the episodes in Part Two of *Don Quixote* partake of play-acting. Among others there are the Cave of Montesinos (described by Salvador de Madariaga as "an illusion within an illusion"); the puppet show; the three elaborate spectacles directed by the Duke and the Duchess (including the present scene, which in part resembles a Renaissance masque); Sancho's brief governorship of Barataria, where the whole town takes part in a gigantic hoax; and Don Quixote's triumphal march into Barcelona, with a sign pinned to his back. The last two sentences in the present chapter have already been cited as underscoring the interplay between illusion and reality, idealism and realism, that marks Part Two. Life as a play or a dream is an idea that seems to have been especially congenial to some of the great writers of the Renaissance—as note Shakespeare's many allusions to the world as a stage, Lope de Vega's drama, *Life Is a Dream*, and Calderon's *Great Theater of the World*. These men, however, were playwrights, and the very notion of working with actors on a stage seems conducive to Hamletian speculations about art and life. Apparently Cervantes was the first to have introduced this *topos* or theme into prose fiction—another token of the greatness of *Don Quixote*, though of course that greatness goes far beyond formal and technical considerations.

Tom Jones (1749)

HENRY FIELDING (1707-1754), born in Somersetshire like the hero of his novel, started life as a poor relation. He was the great-grandson of an earl, the grandson of a church dignitary (and of a judge, on the mother's side), but his father was a professional soldier who, though he rose at last to be a general, could never hold on to a guinea. The future general eloped with an heiress without much profit to himself; her family, with some reluctance, settled a small estate upon their daughter. Henry was the oldest child. When his mother died in 1718, the father went to London, leaving the boy and his four sisters in charge of their maternal grandmother. The boy was sent to Eton, where he did well in the classics. At eighteen he emulated his father by trying, though unsuccessfully, to run off with an heiress. Before he was twenty-one his first play, *Love in Seven Masques*, was performed but not wildly applauded at the Drury Lane Theatre. Shortly afterward he went to Holland and enrolled at the University of Leyden. It was a simple lack of money that brought him back to London in 1729.

There he lost no time in becoming a professional playwright. Always a fast worker, he wrote some twenty-five plays during the next eight years, besides translating two comedies by Molière, an author whose stagecraft he greatly admired. Many of the plays were modeled on Congreve's comedy of manners, though some were sheer burlesque. Fielding also found, however, that the public enjoyed satires with a sharp political edge. Thus, *Rape upon Rape; or, the Justice caught in his own Trap* (1731) satirized the relations between George II and Queen Caroline, with bold thrusts at the ruling Whig Minister, Sir Robert Walpole.

In 1734 Fielding married Charlotte Cradock, who may have served as the model for Sophia Western in *Tom Jones*. She brought him a little money, part of which he invested in a company that played at the Haymarket Theatre. His first plays there enjoyed great popularity. In 1737, however, one of his satires was such a direct attack on the Walpole regime that the government rushed through a Licensing Act, limiting the number of theatres and providing for a censorship that effectively prohibited plays with any political edge. Fielding's theatre was one of its victims; not the only one, for the Act was followed by a general decline in the liveliness of the English stage. Driven from his first profession, Fielding became a law student in the Middle Temple and after three years was admitted to the bar. Meanwhile he meagerly supported his wife and two children by literary hackwork.

It was the appearance of Samuel Richardson's *Pamela* in 1740 that started Fielding on his second and greater career in literature. *Pamela* is a story told in letters; the story is that of Pamela Andrews, a virtuous serving maid employed by Lady B—. The lady's son makes attempts on her honor, which the maid indignantly repels, till at last Squire B— forgoes the attempts and marries her. As a novel, *Pamela* was new in form and new in sentiment, though both innovations came naturally to the author, who had made a profession of composing letters for illiterate servant girls. The book was an immediate and lasting success. For the next half-century authors in all the great European nations would follow Richardson by writing epistolary novels of sentiment. Even Alexander Pope, not usually a sentimentalist, confessed that he had stayed up all night to finish *Pamela*. "It will do more good," he said, "than a great many of the new sermons."

Fielding did not agree. His dislike of *Pamela* may have been caused by his aristocratic disdain for cant, or again it may have expressed his feeling that Richardson's morality could be reduced to the mere principle that it pays off to be sexually virtuous; at any rate it was a violent reaction. Five months after the book appeared, Fielding anonymously published *An Apology for the Life of Mrs. Shamela Andrews* (1741), a parody so bawdy that many scholars refused until recently to believe that Fielding wrote it. There was no such question of authorship in the case of *Joseph Andrews*, which appeared in February 1742. This too began as a parody of *Pamela*—with Lady B—, now called Lady Booby, making attempts on the honor of Joseph, her pure-minded footman—but it ended by meeting the definition that Fielding offered in his Preface: "a comic romance is a comic epic poem in prose." Like the book that engendered it, *Joseph Andrews* was a popular success, with 6500 copies sold within the year.

Fielding next published three volumes of *Miscellanies*, of which the third consisted of *The Life of Jonathan Wilde the Great* (1743), a work that has sometimes been placed among his novels. It is the story of a master thief who had earlier served as a subject for Defoe. Fielding's approach, unlike that of his predecessor, was mock-heroic. Many contemporary readers saw in this "great" hero a bitter caricature of Sir Robert Walpole.

In 1744 his wife died, and he married his housekeeper in 1747. By this time he had become editor of *The True Patriot* (1745-1746), then of *The Jacobite's Journal* (1747-1748), and his strong stand against the Jacobites during and after the Great Rebellion of 1745 doubtless had something to do with his appointment as presiding magistrate of the Bow Street Court. With the aid of his half-brother John, he improved prison conditions, reformed the London police, and reduced the rate of robbery and murder.

His greatest novel, *The History of Tom Jones, a Foundling*, appeared in February 1749 and met with general acclamation. There were dissenting voices, especially in the circle that surrounded Samuel Richardson, who did not forget a grudge. Richardson said that he would not read *Tom Jones*; nevertheless he described it as "a dissolute book" and a "profligate performance." Some of his followers libeled Fielding as a bribe-taking magistrate who had married his cook. But such comments—and those of Dr. Johnson, who said that he "scarcely knew a more corrupt work than *Tom Jones*"—were drowned by the voices of enthusiastic readers, both in Fielding's day and later. There is always Coleridge's accolade: "What a master of composition Fielding was! Upon my word, I think the *Oedipus Tyrannus*, *The Alchemist*, and *Tom Jones*, the three most perfect plots ever planned."

Fielding's next novel was *Amelia* (1751). The first edition of 5000 copies, very large for the time, was quickly exhausted, since readers expected to be entertained by another "comic epic poem in prose." They were disappointed, as later readers have been, to find that *Amelia* was comparatively lacking in comic invention. It is the story of a drunkard's virtuous wife, with painful scenes, drawn from the author's experience as a Bow Street magistrate, that expose the cruelty of the prison system and the immorality of law courts. Fielding wrote no more fiction. Falling seriously ill, he resigned his magistracy, and in 1754 he sailed with his wife and his oldest daughter for Lisbon, where he died. *Journal of a Voyage to Lisbon* was posthumously published in 1755 "for the Benefit of his Wife and Children," since he left no estate.

THE STORY

The *Iliad* has twenty-four books; the *Aeneid* has twelve. Fielding, who kept them both in mind, struck a compromise by dividing his comic epic into eighteen books: six for the beginning, six for the middle, and six for the end.

In the beginning good Squire Allworthy, a widower, comes home to his rich estate in the West Country and finds a newborn infant in his bed. Jenny Jones, once the maid of Allworthy's sister Bridget, is accused of being the child's mother and is sent away. But Allworthy decides to keep the child, henceforth called Tom Jones, and confides it to his sister's keeping. Soon Bridget marries a fortune hunter, Captain Blifil, to whom she bears a son. After the Captain dies, young Blifil and Tom Jones are educated together by two cane-wielding pedagogues, the Reverend Mr. Thwackum and the philosopher Square. Tom is a handsome, open-hearted boy, but wild and lusty. Young Blifil, hypocritical and malignant, seizes on every opportunity to get him into trouble. In early manhood they both court Sophia Western, the daughter of a fox-hunting squire. Tom, though he deeply loves her, has an affair with Molly Seagrim, daughter of Black George, Squire Western's gamekeeper. A distorted version of the affair is presented to Allworthy by Blifil and the two pedagogues, who add some fabrications of their own. Tom is banished from home in Book VI, and Squire Western locks his daughter in her room to keep her from running after him.

The six middle books deal with Tom's adventures on the road to London. He joins the army—for this is the year of the Great Rebellion—and is badly injured by Ensign Northerton in a quarrel over Sophia's honor. After dismissing the surgeon, Tom sends for a barber, and Partridge appears; he is a former schoolmaster who was forced to flee the Allworthy neighborhood when falsely suspected of being Tom's father. Henceforth he will follow Tom as a sort of Sancho Panza (and that is not the only debt to Cervantes in the novel). The scene changes to the inn at Upton. Tom goes there with Mrs. Waters, whom he has rescued from Northerton. He goes to bed with her, but is routed out by Fitzpatrick, a furious Irishman who thinks that Mrs. Waters is his estranged wife. In the general confusion Sophia arrives; she is in flight from her father, who wants her to marry Blifil. Now, when the voluble Partridge reveals that Tom is in bed with a wench, she immediately sets out for London.

In the last six books, Tom suffers the consequences of Blifil's malevolence and of his own follies. These include a final one: Tom lets himself be seduced and supported by a lady of fashion. He manages to get rid of her, but then his misfortunes accumulate. By the next-to-last book he is lying in prison charged with a hanging offense, that of having mortally wounded Fitzgerald in a duel (though it was the other man who had picked the quarrel). A worse blow to Tom is that Sophia has written him to say that his name must never again be mentioned in her presence. A still worse blow is imminent: he learns that Mrs. Waters is the former Jenny Jones, the woman he believes to be his mother. But now comes the classical *peripeteia*, or change of fortune. In Book XVIII Fitzgerald recovers and Tom is set free. Mrs. Waters reveals that he is really the son of Allworthy's sister. Blifil's treachery is exposed, Tom is reconciled with his benefactor, and Sophia gives him her hand.

What follows is the first seven chapters of Book X, which may be regarded as the climax of the novel.

[*The Inn at Upton*]

CHAPTER I

CONTAINING INSTRUCTIONS VERY NECESSARY
TO BE PERUSED BY MODERN CRITICS

Reader, it is impossible we should know what sort of person thou wilt be; for, perhaps, thou may'st be as learned in human nature as Shakespeare himself was, and, perhaps, thou may'st be no wiser than some of his editors. Now, lest this latter should be the case, we think proper, before we go any farther together, to give thee a few wholesome admonitions; that thou may'st not as grossly misunderstand and misrepresent us, as some of the said editors have misunderstood and misrepresented their author.

First, then, we warn thee not too hastily to condemn any of the incidents in this our history as impertinent and foreign to our main design, because thou dost not immediately conceive in what manner such incident may conduce to that design. This work may, indeed, be considered as a great creation of our own; and for a little reptile of a critic to presume to find fault with any of its parts, without knowing the manner in which the whole is connected, and before he comes to the final catastrophe, is a most presumptuous absurdity. The allusion and metaphor we have here made use of we must acknowledge to be infinitely too great for our occasion; but there is, indeed, no other which is at all adequate to express the difference between an author of the first rate and a critic of the lowest.

Another caution we would give thee, my good reptile, is, that thou dost not find out too near a resemblance between certain characters here introduced; as, for instance, between the landlady who appears in the seventh book and her in the ninth. Thou art to know, friend, that there are certain characteristics in which most individuals of every profession and occupation agree. To be able to preserve these characteristics, and at the same time to diversify their operations, is one talent of a good writer. Again, to mark the nice distinction between two persons actuated by the same vice or folly is another; and, as this last talent is found in very few writers, so is the true discernment of it found in as few readers; though, I believe, the observation of this forms a very principal pleasure in those who are capable of the discovery; every person, for instance, can distinguish between Sir Epicure Mammon and Sir Fopling Flutter; but to note the difference between Sir Fopling Flutter and Sir Courtly Nice requires a more exquisite judgment: for want of which, vulgar spectators of plays very often do great injustice in the theatre; where I have sometimes known a poet in danger of being convicted as a thief, upon much worse evidence than the resemblance of hands hath been held to be in the law. In reality, I apprehend every amorous widow on the stage would run the hazard of being condemned as a servile imitation of Dido, but that happily very few of our playhouse critics understand enough of Latin to read Virgil.

In the next place, we must admonish thee, my worthy friend (for, perhaps, thy heart may be better than thy head), not to condemn a character as a bad one because it is not perfectly a good one. If thou dost delight in these models of perfection, there are books enow written to gratify thy taste; but, as we have not, in the course of our conversation, ever happened to meet with any such person, we have not chosen to introduce any such here. To say the truth, I a little question whether mere man ever arrived at this consummate degree of excellence, as well as whether there hath ever existed a monster bad enough to verify that

———*nulla virtute redemptum*
A vitiis———[1]

in Juvenal; nor do I, indeed, conceive the good purposes served
by inserting characters of such angelic perfection, or such diabolical depravity, in any work of invention; since, from contem-
plating either, the mind of man is more likely to be overwhelmed
with sorrow and shame than to draw any good uses from such
patterns; for in the former instance he may be both concerned
and ashamed to see a pattern of excellence in his nature, which
he may reasonably despair of ever arriving at; and in contemplat-
ing the latter he may be no less affected with those uneasy sensations, at seeing the nature of which he is a partaker degraded
into so odious and detestable a creature.

In fact, if there be enough of goodness in a character to en-
gage the admiration and affection of a well-disposed mind, though
there should appear some of those little blemishes *quas humana
parum cavit natura*,[2] they will raise our compassion rather than
our abhorrence. Indeed, nothing can be of more moral use than
the imperfections which are seen in examples of this kind; since
such form a kind of surprise, more apt to affect and dwell upon
our minds than the faults of very vicious and wicked persons.
The foibles and vices of men, in whom there is great mixture of
good, become more glaring objects from the virtues which contrast them and show their deformity; and when we find such vices
attended with their evil consequence to our favourite characters,
we are not only taught to shun them for our own sake, but to
hate them for the mischiefs they have already brought on those
we love.

And now, my friend, having given you these few admonitions,
we will, if you please, once more set forward with our history.

CHAPTER 2
CONTAINING THE ARRIVAL OF AN IRISH GENTLEMAN,
WITH VERY EXTRAORDINARY ADVENTURES
WHICH ENSUED AT THE INN

Now the little trembling hare, which the dread of all her
numerous enemies, and chiefly of that cunning, cruel, carnivo-
rous animal, man, had confined all the day to her lurking-place,

---

[1] Whose vices are not allayed with a single virtue.
[2] Which human nature takes little account of.]

sports wantonly o'er the lawns; now on some hollow tree the owl, shrill chorister of the night, hoots forth notes which might charm the ears of some modern connoisseurs in music; now, in the imagination of the half-drunk clown, as he staggers through the churchyard, or rather charnelyard, to his home, fear paints the bloody hobgoblin; now thieves and ruffians are awake, and honest watchmen fast asleep; in plain English, it was now midnight; and the company at the inn, as well those who have been already mentioned in this history, as some others who arrived in the evening, were all in bed. Only Susan Chambermaid was now stirring, she being obliged to wash the kitchen before she retired to the arms of the fond expecting hostler.

In this posture were affairs at the inn when a gentleman arrived there post. He immediately alighted from his horse, and, coming up to Susan, inquired of her, in a very abrupt and confused manner, being almost out of breath with eagerness, Whether there was any lady in the house? The hour of night, and the behaviour of the man, who stared very wildly all the time, a little surprised Susan, so that she hesitated before she made any answer; upon which the gentleman, with redoubled eagerness, begged her to give him a true information, saying he had lost his wife, and was come in pursuit of her. "Upon my shoul," cries he, "I have been near catching her already in two or three places, if I had not found her gone just as I came up with her. If she be in the house, do carry me up in the dark and show her to me; and if she be gone away before me, do tell me which way I shall go after her to meet her, and, upon my shoul, I will make you the richest poor woman in the nation." He then pulled out a handful of guineas, a sight which would have bribed persons of much greater consequence than this poor wench to much worse purposes.

Susan, from the account she had received of Mrs. Waters, made not the least doubt but that she was the very identical stray whom the right owner pursued. As she concluded, therefore, with great appearance of reason, that she never could get money in an honester way than by restoring a wife to her husband, she made no scruple of assuring the gentleman that the lady he wanted was then in the house; and was presently afterwards prevailed upon (by very liberal promises, and some earnest paid into her hands) to conduct him to the bedchamber of Mrs. Waters.

It hath been a custom long established in the polite world, and that upon very solid and substantial reasons, that a husband shall never enter his wife's apartment without first knocking at the door. The many excellent uses of this custom need scarce be hinted to a reader who hath any knowledge of the world; for by this means the lady hath time to adjust herself, or to remove any disagreeable object, out of the way; for there are some situations in which nice and delicate women would not be discovered by their husbands.

To say the truth, there are several ceremonies instituted among the polished part of mankind, which, though they may, to coarser judgments, appear as matters of mere form, are found to have much of substance in them by the more discerning; and lucky would it have been had the custom above mentioned been observed by our gentleman in the present instance. Knock, indeed, he did at the door, but not with one of those gentle raps which is usual on such occasions. On the contrary, when he found the door locked, he flew at it with such violence that the lock immediately gave way, the door burst open, and he fell headlong into the room.

He had no sooner recovered his legs than forth from the bed, upon his legs likewise, appeared—with shame and sorrow are we obliged to proceed—our hero himself, who, with a menacing voice, demanded of the gentleman who he was, and what he meant by daring to burst open his chamber in that outrageous manner.

The gentleman at first thought he had committed a mistake, and was going to ask pardon and retreat, when, on a sudden, as the moon shone very bright, he cast his eyes on stays, gowns, petticoats, caps, ribbons, stockings, garters, shoes, clogs, etc., all which lay in a disordered manner on the floor. All these operating on the natural jealousy of his temper, so enraged him, that he lost all power of speech; and, without returning any answer to Jones, he endeavoured to approach the bed.

Jones immediately interposing, a fierce contention arose, which soon proceeded to blows on both sides. And now Mrs. Waters (for we must confess she was in the same bed), being, I suppose, awakened from her sleep, and seeing two men fighting in her bedchamber, began to scream in the most violent manner, crying out Murder! robbery! and more frequently Rape! which last, some, perhaps, may wonder she should mention, who do not consider that these words of exclamation are used by ladies

in a fright, as fa, la, la, ra, da, etc., are in music, only as the vehicles of sound, and without any fixed ideas.

Next to the lady's chamber was deposited the body of an Irish
gentleman who arrived too late at the inn to have been mentioned before. This gentleman was one of those whom the Irish
call a calabalaro, or cavalier. He was a younger brother of a good
family, and, having no fortune at home, was obliged to look
abroad in order to get one; for which purpose he was proceeding to the Bath, to try his luck with cards and the women.

This young fellow lay in bed reading one of Mrs. Behn's
novels; for he had been instructed by a friend that he would find
no more effectual method of recommending himself to the ladies
than the improving of his understanding, and filling his mind
with good literature. He no sooner, therefore, heard the violent
uproar in the next room, than he leapt from his bolster, and, taking his sword in one hand, and the candle which burnt by him in
the other, he went directly to Mrs. Waters's chamber.

If the sight of another man in his shirt at first added some
shock to the decency of the lady, it made her presently amends
by considerably abating her fears; for no sooner had the calabalaro entered the room than he cried out, "Mr. Fitzpatrick, what
the devil is the maning of this?" Upon which the other immediately answered, "Oh, Mr. Maclachlan! I am rejoiced you are
here. This villain hath debauched my wife, and is got into bed
with her."—"What wife?" cries Maclachlan; "do not I know Mrs.
Fitzpatrick very well, and don't I see that the lady whom the
gentleman who stands here in his shirt is lying in bed with, is
none of her?"

Fitzpatrick, now perceiving, as well by the glimpse he had of
the lady, as by her voice, which might have been distinguished
at a greater distance than he now stood from her, that he had
made a very unfortunate mistake, began to ask many pardons of
the lady; and then, turning to Jones, he said, "I would have you
take notice I do not ask your pardon, for you have bate me; for
which I am resolved to have your blood in the morning."

Jones treated this menace with much contempt; and Mr. Maclachlan answered, "Indeed, Mr. Fitzpatrick, you may be ashamed
of your own self, to disturb people at this time of night; if all the
people in the inn were not asleep, you would have awakened them
as you have me. The gentleman has served you very rightly.

Upon my conscience, though I have no wife, if you had treated her so, I would have cut your throat."

Jones was so confounded with his fears for his lady's reputation, that he knew neither what to say or do; but the invention of women is, as hath been observed, much readier than that of men. She recollected that there was a communication between her chamber and that of Mr. Jones; relying, therefore, on his honour and her own assurance, she answered, "I know not what you mean, villains! I am wife to none of you. Help! Rape! murder! Rape!" And now, the landlady coming into the room, Mrs. Waters fell upon her with the utmost virulence, saying, "She thought herself in a sober inn, and not in a bawdy-house; but that a set of villains had broke into her room, with an intent upon her honour, if not upon her life; and both, she said, were equally dear to her."

The landlady now began to roar as loudly as the poor woman in bed had done before. She cried, "She was undone, and that the reputation of her house, which was never blown upon before, was utterly destroyed." Then, turning to the men, she cried, "What, in the devil's name, is the reason of all this disturbance in the lady's room?" Fitzpatrick, hanging down his head, repeated, "That he had committed a mistake, for which he heartily asked pardon," and then retired with his countryman. Jones, who was too ingenious to have missed the hint given him by his fair one, boldly asserted, "That he had run to her assistance upon hearing the door broke open, with what design he could not conceive, unless of robbing the lady; which, if they intended, he said, he had the good fortune to prevent."—"I never had a robbery committed in my house since I have kept it," cries the landlady; "I would have you to know, sir, I harbour no highwaymen here; I scorn the word, thof I say it. None but honest, good gentlefolks are welcome to my house; and, I thank good luck, I have always had enow of such customers; indeed as many as I could entertain. Here hath been my Lord—," and then she repeated over a catalogue of names and titles, many of which we might, perhaps, be guilty of a breach of privilege by inserting.

Jones, after much patience, at length interrupted her, by making an apology to Mrs. Waters for having appeared before her in his shirt, assuring her "That nothing but a concern for her safety could have prevailed on him to do it." The reader may inform himself of her answer, and, indeed, of her whole behaviour to the end of the scene, by considering the situation which she affected, it being that of a modest lady, who was awakened out of her sleep by three strange men in her chamber. This was the part which she undertook to perform; and, indeed, she executed it so well, that none of our theatrical actresses could exceed her, in any of their performances, either on or off the stage.

And hence, I think, we may very fairly draw an argument to prove how extremely natural virtue is to the fair sex; for, though there is not, perhaps, one in ten thousand who is capable of making a good actress, and even among these we rarely see two who are equally able to personate the same character, yet this of virtue they can all admirably well put on; and as well those individuals who have it not, as those who possess it, can all act it to the utmost degree of perfection.

When the men were all departed, Mrs. Waters, recovering from her fear, recovered likewise from her anger, and spoke in much gentler accents to the landlady, who did not so readily quit her concern for the reputation of the house, in favour of which she began again to number the many great persons who had slept under her roof; but the lady stopped her short, and having absolutely acquitted her of having had any share in the past disturbance, begged to be left to her repose, which, she said, she hoped to enjoy unmolested during the remainder of the night. Upon which the landlady, after much civility and many courtesies, took her leave.

CHAPTER 3
A DIALOGUE BETWEEN THE LANDLADY AND SUSAN
THE CHAMBERMAID, PROPER TO BE READ BY ALL
INNKEEPERS AND THEIR SERVANTS; WITH THE ARRIVAL, AND
AFFABLE BEHAVIOUR OF A BEAUTIFUL YOUNG LADY;
WHICH MAY TEACH PERSONS OF CONDITION HOW
THEY MAY ACQUIRE THE LOVE OF THE WHOLE WORLD

The landlady, remembering that Susan had been the only person out of bed when the door was burst open, resorted presently to her, to inquire into the first occasion of the disturbance, as well as who the strange gentleman was, and when and how he arrived.

Susan related the whole story which the reader knows already, varying the truth only in some circumstances, as she saw convenient, and totally concealing the money which she had received. But whereas her mistress had, in the preface of her inquiry, spoken much in compassion for the fright which the lady had been in concerning any intended depredations on her virtue, Susan could not help endeavouring to quiet the concern which her mistress seemed to be under on that account, by swearing heartily she saw Jones leap out from her bed.

The landlady fell into a violent rage at these words. "A likely story, truly," cried she, "that a woman should cry out, and endeavour to expose herself, if that was the case! I desire to know what better proof any lady can give of her virtue than her crying out, which, I believe, twenty people can witness for her she did? I beg, madam, you would spread no such scandal of any of my guests; for it will not only reflect on them, but upon the house; and I am sure no vagabonds, nor wicked beggarly people, come here."

"Well," says Susan, "then I must not believe my own eyes." —"No, indeed, must you not always," answered her mistress; "I would not have believed my own eyes against such good gentlefolks. I have not had a better supper ordered this half-year than they ordered last night; and so easy and good-humoured were they, that they found no fault with my Worcestershire perry,[3] which I sold them for champagne; and to be sure it is as well tasted and as wholesome as the best champagne in the kingdom, otherwise I would scorn to give it 'em; and they drank me two bottles. No, no, I will never believe any harm of such sober good sort of people."

Susan being thus silenced, her mistress proceeded to other matters. "And so you tell me," continued she, "that the strange gentleman came post, and there is a footman without with the horses; why, then, he is certainly some of your great gentlefolks too. Why did not you ask him whether he'd have any supper? I think he is in the other gentleman's room; go up and ask whether he called. Perhaps he'll order something when he finds anybody stirring in the house to dress it. Now, don't commit any of your usual blunders, by telling him the fire's out and the fowl's alive. And if he should order mutton, don't blab out that we have none. The butcher, I know, killed a sheep just before I went to bed, and he never refuses to cut it up warm when I desire it. Go,

[3 The fermented juice of pears.]

remember there's all sorts of mutton and fowls; go, open the door with, Gentlemen, d'ye call? and if they say nothing, ask what his honour will be pleased to have for supper? Don't forget his honour. Go; if you don't mind all these matters better, you'll never come to anything."

Susan departed, and soon returned with an account that the two gentlemen were got both into the same bed. "Two gentlemen," says the landlady, "in the same bed! that's impossible; they are two arrant scrubs, I warrant them; and I believe young Squire Allworthy guessed right, that the fellow intended to rob her ladyship; for, if he had broke open the lady's door with any of the wicked designs of a gentleman, he would never have sneaked away to another room to save the expense of a supper and a bed to himself. They are certainly thieves, and their searching after a wife is nothing but a pretence."

In these censures my landlady did Mr. Fitzpatrick great injustice; for he was really born a gentleman, though not worth a groat; and though, perhaps, he had some few blemishes in his heart as well as in his head, yet being a sneaking or a niggardly fellow was not one of them. In reality, he was so generous a man that, whereas he had received a very handsome fortune with his wife, he had now spent every penny of it, except some little pittance which was settled upon her; and, in order to possess himself of this, he had used her with such cruelty, that, together with his jealousy, which was of the bitterest kind, it had forced the poor woman to run away from him.

This gentleman, then, being well tired with his long journey from Chester in one day, with which, and some good dry blows he had received in the scuffle, his bones were so sore, that, added to the soreness of his mind, it had quite deprived him of any appetite for eating; and being now so violently disappointed in the woman whom, at the maid's instance, he had mistaken for his wife, it never once entered into his head that she might nevertheless be in the house, though he had erred in the first person he had attacked. He therefore yielded to the dissuasions of his friend from searching any farther after her that night, and accepted the kind offer of part of his bed.

The footman and post-boy were in a different disposition. They were more ready to order than the landlady was to provide; however, after being pretty well satisfied by them of the real truth of the case, and that Mr. Fitzpatrick was no thief, she was at length prevailed on to set some cold meat before them, which they were devouring with great greediness when Partridge came into the kitchen. He had been first awaked by the hurry which we have before seen; and while he was endeavouring to compose himself again on his pillow, a screech-owl had given him such a serenade at his window, that he leapt in a most horrible affright from his bed, and, huddling on his clothes with great expedition ran down to the protection of the company, whom he heard talking below in the kitchen.

His arrival detained my landlady from returning to her rest; for she was just about to leave the other two guests to the care of Susan; but the friend of young Squire Allworthy was not to be so neglected, especially as he called for a pint of wine to be mulled. She immediately obeyed, by putting the same quantity of perry to the fire; for this readily answered to the name of every kind of wine.

The Irish footman was retired to bed, and the post-boy was going to follow; but Partridge invited him to stay and partake of his wine, which the lad very thankfully accepted. The schoolmaster was indeed afraid to return to bed by himself; and as he did not know how soon he might lose the company of my landlady, he was resolved to secure that of the boy, in whose presence he apprehended no danger from the devil or any of his adherents.

And now arrived another post-boy at the gate; upon which Susan, being ordered out, returned, introducing two young women in riding habits, one of which was so very richly laced, that Partridge and the post-boy instantly started from their chairs, and my landlady fell to her courtesies, and her ladyships, with great eagerness.

The lady in the rich habit said, with a smile of great condescension, "If you will give me leave, madam, I will warm myself a few minutes at your kitchen fire, for it is really very cold; but I must insist on disturbing no one from his seat." This was spoken on account of Partridge, who had retreated to the other end of the room, struck with the utmost awe and astonishment at the splendour of the lady's dress. Indeed, she had a much better title to respect than this, for she was one of the most beautiful creatures in the world.

The lady earnestly desired Partridge to return to his seat, but could not prevail. She then pulled off her gloves, and displayed to the fire two hands, which had every property of snow in them, except that of melting. Her companion, who was indeed her maid, likewise pulled off her gloves, and discovered what bore an exact resemblance, in cold and colour, to a piece of frozen beef.

"I wish, madam," quoth the latter, "your ladyship would not think of going any farther to-night. I am terribly afraid your ladyship will not be able to bear the fatigue."

"Why, sure," cries the landlady, "her ladyship's honour can never intend it. Oh, bless me! farther tonight, indeed! let me beseech your ladyship not to think on't——But, to be sure, your ladyship can't. What will your honour be pleased to have for supper? I have mutton of all kinds, and some nice chicken."

"I think, madam," said the lady, "it would be rather breakfast than supper; but I can't eat anything; and, if I stay, shall only lie down for an hour or two. However, if you please, madam, you may get me a little sack whey, made very small and thin."

"Yes, madam," cries the mistress of the house, "I have some excellent white wine."—"You have no sack, then?" says the lady. —"Yes, an't please your honour, I have; I may challenge the country for that—but let me beg your ladyship to eat something."

"Upon my word, I can't eat a morsel," answered the lady; "and I shall be much obliged to you if you will please to get my apartment ready as soon as possible; for I am resolved to be on horseback again in three hours."

"Why, Susan," cries the landlady, "is there a fire lit yet in the Wild-goose? I am sorry, madam, all my best rooms are full. Several people of the first quality are now in bed. Here's a great young squire, and many other great gentlefolks of quality."— Susan answered, "That the Irish gentlemen were got into the Wild-goose."

"Was ever anything like it?" says the mistress; "why the devil would you not keep some of the best rooms for the quality, when you know scarce a day passes without some calling here?——If they be gentlemen, I am certain, when they know it is for her ladyship, they will get up again."

"Not upon my account," says the lady; "I will have no person disturbed for me. If you have a room that is commonly decent it will serve me very well, though it be never so plain. I beg, madam, you will not give yourself so much trouble on my account."—"Oh, madam!" cries the other, "I have several very good rooms for that matter, but none good enough for your honour's ladyship. However, as you are so condescending to take up with the best I have, do, Susan, get a fire in the Rose this minute. Will your ladyship be pleased to go up now, or stay till the fire is lighted?"—"I think I have sufficiently warmed myself," answered the lady; "so, if you please, I will go now; I am afraid I have kept people, and particularly that gentleman (meaning Partridge), too long in the cold already. Indeed, I cannot bear to think of keeping any person from the fire this dreadful weather." She then departed with her maid, the landlady marching with two lighted candles before her.

When that good woman returned, the conversation in the kitchen was all upon the charms of the young lady. There is indeed in perfect beauty a power which none almost can withstand; for my landlady, though she was not pleased at the negative given to the supper, declared she had never seen so lovely a creature. Partridge ran out into the most extravagant encomiums on her face, though he could not refrain from paying some compliments to the gold lace on her habit. The post-boy sang forth the praises of her goodness, which were likewise echoed by the other post-boy, who was now come in. "She's a true good lady, I warrant her," says he; "for she hath mercy upon dumb creatures; for she asked me every now and tan upon the journey, if I did not think she should hurt the horses by riding too fast; and when she came in she charged me to give them as much corn as ever they would eat."

Such charms are there in affability, and so sure is it to attract the praises of all kinds of people. It may indeed be compared to the celebrated Mrs. Hussey.[4] It is equally sure to set off every female perfection to the highest advantage, and to palliate and conceal every defect. A short reflection, which we could not forbear making in this place, where my reader hath seen the loveliness of an affable deportment; and truth will now oblige us to contrast it by showing the reverse.

CHAPTER 4

CONTAINING INFALLIBLE NOSTRUMS FOR PROCURING
UNIVERSAL DISESTEEM AND HATRED

The lady had no sooner laid herself on her pillow than the waiting-woman returned to the kitchen to regale with some of those dainties which her mistress had refused.

[4] A celebrated mantua-maker in the Strand, famous for setting off the shapes of women.

The company, at her entrance, showed her the same respect which they had before paid to her mistress, by rising; but she forgot to imitate her, by desiring them to sit down again. Indeed, it was scarce possible they should have done so, for she placed her chair in such a posture as to occupy almost the whole fire. She then ordered a chicken to be broiled that instant, declaring, if it was not ready in a quarter of an hour she would not stay for it. Now, though the said chicken was then at roost in the stable, and required the several ceremonies of catching, killing, and picking, before it was brought to the gridiron, my landlady would nevertheless have undertaken to do all within the time; but the guest, being unfortunately admitted behind the scenes, must have been witness to the *fourberie;* the poor woman was therefore obliged to confess that she had none in the house; "but, madam," said she, "I can get any kind of mutton in an instant from the butcher's."

"Do you think, then," answered the waiting-gentlewoman, "that I have the stomach of a horse, to eat mutton at this time of night? Sure you people that keep inns imagine your betters are like yourselves. Indeed, I expected to get nothing at this wretched place. I wonder my lady would stop at it. I suppose none but tradesmen and graziers ever call here." The landlady fired at this indignity offered to her house; however, she suppressed her temper, and contented herself with saying, "Very good quality frequented it, she thanked Heaven!"—"Don't tell me," cries the other, "of quality! I believe I know more of people of quality than such as you. But, prithee, without troubling me with any of your impertinence, do tell me what I can have for supper; for, though I cannot eat horse-flesh, I am really hungry."— "Why, truly, madam," answered the landlady, "you could not take me again at such a disadvantage; for I must confess I have nothing in the house, unless a cold piece of beef, which indeed a gentleman's footman and the post-boy have almost cleared to the bone."—"Woman," said Mrs. Abigail (so for shortness we will call her), "I entreat you not to make me sick. If I had fasted a month, I could not eat what has been touched by the fingers of such fellows. Is there nothing neat or decent to be had in this horrid place?"—"What think you of some eggs and bacon, madam?" said the landlady.—"Are your eggs new laid? are you certain they were laid to-day? and let me have the bacon cut very nice and thin; for I can't endure anything that's gross. Prithee try if you can do a little tolerably for once, and don't think you have a farmer's wife, or some of those creatures, in the house." The landlady began then to handle her knife; but the other stopped her, saying, "Good woman, I must insist upon your first washing your hands; for I am extremely nice, and have been always used from my cradle to have everything in the most elegant manner."

The landlady, who governed herself with much difficulty, began now the necessary preparations; for as to Susan, she was utterly rejected, and with such disdain, that the poor wench was as hard put to it to restrain her hands from violence as her mistress had been to hold her tongue. This, indeed, Susan did not entirely; for, though she literally kept it within her teeth, yet there it muttered many "marry-come-ups, as good flesh and blood as yourself," with other such indignant phrases.

While the supper was preparing, Mrs. Abigail began to lament she had not ordered a fire in the parlour; but, she said, that was now too late. "However," said she, "I have novelty to recommend a kitchen; for I do not believe I ever eat in one before." Then, turning to the post-boys, she asked them, "Why they were not in the stable with their horses? If I must eat my hard fare here, madam," cries she to the landlady, "I beg the kitchen may be kept clear, that I may not be surrounded with all the blackguards in town. As for you, sir," says she to Partridge, "you look somewhat like a gentleman, and may sit still if you please; I don't desire to disturb anybody but mob."

"Yes, yes, madam," cries Partridge, "I am a gentleman, I do assure you, and I am not so easily to be disturbed. *Non semper vox casualis est verbo nominativus.*"—This Latin she took to be some affront, and answered, "You may be a gentleman, sir; but you don't show yourself as one to talk Latin to a woman." Partridge made a gentle reply, and concluded with more Latin; upon which she tossed up her nose, and contented herself by abusing him with the name of a great scholar.

The supper being now on the table, Mrs. Abigail eat very heartily for so delicate a person; and while a second course of the same was by her order preparing, she said, "And so, madam, you tell me your house is frequented by people of great quality?"

The landlady answered in the affirmative, saying, "There were a great many very good quality and gentle-folks in it now. There's young Squire Allworthy, as the gentleman there knows."

"And pray who is this young gentleman of quality, this young Squire Allworthy?" said Abigail.

"Who should he be," answered Partridge, "but the son and heir of the great Squire Allworthy of Somersetshire?"

"Upon my word," said she, "you tell me strange news; for I know Mr. Allworthy of Somersetshire very well, and I know he hath no son alive."

The landlady pricked up her ears at this, and Partridge looked a little confounded. However, after a short hesitation, he answered, "Indeed, madam, it is true, everybody doth not know him to be Squire Allworthy's son; for he was never married to his mother; but his son he certainly is, and will be his heir too, as certainly as his name is Jones." At that word Abigail let drop the bacon which she was conveying to her mouth, and cried out, "You surprise me, sir! Is it possible Mr. Jones should be now in the house?"—"*Quare non?*" answered Partridge, "it is possible, and it is certain."

Abigail now made haste to finish the remainder of her meal, and then repaired back to her mistress, when the conversation passed which may be read in the next chapter.

CHAPTER 5

SHOWING WHO THE AMIABLE LADY, AND HER
UNAMIABLE MAID, WERE

As in the month of June, the damask rose, which chance hath planted among the lilies, with their candid hue mixes his vermilion; or as some playsome heifer in the pleasant month of May diffuses her odoriferous breath over the flowery meadows; or as, in the blooming month of April, the gentle, constant dove, perched on some fair bough, sits meditating on her mate; so, looking a hundred charms and breathing as many sweets, her thoughts being fixed on her Tommy, with a heart as good and innocent as her face was beautiful, Sophia (for it was she herself) lay reclining her lovely head on her hand, when her maid entered the room, and running directly to the bed, cried, "Madam—madam—who doth your ladyship think is in the house?" Sophia, starting up, cried, "I hope my father hath not overtaken us." "No, madam, it is one worth a hundred fathers; Mr. Jones himself is here at this very instant."—"Mr. Jones!" says Sophia, "it is impossible! I cannot be so fortunate." Her maid averred the fact, and was presently detached by her mistress to order him to be called; for she said she was resolved to see him immediately.

Mrs. Honour had no sooner left the kitchen in the manner we have before seen than the landlady fell severely upon her. The poor woman had indeed been loading her heart with foul language for some time, and now it scoured out of her mouth, as filth doth from a mud-cart when the board which confines it is removed. Partridge likewise shovelled in his share of calumny, and (what may surprise the reader) not only bespattered the maid, but attempted to sully the lily-white character of Sophia herself. "Never a barrel the better herring," cries he, "*Noscitur à socio*, is a true saying. It must be confessed, indeed, that the lady in the fine garments is the civiller of the two; but I warrant neither of them are a bit better than they should be. A couple of Bath trulls, I'll answer for them; your quality don't ride about at this time o' night without servants."—"Sbodlikins, and that's true," cries the landlady, "you have certainly hit upon the very matter; for quality don't come into a house without bespeaking a supper, whether they eat or no."

While they were thus discoursing, Mrs. Honour returned and discharged her commission, by bidding the landlady immediately wake Mr. Jones, and tell him a lady wanted to speak with him. The landlady referred her to Partridge, saying, "He was the squire's friend; but, for her part, she never called men-folks, especially gentlemen," and then walked sullenly out of the kitchen. Honour applied herself to Partridge; but he refused, "For my friend," cries he, "went to bed very late, and he would be very angry to be disturbed so soon." Mrs. Honour insisted still to have him called, saying, "She was sure, instead of being angry, that he would be to the highest degree delighted when he knew the occasion."—"Another time, perhaps, he might," cries Partridge; "but *non omnia possumus omnes*. One woman is enough at once for a reasonable man."—"What do you mean by one woman, fellow?" cries Honour.—"None of your fellow," answered Partridge. He then proceeded to inform her plainly that Jones was in bed with a wench, and made use of an expression too indelicate to be here inserted; which so enraged Mrs. Honour, that she called him jackanapes, and returned in a violent hurry to her mistress, whom she acquainted with the success of her errand, and with the account she had received; which, if possible, she exaggerated, being as angry with Jones as if he had pronounced all the words that came from the mouth of Partridge. She discharged a torrent of abuse on the master, and advised her mistress to quit all thoughts of a man who had never shown himself deserving of her. She then ripped up the story of Molly Seagrim, and gave the most malicious turn to his formerly quitting Sophia herself; which, I must confess, the present incident not a little countenanced.

The spirits of Sophia were too much dissipated by concern to enable her to stop the torrent of her maid. At last, however, she interrupted her, saying, "I never can believe this; some villain hath belied him. You say you had it from his friend; but surely it is not the office of a friend to betray such secrets."—"I suppose," cries Honour, "the fellow is his pimp, for I never saw so ill-looked a villain. Besides, such profligate rakes as Mr. Jones are never ashamed of these matters."

To say the truth, this behaviour of Partridge was a little inexcusable; but he had not slept off the effect of the dose which he swallowed the evening before; which had, in the morning, received the addition of above a pint of wine, or indeed rather of malt spirits; for the perry was by no means pure. Now, that part of his head which Nature designed for the reservoir of drink being very shallow, a small quantity of liquor overflowed it, and opened the sluices of his heart; so that all the secrets there deposited run out. These sluices were indeed, naturally, very ill-secured. To give the best-natured turn we can to his disposition, he was a very honest man; for, as he was the most inquisitive of mortals, and eternally prying into the secrets of others, so he very faithfully paid them by communicating, in return, everything within his knowledge.

While Sophia, tormented with anxiety, knew not what to believe, nor what resolution to take, Susan arrived with the sack-whey. Mrs. Honour immediately advised her mistress, in a whisper, to pump this wench, who probably could inform her of the truth. Sophia approved it, and began as follows: "Come hither, child; now answer me truly what I am going to ask you, and I promise you I will very well reward you. Is there a young gentleman in this house, a handsome young gentleman, that——" Here Sophia blushed and was confounded.—"A young gentleman," cries Honour, "that came hither in company with that saucy rascal who is now in the kitchen?"—Susan answered, "There was."—"Do you

know anything of any lady?" continues Sophia, "any lady? I
don't ask you whether she is handsome or no; perhaps she is not;
that's nothing to the purpose; but do you know of any lady?"—
"La, madam," cries Honour, "you will make a very bad exam-
iner. Hark'ee, child," says she, "is not that very young gentleman
now in bed with some nasty trull or other?" Here Susan smiled,
and was silent. "Answer the question, child," says Sophia, "and
here's a guinea for you."—"A guinea! madam," cries Susan; "la,
what's a guinea? If my mistress should know it I shall certainly
lose my place that very instant."—"Here's another for you," says
Sophia, "and I promise you faithfully your mistress shall never
know it." Susan, after a very short hesitation, took the money,
and told the whole story, concluding with saying, "If you have
any great curiosity, madam, I can steal softly into his room, and
see whether he be in his own bed or no." She accordingly did this
by Sophia's desire, and returned with an answer in the negative.

Sophia now trembled and turned pale. Mrs. Honour begged
her to be comforted, and not to think any more of so worthless a
fellow. "Why there," says Susan, "I hope madam, your ladyship
won't be offended; but pray, madam, is not your ladyship's name
Madam Sophia Western?"—"How is it possible you should know
me?" answered Sophia.—"Why, that man that the gentlewoman
spoke of, who is in the kitchen, told about you last night. But
I hope your ladyship is not angry with me."—"Indeed, child,"
said she, "I am not; pray tell me all, and I promise you I'll reward
you."—"Why, madam," continued Susan, "that man told us all
in the kitchen that Madam Sophia Western—indeed I don't know
how to bring it out." Here she stopped, till, having received
encouragement from Sophia, and being vehemently pressed by
Mrs. Honour, she proceeded thus:—"He told us, madam, though
to be sure it is all a lie, that your ladyship was dying for love of
the young squire, and that he was going to the wars to get rid of
you. I thought to myself then he was a false-hearted wretch;
but, now, to see such a fine, rich, beautiful lady as you be, forsaken for such an ordinary woman; for to be sure so she is, and
another man's wife into the bargain. It is such a strange, unnatural thing, in a manner."

Sophia gave her a third guinea, and, telling her she would
certainly be her friend if she mentioned nothing of what had
passed, nor informed any one who she was, dismissed the girl,
with orders to the post-boy to get the horses ready immediately.

Being now left alone with her maid, she told her trusty waiting-woman, "That she never was more easy than at present. I am now convinced," said she, "he is not only a villain, but a low despicable wretch. I can forgive all rather than his exposing my name in so barbarous a manner. That renders him the object of my contempt. Yes, Honour, I am now easy; I am indeed; I am very easy"; and then she burst into a violent flood of tears.

After a short interval spent by Sophia, chiefly in crying, and assuring her maid that she was perfectly easy, Susan arrived with an account that the horses were ready, when a very extraordinary thought suggested itself to our young heroine, by which Mr. Jones would be acquainted with her having been at the inn, in a way which, if any sparks of affection for her remained in him, would be at least some punishment for his faults.

The reader will be pleased to remember a little muff, which hath had the honour of being more than once remembered already in this history. This muff, ever since the departure of Mr. Jones, had been the constant companion of Sophia by day and her bedfellow by night; and this muff she had at this very instant upon her arm; whence she took it off with great indignation, and, having writ her name with her pencil upon a piece of paper which she pinned to it, she bribed the maid to convey it into the empty bed of Mr. Jones, in which, if he did not find it, she charged her to take some method of conveying it before his eyes in the morning.

Then, having paid for what Mrs. Honour had eaten, in which bill was included an account for what she herself might have eaten, she mounted her horse, and, once more assuring her companion that she was perfectly easy, continued her journey.

CHAPTER 6
CONTAINING, AMONG OTHER THINGS, THE INGENUITY
OF PARTRIDGE, THE MADNESS OF TOM JONES,
AND THE FOLLY OF FITZPATRICK

It was now past five in the morning, and other company began to rise and come to the kitchen, among whom were the sergeant and the coachman, who, being thoroughly reconciled, made a libation, or, in the English phrase, drank a hearty cup together.

In this drinking nothing more remarkable happened than the behaviour of Partridge, who, when the sergeant drank a health to

King George, repeated only the word King; nor could he be brought to utter more; for though he was going to fight against his own cause, yet he could not be prevailed upon to drink against it.

Mr. Jones, being now returned to his own bed (but from whence he returned we must beg to be excused from relating), summoned Partridge from this agreeable company, who, after a ceremonious preface, having obtained leave to offer his advice, delivered himself as follows:—

"It is, sir, an old saying, and a true one, that a wise man may sometimes learn counsel from a fool; I wish, therefore, I might be so bold as to offer you my advice, which is to return home again, and leave these *horrida bella*, these bloody wars, to fellows who are contented to swallow gun-powder because they have nothing else to eat. Now, everybody knows your honour wants for nothing at home; when that's the case, why should any man travel abroad?"

"Partridge," cries Jones, "thou art certainly a coward; I wish, therefore, thou wouldst return home thyself, and trouble me no more."

"I ask your honour's pardon," cries Partridge; "I spoke on your account more than my own; for as to me, Heaven knows my circumstances are bad enough, and I am so far from being afraid, that I value a pistol, or a blunderbuss, or any such thing, no more than a pop-gun. Every man must die once, and what signifies the manner how? besides, perhaps I may come off with the loss only of an arm or a leg. I assure you, sir, I was never less afraid in my life; and so, if your honour is resolved to go on, I am resolved to follow you. But, in that case, I wish I might give my opinion. To be sure it is a scandalous way of travelling, for a great gentleman like you to walk afoot. Now here are two or three good horses in the stable, which the landlord will certainly make no scruple of trusting you with; but, if he should, I can easily contrive to take them; and, let the worst come to the worst, the King would certainly pardon you, as you are going to fight in his cause."

Now, as the honesty of Partridge was equal to his understanding, and both dealt only in small matters, he would never have attempted a roguery of this kind had he not imagined it altogether safe; for he was one of those who have more consideration of the gallows than of the fitness of things; but, in reality,

he thought he might have committed this felony without any
danger; for besides that he doubted not but the name of Mr.
Allworthy would sufficiently quiet the landlord, he conceived
they should be altogether safe, whatever turn affairs might take;
as Jones, he imagined, would have friends enough on one side,
and as his friends would as well secure him on the other.

When Mr. Jones found that Partridge was in earnest in this
proposal, he very severely rebuked him, and that in such bitter
terms that the other attempted to laugh it off, and presently
turned the discourse to other matters, saying he believed they
were then in a bawdy-house, and that he had with much ado prevented two wenches from disturbing his honour in the middle of
the night. "Heyday!" says he, "I believe they got into your chamber whether I would or no; for here lies the muff of one of them
on the ground." Indeed, as Jones returned to his bed in the dark,
he had never perceived the muff on the quilt, and, in leaping into
his bed, he had tumbled it on the floor. This Partridge now took
up, and was going to put into his pocket, when Jones desired to
see it. The muff was so very remarkable, that our hero might
possibly have recollected it without the information annexed.
But his memory was not put to that hard office; for the same
instant he saw and read the words Sophia Western upon the
paper which was pinned to it. His looks now grew frantic in a
moment, and he eagerly cried out, "Oh, Heavens! how came
this muff here?"—"I know no more than your honour," cried
Partridge; "but I saw it upon the arm of one of the women who
would have disturbed you, if I would have suffered them."—
"Where are they?" cries Jones, jumping out of bed, and laying
hold of his clothes.—"Many miles off, I believe, by this time,"
said Partridge. And now Jones, upon further inquiry, was sufficiently assured that the bearer of this muff was no other than the
lovely Sophia herself.

The behaviour of Jones on this occasion, his thoughts, his
looks, his words, his actions, were such as beggar all description.
After many bitter execrations on Partridge, and not fewer on himself, he ordered the poor fellow, who was frightened out of his
wits, to run down and hire him horses at any rate; and a very few
minutes afterwards, having shuffled on his clothes, he hastened
downstairs to execute the orders himself which he had just before given.

But before we proceed to what passed on his arrival in the

kitchen, it will be necessary to recur to what had there happened since Partridge had first left it on his master's summons.

The sergeant was just marched off with his party, when the two Irish gentlemen arose and came downstairs; both complaining that they had been so often waked by the noises in the inn, that they had never once been able to close their eyes all night.

The coach which had brought the young lady and her maid, and which, perhaps, the reader may have hitherto concluded was her own, was, indeed, a returned coach belonging to Mr. King, of Bath, one of the worthiest and honestest men that ever dealt in horse-flesh, and whose coaches we heartily recommend to all our readers who travel that road. By which means they may, perhaps, have the pleasure of riding in the very coach, and being driven by the very coachman, that is recorded in this history.

The coachman, having but two passengers, and hearing Mr. Maclachlan was going to Bath, offered to carry him thither at a very moderate price. He was induced to this by the report of the hostler, who said that the horse which Mr. Maclachlan had hired from Worcester would be much more pleased with returning to his friends there than to prosecute a long journey; for that the said horse was rather a two-legged than a four-legged animal.

Mr. Maclachlan immediately closed with the proposal of the coachman, and, at the same time, persuaded his friend Fitzpatrick to accept of the fourth place in the coach. This conveyance the soreness of his bones made more agreeable to him than a horse; and, being well assured of meeting with his wife at Bath, he thought a little delay would be of no consequence.

Maclachlan, who was much the sharper man of the two, no sooner heard that this lady came from Chester, with the other circumstances which he learned from the hostler, than it came into his head that she might possibly be his friend's wife; and presently acquainted him with this suspicion, which had never once occurred to Fitzpatrick himself. To say the truth, he was one of those compositions which nature makes up in too great a hurry, and forgets to put any brains into their heads.

Now it happens to this sort of men, as to bad hounds, who never hit off a fault themselves; but no sooner doth a dog of sagacity open his mouth than they immediately do the same, and, without the guidance of any scent, run directly forwards as fast as they are able. In the same manner, the very moment Mr. Maclachlan had mentioned his apprehension, Mr. Fitzpatrick instantly concurred, and flew directly upstairs, to surprise his wife before he knew where she was, and unluckily (as Fortune loves to play tricks with those gentlemen who put themselves entirely under her conduct) ran his head against several doors and posts to no purpose. Much kinder was she to me, when she suggested that simile of the hounds, just before inserted; since the poor wife may, on these occasions, be so justly compared to a hunted hare. Like that little wretched animal, she pricks up her ears to listen after the voice of her pursuer; like her, flies away trembling when she hears it; and, like her, is generally overtaken and destroyed in the end.

This was not, however, the case at present; for after a long fruitless search, Mr. Fitzpatrick returned to the kitchen, where, as if this had been a real chase, entered a gentleman hallooing as hunters do when the hounds are at a fault. He was just alighted from his horse, and had many attendants at his heels.

Here, reader, it may be necessary to acquaint thee with some matters, which, if thou dost know already, thou art wiser than I take thee to be. And this information thou shalt receive in the next chapter.

CHAPTER 7

IN WHICH ARE CONCLUDED THE ADVENTURES THAT HAPPENED
AT THE INN AT UPTON

In the first place, then, this gentleman just arrived was no other person than Squire Western himself, who was come hither in pursuit of his daughter; and, had he fortunately been two hours earlier, he had not only found her, but his niece into the bargain; for such was the wife of Mr. Fitzpatrick, who had run away with her five years before, out of the custody of that sage lady, Madam Western.

Now this lady had departed from the inn much about the same time with Sophia; for, having been waked by the voice of her husband, she had sent up for the landlady, and being by her apprised of the matter, had bribed the good woman, at an extravagant price, to furnish her with horses for her escape. Such prevalence had money in this family; and though the mistress would have turned away her maid for a corrupt hussy, if she had known as much as the reader, yet she was no more proof against corruption herself than poor Susan had been.

Mr. Western and his nephew were not known to one another; nor indeed would the former have taken any notice of the latter if he had known him; for, this being a stolen match, and consequently an unnatural one in the opinion of the good squire, he had, from the time of her committing it, abandoned the poor young creature, who was then no more than eighteen, as a monster, and had never since suffered her to be named in his presence.

The kitchen was now a scene of universal confusion, Western inquiring after his daughter, and Fitzpatrick as eagerly after his wife, when Jones entered the room, unfortunately having Sophia's muff in his hand.

As soon as Western saw Jones, he set up the same holloa as is used by sportsmen when their game is in view. He then immediately ran up and laid hold of Jones, crying, "We have got the dog fox, I warrant the bitch is not far off." The jargon which followed for some minutes, where many spoke different things at the same time, as it would be very difficult to describe, so would it be no less unpleasant to read.

Jones having, at length, shaken Mr. Western off, and some of the company having interfered between them, our hero protested his innocence as to knowing anything of the lady; when Parson Supple stepped up, and said, "It is folly to deny it; for why, the marks of guilt are in thy hands. I will myself asseverate and bind it by an oath, that the muff thou bearest in thy hand belongeth unto Madam Sophia; for I have frequently observed her, of later days, to bear it about her."—"My daughter's muff!" cries the squire in a rage. "Hath he got my daughter's muff? bear witness the goods are found upon him. I'll have him before a justice of peace this instant. Where is my daughter, villain?"— "Sir," said Jones, "I beg you would be pacified. The muff, I acknowledge, is the young lady's; but, upon my honour, I have never seen her." At these words Western lost all patience, and grew inarticulate with rage.

Some of the servants had acquainted Fitzpatrick who Mr. Western was. The good Irishman, therefore, thinking he had now an opportunity to do an act of service to his uncle, and by that means might possibly obtain his favour, stepped up to Jones, and cried out, "Upon my conscience, sir, you may be ashamed of denying your having seen the gentleman's daughter before my face, when you know I found you there upon the bed together.' Then, turning to Western, he offered to conduct him immediately to the room where his daughter was; which offer being accepted, he, the squire, the parson, and some others, ascended directly to Mrs. Waters's chamber, which they entered with no less violence than Mr. Fitzpatrick had done before.

The poor lady started from her sleep with as much amazement as terror, and beheld at her bedside a figure which might very well be supposed to have escaped out of Bedlam. Such wildness and confusion were in the looks of Mr. Western; who no sooner saw the lady than he started back, showing sufficiently by his manner, before he spoke, that this was not the person sought after.

So much more tenderly do women value their reputation than their persons, that, though the latter seemed now in more danger than before, yet, as the former was secure, the lady screamed not with such violence as she had done on the other occasion. However, she no sooner found herself alone than she abandoned all thoughts of further repose; and, as she had sufficient reason to be dissatisfied with her present lodging, she dressed herself with all possible expedition.

Mr. Western now proceeded to search the whole house, but to as little purpose as he had disturbed poor Mrs. Waters. He then returned disconsolate into the kitchen, where he found Jones in the custody of his servants.

This violent uproar had raised all the people in the house, though it was yet scarcely daylight. Among these was a grave gentleman, who had the honour to be in the commission of the peace for the county of Worcester. Of which Mr. Western was no sooner informed than he offered to lay his complaint before him. The justice declined executing his office, as he said he had no clerk present, nor no book about justice business; and that he could not carry all the law in his head about stealing away daughters, and such sort of things.

Here Mr. Fitzpatrick offered to lend him his assistance, informing the company that he had been himself bred to the law. (And indeed he had served three years as clerk to an attorney in the north of Ireland, when, choosing a genteeler walk in life, he quitted his master, came over to England, and set up that busi-

ness which requires no apprenticeship, namely, that of a gentleman, in which he had succeeded, as hath been already partly
mentioned.)

Mr. Fitzpatrick declared that the law concerning daughters
was out of the present case; that stealing a muff was undoubtedly
felony, and the goods being found upon the person, were sufficient
evidence of the fact.

The magistrate, upon the encouragement of so learned a co-
adjutor, and upon the violent intercession of the squire, was at
length prevailed upon to seat himself in the chair of justice,
where being placed, upon viewing the muff which Jones still
held in his hand, and upon the parson's swearing it to be the
property of Mr. Western, he desired Mr. Fitzpatrick to draw up
a commitment, which he said he would sign.

Jones now desired to be heard, which was at last, with difficulty, granted him. He then produced the evidence of Mr. Partridge as to the finding it; but, what was still more, Susan deposed
that Sophia herself had delivered the muff to her, and had ordered
her to convey it into the chamber where Mr. Jones had found it.

Whether a natural love of justice, or the extraordinary comeli-
ness of Jones, had wrought on Susan to make the discovery, I
will not determine; but such were the effects of her evidence,
that the magistrate, throwing himself back in his chair, declared
that the matter was now altogether as clear on the side of the
prisoner as it had before been against him; with which the parson concurred, saying, the Lord forbid he should be instrumental
in committing an innocent person to durance. The justice then
arose, acquitted the prisoner, and broke up the court.

Mr. Western now gave every one present a hearty curse, and,
immediately ordering his horses, departed in pursuit of his daughter, without taking the least notice of his nephew Fitzpatrick, or
returning any answer to his claim of kindred, notwithstanding all
the obligations he had just received from that gentleman. In the
violence, moreover, of his hurry, and of his passion, he luckily
forgot to demand the muff of Jones; I say luckily; for he would
have died on the spot rather than have parted with it.

Jones likewise, with his friend Partridge, set forward the moment he had paid his reckoning, in quest of his lovely Sophia,
whom he now resolved never more to abandon the pursuit of.
Nor could he bring himself even to take leave of Mrs. Waters; of
whom he detested the very thoughts, as she had been, though

not designedly, the occasion of his missing the happiest interview with Sophia, to whom he now vowed eternal constancy.

As for Mrs. Waters, she took the opportunity of the coach
which was going to Bath; for which place she set out in company
with the two Irish gentlemen, the landlady kindly lending her
clothes; in return for which she was contented only to receive
about double their value as a recompense for the loan. Upon the
road she was perfectly reconciled to Mr. Fitzpatrick, who was a
very handsome fellow, and indeed did all she could to console
him in the absence of his wife.

Thus ended the many odd adventures which Mr. Jones encountered at his inn at Upton, where they talk, to this day, of
the beauty and lovely behaviour of the charming Sophia, by the
name of the Somersetshire angel.

AFTERWORD

Each of the eighteen books that comprise *Tom Jones* opens with
a chapter that serves as a prologue to the action, or to what Fielding
calls the "history." Most of these little essays deal with literary themes:
"Showing what kind of a history this is," "Of the serious in writing,"
"A comparison between the world and the stage." In spite of the bantering
tone, these opening chapters reveal Fielding's concern with the aesthetics
of the novel as a new genre. Thus, at the beginning of Book Ten the
author defends his use of incidents that may seem irrelevant, but are
actually part of a larger design; and what he says reminds us of Coleridge's
praise of *Tom Jones* as containing one of "the three most perfect plots
ever planned." At the same time Fielding is defending himself against
the charge of subverting public morals by depicting a hero whose virtues
are allayed with vices. The vices, he says, make the hero more believable,
and the reader cannot fail to note that they lead to "evil consequences"
for Tom and for those he loves.

Besides offering a defense of Fielding's methods, these prologues
impart a definite tone to the novel as a whole, by maintaining a playful
relation between the narrator and the reader. The former plays tricks
on the latter. In the second paragraph of the present prologue, the
reader is asked to share the narrator's contempt for "a little reptile of
a critic"; in the third he finds himself addressed as "my good reptile." Soon
he will be admonished as "my worthy friend (for, perhaps, thy heart may

be better than thy head)." One might add that this narrating voice is never far from the story, even when the action is most dramatic.

Fielding's editorial intrusions, uttered with the same urbanity and wit that mark the writing of the introductory chapter, often occur at significant points in the action. Thus, in Chapter 2 of the present sequence, when the furious Mr. Fitzpatrick is about to break into the room where Tom and Mrs. Waters are in bed, the action is momentarily suspended while the narrator explains why husbands should always knock at their wives' bedroom doors. Mrs. Waters' cry of "Murder! Rape!" when men storm into her room is followed by a similar comment ("these words of exclamation are used by ladies in a fright, as fa, la, la, ra, da, etc., are used in music"); and later in the chapter there are wry remarks about the ease with which women can feign virtue. Such remarks, offered at moments of potential seriousness, quickly return us to an essentially comic world in which everything turns out well enough in the end. They keep us from being emotionally involved with the characters, even when their situations are rich in emotional possibilities: Sophia seeking the young man she loves; Tom pursuing Sophia, but caught in an act of folly that began with his rescue of a women in distress; an angry father determined to save his only daughter from marrying a penniless scamp; and a husband trying to find his runaway wife.

Many critics have pointed out that Fielding had a way of mingling high and low styles of rhetoric. He was writing, in effect, for a double audience; it consisted partly of gentlefolk who had or pretended to some familiarity with the classics, and partly of persons from the new middle classes who wanted first of all a good, racy story. For readers of the first type there are those Latin quotations in Chapter 1, as well as many echoes of the formal literary epic. For the second type there is the plain style of his narrative passages. Often Fielding plays one style against the other for humorous effect, as at the beginning of Chapter 2. "Now the little trembling hare," he writes, ". . . sports wantonly o'er the lawns; now on some hollow tree the owl, shrill chorister of the night, hoots forth notes which might charm the ears of some modern connoisseur of music"; then, after two more of these elegant statements, he writes, "in plain English, it was now midnight. . . . Only Susan Chambermaid was now stirring, she being obliged to wash the kitchen before she retired to the arms of the fond expecting hostler."

Susan Chambermaid—overworked, bribable, beddable, but goodhearted—is like other figures that Fielding had used in his comedies, and in fact the present sequence is full of stage types: the angry father, the lady's maid determined to outlady her mistress, the landlady serving perry for champagne, and the husband furious at being cuckolded, who is also, in this case, the stage Irishman. One might go further and say that Fielding has treated the whole sequence as a knockabout farce. "The kitchen was now a scene of universal confusion," he says; and one pictures the scene enacted while the audience howls. As in stage comedies, there is no formal description. The few objects presented—for example, "a cold piece of beef, which indeed a gentleman's footman and the post-boy have almost cleared to the bone," and notably Sophia's muff, which plays an important part in the action—all have the quality of being stage properties. Except for the author's comments in his role of stage director, everything depends on what we see and what we hear.

The dialect, though partly indirect, is lively and true to the status and character of the speaker. Partridge brings in his tags of Latin at opportunely inopportune moments. Mr. Maclachlan, the Irish "calabalaro," speaks in Irish bulls. "Do not I know Mrs. Fitzpatrick very well," he cries to her husband, "and don't I see that the lady whom the gentleman who stands here in his shirt is lying in bed with, is none of her?" Squire Western speaks as a fox-hunting man. "We have got the dog fox," he roars as he lays hold of Jones, "I warrant the bitch is not far off." For her father, poor Sophia is the hunted bitch. With her world in ruins, she cries to her maid, "Yes, Honour, I am now easy; I am indeed; I am very easy"; and then, Fielding tells us, "she burst into violent tears." One can imagine what a gifted ingenue would do with the scene. Among the many achievements of Fielding, a banned playwright, was that of adapting stage techniques, and capturing much of the stage audience, for the new art of the novel.

The Sorrows of Young Werther (1774)

JOHANN WOLFGANG VON GOETHE (1749-1832) was not yet twenty-five when he wrote this novel, but already he was widely known as a poet and as the leader of a new literary movement, *Sturm und Drang*, Storm and Stress, a passionate revolt against the neoclassical standards that had prevailed all over Europe. Nature, love, freedom, the bruised heart, the primacy of feeling over form, and the miseries of genius when oppressed by conventional society: these were some of its favorite themes. Goethe had written a Shakespearean drama, *Götz von Berlichingen* (1773), that would furnish a pattern for the dramatists of the movement. In the same way *Werther*, his first novel, would become a model for the novelists.

It was a model based largely on his own adventures of the heart. Fiction and truth—or *Dichtung und Wahrheit*, the phrase that Goethe was to use as the title of his autobiography (1811-1833)—come relatively close in *Werther*, a fact that the author himself made clear from the first. Beginning in May 1772, he had spent four months in the little town of Wetzlar, which seemed to him idyllically provincial. There he became closely acquainted with Charlotte (or Lotte) Buff, daughter of the local magistrate, and J. C. Kestner, to whom she was engaged. Goethe was so much attracted by Charlotte that an older friend advised him to leave Wetzlar before the situation became tragic. He did leave in September, not without desperate thoughts of suicide. Charlotte and Kestner were married the following April, and a week later Goethe wrote to the bridegroom that he intended "to put you both on the stage with the most striking features." In his usual literary fashion, he was transmuting an unhappy experience into art. "All my works," he was to say much later, "are fragments of one great confession." It might be added that, in his usual amatory fashion, he soon fell in love with Maximiliane von Laroche and then with Lili Schönemann.

Another man's sorrowful life also contributed to *Werther*. In October 1772, a brilliant middle-class youngster named Karl Wilhelm Jerusalem committed suicide, and Goethe heard the story. There had been two reasons for Jerusalem's despair: he felt scorned by the elegant society in which, as secretary to a count, he was expected to move, and he was also in love with another man's wife. In the same way Werther's sorrows (Goethe used the plural) are doubly rooted in unrequited love and social ostracism. Napoleon did not think that the latter was a true cause for grief. When he met Goethe in 1808, he said that he had read the book seven times, but that, much as he admired it, he still resented Werther's hurt pride and his sense of being held in contempt by the local aristocrats. After the meeting, however, Napoleon also said, "There is a man!"

Goethe's career in letters, which covered sixty-five years, was extraordinarily fruitful. Besides making great contributions to lyric poetry, dramatic poetry and prose, autobiography, travel writing, and even science, he also wrote other novels, one of which has widely affected the history of fiction. *The Apprenticeship of Wilhelm Meister* (1796) was to become the prototype of the *Bildungsroman* or apprenticeship novel, a genre that has been especially popular among German authors; an outstanding example is Thomas Mann's *The Magic Mountain* (1924). In English and French the genre has produced such famous works as Samuel Butler's *The Way of All Flesh* (1903), Joyce's *Portrait of the Artist as a Young Man* (1916), and Gide's *The Counterfeiters* (1926). It was with *Werther*, however, and not with *The Apprenticeship*, that Goethe produced the greatest emotional impact on his own times. "Wertheriads" were sung at Jerusalem's grave, which, shaded as it was by two linden trees, resembled Werther's own. Werther's blue coat, yellow waistcoat, and gray hat became the costume of every young man who felt stifled by a class-bound social order. His death called forth a comment from Mme. de Staël: "Werther has caused more suicides than the most beautiful woman in the world."

THE STORY

Goethe's choice of an epistolary form for the novel had countless eighteenth-century precedents, beginning with Richardson's *Pamela* (1740) and *Clarissa Harlowe* (1747-1748). Often the form seems artificial, but in *Werther* the substance of the story is in such harmony with the manner of presentation that it seems to justify Goethe's remark: "Gloom is the offspring of solitude and the parent of letter writing." The fact that there is little action enables Goethe to concentrate on what the Germans call "soul painting," *Seelenmahlerei*. The book conveys a sense of moving toward inevitable tragedy, and this feeling is reinforced by the dating of Werther's letters, which are written to his friend Wilhelm and which run from May 1771 to the following December. His love blooms in the spring, his hopes decline in the autumn, and, with a note of irony, his suicide takes place at midnight on Christmas day.

In May Werther goes to the country to recover from an unfortunate love affair. Soon after he meets Lotte, and his love for her blossoms amid scenes reminiscent of the Dutch genre painters. But Lotte is married to Albert, and when he appears even benevolent Nature cannot assuage Werther's jealousy and grief. At the end of Part One he says farewell. At the beginning of Part Two he is the secretary of an ambassador. He is snubbed at a party given by the local aristocrats, abandons his position, and returns to Lotte and Albert. When he declares his love for Lotte and presses on her his first and only kisses, she severs their relation. "This is the last time, Werther!" she cries. "You shall never see me again!" He writes her a final letter announcing that he will kill himself. The passage that follows is the conclusion of the novel.

The modern translation is by Victor Lange and is published by Holt, Rinehart and Winston (New York, 1949).

[*Werther's Last Day*]

About eleven o'clock Werther asked his servant if Albert had returned. He answered: "Yes," he had seen his horse go past; upon which Werther sent him the following note, unsealed:

"Would you lend me your pistols for a journey I am about to undertake? Adieu."

Charlotte had slept little that night. Her fears were realized in a way that she could neither have foreseen nor have avoided. She, who was usually so tranquil, was feverishly disturbed. A thousand painful sensations rent her heart. Was it the passion of Werther's embraces? Was it anger at his daring? Was it the contrast between her present condition and those days of innocence, peace and self-confidence? How could she face her husband, and confess a scene which she had no reason to conceal, and which she yet felt unwilling to avow? They had so long preserved a silence toward each other—and should she be the first to break it by this unexpected admission? She was afraid that the very news of Werther's visit would annoy him, and now—this sudden catastrophe! Dared she hope that he would see her in the true light and judge her without prejudice? Should she wish that he read her inmost soul? On the other hand, could she deceive him to whom all her thoughts had ever been as clear as a crystal, and from whom she never would or could conceal a single thought? All this made her anxious and distressed. Again and again her mind returned to Werther, who was now lost to her, but whom she could not bring herself to let go, and for whom she knew nothing was left but despair if she should be lost to him.

A shadow of that estrangement which had lately come between herself and Albert fell over her thoughts. Two such intelligent and well-meaning people had begun to keep silent because of certain unspoken differences of opinion—each preoccupied with his own right and the other's wrong, making things worse and worse until eventually it became impossible to disentangle the knot at the crucial moment on which all seemed to depend. If mutual trust had earlier brought them together again, if love and understanding had helped them open their hearts to each other, our friend might still have been saved.

But we must not forget one other curious circumstance. As we can gather from Werther's correspondence, he had never concealed his anxious desire to quit this world. He had often discussed the subject with Albert; and between Charlotte and Werther it had often been a topic of conversation. Albert was so opposed to the very idea that, with a kind of irritation unusual in him, he had more than once given Werther to understand that he doubted the seriousness of his threats, and not only turned them into ridicule but persuaded Charlotte to share his feelings. Her heart was thus fairly at ease when she thought of the melancholy subject, but she never communicated to her husband the fears she felt at that time.

Albert returned and was greeted by Charlotte with an embarrassed embrace. He was himself in a bad mood; his business was unfinished, and he had found the neighboring official, with whom he had to deal, an obstinate and narrow-minded person. The bad roads, too, had provoked him.

He enquired whether anything had happened during his absence, and Charlotte hastily answered that Werther had been there on the evening before. He then asked for his letters, and was answered that several packages had been left in his study. He thereupon retired, leaving Charlotte alone.

The presence of her husband, whom she loved and honored, made a fresh impression on her heart. The recollection of his generosity, kindness, and affection calmed her agitation; a secret impulse prompted her to follow him; she took her work and went to his study, as was often her custom. He was busy opening and reading his letters. It seemed as if some of them contained disagreeable news. She asked some question; he gave short answers and went to his desk to write.

Several hours passed, and Charlotte's feelings became more and more melancholy. She felt the extreme difficulty of explaining to her husband, even if he were in a better mood, the weight that lay upon her heart; and her depression became all the more distressing as she tried to hide her grief and to control her tears.

The arrival of Werther's boy caused her the greatest embarrassment. He gave Albert a note, which the latter coldly handed to his wife, saying, "Give him the pistols—I wish him a pleasant journey," he added, turning to the servant. These words fell upon Charlotte like thunder; she rose from her seat, half conscious of what she did. She walked slowly to the wall, took down the pistols with a trembling hand, wiped the dust from them, and hesitated. She would have delayed longer had not Albert hastened her by an impatient look. She gave the fatal weapons to the boy without being able to utter a word. As soon as he had gone, she folded up her work and went to her room, in a state of immeasurable uncertainty. Her heart prophesied all sorts of catastrophes. At one moment she was on the point of going to her husband, throwing herself at his feet, and confessing everything: all that had happened on the previous evening, her own guilt, her apprehensions; then she saw that such a step would be useless; she could not hope to induce Albert to visit Werther. The table was laid; and a kind friend who had come to ask a question or two helped to sustain the conversation. They pulled themselves together, talked about this and that, and were able to forget.

When the servant brought the pistols to Werther, the latter received them with transports of delight when he heard that Charlotte had given them to him with her own hand. He had bread and wine brought in, sent his servant to dinner, and then sat down to write:

"They have passed through your hands—you have wiped the dust from them. I kiss them a thousand times—you have touched them. Heavenly Spirits favor my design—and you, Charlotte, offer me the weapon. You, from whose hands I wished to receive my death. Now—my wish is gratified. I asked my servant. You trembled when you gave him the pistols, but you bade me no farewell. Alas, alas! Not one farewell! How could you shut your heart against me on account of that one moment which made you mine forever? Oh, Charlotte, ages cannot efface the impression—I feel you cannot hate him who loves you so!"

After dinner he called his servant, told him to finish packing, destroyed many papers, and then went out to settle some small debts. He returned home, then went out again beyond the gate in spite of the rain, walked for some time in the Count's garden, and farther into the neighborhood. Toward evening he came back and wrote:

"Wilhelm, I have for the last time seen fields, wood, and sky. Farewell, you, too! And you, dearest mother, forgive me! Console her, Wilhelm. God bless you both! I have settled all my affairs! Farewell! We shall meet again, and be happier."

"I have ill rewarded you, Albert; but you will forgive me. I have disturbed the peace of your house. I have sowed distrust between you. Farewell! I will end it all. And oh! that my death may restore your happiness! Albert, Albert! make the angel happy, and may God's blessing be upon you!"

He spent the rest of the evening going through his papers; he tore and burned a great many; he sealed a few packages and addressed them to Wilhelm. They contained some short essays and disconnected aphorisms, some of which I have seen. At ten o'clock he ordered his fire to be made up, and a bottle of wine to be brought to him. He then sent his servant to bed; his room, as well as the apartments of the rest of the domestics, was situated in the back of the house. The boy lay down without undressing that he might be the sooner ready for his journey in the morning, as his master had told him that the coach horses would be at the door before six o'clock.

"*After eleven*

"All is silent around me, and my soul is calm. I thank Thee, God, that Thou has given me strength and courage in these last moments! I step to the window, my dearest, and can see a few stars through the passing storm clouds. No, you will not fall. The Almighty sustains you, and me. I see the brightest lights of the Great Bear, my favorite constellation. When I left you, Charlotte, and went out from your gate, it always was in front of me. With what rapture have I so often looked at it! How many times have I implored it with raised hands to witness my happiness! and still—But what is there, Charlotte, that does not remind me of you? Are you not everywhere about me? and have I not, like a child, treasured up every trifle which your saintly hands have touched?

"Beloved silhouette! I now return it to you; and I pray you to preserve it. Thousands of kisses have I pressed upon it, and a thousand times did it gladden my heart when I have left the house or returned.

"I have asked your father in a note to protect my body. At one corner of the churchyard, looking towards the fields, there are two linden trees—there I wish to lie. Your father can, and doubtless will, do this for his friend. You ask him, too! I will not expect it of pious Christians that their bodies should be buried near the corpse of a poor, unhappy wretch like me. I could wish to lie in some remote valley by the wayside, where priest and Levite may bless themselves as they pass by my tomb, and the Samaritan shed a tear.

"See, Charlotte, I do not shudder to take the cold and fatal cup, from which I shall drink the draught of death. Your hand gave it to me, and I do not tremble. All, all the wishes and the hopes of my life are fulfilled. Cold and stiff I knock at the brazen gates of Death.

"Oh that I might have enjoyed the bliss of dying for you! how gladly would I have sacrificed myself for you, Charlotte! And could I but restore your peace and happiness, with what resolution, with what joy, would I not meet my fate! But it is given to but a chosen few to shed their blood for those they loved, and by their death to kindle a hundred-fold the happiness of those by whom they are beloved.

"Charlotte, I wish to be buried in the clothes I wear at present; you have touched them, blessed them. I have begged this same favor of your father. My spirit soars above my coffin. I do not wish my pockets to be searched. This pink bow which you wore the first time I saw you, surrounded by the children—Oh, kiss them a thousand times for me, and tell them the fate of their unhappy friend! I think I see them playing around me. The darling children! How they swarm about me! How I attached myself to you, Charlotte! From the first hour I saw you, I knew I could not leave you! Let this ribbon be buried with me; it was a present from you on my birthday. How eagerly I accepted it all! I did not think that it would all lead to this! Be calm! I beg you, be calm!

"They are loaded—the clock strikes twelve. So be it! Charlotte! Charlotte, farewell, farewell!"

A neighbor saw the flash, and heard the shot; but, as everything remained quiet, he thought no more of it.

At six in the morning, the servant entered Werther's room with a candle. He found his master stretched on the floor, blood about him, and the pistol at his side. He called to him, took him in his arms, but there was no answer, only a rattling in the throat. The servant ran for a surgeon, for Albert. Charlotte heard the bell; a shudder seized her. She awakened her husband; both arose. The servant, in tears, stammered the dreadful news. Charlotte fell senseless at Albert's feet.

When the surgeon arrived, Werther was lying on the floor; his pulse beat, but his limbs were paralyzed. The bullet had entered the forehead over the right eye; his brains were protruding. He was bled in the arm; the blood came, and he breathed.

From the blood on the chair, it could be inferred that he had committed the deed sitting at his desk, and that he had afterwards fallen on the floor and had twisted convulsively around the chair. He was found lying on his back near the window. He was fully dressed in his boots, blue coat and yellow waistcoat.

The house, the neighbors, and the whole town were in commotion. Albert arrived. They had laid Werther on the bed. His head was bandaged, and the pallor of death was upon his face. His limbs were motionless; a terrible rattling noise came from his lungs, now strongly, now weaker. His death was expected at any moment.

He had drunk only one glass of the wine. "Emilia Galotti" lay open on his desk.

Let me say nothing of Albert's distress or of Charlotte's grief.

The old judge hastened to the house upon hearing the news; he kissed his dying friend amid a flood of tears. His eldest boys soon followed him on foot. In speechless sorrow they threw themselves on their knees by the bedside, and kissed his hands and face. The eldest, who was his favorite, clung to his lips till he was gone; even then the boy had to be taken away by force. At noon Werther died. The presence of the judge, and the arrangements he had made prevented a disturbance; that night, at the hour of eleven he had the body buried in the place that Werther had chosen.

The old man and his sons followed the body to the grave. Albert could not. Charlotte's life was in danger. The body was carried by workmen. No clergyman attended.

AFTERWORD

This volume offers two examples of epistolary narrative; the other is the series of letters from Laclos' *Dangerous Liaisons*. As the first major practitioner of the form, Richardson might have been chosen instead. Our two examples, however, illustrate what strikingly different effects can be produced within the constricting limits of the form. *Werther* leads to the Romantic novel with its emotionalism and subjectivity, while *Dangerous Liaisons* points toward Stendhal and Proust and the cerebrations of modern fiction.

The epistolary novel virtually disappeared half a century after *Werther*, though one can think of such later examples as Henry James's charming *Bundle of Letters* (1879)—which is of course a novella—and Thornton Wilder's *The Ides of March* (1948). Still later novelists often *use* letters effectively, as Lawrence Durrell does in *The Alexandria Quartet* (1957–1960) and Saul Bellow in *Herzog* (1964), but with very rare exceptions they do not rely on letters as the principal means of narration.

There were many reasons for the disappearance of the form. One was that after the novel became literarily respectable authors stopped pretending that they had discovered letters by "real" persons, which they, as "editors," were offering to the reading public. Verisimilitude no longer required such a pretense. Another reason is that novelists found a better means of achieving the same effects. The early novel from Cervantes through Fielding had been essentially dramatic, in that characters talked and acted but seldom *thought*. The novel in letters had the advantage of permitting characters to be introspective. After exploring this possibility, however, novelists began trying to penetrate more deeply into the minds of their heroes, and many of them ended by adopting the inner monologue as a better means of revealing the psyche than letters could offer.

Still another reason for the disappearance of the form is that the epistolary novel required a highly literate and, in general, an upper-class assortment of characters, with leisure enough to write interesting letters. By the mid-nineteenth century, however, the novel was portraying middle-class people for its middle-class readers. "Everything goes to the people," the Goncourt brothers complained in 1866, "and deserts the kings—even literary themes, which descend from royal misfortunes to private misfortunes." In the new world of the middle class, work and the pursuit of happiness, as variously conceived, afforded little time for epistolary intercourse.

The form also had a technical limitation. It required letters to bear the burden of more description than readers of any era would expect to find in them. They were also forced to report most of the action as having already taken place. This necessary retrospection may be effective in *Werther*, where the hero reflects poignantly on what he has done and seen, as also in *Dangerous Liaisons*, where Valmont analyzes his attempts at seduction in the manner of a general assessing his former campaigns. But it could also lead to improbabilities, as when Richardson's Clarissa composes frantic but rather elegant letters to her friend while Lovelace is panting outside her boudoir. And so the form disappeared, in the end, for much the same reason it had been widely adopted, that is, in the search for greater verisimilitude.

As for the present scene from *Werther*, it illustrates, among other things, the problems in point of view that often faced the author of an epistolary novel. The beginning of the scene is written by Wilhelm, the recipient of Werther's letters; and Goethe thereupon assumes the role of omniscient narrator when he has Wilhelm project himself into Charlotte's distraught mind. Wilhelm also describes a scene between Charlotte and Albert that he could not possibly have witnessed. An ironic note is struck when Charlotte gives the servant the pistols with which Werther will end his life. The servant's return to Werther's lodging takes us back to the epistolary framework; we read that Werther "sat down to write." What follows is his last letter to Charlotte. It recapitulates themes that had been introduced in the previous correspondence: Werther's clothes, Lotte's silhouette, the pink bow she gave him, the children he kissed with such rapture, and the pistols that he now fondles once more, since they have been blessed by the touch of her hands.

With the last two pages of the book, the point of view shifts once again. The pages are written by a third-person narrator, who reports at length on Werther's death throes, writing factually but in such a manner as to extract from them the last drop of emotion. We learn that the book lying beside his body was a copy of Lessing's *Emilia Galotti*, another tale of unhappy love in which social differences play a part. How often have novelists, beginning with Cervantes, exploited the importance of literature in shaping the ideas and attitudes of their characters—offering, as it were, a special plea for their own creations! The last paragraph is a series of laconic statements that contrast with the hero's earlier effusions. It makes for an effective coda; and the final sentence, "No clergyman attended," underscores Werther's alienation from society in death as well as in life.

Dangerous Liaisons (1782)

PIERRE CHODERLOS DE LACLOS (1741-1803) spent his adult life in the army. A member of the minor nobility, he became a sub-lieutenant in 1761, and in 1799, toward the end of his military career, Napoleon made him a general. During the French Revolution, he first supported Louis XVI, then advocated a constitutional monarchy, then spoke for republicanism, then finally swore loyalty to Napoleon. He was twice imprisoned for political reasons and, like many others, learned how difficult it was merely to survive in a revolutionary era when, to paraphrase Lewis Carroll, it took all the running a man could do to stand in the same place.

The one-volume Pléiade edition of Laclos' complete works, standard in France, contains *Dangerous Liaisons*, which takes more than half of the volume, a dull essay "On the Education of Women," some highly conventional poems, a few political essays, with two on literary themes, libretti for two comic operas, only one of which was performed, and a long panegyric of Marshal Vauban, the great military architect. In short, Laclos was "a one-book man"; but that book was a novel described in our time by Jean Giraudoux as "a betrayal and a denunciation of the eighteenth century . . . the only French novel that gives you the impression of danger."

Not long before his death he met Stendhal, then a youngster serving with the French army in Italy. Stendhal's novels were to show that he owed a considerable debt to Laclos, perhaps including the habit, common to both authors, of describing a love affair as if it were a military campaign. In *The Life of Henri Brulard*, an autobiographical work with a strong admixture of fiction, Stendhal tells us that in his native Grenoble he had known a Mme. de Montmart, who, so he claims, was the model for Mme. de Merteuil in the *Liaisons*. He says of her that she "was worthy of the times of the most insatiable of the Roman empresses." The story is also told that the Marquise de Conflans, who flattered herself—probably without good reason—that *she* was the model for the Marquise de Merteuil, shut her door to Laclos, saying that she feared to be alone with him. If one can believe Laclos' friend Tilly when he describes the novelist as "a large, thin, yellow gentleman, dressed in black . . . a virtuous man, a good son, a good father, an excellent husband," then Mme. de Conflans was confusing fiction with life.

Dangerous Liaisons ran through fifty editions in Laclos' lifetime. Marie Antoinette, herself expert in the art of love, owned a copy, with the title and the author's name discreetly excised. French authorities twice ordered the book destroyed, in 1824 and in 1865, on the ground that it was an outrage to good conduct. Not many years ago a film was made of it, which the authorities were loath to release for foreign distribution, this time on the ground that it would give a false and excessively erotic picture of the French character. Plainly the wish was realized that Laclos expressed in a letter to Tilly: "I resolved to produce a work that would depart from the ordinary path; that would make some noise and would still reverberate on the earth after I am gone."

Dangerous Liaisons is an incredibly brutal book. Laclos strips off the elegant façade of the era and denies its claims to *politesse* and decorum. The world of graceful architecture, elegant clothes, stately minuets—visually portrayed by painters like Boucher, Fragonard, and Watteau—is all there. Beneath the exterior, however, we sense complete moral corruption and a cold calculus of values having to do with love, lust, and cruelty. Nearly a hundred years after the book appeared, the Goncourt brothers described it as being to eighteenth-century ethics in matters of love what Machiavelli's *The Prince* had been to political conduct in sixteenth-century Italy.

THE STORY

The Marquise de Merteuil is the heroine and villainess of the book; the Vicomte de Valmont is its hero and villain. Merteuil has been the mistress of the Comte de Gercourt, then of Valmont, and now she has taken another lover, the Chevalier de Belleroche ("my Chevalier" in Letter 20). Gercourt plans to marry the young, beautiful, and wealthy Cécile de Volanges (Letter 22 is addressed to her mother). But Cécile and the young Chevalier de Danceny have fallen in love with each other, and indeed they represent the only "good" love relation in the novel.

Valmont seizes on the idea of seducing Mme. de Tourvel, a sincerely religious married woman. He asks Merteuil to help him. Their letters consist of her advice to him, and his reports of progress in the amatory campaign. She also asks him to seduce Cécile, to whom she pretends to act as confidante (and here her motives stem from pure nastiness). She herself manages to seduce the much younger Danceny, thus breaking up the ideal romance of the young couple. After Valmont gets Cécile pregnant, she miscarries and retires to a convent. He also succeeds in breaking down the resistance of Mme. de Tourvel, who then goes mad and dies soon after. Danceny kills Valmont in a duel. The Marquise de Merteuil contracts smallpox, loses an eye, falls into bankruptcy, and leaves France for Holland. Poetic justice is dispensed, but at what a cost!

Dangerous Liaisons consists of 175 letters, from which we have selected Letters 20 through 23. Valmont has left Paris for an extended visit to the château of his very old aunt, Mme. de Rosemonde, who is also entertaining Mme. de Tourvel in the absence of her husband. The modern English version, published by Bantam Books, is the work of Lowell Bair.

[*A Deed of Virtue*]

LETTER 20

FROM THE MARQUISE DE MERTEUIL

TO THE VICOMTE DE VALMONT

August 20, 17—

Ah, you rascal, you flatter me for fear I may mock you! But I shall be kind: you have written to me so many extravagant things that I am forced to forgive you for the sobriety in which you are being kept by your Madame de Tourvel. I do not think my Chevalier would be as indulgent as I am: he would be capable of not approving the renewal of our lease, and of finding nothing amusing in your wild idea. It made me laugh heartily, however, and I was sorry that I had to laugh all alone. If you had been here, I do not know how far my gaiety might have led me; but I have now had time to reflect, and I have armed myself with severity. Not that I refuse forever; but I insist on a postponement, and I am right. My vanity might become involved, and once I had been caught up in the game, it is impossible to say where it would stop. I might enchain you again, and make you forget your Madame de Tourvel; and think how scandalous it would be if I, unworthy as I am, should make you disgusted with virtue! To avoid this danger, here are my conditions.

As soon as you have possessed your pious beauty and can prove it to me, come to me and I shall be yours. But, as you know, in important matters only written proof is accepted. By this arrangement, on the one hand, I shall be a reward rather than a consolation, and that idea pleases me more; and on the other hand, your success will be all the more piquant because it will be in itself a means of infidelity. Come, come as soon as you can and bring me a token of your triumph, like those gallant knights of old who used to lay at their ladies' feet the splendid fruits of their victory. Seriously, I am curious to know what a prude will write after such a moment, and what veil she will throw over her words after having left none on her body. It is for you to see whether I have placed too high a price on myself; but I warn you that it will not be lowered. Until then, my dear Vicomte, you will forgive me if I remain faithful to my Chevalier and amuse myself by making him happy, despite the slight distress it causes you.

However, if I were less moral, I believe he would now have a dangerous rival: little Cécile Volanges. I adore that child; it is a real passion. If I am not mistaken, she will become one of our most fashionable women. I can see her little heart developing, and it is a delightful sight. She is already madly in love with her Danceny, but she does not know it yet. And although he is also very much in love, he still has the shyness of his age and does not dare to speak too openly. They both worship me. She, especially, is eager to tell me her secret. Particularly in the past few days I have seen that she is really oppressed by it, and I would have done her a great service by helping her a little; but I have not forgotten that she is only a child and I do not want to compromise myself. Danceny has spoken to me a little more clearly, but my mind is made up: I will not listen to him. As for her, I am often tempted to make her my pupil; it is a service I would like to render Gercourt. He has given me enough time, since he will be in Corsica until October. I have a notion that I shall make good use of that time, and that we shall give him a fully developed woman instead of his innocent schoolgirl. What insolent confidence on the part of that man who dares to sleep peacefully while a woman who has reason to complain of him has not yet avenged herself! If that girl were here at this moment, I do not know what I might say to her.

Good-by, Vicomte; good night and good luck; but in the name of God, make some progress! Remember that if you fail to have that woman, others will blush at having had you.

LETTER 21

FROM THE VICOMTE DE VALMONT

TO THE MARQUISE DE MERTEUIL

August 20, 17—

At last, my fair friend, I have taken a step forward, a large step which, although it has not led me to my goal, has at least showed me that I am on the right path, and has banished my fear that I had gone astray. I have finally declared my love, and although she has maintained a stubborn silence, I have obtained what is perhaps the least ambiguous and most flattering reply possible. But let us not anticipate; let us go back to the beginning.

You will recall that my actions were being spied upon. Well, I decided to make that scandalous procedure serve the cause of public edification, and here is what I did. I told my valet to find in the vicinity some unfortunate person who needed help. It was not a difficult mission to accomplish. Yesterday afternoon he informed me that this morning the authorities were going to seize the personal property of an entire family who could not pay their taxes. I made sure there was no girl or woman in that family whose age or appearance might cast suspicion on my act, and when I was well informed I declared at supper that I intended to go hunting the next day. Here I must do justice to my Madame de Tourvel: she no doubt regretted to some extent the orders she had given, and while she did not have the strength to overcome her curiosity, she at least had enough to oppose my desire. It would be an extremely hot day, I would run the risk of falling ill, I would kill nothing, I would tire myself in vain; and during this speech her eyes, which perhaps spoke better than she wished, showed me that she wanted me to take these bad reasons for good ones. I had no intention of giving in to them, as you may well imagine, and I also resisted a little diatribe against hunting and hunters, as well as a little cloud of ill-humor which darkened her heavenly face all evening. For a moment I was afraid her orders might be rescinded and that her delicacy might harm me. I reckoned without a woman's curiosity, so I was mistaken. My valet reassured me that same evening, and I went to bed satisfied.

I got up at dawn and left. I was scarcely fifty paces from the château when I saw my spy following me. Pretending to be hunting, I set out across the fields toward the village I wanted to reach. My only pleasure on the way was to force the rascal who was following me to run: since he did not dare to leave the roads, he often had to cover, at top speed, a distance three times as great as mine. I exercised him so much that I myself became overheated and sat down at the foot of a tree. He then had the insolence to slip behind a bush no more than twenty paces from me and sit down too! For a moment I was tempted to take a shot at him; although my gun was loaded only with bird shot, it would have given him a sufficient lesson on the dangers of curiosity. Fortunately for him, I remembered that he was useful and even necessary to my plans; this reflection saved him.

When I arrived in the village I saw a commotion. I went forward, asked questions and was told what was happening. I sent for the tax collector and, yielding to my generous compassion, I nobly paid fifty-six francs, for which five people were about to be reduced to abject poverty and despair. After this simple act you cannot imagine what a chorus of benedictions echoed around me from the spectators! What tears of gratitude flowed from the eyes of the aged head of the family and embellished his patriarchal face, which had been rendered truly hideous only a moment before by the savage imprint of despair! I was watching this spectacle when a younger peasant hurried toward me leading a woman and two children by the hand and said to them, "Let us all fall at the feet of this image of God." In a moment I was surrounded by the family prostrate at my knees. I admit my weakness: my eyes filled with tears and I felt an involuntary but delightful surge of emotion. I was surprised by the pleasure it gives one to do good; I am tempted to believe that those whom we call virtuous do not have as much merit as many are fond of attributing to them. Be that as it may, I thought it only right that I should pay those poor people for the pleasure they had just given me. I handed them the ten louis I had brought with me.

Their thanks began again, but with less emotion: necessity had produced the great, the true effect; the rest was merely an expression of gratitude and surprise for superfluous gifts.

Meanwhile, amid the family's wordy benedictions, I was not unlike the hero of a drama in the final scene. I must point out to you that the faithful spy was in the crowd. My purpose had been accomplished: I disengaged myself from them and went back to the château. All things considered, I congratulate myself on my stratagem. That woman is certainly worth all the pains I have taken; they will some day be my claims on her, and having thus paid for her in advance, as it were, I shall have the right to dispose of her according to my fancy, without having to reproach myself in any way.

I forgot to tell you that, in order to turn everything to my profit, I asked those good people to pray to God for the success of my plans. You will see whether their prayers have not been partly granted already. . . . But I have just been told that supper is served, and it would be too late for this letter to leave if I did not finish it until I returned to my room, so the rest will have to wait until the next post. I am sorry, because the rest is the best part. Good-by, my fair friend. You are stealing from me a moment of the pleasure of seeing her.

LETTER 22
FROM MADAME DE TOURVEL
TO MADAME DE VOLANGES

August 20, 17—

You will no doubt be glad, Madame, to hear of an act on the part of Monsieur de Valmont which, it seems to me, is in strong contrast with all those by which he has been represented to you. It is so painful to think unfavorably of anyone, so sad to find only vices in those who could have all the qualities needed to make virtue cherished! And you are so fond of forbearance that it is rendering you a service to give you reasons for revising a judgment that was too harsh. It seems to me that Monsieur de Valmont is entitled to hope for that favor, I might almost say that justice, and this is why I think so.

This morning he went off on one of those walks which might have led one to suspect that he was pursuing some intrigue in the vicinity, as it occurred to you that he might be. Fortunately for him, and still more fortunately for us, since it saves us from being unjust, one of my servants had to go in the same direction,[1] and it was through him that my reprehensible but fortunate curiosity was satisfied. He reported to us that Monsieur de Valmont, having found in the village of ———— an unfortunate family whose personal property was about to be sold because they could not pay their taxes, not only hastened to pay off the debt of those poor people, but gave them a considerable sum of money as well. My servant witnessed this virtuous act, and he also reported to me that the peasants, in talking among themselves and with him, had said that a servant, whom they described, and who my own servant thinks is Monsieur de Valmont's, made inquiries yesterday concerning those inhabitants of the village who might be in need of help. If this is true, it was not merely a passing compassion aroused by circumstances, but a deliberate plan to do good; it shows the solicitude of charity, the finest virtue of the finest souls. But whether it happened by chance or according to a plan, it was still a good and praiseworthy act, and merely listening to an account of it moved me to tears. I shall further add, still in the interest of justice, that when I spoke to him about that act, which he had not mentioned, he began by denying it, and when he finally admitted it he seemed to place so little value on it that his modesty doubled its merit.

Now tell me, my worthy friend, if Monsieur de Valmont is indeed an incorrigible libertine, if he is nothing but that, yet conducts himself in this way, what is left for decent people? What! Do the wicked share the sacred pleasure of charity with the virtuous? Would God permit a scoundrel to give an honorable family aid for which they would render thanks to His divine Providence? And could He be pleased to hear pure lips shed their blessings upon a reprobate? No, I prefer to believe that certain errors, though long-lived, are not eternal; and I cannot think that a man who does good is an enemy of virtue. Monsieur de Valmont is perhaps only one more example of the danger of bad associations. I shall end with this idea, which pleases me. If, on the one hand, it may serve to justify him in your mind, on the other, it makes more and more precious to me that friendship which unites me with you for life.

[1] Does Madame de Tourvel not dare to say that it was by her order? [Author's note.]

I have the honor of being, etc.

P.S.—Madame de Rosemonde and I are about to go to see the honest and unfortunate family and join our belated aid to that of Monsieur de Valmont. We shall take him with us. We shall at least give those good people the pleasure of seeing their benefactor again; that, I believe, is all he has left us to do.

LETTER 23
FROM THE VICOMTE DE VALMONT
TO THE MARQUISE DE MERTEUIL

August 21, 17—, at four o'clock in morning

We broke off at my return to the château; I shall continue my story from there.

I had only a short time in which to change my clothes. I went into the drawing room, where my fair lady was doing tapestry work while the local priest read the newspaper to my old aunt. I sat down near the tapestry frame. Glances that were even softer than usual, and almost caressing, soon led me to assume that the servant had already given an account of my mission. Indeed, my inquisitive beauty was unable to keep the secret she had stolen from me: without fearing to interrupt the venerable priest, even though his reading sounded like a sermon, she said, "I, too, have news to tell," and immediately related my adventure with an accuracy that honored the intelligence of her historian. You can imagine how I displayed all my modesty; but who could stop a woman when she is unknowingly praising the man she loves? And so I allowed her to continue. It was as though she were preaching the panegyric of a saint. Meanwhile I was observing, not without hope, all that was promised to love by her animated looks, her freer gestures, and especially the tone of her voice, which by an already perceptible alteration betrayed the agitation of her soul. She had scarcely finished speaking when Madame de Rosemonde said, "Come, nephew, let me embrace you!" I realized immediately that the pretty preacher could not prevent herself from being embraced also. She tried to flee, but she was soon in my arms, and far from having the strength to resist, she hardly had enough to stand. The more I observe that woman, the more desirable she seems to me. She quickly went back to her tapestry frame and seemed to everyone else to be beginning her work again; but I saw clearly that her trembling hands would not allow her to go on.

After dinner, the ladies decided to visit the unfortunate family I had so piously aided. I accompanied them. I shall spare you the boredom of that second scene of gratitude and praise. My heart, urged on by a delightful memory, hastens to the time when we returned to the château. On the way, my lovely lady, more thoughtful than usual, did not say a word. Preoccupied with trying to find some means of profiting from the day's event, I also remained silent. Only Madame de Rosemonde spoke, and received only short and rare answers from us. We must have bored her; that was my plan and it succeeded. When we got out of the carriage, she went to her room and left me alone with my fair lady in a dimly lighted drawing room—sweet darkness which emboldens timid love!

I had no difficulty in leading the conversation to where I wanted it to go. My charming preacher's fervor served me better than my own adroitness could have done. "When someone is so worthy of doing good," she said, fixing her gentle gaze on me, "how can he spend his life doing evil?" And I answered, "I deserve neither that praise nor that censure, and it is a mystery to me why, with all your intelligence, you have not yet understood me. Even though my confidence may harm me with you, you are too worthy of it for me to be able to refuse it to you. You will find the key to my conduct in a character which is unfortunately too easily influenced. Surrounded by immoral people, I imitated their vices; I may even have made it a point of pride to surpass them. Here I have fallen under the influence of virtue in the same way, and although I have no hope of being able to reach your level, I have at least tried to follow you. And perhaps the act for which you praise me today would lose all its value in your eyes if you knew its real motive!" (You can see, my fair friend, how close I was to the truth!) "It is not to me," I continued, "that those unfortunate people owe the aid I gave them. Where you see a praiseworthy act, I sought only a means of pleasing. I must tell you that I was only a weak agent of the divinity I worship." (At this point she tried to interrupt me, but I did not give her time.) "At this very moment," I added, "my secret has escaped from me only through weakness. I was determined not to reveal it to you; I found my happiness in rendering to your virtues and your charms a pure tribute of which you would always be unaware. But since I am incapable of deceiving when I have the example of candor before my eyes, I shall not have to reproach myself for a sinful dissimulation with regard to you. Do not think that I insult you by a criminal hope. I shall be unhappy, I know it; but my suffering will be dear to me because it will prove to me the intensity of my love. It is at your feet and in your bosom that I shall pour out my sorrows. There I shall draw fresh strength for suffering anew; there I shall find compassionate kindness, and I shall consider myself consoled because you have pitied me. O you whom I adore, hear me, pity me, help me!" I was by now at her knees, clasping her hands in mine; but she suddenly withdrew them and held them over her eyes with an expression of despair. "Oh, how wretched I am!" she exclaimed; then she burst into tears. Fortunately I had thrown myself into my speech so wholeheartedly that I was weeping too. I took her hands again and bathed them in my tears. This was a very necessary precaution, for she was so absorbed in her own sorrow that she would not have noticed mine if I had not found this means of bringing it to her attention. I also gained an opportunity to gaze at leisure upon her charming face, made still more beautiful by the powerful attraction of tears. I became carried away and lost my self-control to such an extent that I was tempted to take advantage of that moment.

How great is our weakness! How great is the power of circumstances when I forgot my plans and risked losing, by a premature triumph, the charm of long struggles and the details of a painful defeat; when, overcome by desire like an adolescent boy, I nearly exposed the conqueror of Madame de Tourvel to the danger of gathering as the fruit of his labors nothing but the insipid advantage of having had one more woman! Ah, I want her to yield, but I also want her to struggle! I want her to have strength enough to resist but not to conquer. I want her to savor at leisure the feeling of her weakness, and be forced to admit defeat. Let the obscure poacher kill the deer he has ambushed: the real hunter must bring it to bay. A sublime plan, is it not? But I might now be regretting that I had not followed it if chance had not come to the aid of my prudence.

We heard a noise. Someone was coming toward the drawing room. Madame de Tourvel was terrified; she leapt to her feet, took one of the candlesticks and walked out. I had to let her go. It was only a servant. As soon as I had ascertained this, I followed her. I had taken only a few steps when, whether because she recognized me or from a vague feeling of fear, I heard her quicken her pace, rush into her room and close the door behind her. I went up to it, but it was locked from inside. I did not knock, because that would have given her an opportunity to resist too easily. I had the simple and fortunate idea of looking through the keyhole, and I saw that adorable woman on her knees, bathed in tears and praying fervently! What god was she daring to invoke? Is there one who is sufficiently powerful against love? She now seeks outside help in vain: it is I who shall determine her fate.

Thinking I had done enough for one day, I also went to my room and began writing to you. I hoped to see her again at supper, but she sent word that she was indisposed and had gone to bed. Madame de Rosemonde wanted to go up to her room, but the malicious invalid claimed to have a headache which would not allow her to see anyone. As you may well imagine, I spent little time with my aunt after supper, and I, too, had a headache. When I retired to my room, I wrote Madame de Tourvel a long letter complaining of her harshness, then I went to bed, intending to give it to her this morning. I slept badly, as you can see from the date of this letter. I got up and reread my epistle. I saw that I had not been circumspect enough in it, that I showed more ardor than love, and more resentment than sadness. I ought to rewrite it, but I would have to be calmer.

I now see the first light of dawn, and I hope that the coolness which accompanies it will bring me sleep. I am going back to bed. No matter how strong Madame de Tourvel's dominion over me, I promise you that I shall never become so preoccupied with her that I do not have time to think about you a great deal.

AFTERWORD

In Goethe's *Werther*, the epistolary form was eminently successful in revealing states of feeling. Even in *Dangerous Liaisons*, the letters of Mme. de Tourvel—No. 22, for example—as well as those of Cécile and Danceny are rich in emotional content. But most of the novel consists of letters exchanged by Valmont and Mme. de Merteuil, and these are devoted to the cold cerebral dissection of motives. Laclos was only a few years older than Goethe, yet he belonged, as Goethe did not, to the Age of Reason then drawing to its end. He resembled many philosophers of that age—Hume or Diderot, for example—in his fashion of picking the mind to pieces, then trying to put it together again. An examination of Letter 20 alone reveals a complicated ratiocinative activity: Mme. de Merteuil details a series of relationships between herself and the other characters in the objective spirit of a behavioral psychologist surveying his rats in their mazes.

The relative lack of physical description throughout the novel was characteristic of many writers—Fielding, for example—affected by the neoclassical tradition of the eighteenth century. In the case of Laclos, the lack had a special value: it enabled him to concentrate his attention on the inner lives of his characters. The longest scene in the novel that is played against a natural background is the quasi-Rousseauistic tableau in Letter 21, cynically described by Valmont to Mme. de Merteuil, then sentimentally retold by Mme. de Tourvel in the next letter. Here the deed of virtue—paying off the taxes of a destitute village family—has been contrived by Valmont merely as a step in his conquest of Mme. de Tourvel.

Rousseau had earlier stated that sensibility cannot be counterfeited; this was a principle he had tried to illustrate in his tremendously influential novels, *La Nouvelle Héloïse* (1761) and *Emile* (1762). Laclos, in presenting the village tableau and its consequences, neatly gives the lie to Rousseau. The counterfeit sensibility of Valmont is accepted at its face value by Mme. de Tourvel. "I cannot think," she says, "that a man who does good is an enemy to virtue." In her letter to Mme. de Volanges (No. 22) she expresses genuine moral feelings; she is the sort of woman whom Rousseau would have presented with utter sympathy. For Laclos she becomes a means of enforcing his own cynical thesis: that sensibility and the pure but uninformed heart can lead to catastrophe in the world as it really exists. The simple Christian faith of Mme. de Tourvel ("Would God permit a scoundrel to give an honorable family aid for which they would render thanks for His divine Providence?") makes her a prey to Valmont's terrifying atheism. Earlier in the novel he has written to Mme. de Merteuil: "I shall dare to ravish her from the God she adores."

In the correspondence between the two leading characters, we find neither self-delusion nor attempts to deceive. While treating the rest of the world with intellectual arrogance, they are honest with each other. Merteuil and Valmont regard life as a play and other persons as actors under their joint direction. For them there is no romantic "love," but merely the amusing and never serious art of sexual satisfaction. Valmont in particular likes to speak of his actions as stratagems to be adopted in warfare or the chase. The boudoir replaces the battlefield, the tilting ground, and the forest where hunters seek their prey. "Bring me a token of your triumph, like those gallant knights of old," Merteuil orders him in Letter 20. "I congratulate myself on my stratagem," Valmont says in Letter 21. "Let the obscure poacher kill the deer he has ambushed," he tells Merteuil in Letter 23: "the real hunter must bring it to bay." Such remarks bear out the severe code that Valmont has imposed on himself: he must not yield to his emotions, and he must win.

Pride and Prejudice (1813)

JANE AUSTEN (1775-1817), seventh child of a scholarly country rector, spent her childhood and adolescence in rural Hampshire. All her novels chronicle the upper-middle-class world she knew at first hand: tea parties, county balls, family gatherings, occasional walks in a countryside where one imagines not so much the landscape of her contemporary Wordsworth (romantic lakes, streams, and mountains) as rather Pope's "nature methodized" into formal gardens, terraced lawns with well-groomed deer, and trimmed shrubs with neat herbaceous borders.

She once stated that her craft consisted of "a little bit (two inches wide) of Ivory on which I work with so firm a brush." This cameo-like quality of her novels was reflected by her circumspect life. Geographically she saw but a small portion of England. The family moved to Bath in 1801, later to Southampton, then back to the country; but they never made the Grand Tour to the Continent or an extended stay in London. She lived with her mother and her sisters until they married, and with her brother Henry, a failure in business who later entered the Anglican ministry. We know of a marriage proposal, which she refused, by one Harrison Bigg-Wither in 1802. In his old age, Dr. Lyster Lefrey, Lord Chief Justice of Ireland, said that he had once been in love with her, "but it was a boy's love." After her father died in 1805, there was always the fear of genteel poverty and the hope of inheritances which never materialized. She died, so the legend goes, in the arms of her sister Cassandra.

Like her private life, her literary associations were limited. She numbered no *literati* among her close friends; nor did she belong to a literary group or school, something that sets her apart from her contemporaries—Wordsworth, Southey, Coleridge; later Shelley, Keats, Byron, Lamb, Leigh Hunt, and Hazlitt—who felt that they belonged to a guild and were introducing a new literature and a new aesthetic. Her own values, as well as her style, reflected the past, being derived from the Augustans: Dr. Johnson, Addison, and Steele.

Two anecdotes relate Jane Austen, albeit tenuously, to the literary scene. A year before *Emma* appeared in 1816, she was asked by the Reverend J. S. Clarke, librarian to the Prince Regent, later George IV, to write a historical romance about the royal family. She declined the task, which would have been far more congenial to Sir Walter Scott, with his sense of the broad scope of history. Indeed it seems appropriate to quote Scott on Austen: "The big bow-wow strain I can do like any now going; but the exquisite touch, which renders ordinary commonplace things and characters interesting, from the truth of the description and the sentiment, is denied to me." The other anecdote is that she was invited to Carlton House, the Prince Regent's dwelling, to meet the leading female intellectual of the Continent, Mme. de Staël, the friend of Goethe and the writer who did most to acquaint French readers with German literature at the turn of the century. Miss Austen did not attend. No doubt the formidable Mme. de Staël would have triumphed over the demure spinster, but there is a nice irony in Jane Austen's posthumous victory. Who today reads Staël's *Delphine* (1802) or *Corinne* (1807)?

It has been suggested that parody, often unconscious, is an essential element in the history of the novel as a genre. Austen's first attempt at prose fiction, *Love and Friendship* [sic], written when she was fourteen, was a spoof on the popular "lady's novel" of the period. She may have taken the title *Pride and Prejudice* from a novel of that type, Fanny Burney's *Cecilia* (1782): "The whole of this unfortunate business has been the result of Pride and Prejudice." To read Burney's effusions of sentiment and then to read Austen is revealing; in both books we are moving in much the same milieu, but Austen has tempered it with satire and irony.

Her first full-length prose fiction, *Elinor and Marianne*, was written in epistolary form. Later it was rewritten as a straight narrative, and it was published in 1811, at her own expense, as *Sense and Sensibility*. Her next novel, *First Impressions*, was probably written in 1796-97. At first rejected for publication, it appeared after extensive revision as *Pride and Prejudice* in 1813. *Mansfield Park*, begun in 1811, was published in 1814, two years before *Emma. Northanger Abbey*, a satire on the popular Gothic novel, and *Persuasion* both came out posthumously in 1818.

Jane Austen lived during one of the most exciting eras in modern history—the French Revolution and its Napoleonic aftermath—yet her novels are serenely devoid of reference to those upheavals. In *Pride and Prejudice* only the reader with a keen historical nose smells out that the militia (not the "regulars") is stationed in the resort town of Brighton; it is there because Napoleon's *Grande Armée* has assembled across the Channel and threatens an immediate invasion. In Austen's book the presence of the military merely provides officers as dancing partners for the Bennet sisters.

THE STORY

Mr. and Mrs. Bennet and their five daughters live in Hertfordshire. The nearby estate of Netherfield is acquired by Mr. Bingley, unmarried and wealthy. Immediately his eligibility, and that of his arrogant friend Darcy, attract the interest of all the local families with marriageable daughters. The complicated plot has Bingley, intended for Darcy's sister Georgiana, courting Jane Bennet; and Darcy eventually courting Elizabeth Bennet. The more important pair—Darcy and Elizabeth—is separated by Darcy's "pride"—which takes the form of dismay at the Bennet family's seeming vulgarity—and Elizabeth's "prejudice" against him, which results from her false impression of his character.

Complications are introduced that feed the respective vice of each. (1) The pompous clergyman Mr. Collins, cousin and suitor to Elizabeth, but finally husband to her friend Charlotte Lucas, has his living on the estate of Darcy's aunt, Lady Catherine de Bourgh. Her daughter is intended for Darcy. (2) It transpires that Wickham, an officer in the militia and a friend of Elizabeth, was an ungrateful protegé of Darcy's family and once nearly succeeded in eloping with Darcy's sister Georgiana. He now ingratiates himself with the Bennets and eventually runs off with Lydia Bennet.

Although Wickham is a fairly minor character, he is the one who keeps the other couples apart. His faults are unknown to the Bennet family and hence Elizabeth dislikes Darcy because she feels he is unfair to Wickham. Wickham's connection with the Bennet family distresses the Bingleys and Darcy and adds to their aloofness and sense of superiority. Resolving the difficulty of Wickham allows Jane and Bingley, and Elizabeth and Darcy, to marry. Darcy secretly provides the money Wickham demands for marrying Lydia and, when Elizabeth discovers this, the last vestige of her "prejudice" disappears.

The famous scene that follows, that of the ball at Netherfield, is Chapter 18 of the novel, which has sixty-one chapters.

[*The Ball at Netherfield*]

Till Elizabeth entered the drawing-room at Netherfield and looked in vain for Mr. Wickham among the cluster of red coats there assembled, a doubt of his being present had never occurred to her. The certainty of meeting him had not been checked by any of those recollections that might not unreasonably have alarmed her. She had dressed with more than usual care, and prepared in the highest spirits for the conquest of all that remained unsubdued of his heart, trusting that it was not more than might be won in the course of the evening. But in an instant arose the dreadful suspicion of his being purposely omitted for Mr. Darcy's pleasure in the Bingleys' invitation to the officers; and though this was not exactly the case, the absolute fact of his absence was pronounced by his friend Mr. Denny, to whom Lydia eagerly applied, and who told them that Wickham had been obliged to go to town on business the day before, and was not yet returned; adding, with a significant smile,

"I do not imagine his business would have called him away just now, if he had not wished to avoid a certain gentleman here."

This part of his intelligence, though unheard by Lydia, was caught by Elizabeth, and as it assured her that Darcy was not less answerable for Wickham's absence than if her first surmise had been just, every feeling of displeasure against the former was so sharpened by immediate disappointment, that she could hardly reply with tolerable civility to the polite inquiries which he directly afterwards approached to make.—Attention, forbearance, patience with Darcy, was injury to Wickham. She was resolved against any sort of conversation with him, and turned away with a degree of ill-humour, which she could not wholly surmount even in speaking to Mr. Bingley, whose blind partiality provoked her.

But Elizabeth was not formed for ill-humour; and though every prospect of her own was destroyed for the evening, it could not dwell long on her spirits; and having told all her griefs to

Charlotte Lucas, whom she had not seen for a week, she was soon able to make a voluntary transition to the oddities of her cousin, and to point him out to her particular notice. The two first dances, however, brought a return of distress; they were dances of mortification. Mr. Collins, awkward and solemn, apologising instead of attending, and often moving wrong without being aware of it, gave her all the shame and misery which a disagreeable partner for a couple of dances can give. The moment of her release from him was ecstasy.

She danced next with an officer, and had the refreshment of talking of Wickham, and of hearing that he was universally liked. When those dances were over she returned to Charlotte Lucas, and was in conversation with her, when she found herself suddenly addressed by Mr. Darcy, who took her so much by surprise in his application for her hand, that, without knowing what she did, she accepted him. He walked away again immediately, and she was left to fret over her own want of presence of mind; Charlotte tried to console her.

"I dare say you will find him very agreeable."

"Heaven forbid!—*That* would be the greatest misfortune of all!—To find a man agreeable whom one is determined to hate!— Do not wish me such an evil."

When the dancing recommenced, however, and Darcy approached to claim her hand, Charlotte could not help cautioning her in a whisper not to be a simpleton and allow her fancy for Wickham to make her appear unpleasant in the eyes of a man of ten times his consequence. Elizabeth made no answer, and took her place in the set, amazed at the dignity to which she was arrived in being allowed to stand opposite to Mr. Darcy, and reading in her neighbours' looks their equal amazement in beholding it. They stood for some time without speaking a word; and she began to imagine that their silence was to last through the two dances, and at first was resolved not to break it; till suddenly fancying that it would be the greater punishment to her partner to oblige him to talk, she made some slight observation on the dance. He replied, and was again silent. After a pause of some minutes she addressed him a second time with:—

"It is *your* turn to say something now, Mr. Darcy.—*I* talked about the dance, and *you* ought to make some kind of remark on the size of the room, or the number of couples."

He smiled, and assured her that whatever she wished him to say should be said.

"Very well.—That reply will do for the present.—Perhaps by and by I may observe that private balls are much pleasanter than public ones.—But *now* we may be silent."

"Do you talk by rule then, while you are dancing?"

"Sometimes. One must speak a little, you know. It would look odd to be entirely silent for half an hour together, and yet for the advantage of *some*, conversation ought to be so arranged as that they may have the trouble of saying as little as possible."

"Are you consulting your own feelings in the present case, or do you imagine that you are gratifying mine?"

"Both," replied Elizabeth archly; "for I have always seen a great similarity in the turn of our minds.—We are each of an unsocial, taciturn disposition, unwilling to speak, unless we expect to say something that will amaze the whole room, and be handed down to posterity with all the éclat of a proverb."

"This is no very striking resemblance of your own character, I am sure," said he. "How near it may be to *mine*, I cannot pretend to say.—*You* think it a faithful portrait undoubtedly."

"I must not decide on my own performance."

He made no answer, and they were again silent till they had gone down the dance, when he asked her if she and her sisters did not very often walk to Meryton. She answered in the affirmative, and, unable to resist the temptation, added, "When you met us there the other day, we had just been forming a new acquaintance."

The effect was immediate. A deeper shade of hauteur overspread his features, but he said not a word, and Elizabeth, though blaming herself for her own weakness, could not go on. At length Darcy spoke, and in a constrained manner said,

"Mr. Wickham is blessed with such happy manners as may ensure his *making* friends—whether he may be equally capable of *retaining* them, is less certain."

"He has been so unlucky as to lose *your* friendship," replied Elizabeth with emphasis, "and in a manner which he is likely to suffer from all his life."

Darcy made no answer, and seemed desirous of changing the subject. At that moment Sir William Lucas appeared close to them, meaning to pass through the set to the other side of the room; but on perceiving Mr. Darcy he stopt with a bow of superior courtesy to compliment him on his dancing and his partner.

"I have been most highly gratified indeed, my dear Sir. Such very superior dancing is not often seen. It is evident that you belong to the first circles. Allow me to say, however, that your fair partner does not disgrace you, and that I must hope to have this pleasure often repeated, especially when a certain desirable event, my dear Miss Eliza, (glancing at her sister and Bingley,) shall take place. What congratulations will then flow in! I appeal to Mr. Darcy:—but let me not interrupt you, Sir.—You will not thank me for detaining you from the bewitching converse of that young lady, whose bright eyes are also upbraiding me."

The latter part of this address was scarcely heard by Darcy; but Sir Williams's allusion to his friend seemed to strike him forcibly, and his eyes were directed with a very serious expression towards Bingley and Jane, who were dancing together. Recovering himself, however, shortly, he turned to his partner, and said,

"Sir William's interruption has made me forget what we were talking of."

"I do not think we were speaking at all. Sir William could not have interrupted any two people in the room who had less to say for themselves.—We have tried two or three subjects already without success, and what we are to talk of next I cannot imagine."

"What think you of books?" said he, smiling.

"Books—Oh! no.—I am sure we never read the same, or not with the same feelings."

"I am sorry you think so; but if that be the case, there can at least be no want of subject.—We may compare our different opinions."

"No—I cannot talk of books in a ball-room; my head is always full of something else."

"The *present* always occupies you in such scenes—does it?" said he, with a look of doubt.

"Yes, always," she replied, without knowing what she said, for her thoughts had wandered far from the subject, as soon afterwards appeared by her suddenly exclaiming, "I remember hearing you once say, Mr. Darcy, that you hardly ever forgave, that your resentment once created was unappeasable. You are very cautious, I suppose, as to its *being created*."

"I am," said he, with a firm voice.

"And never allow yourself to be blinded by prejudice?"

"I hope not."

"It is particularly incumbent on those who never change their opinion, to be secure of judging properly at first."

"May I ask to what these questions tend?"

"Merely to the illustration of *your* character," said she, endeavouring to shake off her gravity. "I am trying to make it out."

"And what is your success?"

She shook her head. "I do not get on at all. I hear such different accounts of you as puzzle me exceedingly."

"I can readily believe," answered he gravely, "that report may vary greatly with respect to me; and I could wish, Miss Bennet, that you were not to sketch my character at the present moment, as there is reason to fear that the performance would reflect no credit on either."

"But if I do not take your likeness now, I may never have another opportunity."

"I would by no means suspend any pleasure of yours," he coldly replied. She said no more, and they went down the other dance and parted in silence; on each side dissatisfied, though not to an equal degree, for in Darcy's breast there was a tolerable powerful feeling towards her, which soon procured her pardon, and directed all his anger against another.

They had not long separated when Miss Bingley came towards her, and with an expression of civil disdain thus accosted her:—

"So, Miss Eliza, I hear you are quite delighted with George Wickham!—Your sister has been talking to me about him, and asking me a thousand questions; and I find that the young man forgot to tell you, among his other communications, that he was the son of old Wickham, the late Mr. Darcy's steward. Let me recommend you, however, as a friend, not to give implicit confidence to all his assertions; for as to Mr. Darcy's using him ill, it is perfectly false; for, on the contrary, he has been always remarkably kind to him, though George Wickham has treated Mr. Darcy in a most infamous manner. I do not know the particulars, but I know very well that Mr. Darcy is not in the least to blame, that he cannot bear to hear George Wickham mentioned, and that though my brother thought he could not well avoid including him in his invitation to the officers, he was excessively glad to find that he had taken himself out of the way. His coming into the country at all, is a most insolent thing indeed, and I wonder how he could presume to do it. I pity you, Miss Eliza, for this discovery of your favourite's guilt; but really considering his descent, one could not expect much better."

"His guilt and his descent appear by your account to be the same," said Elizabeth angrily; "for I have heard you accuse him of nothing worse than of being the son of Mr. Darcy's steward, and of *that*, I can assure you, he informed me himself."

"I beg your pardon," replied Miss Bingley, turning away with a sneer. "Excuse my interference.—It was kindly meant."

"Insolent girl!" said Elizabeth to herself.—"You are much mistaken if you expect to influence me by such a paltry attack as this. I see nothing in it but your own wilful ignorance and the malice of Mr. Darcy." She then sought her eldest sister, who had undertaken to make inquiries on the same subject of Bingley. Jane met her with a smile of such sweet complacency, a glow of such happy expression, as sufficiently marked how well she was satisfied with the occurrences of the evening.—Elizabeth instantly read her feelings, and at that moment solicitude for Wickham, resentment against his enemies, and every thing else gave way before the hope of Jane's being in the fairest way for happiness.

"I want to know," said she, with a countenance no less smiling than her sister's, "what you have learnt about Mr. Wickham. But perhaps you have been too pleasantly engaged to think of any third person; in which case you may be sure of my pardon."

"No," replied Jane, "I have not forgotten him; but I have nothing satisfactory to tell you. Mr. Bingley does not know the whole of his history, and is quite ignorant of the circumstances which have principally offended Mr. Darcy; but he will vouch for the good conduct, the probity and honour of his friend, and is perfectly convinced that Mr. Wickham has deserved much less attention from Mr. Darcy than he has received; and I am sorry to say that by his account as well as his sister's, Mr. Wickham is by no means a respectable young man. I am afraid he has been very imprudent, and has deserved to lose Mr. Darcy's regard."

"Mr. Bingley does not know Mr. Wickham himself?"

"No; he never saw him till the other morning at Meryton."

"This account then is what he has received from Mr. Darcy. I am perfectly satisfied. But what does he say of the living?"

"He does not exactly recollect the circumstances, though he has heard them from Mr. Darcy more than once, but he believes that it was left to him *conditionally* only."

"I have not a doubt of Mr. Bingley's sincerity," said Elizabeth warmly; "but you must excuse my not being convinced by assurances only. Mr. Bingley's defence of his friend was a very able one I dare say, but since he is unacquainted with several parts of the story, and has learnt the rest from that friend himself, I shall venture still to think of both gentlemen as I did before."

She then changed the discourse to one more gratifying to each, and on which there could be no difference of sentiment. Elizabeth listened with delight to the happy, though modest hopes which Jane entertained of Bingley's regard, and said all in her power to heighten her confidence in it. On their being joined by Mr. Bingley himself, Elizabeth withdrew to Miss Lucas; to whose inquiry after the pleasantness of her last partner she had scarcely replied, before Mr. Collins came up to them and told her with great exultation that he had just been so fortunate as to make a most important discovery.

"I have found out," said he, "by a singular accident, that there is now in the room a near relation of my patroness. I happened to overhear the gentleman himself mentioning to the young lady who does the honours of this house the names of his cousin Miss de Bourgh, and of her mother Lady Catherine. How wonderfully these sort of things occur! Who would have thought of my meeting with—perhaps—a nephew of Lady Catherine de Bourgh in this assembly!—I am most thankful that the discovery is made in time for me to pay my respects to him, which I am now going to do, and trust he will excuse my not having done it before. My total ignorance of the connection must plead my apology."

"You are not going to introduce yourself to Mr. Darcy?"

"Indeed I am. I shall intreat his pardon for not having done it earlier. I believe him to be Lady Catherine's *nephew*. It will be in my power to assure him that her ladyship was quite well yesterday se'nnight."

Elizabeth tried hard to dissuade him from such a scheme; assuring him that Mr. Darcy would consider his addressing him without introduction as an impertinent freedom, rather than a compliment to his aunt; that it was not in the least necessary there should be any notice on either side, and that if it were, it must belong to Mr. Darcy, the superior in consequence, to begin the acquaintance.—Mr. Collins listened to her with the determined air of following his own inclination, and when she ceased speaking, replied thus,

"My dear Miss Elizabeth, I have the highest opinion in the

world of your excellent judgment in all matters within the scope
of your understanding, but permit me to say that there must be
a wide difference between the established forms of ceremony
amongst the laity, and those which regulate the clergy; for give me
leave to observe that I consider the clerical office as equal in point
of dignity with the highest rank in the kingdom—provided that a
proper humility of behaviour is at the same time maintained. You
must therefore allow me to follow the dictates of my conscience
on this occasion, which leads me to perform what I look on as a
point of duty. Pardon me for neglecting to profit by your advice,
which on every other subject shall be my constant guide, though
in the case before us I consider myself more fitted by education
and habitual study to decide on what is right than a young lady
like yourself." And with a low bow he left her to attack Mr. Darcy,
whose reception of his advances she eagerly watched, and whose
astonishment at being so addressed was very evident. Her cousin
prefaced his speech with a solemn bow, and though she could not
hear a word of it, she felt as if hearing it all, and saw in the motion
of his lips the words "apology," "Hunsford," and "Lady Catherine de Bourgh."—It vexed her to see him expose himself to such
a man. Mr. Darcy was eyeing him with unrestrained wonder, and
when at last Mr. Collins allowed him time to speak, replied with
an air of distant civility. Mr. Collins, however, was not discouraged from speaking again, and Mr. Darcy's contempt seemed abundantly increasing with the length of his second speech, and at
the end of it he only made him a slight bow, and moved another
way. Mr. Collins then returned to Elizabeth.

"I have no reason, I assure you," said he, "to be dissatisfied
with my reception. Mr. Darcy seemed much pleased with the attention. He answered me with the utmost civility, and even paid
me the compliment of saying, that he was so well convinced of
Lady Catherine's discernment as to be certain she could never bestow a favour unworthily. It was really a very handsome thought.
Upon the whole, I am much pleased with him."

As Elizabeth had no longer any interest of her own to pursue,
she turned her attention almost entirely on her sister and Mr.
Bingley, and the train of agreeable reflections which her observations gave birth to, made her perhaps almost as happy as Jane.
She saw her in idea settled in that very house in all the felicity
which a marriage of true affection could bestow; and she felt
capable under such circumstances, of endeavouring even to like

Bingley's two sisters. Her mother's thoughts she plainly saw were bent the same way, and she determined not to venture near her, lest she might hear too much. When they sat down to supper, therefore, she considered it a most unlucky perverseness which placed them within one of each other; and deeply was she vexed to find that her mother was talking to that one person (Lady Lucas) freely, openly, and of nothing else but of her expectation that Jane would be soon married to Mr. Bingley.—It was an animating subject, and Mrs. Bennet seemed incapable of fatigue while enumerating the advantages of the match. His being such a charming young man, and so rich, and living but three miles from them, were the first points of self-gratulation; and then it was such a comfort to think how fond the two sisters were of Jane, and to be certain that they must desire the connection as much as she could do. It was, moreover, such a promising thing for her younger daughters, as Jane's marrying so greatly must throw them in the way of other rich men; and lastly, it was so pleasant at her time of life to be able to consign her single daughters to the care of their sister, that she might not be obliged to go into company more than she liked. It was necessary to make this circumstance a matter of pleasure, because on such occasions it is the etiquette; but no one was less likely than Mrs. Bennet to find comfort in staying at home at any period of her life. She concluded with many good wishes that Lady Lucas might soon be equally fortunate, though evidently and triumphantly believing there was no chance of it.

In vain did Elizabeth endeavour to check the rapidity of her mother's words, or persuade her to describe her felicity in a less audible whisper; for to her inexpressible vexation, she could perceive that the chief of it was overheard by Mr. Darcy, who sat opposite to them. Her mother only scolded her for being nonsensical.

"What is Mr. Darcy to me, pray, that I should be afraid of him? I am sure we owe him no such particular civility as to be obliged to say nothing *he* may not like to hear."

"For heaven's sake, madam, speak lower.—What advantage can it be to you to offend Mr. Darcy?—You will never recommend yourself to his friend by so doing."

Nothing that she could say, however, had any influence. Her mother would talk of her views in the same intelligible tone. Elizabeth blushed and blushed again with shame and vexation. She could not help frequently glancing her eye at Mr. Darcy, though every glance convinced her of what she dreaded; for though he was not always looking at her mother, she was convinced that his attention was invariably fixed by her. The expression of his face changed gradually from indignant contempt to a composed and steady gravity.

At length however Mrs. Bennet had no more to say; and Lady Lucas, who had been long yawning at the repetition of delights which she saw no likelihood of sharing, was left to the comforts of cold ham and chicken. Elizabeth now began to revive. But not long was the interval of tranquillity; for when supper was over, singing was talked of, and she had the mortification of seeing Mary, after very little entreaty, preparing to oblige the company. By many significant looks and silent entreaties, did she endeavour to prevent such a proof of complaisance,—but in vain; Mary would not understand them; such an opportunity of exhibiting was delightful to her, and she began her song. Elizabeth's eyes were fixed on her with most painful sensations; and she watched her progress through the several stanzas with an impatience which was very ill rewarded at their close; for Mary, on receiving amongst the thanks of the table, the hint of a hope that she might be prevailed on to favour them again, after the pause of half a minute began another. Mary's powers were by no means fitted for such a display; her voice was weak, and her manner affected.—Elizabeth was in agonies. She looked at Jane, to see how she bore it; but Jane was very composedly talking to Bingley. She looked at his two sisters, and saw them making signs of derision at each other, and at Darcy, who continued however impenetrably grave. She looked at her father to entreat his interference, lest Mary should be singing all night. He took the hint, and when Mary had finished her second song, said aloud,

"That will do extremely well, child. You have delighted us long enough. Let the other young ladies have time to exhibit."

Mary, though pretending not to hear, was somewhat disconcerted; and Elizabeth sorry for her, and sorry for her father's speech, was afraid her anxiety had done no good.—Others of the party were now applied to.

"If I," said Mr. Collins, "were so fortunate as to be able to sing, I should have great pleasure, I am sure, in obliging the company with an air; for I consider music as a very innocent diversion, and perfectly compatible with the profession of a clergyman.—I do not mean however to assert that we can be justified in devoting too much of our time to music, for there are certainly other things to be attended to. The rector of a parish has much to do.—In the first place, he must make such an agreement for tythes as may be beneficial to himself and not offensive to his patron. He must write his own sermons; and the time that remains will not be too much for his parish duties, and the care and improvement of his dwelling, which he cannot be excused from making as comfortable as possible. And I do not think it of light importance that he should have attentive and conciliatory manners towards every body, especially towards those to whom he owes his preferment. I cannot acquit him of that duty; nor could I think well of the man who should omit an occasion of testifying his respect towards any body connected with the family." And with a bow to Mr. Darcy, he concluded his speech, which had been spoken so loud as to be heard by half the room.—Many stared.—Many smiled; but no one looked more amused than Mr. Bennet himself, while his wife seriously commended Mr. Collins for having spoken so sensibly, and observed in a half-whisper to Lady Lucas, that he was a remarkably clever, good kind of young man.

To Elizabeth it appeared, that had her family made an agreement to expose themselves as much as they could during the evening, it would have been impossible for them to play their parts with more spirit, or finer success; and happy did she think it for Bingley and her sister that some of the exhibition had escaped his notice, and that his feelings were not of a sort to be much distressed by the folly which he must have witnessed. That his two sisters and Mr. Darcy, however, should have such an opportunity of ridiculing her relations was bad enough, and she could not determine whether the silent contempt of the gentleman, or the insolent smiles of the ladies, were more intolerable.

The rest of the evening brought her little amusement. She was teazed by Mr. Collins, who continued most perseveringly by her side, and though he could not prevail with her to dance with him again, put it out of her power to dance with others. In vain did she entreat him to stand up with somebody else, and offer to introduce him to any young lady in the room. He assured her that as to dancing, he was perfectly indifferent to it; that his chief object was by delicate attentions to recommend himself to her, and that he should therefore make a point of remaining close to her the whole evening. There was no arguing upon such a project.

She owed her greatest relief to her friend Miss Lucas, who often joined them, and good-naturedly engaged Mr. Collins's conversation to herself.

She was at least free from the offence of Mr. Darcy's farther notice; though often standing within a very short distance of her, quite disengaged, he never came near enough to speak. She felt it to be the probable consequence of her allusions to Mr. Wickham, and rejoiced in it.

The Longbourn party were the last of the company to depart; and by a manoeuvre of Mrs. Bennet had to wait for their carriages a quarter of an hour after every body else was gone, which gave them time to see how heartily they were wished away by some of the family. Mrs. Hurst and her sister scarcely opened their mouths except to complain of fatigue, and were evidently impatient to have the house to themselves. They repulsed every attempt of Mrs. Bennet at conversation, and by so doing, threw a languor over the whole party, which was very little relieved by the long speeches of Mr. Collins, who was complimenting Mr. Bingley and his sisters on the elegance of their entertainment, and the hospitality and politeness which had marked their behaviour to their guests. Darcy said nothing at all. Mr. Bennet, in equal silence, was enjoying the scene. Mr. Bingley and Jane were standing together, a little detached from the rest, and talked only to each other. Elizabeth preserved as steady a silence as either Mrs. Hurst or Miss Bingley; and even Lydia was too much fatigued to utter more than the occasional exclamation of "Lord, how tired I am!" accompanied by a violent yawn.

When at length they arose to take leave, Mrs. Bennet was most pressingly civil in her hope of seeing the whole family soon at Longbourn; and addressed herself particularly to Mr. Bingley, to assure him how happy he would make them, by eating a family dinner with them at any time, without the ceremony of a formal invitation. Bingley was all grateful pleasure, and he readily engaged for taking the earliest opportunity of waiting on her, after his return from London, whither he was obliged to go the next day for a short time.

Mrs. Bennet was perfectly satisfied; and quitted the house under the delightful persuasion that, allowing for the necessary preparations of settlements, new carriages and wedding clothes, she should undoubtedly see her daughter settled at Netherfield, in the course of three or four months. Of having another daughter married to Mr. Collins, she thought with equal certainty, and with considerable, though not equal, pleasure. Elizabeth was the least dear to her of all her children; and though the man and the match were quite good enough for *her*, the worth of each was eclipsed by Mr. Bingley and Netherfield.

AFTERWORD

The ball at Netherfield, with its ceremony and decorum, its comic blunders and savagely wounded sensibilities, epitomizes much that is characteristic of this novel in particular and of Austen's writing in general. The chapter is neatly framed: it starts with Elizabeth's solo entrance into the drawing-room and ends with the mass exit of the Bennet family. The final passage of three paragraphs also serves as an epilogue in which the novelist surveys the tableau, focusing on Mrs. Bennet's absurdities as if to remind us that despite some "serious" moments in the chapter, we still exist in a world of comedy.

For Elizabeth it is a painful comedy. She has suffered three "mortifications" at the hands of Mr. Collins: her dance with him, his insistence on introducing himself to Darcy, and his final speech chiefly directed at Darcy, though overheard by half the assembly, about the nature of the clergyman's profession. This last display has been preceded by other "mortifications" inflicted on Elizabeth, in this case by her immediate family: her mother's conversation at supper, her sister Mary's dismal musical performance, and even Mr. Bennet's rebuke to his weak-voiced daughter. The two longest episodes containing dialogue are the heroine's dance with Darcy and her exchange with Miss Bingley. These are balanced against shorter scenes in which Elizabeth talks first with Charlotte Lucas, then with her sister Jane.

The problem of point of view, which was to become acute for novelists beginning with Flaubert, is one that Austen ignores. Here as throughout the book, she simply lingers more over Elizabeth's thoughts than over those of the other characters. There is only one revelation of Darcy's sentiments: ". . . in Darcy's breast there was a tolerable powerful feeling towards her." Mrs. Bennet's thoughts are revealed at the very end of the chapter in an example of Austen's irony; she quits the house "under the delightful persuasion that . . . she should undoubtedly see her daughter [Jane] settled at Netherfield." Actually the chapter contains few examples of the irony for which Austen is noted. The two outstanding ones are Collins' conviction that Darcy responded to him "with the utmost civility" and Mrs. Bennet's comment on Collins' fatuous address. After commending him "for having spoken so sensibly, [she] observed in a half-whisper to Lady Lucas that he was a remarkable clever, good kind of young man."

It is typical of Austen's method that she refrains from physical description of either persons or things. Many readers have noted that only once in this novel does she extend herself in a fashion suggesting Sir Walter Scott; the occasion is when Elizabeth visits Darcy's estate and there meets the hero unexpectedly, a turning point in the book. At the Netherfield ball, Austen does no more than occasionally qualify how her characters speak: "He smiled," "replied Elizabeth archly," "a deeper shade of hauteur overspread his features," "Mr. Collins listened to her with the determined air of following his own inclination." Even these qualifications are the merest pointers to the reader, leaving his imagination to supply any more precise visual details. Consider how Dickens would have treated the supper that follows the dance and then recall Austen's one mention of food, this in a phrase worthy of Alexander Pope. (Reuben Brower has said that many of her pages are "Pope without couplets.") The mention occurs after Mrs. Bennet has been jubilating over the prospects of Jane's marriage to Bingley. "At length however Mrs. Bennet had no more to say; and Lady Lucas, who had long been yawning at the repetition of delights which she saw no likelihood of sharing, was left to the comforts of cold ham and chicken."

To speak of Pope in this connection reminds us of Austen's admiration for the Augustan prose writers, especially Dr. Johnson: like them she was fond of formal balance, antithesis, and contrasts expressed in parallel phrases. Like them she had a decorous but forthright manner of passing judgment on others by making the sort of general statements that we moderns are likely to associate with intellectual arrogance. Some of her characters express themselves in the same Augustan style. Elizabeth, for example, is speaking in character, speaking from "prejudice," but indirectly speaking for the author when she offers two aphoristic statements in judgment of Darcy's "pride." "For the advantage of *some*," she says, "conversation ought to be so arranged as that they may have the trouble of saying as little as possible." Again she says, "It is particularly incumbent on those who never change their opinion, to be secure of judging properly at first." Dr. Johnson himself might be pontificating.

Mark Schorer has commented on Austen's use of "words that suggest number or money, physical size or material value." These "hidden and dead metaphors," he says, help to reveal that on one level *Pride and Prejudice* is a serious picture of "marriage as a kind of symbol of economic merging, of one class rising and another sinking; and then [of] marriage as a brutal economic fact in an essentially materialistic society." This chapter offers a few illustrations of Schorer's thesis. Wickham is in "town on business"; Charlotte advises Elizabeth not to offend Darcy, "a man of ten times his [Wickham's] consequence"—a word used here to indicate social or economic rank; Collins speaks of a clergyman with "tythes as may be beneficial to himself." The chapter is even richer, however, in words that have to do with manners and social behavior. "Civil" and "civility" appear at least five times. Darcy's "slight bow" is played against Collins' "low bow" to Elizabeth and "solemn bow" to Darcy, as against that "bow of superior courtesy" executed by Sir William Lucas. Darcy says ironically of the character who comes closest to being the villain of the piece, "Mr. Wickham is blessed with such happy manners. . . ."

Deliberate irony, the mark of a superior intelligence, is never practised by Austen's foolish characters, as represented in this chapter by Mrs. Bennet, Mr. Collins, and Sir William Lucas. Mrs. Bennet is made to speak breathlessly and incoherently, as in her reported conversation with Lady Lucas about Jane's prospective match. Collins is a master of the double negative, which give his two recitations an air of rotund, academic pomposity. Sir William is longwinded and cliché-ridden ("fair partner," "desirable event") and Austen loads his remarks with adjectives and adverbs, parts of speech that are seldom employed by the characters whom she hopes that the reader will regard with admiration and sympathy.

This note began by hazarding that the ball at Netherfield epitomizes the book. Perhaps the *danses hautes* ("elegant dances" as against "country dances") of Jane Austen's time provide another analogy for the action in *Pride and Prejudice*. Quadrilles, cotillions, and minuets meant that pairs of partners (Elizabeth and Darcy, Jane and Bingley) moved decorously through elaborate figures or "sets," often separating, but always returning at stated intervals, until they were reunited at the end.

The Heart of Midlothian (1818)

SIR WALTER SCOTT (1771-1832), often called the Wizard of the North, was descended on both sides from small lairds of the Scottish Border who had lived partly by raising sheep and partly by deeds of warfare that included stealing sheep from their English neighbors. His father was the first of the Scott family to live in Edinburgh, where he became a methodical and prosperous attorney. The son recovered from an early attack of infantile paralysis, but it left him permanently lame. Often kept home from school because of his health, he became an avid reader, especially of romances, and also an avid listener to legends of the Border, which he heard from old women during long periods spent at his grandfather's farm. It was all preparation for the books he would later write with unexampled ease.

The preparation continued at the famous high school in Edinburgh, where he was an indifferent scholar in Latin and refused to study Greek. By contrast he taught himself enough French to read romances that were not available in English; then some Italian for the sake of Dante and Ariosto. While still in his teens he puzzled through Cervantes in the original and conceived the notion of writing about a Scottish Jacobite Don Quixote. He attended classes at the university during the years when Edinburgh was known as the Athens of the North. Robert Burns appeared and was briefly lionized—but not fed or clothed—by Edinburgh society. Scott was impressed by him, but was more immediately affected by Henry Mackenzie, the scholarly author of sentimental novels, among them *The Man of Feeling* (1771). After hearing Mackenzie lecture on the new German literature, Scott determined to learn still another language. His first published work was a translation of German ballads, and in 1799 he translated one of Goethe's historical plays, *Götz von Berlichingen*. That inspired him with still another ambition: to do for Border manners what Goethe had done for feudalism on the Rhine.

Meanwhile Scott had been admitted to the bar and had married a young Frenchwoman brought to England as a child. He had also made an imposing collection of ballads, which he published in 1802 as *Minstrelsy of the Scottish Border*, and he was casting about for the subject of a long original poem. The subject having been found, and the form as well—four-beat couplets modeled after those of Coleridge's *Christabel* —the poem appeared in 1805; it was *The Lay of the Last Minstrel*, which had an unprecedented sale. *Marmion* (1808) and *The Lady of the Lake* (1810) were equally popular. In 1812 Scott began drawing a generous salary as clerk of the Court of Session. He was also sleeping partner in a printing house and a publishing house, from both of which he expected great profits, and he felt rich enough to start building a baronial house at Abbotsford.

His first novel, *Waverley* (1814), dealt with Scotland in the days of Bonnie Prince Charlie. It was published without his name—perhaps because he feared that writing novels would be regarded as an undignified occupation for an officer of the reverend Court of Session—and became an immediate success. Scott had invented what was practically a new form. *The Scottish Chiefs* (1810), by Jane Porter, was a romanticized life of Sir William Wallace and might be mentioned as a predecessor of *Waverley*. On another side its ancestry might be traced in the Gothic or "horror" novels of the eighteenth century: such books as Horace Walpole's *The Castle of Otranto* (1765), Anne Radcliffe's *The Mysteries of Udolpho* (1794), and M. G. Lewis's *The Monk* (1796). These also dealt with times long past, but they showed no concern with historical accuracy in presenting such characters as lascivious monks, cruel noblemen, and persecuted females. Scott often resorted to the same tricks of melodrama, but he combined them with a serious effort to depict the manners of the age with which he was dealing. In the modern sense, *Waverley* was the first historical novel.

Scott quickly followed it with others: *Guy Mannering* (1815); then *The Antiquary*, *The Black Dwarf*, and *Old Mortality*, all published in 1816; then in 1818 *Rob Roy*, which Stevenson was to plunder for his *Kidnapped*, and *The Heart of Midlothian*, which is in many ways Scott's most appealing novel. The following year he published *The Bride of Lammermoor* and *The Legend of Montrose*. All these had dealt with

Scotland in the seventeenth or eighteenth centuries, but it was also in 1819 that he wrote—or rather dictated to an amanuensis during shrieks of pain from an almost fatal siege of stomach cramps—his first novel with an English setting, *Ivanhoe*, which vastly increased his audience in England. After six additional novels in four years, he made another departure in 1823 by writing *Quentin Durward*, with its scene laid in France during the reign of Louis XI. It gained a new audience for Scott on the continent of Europe.

With his brilliantly tireless energy he was then leading five lives, any one of which might have satisfied a less ambitious man. First he was clerk of Session and sheriff deputy of Selkirkshire; then he was laird of Abbotsford, entertaining flocks of visitors while continually refurbishing and remodeling his mansion; then, under his own name, he was the most famous poet of his day after Byron, besides being a respected scholar and editor; then, without his authorship's being acknowledged, he was writing novels unexampled in their popular success; then finally he was silent partner in a printing and publishing company allied with the great English house of Constable. While the other careers marched ahead, this publishing venture met with disaster during a business depression. At the end of 1825 Scott found himself responsible for debts of £130,000, equivalent to more than $1.5 million in present American currency.

He might have gone through bankruptcy without dishonor, since most of the debts were not of his making. Instead he tried to satisfy all his creditors and write himself back to solvency. Books came streaming from his desk in the next six years, not only five more novels and a book of stories but also a history of Scotland, an extended series of historical tales for children, and a nine-volume *Life of Napoleon Buonaparte*. By 1829 he had turned over some £40,000 to his creditors. He suffered a series of paralytic strokes and still he kept on working; he was writing himself to death. As a matter of fact, his debts were paid in full by the sale of his copyrights, but not until after he died.

Scott was the first novelist to be given a title—that of baronet—as reward for his literary work. In effect the throne itself was recognizing that he had carried the novel to a new position in the national life. His example inspired novelists all over the world to be the Sir Walter Scotts of their own countries. Cooper in America and Sienkiewicz in Poland are obvious instances, but Manzoni, Balzac, and Tolstoy were also deeply affected. Hawthorne read all the Waverley novels twice, the second time aloud to his family. Once, after a pilgrimage to Abbotsford, he wrote of the return journey by train, "Probably every pant of the engine carried us over some spot of ground which Scott has made fertile with poetry. For Scotland—cold, cloudy, barren, insignificant little bit of earth that it is—owes all the interest that the world feels in it to him. Few men have done so much for their country as he."

THE STORY

In what we have called Scott's most appealing novel, the center of action is the old Edinburgh tolbooth, or prison, regarded by many as the very heart of the shire of Midlothian. Here Effie Deans, the daughter of a "cow feeder" or dairyman, is awaiting trial under a stern Scots law: since she bore a child in secret and the child disappeared, she is presumed guilty of murder. Here too Captain Porteous is imprisoned. A brutal soldier, he has been sentenced to death for ordering his men to fire on an Edinburgh crowd, but he is now waiting to be released under a pardon from Queen Caroline. Effie's lover, an outlaw known as Geordie Robertson, organizes a mob to storm the tolbooth and lynch Porteous. His real purpose is to save Effie, but she refuses to leave her cell. At her trial the decisive question is whether she had completely concealed her pregnancy. If she had confessed it to anyone— even to her older sister Jeanie, the heroine of the novel—she will not be executed. Thus, her life is in Jeanie's hands; by telling a white lie (for Effie had never confessed) Jeanie can save her. Jeanie is a pious girl and, in the trial scene that is the climax of the novel, she refuses to perjure herself. Nevertheless she is tender-hearted. After her sister has been convicted, Jeanie walks barefoot to London to plead for Effie's life.

It is an adventurous journey, in the course of which she discovers that Geordie Robertson is really George Staunton, the heir of an English baronet. In London the great Duke of Argyle listens to Jeanie's story and obtains for her a private audience with Queen Caroline (the scene reprinted here). Effie receives her pardon and runs off to marry George Staunton. Jeanie goes back to Scotland in the Duke of Argyle's calash and has a happy reunion with her suitor, the young clergyman Reuben Butler, whom the Duke has installed in a comfortable parish. The last five chapters are a sort of epilogue. Jeanie is a minister's wife, happy with her family; Effie has become the great Lady Staunton, but is childless and miserable. She still hopes to find the son who was spirited away from her a few days after his birth. He is rumored to be hiding near Reuben Butler's parish, where Sir George comes to look for him. But the lost son has become an outlaw, and during an attempt at highway robbery he kills his own father. Lady Staunton retires to a convent.

The scene that follows is Chapter 37 of *The Heart of Midlothian*.

Just as the courtroom scene was the climax of the novel, so the audience with Queen Caroline is its peripety, or change of fortune. Henceforth, with Argyle as her patron, everything will go well with Jeanie, her dour father, and her clerical suitor.

[*A Scottish Peer, an English Queen*]

> ————I beseech you—
> These tears beseech you, and these chaste hands woo you,
> That never yet were heaved but to things holy—
> Things like yourself—You are a God above us;
> Be as a God, then, full of saving mercy!
> *The Bloody Brother.*

Encouraged as she was by the courteous manners of her noble countryman, it was not without a feeling of something like terror that Jeanie felt herself in a place apparently so lonely, with a man of such high rank. That she should have been permitted to wait on the Duke in his own house, and have been there received to a private interview, was in itself an uncommon and distinguished event in the annals of a life so simple as hers; but to find herself his travelling companion in a journey, and then suddenly to be left alone with him in so secluded a situation, had something in it of awful mystery. A romantic heroine might have suspected and dreaded the power of her own charms; but Jeanie was too wise to let such a silly thought intrude on her mind. Still, however, she had a most eager desire to know where she now was, and to whom she was to be presented.

She remarked that the Duke's dress, though still such as indicated rank and fashion (for it was not the custom of men of quality at that time to dress themselves like their own coachmen or grooms), was nevertheless plainer than that in which she had seen him upon a former occasion, and was divested, in particular, of all those badges of external decoration which intimated superior consequence. In short, he was attired as plainly as any gentleman of fashion could appear in the streets of London in a morning; and this circumstance helped to shake an opinion which Jeanie began to entertain, that, perhaps, he intended she should plead her cause in the presence of royalty itself. "But, surely," said she to herself, "he wad hae putten on his braw star and garter, an he had thought o' coming before the face of Majesty—and after a', this is mair like a gentleman's policy[1] than a royal palace."

There was some sense in Jeanie's reasoning; yet she was not sufficiently mistress either of the circumstances of etiquette, or the particular relations which existed betwixt the government and the Duke of Argyle, to form an accurate judgment. The Duke, as we have said, was at this time in open opposition to the administration of Sir Robert Walpole, and was understood to be out of favour with the royal family, to whom he had rendered such important services. But it was a maxim of Queen Caroline, to bear herself towards her political friends with such caution, as if there was a possibility of their one day being her enemies, and towards political opponents with the same degree of circumspection, as if they might again become friendly to her measures. Since Margaret of Anjou, no queen-consort had exercised such weight in the political affairs of England, and the personal address which she displayed on many occasions, had no small share in reclaiming from their political heresy many of those determined Tories, who, after the reign of the Stuarts had been extinguished in the person of Queen Anne, were disposed rather to transfer their allegiance to her brother the Chevalier de St. George, than to acquiesce in the settlement of the crown on the Hanover family. Her husband, whose most shining quality was courage in the field of battle, and who endured the office of King of England, without ever being able to acquire English habits, or any familiarity with English dispositions, found the utmost assistance from the address of his partner; and while he jealously affected to do everything according to his own will and pleasure, was in secret prudent enough to take and follow the advice of his more adroit consort. He entrusted to her the delicate office of determining the various degrees of favour necessary to attach the wavering, or to confirm such as were already friendly, or to regain those whose good-will had been lost.

With all the winning address of an elegant, and, according to the times, an accomplished woman, Queen Caroline possessed the masculine soul of the other sex. She was proud by nature, and even her policy could not always temper her expressions of displeasure, although few were more ready at repairing any false

[1 A gentleman's park or estate.]

step of this kind, when her prudence came up to the aid of her passions. She loved the real possession of power, rather than the show of it, and whatever she did herself that was either wise or popular, she always desired that the king should have the full credit as well as the advantage of the measure, conscious that, by adding to his respectability, she was most likely to maintain her own. And so desirous was she to comply with all his tastes, that, when threatened with the gout, she had repeatedly had recourse to checking the fit, by the use of the cold bath, thereby endangering her life, that she might be able to attend the king in his walks.

It was a very consistent part of Queen Caroline's character, to keep up many private correspondences with those to whom in public she seemed unfavourable, or who, for various reasons, stood ill with the court. By this means she kept in her hands the threat of many a political intrigue, and, without pledging herself to anything, could often prevent discontent from becoming hatred, and opposition from exaggerating itself into rebellion. If by any accident her correspondence with such persons chanced to be observed or discovered, which she took all possible pains to prevent, it was represented as a mere intercourse of society, having no reference to politics; an answer with which even the prime minister, Sir Robert Walpole, was compelled to remain satisfied, when he discovered that the Queen had given a private audience to Pulteney, afterwards Earl of Bath, his most formidable and most inveterate enemy.

In thus maintaining occasional intercourse with several persons who seemed most alienated from the crown, it may readily be supposed, that Queen Caroline had taken care not to break entirely with the Duke of Argyle. His high birth, his great talents, the estimation in which he was held in his own country, the great services which he had rendered the house of Brunswick in 1715, placed him high in that rank of persons who were not to be rashly neglected. He had, almost by his single and unassisted talents, stopped the irruption of the banded force of all the Highland chiefs; there was little doubt, that, with the slightest encouragement, he could put them all in motion, and renew the civil war; and it was well known that the most flattering overtures had been transmitted to the Duke from the court of St. Germains. The character and temper of Scotland were still little known, and it was considered as a volcano, which might, indeed, slumber for a series of years but was still liable, at a moment the least expected, to break out into a wasteful eruption. It was, therefore, of the highest importance to retain some hold over so important a personage as the Duke of Argyle, and Caroline preserved the power of doing so by means of a lady, with whom, as wife of George II., she might have been supposed to be on less intimate terms.

It was not the least instance of the Queen's address, that she had contrived that one of her principal attendants, Lady Suffolk, should unite in her own person the two apparently inconsistent characters, of her husband's mistress, and her own very obsequious and complaisant confidant. By this dexterous management the Queen secured her power against the danger which might most have threatened it—the thwarting influence of an ambitious rival; and if she submitted to the mortification of being obliged to connive at her husband's infidelity, she was at least guarded against what she might think its most dangerous effects, and was besides at liberty, now and then, to bestow a few civil insults upon "her good Howard," whom, however, in general, she treated with great decorum.[2] Lady Suffolk lay under strong obligations to the Duke of Argyle, for reasons which may be collected from Horace Walpole's Reminiscences of that reign, and through her means the Duke had some occasional correspondence with Queen Caroline, much interrupted, however, since the part he had taken in the debate concerning the Porteous mob, an affair which the Queen, though somewhat unreasonably, was disposed to resent, rather as an intended and premeditated insolence to her own person and authority, than as a sudden ebullition of popular vengeance. Still, however, the communication remained open betwixt them, though it had been of late disused on both sides. These remarks will be found necessary to understand the scene which is about to be presented to the reader.

From the narrow alley which they had traversed, the Duke turned into one of the same character, but broader and still longer. Here, for the first time since they had entered these gardens, Jeanie saw persons approaching them.

They were two ladies; one of whom walked a little behind the other, yet not so much as to prevent her from hearing and replying to whatever observation was addressed to her by the lady who walked foremost, and that without her having the trouble to turn her person. As they advanced very slowly, Jeanie had time to study

[2] See Horace Walpole's Reminiscences. [Scott's note.]

their features and appearance. The Duke also slackened his pace, as if to give her time to collect herself, and repeatedly desired her not to be afraid. The lady who seemed the principal person had remarkably good features, though somewhat injured by the small-pox, that venomous scourge, which each village Esculapius (thanks to Jenner) can now tame as easily as their tutelary deity subdued the Python. The lady's eyes were brilliant, her teeth good, and her countenance formed to express at will either majesty or courtesy. Her form, though rather *embonpoint*, was nevertheless graceful; and the elasticity and firmness of her step gave no room to suspect, what was actually the case, that she suffered occasionally from a disorder the most unfavourable to pedestrian exercise. Her dress was rather rich than gay, and her manner commanding and noble.

Her companion was of lower stature, with light-brown hair and expressive blue eyes. Her features, without being absolutely regular, were perhaps more pleasing than if they had been critically handsome. A melancholy, or at least a pensive expression, for which her lot gave too much cause, predominated when she was silent, but gave way to a pleasing and good-humoured smile when she spoke to any one.

When they were within twelve or fifteen yards of these ladies, the Duke made a sign that Jeanie should stand still, and stepping forward himself, with the grace which was natural to him, made a profound obeisance, which was formally, yet in a dignified manner, returned by the personage whom he approached.

"I hope," she said, with an affable and condescending smile, "that I see so great a stranger at court, as the Duke of Argyle has been of late, in as good health as his friends there and elsewhere could wish him to enjoy."

The Duke replied, "That he had been perfectly well"; and added, "that the necessity of attending to the public business before the House, as well as the time occupied by a late journey to Scotland, had rendered him less assiduous in paying his duty at the levee and drawing-room than he could have desired."

"When your Grace *can* find time for a duty so frivolous," replied the Queen, "you are aware of your title to be well received. I hope my readiness to comply with the wish which you expressed yesterday to Lady Suffolk, is a sufficient proof that one of the royal family, at least, has not forgotten ancient and important services, in resenting something which resembles recent neglect."

This was said apparently with great good-humour, and in a tone which expressed a desire of conciliation.

The Duke replied, "That he would account himself the most unfortunate of men, if he could be supposed capable of neglecting his duty, in modes and circumstances when it was expected, and would have been agreeable. He was deeply gratified by the honour which her Majesty was now doing to him personally; and he trusted she would soon perceive that it was in a matter essential to his Majesty's interest, that he had the boldness to give her this trouble."

"You cannot oblige me more, my Lord Duke," replied the Queen, "than by giving me the advantage of your lights and experience on any point of the King's service. Your Grace is aware, that I can only be the medium through which the matter is subjected to his Majesty's superior wisdom; but if it is a suit which respects your Grace personally, it shall lose no support by being preferred through me."

"It is no suit of mine, madam," replied the Duke; "nor have I any to prefer for myself personally, although I feel in full force my obligation to your Majesty. It is a business which concerns his Majesty, as a lover of justice and of mercy, and which, I am convinced, may be highly useful in conciliating the unfortunate irritation which at present subsists among his Majesty's good subjects in Scotland."

There were two parts of this speech disagreeable to Caroline. In the first place, it removed the flattering notion she had adopted, that Argyle designed to use her personal intercession in making his peace with the administration, and recovering the employments of which he had been deprived; and next, she was displeased that he should talk of the discontents in Scotland as irritations to be conciliated, rather than suppressed.

Under the influence of these feelings, she answered hastily, "That his Majesty has good subjects in England, my Lord Duke, he is bound to thank God and the laws—that he has subjects in Scotland, I think he may thank God and his sword."

The Duke, though a courtier, coloured slightly, and the Queen, instantly sensible of her error, added, without displaying the least change of countenance, and as if the words had been an original branch of the sentence—"And the swords of those real Scotchmen who are friends to the House of Brunswick, particularly that of His Grace of Argyle."

"My sword, madam," replied the Duke, "like that of my fathers, has been always at the command of my lawful king, and of my native country—I trust it is impossible to separate their real rights and interests. But the present is a matter of more private concern, and respects the person of an obscure individual."

"What is the affair, my lord?" said the Queen. "Let us find out what we are talking about, lest we should misconstrue and misunderstand each other."

"The matter, madam," answered the Duke of Argyle, "regards the fate of an unfortunate young woman in Scotland, now lying under sentence of death, for a crime of which I think it highly probable that she is innocent. And my humble petition to your Majesty is, to obtain your powerful intercession with the King for a pardon."

It was now the Queen's turn to colour, and she did so over cheek and brow—neck and bosom. She paused a moment, as if unwilling to trust her voice with the first expression of her displeasure; and on assuming an air of dignity and an austere regard of control, she at length replied, "My Lord Duke, I will not ask your motives for addressing to me a request which circumstances have rendered such an extraordinary one. Your road to the King's closet, as a peer and a privy-councillor, entitled to request an audience, was open, without giving me the pain of this discussion. I, at least, have had enough of Scotch pardons."

The Duke was prepared for this burst of indignation, and he was not shaken by it. He did not attempt a reply while the Queen was in the first heat of displeasure, but remained in the same firm, yet respectful posture, which he had assumed during the interview. The Queen, trained from her situation to self-command, instantly perceived the advantage she might give against herself by yielding to passion; and added, in the same condescending and affable tone in which she had opened the interview, "You must allow me some of the privileges of the sex, my Lord; and do not judge uncharitably of me, though I am a little moved at the recollection of the gross insult and outrage done in your capital city to the royal authority, at the very time when it was vested in my unworthy person. Your Grace cannot be surprised that I should both have felt it at the time, and recollected it now."

"It is certainly a matter not speedily to be forgotten," answered the Duke. "My own poor thoughts of it have been long before your Majesty, and I must have expressed myself very ill if I did not convey my detestation of the murder which was committed under such extraordinary circumstances. I might, indeed, be so unfortunate as to differ with his Majesty's advisers on the degree in which it was either just or politic to punish the innocent instead of the guilty. But I trust your Majesty will permit me to be silent on a topic in which my sentiments have not the good fortune to coincide with those of more able men."

"We will not prosecute a topic on which we may probably differ," said the Queen. "One word, however, I may say in private —You know our good Lady Suffolk is a little deaf—the Duke of Argyle, when disposed to renew his acquaintance with his master and mistress, will hardly find many topics on which we should disagree."

"Let me hope," said the Duke, bowing profoundly to so flattering an intimation, "that I shall not be so unfortunate as to have found one on the present occasion."

"I must first impose on your Grace the duty of confession," said the Queen, "before I grant you absolution. What is your particular interest in this young woman? She does not seem" (and she scanned Jeanie, as she said this, with the eye of a connoisseur) "much qualified to alarm my friend the Duchess's jealousy."

"I think your Majesty," replied the Duke, smiling in his turn, "will allow my taste may be a pledge for me on that score."

"Then, though she has not much the air *d'une grande dame*, I suppose she is some thirtieth cousin in the terrible chapter of Scottish genealogy?"

"No, madam," said the Duke; "but I wish some of my nearer relations had half her worth, honesty, and affection."

"Her name must be Campbell, at least?" said Queen Caroline.

"No, madam; her name is not quite so distinguished, if I may be permitted to say so," answered the Duke.

"Ah! but she comes from Inverary or Argyleshire?" said the sovereign.

"She has never been farther north in her life than Edinburgh, madam."

"Then my conjectures are all ended," said the Queen, "and your Grace must yourself take the trouble to explain the affair of your protégée."

With that precision and easy brevity which is only acquired by habitually conversing in the higher ranks of society, and which is the diametrical opposite of that protracted style of disquisition,

Which squires call potter, and which men call prose,

the Duke explained the singular law under which Effie Deans had received sentence of death, and detailed the affectionate exertions which Jeanie had made in behalf of her sister, for whose sake she was willing to sacrifice all but truth and conscience.

Queen Caroline listened with attention; she was rather fond, it must be remembered, of an argument, and soon found matter in what the Duke told her for raising difficulties to his request.

"It appears to me, my Lord," she replied, "that this is a severe law. But still it is adopted upon good grounds, I am bound to suppose, as the law of the country, and the girl has been convicted under it. The very presumptions which the law construes into a positive proof of guilt exist in her case, and all that your Grace has said concerning the possibility of her innocence may be a very good argument for annulling the Act of Parliament, but cannot, while it stands good, be admitted in favour of any individual convicted upon the statute."

The Duke saw and avoided the snare; for he was conscious, that, by replying to the argument, he must have been inevitably led to a discussion, in the course of which the Queen was likely to be hardened in her own opinion, until she became obliged, out of mere respect to consistency, to let the criminal suffer. "If your Majesty," he said, "would condescend to hear my poor countrywoman herself, perhaps she may find an advocate in your own heart, more able than I am, to combat the doubts suggested by your understanding."

The Queen seemed to acquiesce, and the Duke made a signal for Jeanie to advance from the spot where she had hitherto remained watching countenances, which were too long accustomed to suppress all apparent signs of emotion, to convey to her any interesting intelligence. Her Majesty could not help smiling at the awe-struck manner in which the quiet demure figure of the little Scotchwoman advanced towards her, and yet more at the first sound of her broad northern accent. But Jeanie had a voice low and sweetly toned, an admirable thing in woman, and eke besought "her Leddyship to have pity on a poor misguided young creature," in tones so affecting, that, like the notes of some of her native songs, provincial vulgarity was lost in pathos.

"Stand up, young woman," said the Queen, but in a kind tone, "and tell me what sort of a barbarous people your countryfolk are, where child-murder is become so common as to require the restraint of laws like yours?"

"If your Leddyship pleases," answered Jeanie, "there are mony places beside Scotland where mothers are unkind to their ain flesh and blood."

It must be observed, that the disputes between George the Second, and Frederick, Prince of Wales, were then at the highest, and that the good-natured part of the public laid the blame on the Queen. She coloured highly, and darted a glance of a most penetrating character first at Jeanie, and then at the Duke. Both sustained it unmoved; Jeanie from total unconsciousness of the offence she had given, and the Duke from his habitual composure. But in his heart he thought, My unlucky protégée has, with this luckless answer, shot dead, by a kind of chance medley, her only hope of success.

Lady Suffolk, good-humouredly and skilfully, interposed in this awkward crisis. "You should tell this lady," she said to Jeanie, "the particular causes which render this crime common in your country."

"Some thinks it's the Kirk-Session—that is—it's the—it's the cutty-stool, if your Leddyship pleases," said Jeanie, looking down, and courtesying.

"The what?" said Lady Suffolk, to whom the phrase was new, and who besides was rather deaf.

"That's the stool of repentance, madam, if it please your Leddyship," answered Jeanie, "for light life and conversation, and for breaking the seventh command." Here she raised her eyes to the Duke, saw his hand at his chin, and, totally unconscious of what she had said out of joint, gave double effect to the innuendo, by stopping short and looking embarrassed.

As for Lady Suffolk, she retired like a covering party, which, having interposed betwixt their retreating friends and the enemy, have suddenly drawn on themselves a fire unexpectedly severe.

The deuce take the lass, thought the Duke of Argyle to himself: there goes another shot—and she has hit with both barrels right and left!

Indeed the Duke had himself his share of the confusion, for, having acted as master of ceremonies to this innocent offender, he felt much in the circumstances of a country squire, who, having introduced his spaniel into a well appointed drawing-room, is doomed to witness the disorder and damage which arises to china and to dress-gowns, in consequence of its untimely frolics. Jeanie's last chance hit, however, obliterated the ill impression which had arisen from the first; for her Majesty had not so lost the feelings of a wife in those of a Queen, but that she could enjoy a jest at the expense of "her good Suffolk." She turned towards the Duke of Argyle with a smile, which marked that she enjoyed the triumph, and observed, "the Scotch are a rigidly moral people." Then again applying herself to Jeanie, she asked how she traveled up from Scotland.

"Upon my foot mostly, madam," was the reply.

"What, all that immense way upon foot?—How far can you walk in a day?"

"Five-and-twenty miles and a bittock."

"And a what?" said the Queen, looking towards the Duke of Argyle.

"And about five miles more," replied the Duke.

"I thought I was a good walker," said the Queen, "but this shames me sadly."

"May your Leddyship never hae sae weary a heart, that ye canna be sensible of the weariness of the limbs!" said Jeanie.

That came better off, thought the Duke; it's the first thing she has said to the purpose.

"And I didna just a'thegither walk the haill way neither, for I had whiles the cast of a cart; and I had the cast of a horse from Ferrybridge—and divers other easements," said Jeanie, cutting short her story, for she observed the Duke made the sign he had fixed upon.

"With all these accommodations," answered the Queen, "you must have had a very fatiguing journey, and, I fear, to little purpose; since, if the King were to pardon your sister, in all probability it would do her little good, for I suppose your people of Edinburgh would hang her out of spite."

She will sink herself now outright, thought the Duke.

But he was wrong. The shoals on which Jeanie had touched in this delicate conversation lay underground, and were unknown to her; this rock was above water, and she avoided it.

"She was confident," she said, "that baith town and country wad rejoice to see his Majesty taking compassion on a poor unfriended creature."

"His Majesty has not found it so in a late instance," said the Queen; "but, I suppose, my Lord Duke would advise him to be guided by the votes of the rabble themselves, who should be hanged and who spared?"

"No, madam," said the Duke; "but I would advise his Majesty to be guided by his own feelings, and those of his royal consort; and then, I am sure, punishment will only attach itself to guilt, and even then with cautious reluctance."

"Well, my Lord," said her Majesty, "all these fine speeches do not convince me of the propriety of so soon showing any mark of favour to your—I suppose I must not say rebellious?—but, at least, your very disaffected and intractable metropolis. Why, the whole nation is in a league to screen the savage and abominable murderers of that unhappy man; otherwise, how is it possible but that, of so many perpetrators, and engaged in so public an action for such a length of time, one at least must have been recognised? Even this wench, for aught I can tell, may be a depository of the secret.—Hark you, young woman, had you any friends engaged in the Porteous mob?"

"No, madam," answered Jeanie, happy that the question was so framed that she could, with a good conscience, answer it in the negative.

"But I suppose," continued the Queen, "if you were possessed of such a secret, you would hold it matter of conscience to keep it to yourself?"

"I would pray to be directed and guided what was the line of duty, madam," answered Jeanie.

"Yes, and take that which suited your own inclinations," replied her Majesty.

"If it like you, madam," said Jeanie, "I would hae gaen to the end of the earth to save the life of John Porteous, or any other unhappy man in his condition; but I might lawfully doubt how far I am called upon to be the avenger of his blood, though it may become the civil magistrate to do so. He is dead and gane to his place, and they that have slain him must answer for their ain act. But my sister, my puir sister Effie, still lives, though her days and hours are numbered!—She still lives, and a word of the King's mouth might restore her to a broken-hearted auld man, that never, in his daily and nightly exercise, forgot to pray that his Majesty might be blessed with a long and a prosperous reign, and that his throne, and the throne of his posterity, might be established in righteousness. Oh, madam, if ever ye kend what it was to sorrow for and with a sinning and a suffering creature, whose mind is sae tossed that she can be neither ca'd fit to live or die, have some compassion on our misery!—Save an honest house from dishonour, and an unhappy girl, not eighteen years of age, from an early and dreadful death! Alas! it is not when we sleep soft and wake merrily ourselves, that we think on other people's sufferings. Our hearts are waxed light within us then, and we are for righting our ain wrangs and fighting our ain battles. But when the hour of trouble comes to the mind or to the body—and seldom may it visit your Leddyship—and when the hour of death comes, that comes to high and low—lang and late may it be yours—Oh, my Leddy, then it isna what we hae dune for oursells, but what we hae dune for others, that we think on maist pleasantly. Ahd the thoughts that ye hae intervened to spare the puir thing's life will be sweeter in that hour, come when it may, than if a word of your mouth could hang the haill Porteous mob at the tail of ae tow."[3]

Tear followed tear down Jeanie's cheeks, as, her features glowing and quivering with emotion, she pleaded her sister's cause with a pathos which was at once simple and solemn.

"This is eloquence," said her Majesty to the Duke of Argyle. "Young woman," she continued, addressing herself to Jeanie, "I cannot grant a pardon to your sister—but you shall not want my warm intercession with his Majesty. Take this housewife case," she continued, putting a small embroidered needle case into Jeanie's hands; "do not open it now, but at your leisure you will find something in it which will remind you that you have had an interview with Queen Caroline."

Jeanie, having her suspicions thus confirmed, dropped on her knees, and would have expanded herself in gratitude; but the Duke, who was upon thorns lest she should say more or less than just enough, touched his chin once more.

"Our business is, I think, ended for the present, my Lord Duke," said the Queen, "and, I trust, to your satisfaction. Hereafter I hope to see your Grace more frequently, both at Richmond and St. James's.—Come, Lady Suffolk, we must wish his Grace good morning."

They exchanged their parting reverences, and the Duke, so

[3 Rope.]

soon as the ladies had turned their backs, assisted Jeanie to rise from the ground, and conducted her back through the avenue, which she trode with the feeling of one who walks in her sleep.

AFTERWORD

This chapter, as we have said, is the peripety of the novel, the moment when Jeanie's fortunes change for the better, and Scott rises to the moment. His technical mastery—the economy of description, the psychological acumen, and the formal inventiveness—may be surprising to those readers who associate the Waverley novels with romantic scenery, elaborate documentation (one recalls Scott's historical footnotes), and an eighteenth-century rhetoric used indiscriminately for all types of characters. Even Robert Louis Stevenson, in many ways Scott's closest literary descendant, twigged his master for "tushery": "'Tush,' quoth he." The contemporary critic V.S. Pritchett once remarked of the passages meant to represent Lowland Scots that "we would as soon read phonetics." These accusations, valid for some of Scott's writing, do not seem applicable here. The formal language of the Queen and the Duke of Argyle befits their personalities as Scott reveals them, and Jeanie Deans's speeches— even her inner thoughts expressed in dialect—are efforts to catch the tone of the spoken voice, always a problem for the novelist writing dialogue.

Details of the landscape are confined to a few bare mentions of alleys and avenues in the royal park. The three members of the court are seen through Jeanie's naïve yet surprisingly shrewd eyes: the Duke's plain costume, giving her the notion that perhaps he intends her to plead her own cause (as indeed he does); the Queen's handsome, pockmarked face; and the melancholy look of Lady Suffolk (though Jeanie cannot know what we are told, that the look reveals the discomfort of her double position as the Queen's confidante and the King's mistress). Except for the "coloring" of first the Duke and then Queen Charlotte when they discuss relations between Scotland and England, and the two times Argyle touches his chin, using a prearranged signal to warn Jeanie that she should stop talking, there is little stage movement.

The dialogue is something like an operatic quartet: first comes the exchange between the Duke and the Queen, then another between Jeanie and the Queen, with Lady Suffolk given a scant two lines and the Duke one brief interpolation. But the only stage direction that refers to sound is the author's double remark about Jeanie's voice: first he calls it "low and sweetly toned, an admirable thing in woman," then he compares it to "the notes of her native songs." The first part of the remark, echoing a line in Shakespeare, has the effect of exalting the heroine; the second evokes the whole tradition of Scottish folk poetry. What is more important, the double remark prepares us for Jeanie's great speech—almost an aria—at the end of the chapter. "This is eloquence," her Majesty says to the Duke of Argyle—and to the reader, too, since she is telling us what our response should be.

Often the historical novelist is taken to task for attributing attitudes, thoughts, and words to real persons on occasions on which no evidence exists as to what they were feeling or saying. Properly this is an extra-literary problem. Scott's real problem as a novelist dealing in part with historical personages was how to humanize them without diminishing their political importance. He solves the problem here by a number of expedients. After two paragraphs about Jeanie's surmises, he enters into a long authorial digression about the political situation, but this is not merely to impart historical knowledge; most of the facts bear relevance to the dramatized scene that follows. In the course of the scene he gives us many human touches. There is, for example, the Queen's gout, a homely detail picked up when Jeanie notes the "elasticity and firmness of her step" (despite the ailment of which we, not the heroine, have knowledge), and again in the Queen's remark, "I thought I was a good walker." There is the Queen's relation to Lady Suffolk. What could better demonstrate Caroline's firm conviction that the state comes before all personal considerations than her appointing the King's mistress as her personal attendant? She tells the Duke that Jeanie's plain looks are not calculated to arouse jealousy in his wife, thus making a wry comment on her own situation. Jeanie's inadvertent reference to adultery, which causes some dismay to Lady Suffolk, comes after her equally innocent remark about mothers' being unkind to their own children, which the Queen first takes as reference to her uneasy relations with the Prince of Wales. Thus, affairs of state and personal affairs are persuasively inter-mingled.

Something should be said about the political lessons implied by the chapter. Scott was a romantic tory, though a moderate one who had conflicting feelings. One of the conflicts, often noted by critics, was between his sympathy for those arch-tories, the Scottish Jacobites, and his loyalty to the house of Hanover; this adds dramatic tension to many of his novels, beginning with *Waverley*. In the present chapter—to Scott's evident pleasure—the conflict is resolved in the person of John,

Duke of Argyle, who is both a patriotic Scots peer and a loyal servant of the English king. At the moment of Jeanie's changing fortunes, it is the Duke who saves her, thus becoming a god from the machine (and we remember that Richard the Lion-Heart, in *Ivanhoe*, was another *deus ex machina*). The most obvious lesson of the chapter is a tory lesson, namely, that mistakes of common people—such as Scottish lawmakers and judges—can be rectified by those whom God has endowed with power in keeping with their high descent; some of those personages are villains in Scott's novels, but others display true wisdom, generosity, and moral and martial courage.

Scott's toryism infected a good half of the romantic writers who followed him, though the other half were revolutionary democrats. It had even more effect on his susceptible readers—especially those in the Southern states, who pictured themselves as great lords, highborn ladies, and knights jousting in tournaments. Mark Twain was exaggerating even more than was his custom, but nevertheless he had some reason for saying that the Waverley novels were responsible for the Civil War. Still, there was another conflict in Scott's feelings. Much as he admired lords and ladies of high degree, he also had a sense of the common people and their stake in history. *The Heart of Midlothian* is first of all a novel about the Scottish peasantry and petty bourgeoisie. Jeanie Deans is its heroine, not Queen Caroline. Jeanie's great speech raises her to a kind of moral grandeur when it reveals her own half-conscious, half-articulated feeling of her political mission. In fiction as in life the bestowing of gifts often has a symbolic value, and the sewing case that the Queen gives to Jeanie is a token that some of the royal virtue or mana is being transferred to the cow feeder's daughter.

The Red and the Black (1830)

STENDHAL, the misspelled name of a small East German city, is the pseudonym under which the works of MARIE HENRI BEYLE (1783-1842) have long outlived their author. Beyle or Stendhal was fond of pseudonyms, and it has been estimated that he used more than three hundred of them, counting those signed to letters. The famous one was first attached to *Rome, Naples, and Florence* (1817), a travel book full of bold reflections and wild stories. Two months earlier, under a different pseudonym, Stendhal had published a *History of Painting in Italy* that was largely copied from an Italian art historian, the Abbé Lanza. In writing supposedly factual works, Stendhal could seldom resist plagiarizing and fabricating, or lying; but "The truth, the dry truth" is the motto affixed to *The Red and the Black*, and one can apply it to all his fiction.

He was born in Grenoble, a very old provincial city that he remembered as if it were "an abominable attack of indigestion; there is nothing dangerous about it, but it is utterly disgusting." His parents belonged to the prosperous upper bourgeoisie. "My mother," he writes in a pseudonymous autobiography, *The Life of Henri Brulard*, ". . . was a charming woman and I was in love with her." But she died when he was seven years old, and he felt nothing but hatred for his father. Since the father was a devout Catholic and a royalist, little Henri soon became a republican and an agnostic. He was not allowed to have playmates. For many years his only close friend was his maternal grandfather, Dr. Gagnon, a disciple of Voltaire's who listened to his confidences and gave him the run of his library. There, at the age of twelve, he read *Dangerous Liaisons* and remembered it all his life.

For three years he attended the École Centrale de Grenoble, one of the new public high schools opened by the Republic and later closed by Napoleon. He displayed such brilliance in mathematics that his father sent him to Paris, at sixteen, to enter the École Polytechnique, where engineers and army officers were trained. He stayed away from the entrance examinations, however, since he preferred to walk the Paris streets dreaming of love and glory. A second cousin of Stendhal's, Pierre Daru, was directing the service of supply for the army that Napoleon had secretly assembled to invade Italy. Daru obtained for him a commission as second lieutenant of dragoons, and the youngster followed Napoleon over Saint Bernard Pass into the plains of Lombardy. It was the most romantic period of his life, for he was serving in an army of liberation, while at the same time he was in love with Italy, with Milan, and with a beautiful Milanese. But the beauty repulsed him, the army assigned him to garrison duty away from Milan, and after less than two years he resigned his commission.

The next three years, 1802-1805, he spent in Paris, living alone on a small allowance from his father and studying hard to make himself a comic dramatist on the order of Molière or perhaps a bold revolutionary philosopher; he wavered between the two ambitions. Then, after a stormy love affair in Marseilles, he re-entered military service. By cultivating his relation to the Daru family, he obtained an important post in Germany, and later he served with distinction in the army commissariat during the Austrian campaign. In 1811 he was back in Paris, there living grandly as an official of Napoleon's court. In 1812 he joined the Grande Armée when it invaded Russia; he saw the burning of Moscow and barely survived the disastrous retreat. Those experiences were the climax of his military career, but he was never to write about them. After Napoleon abdicated, he preferred a self-imposed exile to begging for a place under the restored Bourbon monarchy. "I fell with Napoleon," he later said.

His place of exile was Milan, now ruled again by the Austrians, who were even more repressive than the Bourbons. During the Milanese years, 1814-1821, Stendhal published his first three books, but only the third of these, *Rome, Naples, and Florence*, was completely his own. Chiefly he occupied himself with conversation (which often took a political turn, since many of his friends were revolutionaries), attendance at the opera, and affairs of the heart. "Love is to me the greatest of all concerns, or perhaps the only one," he said. Balzac, his younger contemporary, showed an equally great concern with money, but was never able to handle it. In the same way Stendhal was often a most unfortunate lover. In Milan, for example, he renewed his acquaintance with the beauty who had repulsed him in 1801. Now she became his mistress, but she deceived him on such a grand scale that Stendhal felt himself to be the butt of ridicule. Later he fell desperately in love with the Countess Metilda Dembowska, but she rejected his advances. Metilda was an ardent revolutionary and, partly because of his connections with her circle, Stendhal himself fell under suspicion. In 1821 the Austrians warned him to leave Italy.

Back in Paris with little money and no prospect of advancement under the Bourbons, he became a more or less professional writer. His new career started inauspiciously with *De l'Amour* (1822), a sort of anatomy and natural history of love. Stendhal was proud of the book, with its analysis of his own passions, but it went unnoticed. Long afterward his bookseller told him that seventeen copies had been sold in twelve years. *A Life of Rossini* (1823) was full of scandalous anecdotes and proved to be more successful; it had a second printing and was also published in England. In those day Stendhal was earning much of his small income by writing for English magazines. He tried his hand at a novel, *Armance* (1827), based on the same situation that Hemingway was to use in *The Sun Also Rises*, an impotent man in love, but the book was scathingly reviewed and had no sale. To restore his standing with the booksellers, Stendhal wrote a travel book, *Promenades in Rome* (1829), which had a modest success. Then he set to work on another novel that was vastly more ambitious than *Armance* and, from the commercial standpoint, still more impractical, since it was sure to be suppressed while a Bourbon was on the throne.

At this point Stendhal—and France—had a stroke of political good fortune. The Bourbon king, Charles X, was deposed in the July Days of 1830, and Louis Philippe, who succeeded him, promised a series of reforms. Stendhal's novel, *The Red and the Black*, could now be placed on sale in spite of the subversive story it told. That story—the rise of a peasant's son in French society by playing a part and by concealing his radical opinions—was one that permitted the author to use all his accumulated knowledge of love and politics, of military life and social intrigue. The hero embodied the conflicting elements of Stendhal's own character: cynicism and idealism, realism and romanticism, a coldly calculating mind in the service of violent passions. His complexity baffled and horrified the critics, one of whom—Jules Janin, then the most influential—compared the book to "an amphitheater for the dissection of moral leprosy." *The Red and the Black* had a sale of only 1500 copies and then went out of print for more than twenty years.

Meanwhile the new government, urged on by Stendhal's friends, had appointed him to the consular service. After being sent to Trieste, where the Austrians refused to accept him because of his political record, he was transferred to Civitavecchia, a sleepy port in what were then the Papal States. He was consul there for the rest of his life, though with long leaves of absence in Paris. With few duties to perform and hardly any friends in reach, he found time for an amazing quantity of writing. Only two of the books he started during those later years were published during his lifetime: the first was *Memoirs of a Tourist* (1838), which had the same modest success as his earlier travel books; the second was *The Charterhouse of Parma* (1839), his other great novel. Its plot is based on the adventurous early life of Alessandro Farnese, a wastrel who became devout and was elected Pope in 1534, but Stendhal transferred his story into the nineteenth century. Although *The Charterhouse* called forth an enthusiastic tribute from Balzac, its sale was disappointing. Stendhal consoled himself by saying again (in English) that his books were "For the happy few," a phrase he may have found in Shakespeare. He also said, "I shall be read only in 1880 or 1900." As a simple fact, the books he left in manuscript were published between those two dates: *Lamiel*, an unfinished novel, in 1889; *Lucien Leuwen*, a longer novel, also unfinished, in 1894; *Memoirs of an Egotist* in 1892; and *The Life of Henri Brulard*, an extraordinary book about his boyhood and his family, in 1894. By that time Stendhal himself had been dead for more than fifty years.

THE STORY

In the title of the novel, "Red" stands for the military profession and also for the revolutionary element in French society, since the soldiers of '93 wore red uniforms. "Black" stands for the clergy and also for reaction and repression. Julien Sorel, the hero of the novel, is the gifted and fiercely ambitious son of an avaricious peasant who owns a sawmill. Although he dreams of a military career, Julien coldly decides to become a priest, since that is the only career open to talents under the restored Bourbon monarchy. But first he is hired as a tutor to the children of M. de Rênal, the mayor of a little manufacturing town. Julien falls in love with the mayor's wife and, timid as he is in reality, forces himself to seduce her. After a time the lovers are betrayed by one of the household servants, but Mme. de Rênal manages the situation so well that Julien, instead of being turned away, is sent to a seminary. He distinguishes himself in his studies and soon is invited to Paris by a great nobleman, the Marquis de la Mole, who makes Julien his confidential secretary. The Marquis has a daughter, Mathilde, and Julien seduces her. When she becomes pregnant the Marquis tries to avoid a public scandal; he obtains a commission in the dragoons for Julien, has him ennobled, and prepares for a wedding. At this moment when Julien has reached the goal of his ambition, a letter arrives from Mme. de Rênal denouncing him. In disgrace and mad with rage, he tries to kill her while she is at church; then he practically insists on being condemned to death for the crime. He becomes reconciled with Mme. de Rênal while awaiting execution. After his death Mathilde buries her lover's severed head with her own hands.

The two chapters that follow, 9 and 15, both set in the Rênals' big country house, recount the seduction of Mme. de Rênal. (In one of the intervening chapters, Julien shocks and frightens her by stealing a kiss). The new and idiomatic translation was made by Lloyd Parks for the New American Library.

[*Chapter 9. An Evening in the Country*]

—M. Guérin's Dido, a charming sketch!—*Strombeck*

When he saw Mme. de Rênal again, the next morning, he had a peculiar look in his eye; he watched her as if she were an enemy with whom he would soon have to do battle. His expression, so different from that of the night before, threw her into a state of confusion; she had been so good to him and he seemed angry. She could not take her eyes off his.

Mme. Derville's presence allowed Julien to talk less and give more attention to what was on his mind. His only real concern, all that day, was to fortify himself by reading in the inspired book which tempered his soul anew.[1]

He cut the children's lessons very short, and later on, when Mme. de Rênal's presence reminded him to look to his own glory, decided it was absolutely essential that tonight she should allow her hand to remain in his. The sun setting, bringing the decisive

[1 The "inspired book" was about Julien's hero, Napoleon: *The Memorial of St. Helena*, by the Count de Las Cases.]

moment closer and closer, made his heart beat strangely. Night came. He observed with joy, relieved of the immense weight on his chest, that it was very dark. The sky, heavy with big clouds driven by a hot breeze, seemed to forecast a storm. The two cousins prolonged their stroll in the garden. To Julien, everything they did this evening seemed out of the ordinary. They delighted in such weather, the kind which, for certain delicate sensibilities, seems to enhance the pleasure of being in love.

Finally they sat down: Mme. de Rênal beside Julien and Mme. Derville next to her cousin. Preoccupied with the attempt he was about to make, Julien could find nothing to say. The conversation flagged.

"Will I shake like this and feel so wretched the first time I have to fight a duel?" Julien wondered; for he had too little confidence either in himself or in others not to see the state he was in.

In his mortal agony, any danger would have seemed preferable. How many times had he wished that something unexpected would come up and oblige Mme. de Rênal to go back into the house, and leave the garden! The violence Julien was obliged to do his feelings was too great for his voice not to be markedly altered. Soon Mme. de Rênal's voice was trembling too, but Julien didn't notice it. The frightful combat going on in his breast, waged by duty against timidity, was so painful that he was in no condition to observe anything outside himself. A quarter to ten had just sounded in the clock-tower, without his having yet dared anything. Shocked at his own cowardice, Julien told himself: "At the exact moment the clock strikes ten, I will carry out the plan I have been promising myself all day that I would execute tonight, or I will go to my room and blow out my brains."

After one last minute of waiting and anxiety, during which the excess of his emotion almost drove Julien out of his mind, ten o'clock sounded from the tower over his head. Each stroke of the fatal bell echoed in his chest, causing there a sort of physical impulsion.

Finally, while the last stroke of ten was still vibrating, he reached out and took the hand of Mme. de Rênal, who pulled it away at once. Hardly aware of what he was doing, Julien seized it again. Though deeply agitated himself, he was struck by the icy coldness of the hand in his grasp; he squeezed it convulsively. A last effort was made to wrest it from him; but in the end the hand was his.

His soul was flooded with happiness, not because he loved Mme. de Rênal, but because a horrible torture had come to an end. He felt obliged to speak, so that Mme. Derville would not notice anything; this time his voice was strong and resonant. Mme. de Rênal's, on the contrary, betrayed so much emotion, her friend thought she must be ill and suggested going indoors. Julien saw his danger: "If Mme. de Rênal goes into the drawing-room now, I will be back in the same horrible position I've been in all day. I've held this hand too short a time to claim a decided victory."

When Mme. Derville repeated her suggestion that they return to the drawing-room, Julien gave the hand that had been abandoned to him a hard squeeze.

Mme. de Rênal, who was already getting up, sat down again, saying in a dying voice: "To tell the truth, I don't feel very well. . . . But the fresh air is doing me good."

These words confirmed Julien's happiness, which, for the moment, was immense. He talked; he forgot to feign; to the two friends who were listening, he seemed the most charming of men. And yet, in this sudden flow of eloquence, there was still some want of courage, an apprehension. He was deathly afraid that Mme. Derville, tired by the rising wind that preceded the storm, might decide to go back to the drawing-room by herself. Then he would be left in a tête-à-tête with Mme. de Rênal. Almost by chance he had found the blind courage it takes for action; but he felt it was beyond his power to utter the simplest word to Mme. de Rênal. However inconsequential her reproaches might be, he would be beaten, and the advantage he had just gained would be wiped out.

Luckily for him, his speech, emphatic and moving tonight, won over Mme. Derville, who as a rule found him awkward as a child and by no means amusing. As for Mme. de Rênal, her hand in Julien's, she hadn't a thought in the world; she was letting herself live. The hours they spent beneath that great linden tree, which, as local tradition would have it, was planted by Charles the Bold, were for her a time of bliss. She listened delightedly to the wind moaning in the tree's thick foliage, and to the sound of the first few scattered drops that were beginning to fall on its lowest leaves. Julien failed to remark one detail that might well have reassured him; Mme. de Rênal, who had been forced to take her hand out of his, so she could get up to help her cousin right a pot of flowers which the wind had knocked over at their feet, was scarcely seated again when she gave him back her hand, with almost no fuss, as if it were already a thing agreed upon between them.

Midnight had struck long ago; it was high time to leave the garden; they separated. Mme. de Rênal, transported by the joys of love, was so ignorant that she hardly blamed herself at all. Happiness robbed her of sleep. Julien, tired to death by the pitched battle between timidity and pride that had been raging in his heart all day long, was carried off by a sleep like lead.

The next morning he was awakened at five o'clock, and though Mme. de Rênal would have suffered cruelly had she known it, he barely gave her a thought. He had done *his duty, a heroic duty*. Filled with joy by this sentiment, he locked the door to his room and, with an entirely new pleasure, gave himself over to reading about the exploits of his hero.

By the time the bell for lunch was rung, he had forgotten, while reading the reports of the Grand Army, all the advantages he had won the night before. He said to himself, in an offhand way, as he went down to the drawing-room: "I must tell this woman I love her."

Instead of the passionate gaze he was expecting to meet, he found the stern face of M. de Rênal, who, having arrived from Verrières two hours before, took no pains to hide his displeasure at Julien's having spent the entire morning without a thought to his children. Nothing could be uglier than this important man, in a bad temper and sure of his right to show it.

Every one of her husband's harsh remarks pierced Mme. de Rênal to the heart. Julien, on the other hand, was still so deeply immersed in his ecstasy, so full of the great events which, for the past several hours, had been taking place before his eyes, that at first he was hardly able to lower his attention enough to listen to the hard language M. de Rênal was directing at him. At length he told him, sharply enough:

"I was sick."

The tone of his reply might have nettled a man far less touchy than the Mayor of Verrières. The thought crossed his mind to answer Julien by turning him out, then and there. He was restrained only by the rule he had laid down for himself: never be hasty in business matters.

"The young fool," he soon concluded, "has made a sort of

reputation for himself in my house. If I dismiss him, Valenod may take him on, or else he will marry Elisa; in either case, he will be able to laugh up his sleeve at me."

Despite the wisdom of these reflections, M. de Rênal's annoyance erupted in a series of coarse expressions which, little by little, succeeded in irritating Julien. Mme. de Rênal was on the point of tears. Lunch hardly over, she asked Julien to give her his arm for the walk. She leaned on it in a friendly manner. To everything Mme. de Rênal said to him, Julien would only mutter:

"That's the rich for you."

M. de Rênal was walking close by them; his presence increased Julien's wrath. Suddenly he became aware that Mme. de Rênal was leaning on his arm in an obvious way. Horrified by this gesture, he pushed her away and freed his arm.

Fortunately, M. de Rênal did not see this fresh bit of impertinence; only Mme. Derville noticed it. Her friend burst into tears. At this moment M. de Rênal began throwing stones at a little peasant girl who was taking a short-cut across a corner of his orchard.

"Monsieur Julien, for heaven's sake, control yourself. Remember that we all lose our temper at times," said Mme. Derville quickly.

Julien looked at her coldly, his face a picture of the most sovereign contempt.

His look astonished Mme. Derville and would have surprised her even more could she have guessed its full import. In it she might have read a vague hope for the most atrocious kind of vengeance. It is, no doubt, such moments of humiliation that have produced our Robespierres.

"Your Julien is a violent man; he frightens me," Mme. Derville whispered to her friend.

"He has a right to be angry," replied the latter. "After the amazing progress the children have made with him, what difference does it make if he goes for a morning without speaking to them? You must admit that men are very hard."

For the first time in her life, Mme. de Rênal felt a sort of desire to be revenged against her husband. The intense hatred Julien bore the rich was going to burst out before long. Luckily, M. de Rênal summoned his gardener and stayed behind to help him set up a barrier of thorn branches across the illegal path through his orchard. During the rest of the stroll, Julien did not respond by so much as a word to all the little attentions that were shown him. No sooner had M. de Rênal left than the two ladies, on the pretext of being tired, asked him each for an arm.

Between these two women, who were both deeply disturbed and whose cheeks were flushed with embarrassment, Julien's haughty pallor, his determined and somber air, made a strange contrast. He despised these ladies and all tender feelings.

"What!" he said to himself, "not even five hundred francs a year to finish my education! Ah! how I'd love to tell him off!"

Absorbed in these hard thoughts, the little he condescended to take in of the two friends' well-intended remarks displeased him as void of meaning, silly, weak—in a word, *feminine*.

By dint of talking for the sake of talking, to keep the conversation from dying, Mme. de Rênal happened to mention that her husband came out from Verrières because he had made a bargain with one of his tenant farmers for some corn husks. (In that region they use husks to fill their mattresses.)

"My husband will not join us again," added Mme. de Rênal. "He is going with his gardener and valet to see to it that the rest of the mattresses in the house are changed. This morning he put fresh husks in all the beds on the second floor; now he is on the third."

Julien changed color; he gave Mme. de Rênal an odd look and shortly afterward took her aside, so to speak, by doubling his pace. Mme. Derville let them go on.

"Save my life," Julien said to Mme. de Rênal, "Only you can do it. For you know that the valet hates the sight of me. I must confess, Madam, that I have a portrait; I've hidden it in the mattress on my bed."

At this information, Mme. de Rênal also turned pale.

"You alone, Madam, can go into my room right now. Feel, without letting anyone see you, in the corner of the mattress nearest the window; there you will find a small, shiny, black cardboard box."

"It contains a portrait!" said Mme. de Rênal, hardly able to stand.

Her disheartened air did not escape Julien, who was quick to take advantage of it.

"I have a second favor to ask of you, Madam: I beg you not to look at that portrait. It is my secret."

"It is a secret," repeated Mme. de Rênal, in a barely audible voice.

Although she had been brought up among people who were proud of their fortunes and sensitive to money matters alone, love had already introduced some notion of generosity into her soul. Though cruelly wounded, it was with an air of the simplest devotion that Mme. de Rênal asked Julien the questions she had to, if she was to do his errand properly.

"So," she said to him as she was leaving, "a small, round box, made of black cardboard . . . shiny."

"Yes, Madam," replied Julien, with that hard look danger imparts to men.

She climbed to the third floor of the château, pale as if she were going to her death. To crown her misery, she felt as if she were about to faint; but the necessity of doing a good turn for Julien restored her strength.

"I must have that box," she said, quickening her step. She heard her husband speaking to his valet, in Julien's room itself. As luck would have it, they moved on to the children's bedroom. She raised the mattress and thrust her hand into the stuffing so violently that she skinned her fingers. But, though very sensitive to little hurts of that nature, she was unconscious of this one, for almost simultaneously she felt the slick surface of the cardboard box. She seized it and disappeared.

No sooner was she delivered from her dread of being discovered by her husband than the horror inspired by that box made her feel that she was definitely on the point of fainting.

"So, Julien is in love, and I have here a portrait of the woman he loves!"

Seated on a chair in the antechamber of the apartment, Mme. de Rênal became a prey to all the torments of jealousy, but her extreme ignorance was again useful to her at this juncture; astonishment tempered her suffering. Julien appeared, seized the box without thanking her, without saying a word, and ran into his bedroom, where he made a fire and burned it in a minute. He was pale, wrung out; he exaggerated the extent of the risk he had just run.

"Imagine," he said to himself shaking his head, "Napoleon's portrait found hidden in the room of a man who professes nothing but hatred for the usurper! found by M. de Rênal, so *ultra* and so irritated! and—the height of recklessness—on its white cardboard backing, lines written in my own hand, which can leave no doubt about the warmth of my admiration, and each of these raptures of love is dated! . . . one from the day before yesterday.

"My whole reputation ruined, wrecked in a moment!" thought Julien, as he watched the box burn up. "And my reputation is all I have; my living depends on it . . . and what a living at that! good God!"

Weariness and self-pity inclined him an hour later to tenderness. Coming across Mme. de Rênal, he took her hand and kissed it with more sincerity than he had ever felt before. She blushed with delight, but, almost instantly, pushed Julien away in a jealous rage. His pride, so recently wounded, made a fool of Julien in that moment. All he could see in Mme. de Rênal was the rich woman; letting her hand drop disdainfully, he walked away. He went out for a thoughtful stroll in the garden. Before long a bitter smile appeared on his lips.

"Here I am, taking a walk, at my ease, like a man who is master of his own time! I am neglecting the children! I am exposing myself to M. de Rênal's humiliating criticism—and he will have good reason!" He ran to the children's room.

The affection of the youngest boy, of whom he was very fond, did much to calm his searing pain.

"This one doesn't despise me yet," thought Julien. But he was soon reproaching himself for this diminution of his pain, as for a new weakness. "These children hug me just as they would hug the hound puppy their father bought yesterday."

[*Chapter 15. Cock's Crow*]

> Amour en latin faict amor;
> Or donc provient d'amour la mort,
> Et, par avant, soulcy qui mord,
> Deuil, plours, pieges, forfaitz, remord.
> *Blason d'amour*

If Julien had a little of that cleverness he so freely imputed to himself, he might have congratulated himself the next day on the effect produced by his trip to Verrières. Absence caused the ladies to forget his bungling. All that day too, he was sullen; toward evening, an absurd idea crossed his mind, and he communicated it to Mme. de Rênal with rare intrepidity.

They were no more than seated in the garden, when Julien, not waiting until it was dark enough, but his mouth to Mme. de Rênal's ear and, at the risk of compromising her horribly, said:

"Madam, tonight, at two o'clock, I am coming to your room; there's something I must tell you."

Julien was shaking for fear that his request be granted; the role of seducer weighed on him so heavily that had he been free to follow his own inclination, he would have retired to his room for several days and would not have seen those ladies again. He realized that yesterday's subtle tactics spoiled the fine impression made the day before, and really he didn't know which way to turn.

Mme. de Rênal responded with a real and by no means exaggerated indignation to the impertinent announcement Julien had had the audacity to make. He thought he detected scorn in her curt answer. It's certain that in this reply, spoken in a whisper, the words *for shame* had occurred. Under the pretext of having something to tell the children, Julien went to their bedroom and, on his return, sat down beside Mme. Derville, a good distance from Mme. de Rênal. Thus he removed any possibility of taking her hand. The conversation was serious, and Julien held up his own end of it very well, if we except a few moments of silence, during which he was racking his brains. "Why," he was asking himself, "can't I think up some fine maneuver and force Mme. de Rênal into showing me once more those unmistakable signs of affection that, three days ago, led me to believe she was mine!"

Julien was dismayed at the almost desperate state of affairs into which he had got himself. Yet nothing would have embarrassed him more than success.

When the company parted at midnight, his pessimism made him believe that he enjoyed Mme. Derville's contempt, and that he was probably not on much better terms with Mme. de Rênal. Humiliated and in a foul temper, Julien didn't sleep. Yet he was a thousand miles away from any thought of forswearing all sham, all his schemes, and of living with Mme. de Rênal on a day-to-day basis, contenting himself like a child with the happiness each day might bring.

He wearied his brain trying to think up expert maneuvers; a moment later they would all seem ridiculous. He was, in short, thoroughly miserable when the château clock struck two.

This sound roused him, just as the cock's crow roused St. Peter. In that instant he saw himself at the most painful juncture of his life. He hadn't given another thought to his impudent proposition since he made it; it had been so poorly received! "I told her I would go to her room at two o'clock," he said to himself as he got up. "I am as inexperienced and boorish as a peasant's son should be. Mme. Derville made that clear enough; but at least I won't be weak."

Julien had reason to think highly of his courage; he had never forced himself to do anything so painful. When he opened his door, he was shaking so that his knees gave way beneath him, and he was obliged to lean against the wall.

He was barefoot. He went to listen at M. de Rênal's door; he could make out his snoring. He was sorry, indeed. So, there was no longer any excuse for not going to her room. But, good God! what would he do there? He had no plan, and even if he had one, he felt so upset that he would have been in no condition to follow it through. At last, suffering a thousand times more than if he were walking to his death, he stepped into the short corridor just off Mme. de Rênal's room. With a trembling hand and making a frightful racket, he opened her door.

There was light; a night-light was burning in the fireplace; he was not prepared for this fresh calamity. On seeing him enter, Mme. de Rênal jumped out of bed. "Wretch!" she cried. There was a moment's confusion. Julien forgot his useless plan and reverted to his natural self. Not to find favor in the eyes of such a lovely woman seemed to him the worst of misfortunes. His only answer to her reproaches was to throw himself at her feet and clasp her knees. Since she said some very harsh things to him, he burst into tears.

When Julien left Mme. de Rênal's bedroom some hours later, it might be said, in the style of the novel, that he had nothing more to desire. He was, in fact, indebted to the love he had inspired, and to the unexpected impression her seductive charms had made on him, for a conquest that all his clumsy maneuvering could never have brought off.

Yet, even at the tenderest moments, victim of a bizarre pride, he still aspired to the role of a man who is used to subjugating women. He applied himself with incredible effort to spoiling whatever was likable about him. Instead of being attentive to the raptures he had awakened and to the remorse that only heightened their intensity, he could think of nothing but his *duty*. He dreaded the terrible regret and sense of everlasting ridicule that must follow, should he lose sight of the model he had proposed for himself. In a word, what made Julien a superior fellow was precisely that which kept him from relishing the happiness that lay at his feet. He was like the sixteen-year-old girl with a lovely complexion who, when she goes to a ball, has the crazy notion of putting rouge on her face.

At first mortally terrified by Julien's appearance, Mme. de Rênal was soon a prey to the most agonizing fears. Julien's despair and his tears troubled her profoundly.

Even when she had nothing left to refuse him, she kept pushing Julien away, out of real indignation, and would then fling herself into his arms. There was no design apparent in this behavior. She believed she was damned beyond remission and kept trying to hide from her vision of hell by covering Julien with the most passionate kisses. In short, nothing would have been wanting to our hero's happiness, not even a burning tenderness in the woman he had just swept off her feet, had he but known how to enjoy it. Julien's departure did not put an end to the raptures that kept surging through her, in spite of herself, or her struggles against a feeling of remorse that was tearing her apart.

"My God! to be happy, to be loved, is that all there is to it?" Such was Julien's first thought when he got back to his room. He was in that state of astonishment and uneasiness into which a man may lapse just after obtaining what he has long desired. He is used to desiring, has nothing more to desire, and hasn't, as yet, any memories. Like the soldier who comes back from a parade, Julien was busy reviewing every detail of his conduct.

"Have I failed in any way with respect to what I owe myself? Have I played my part well?"

Which part? That of a man who is used to having his way with women.

AFTERWORD

The selection from *The Red and the Black* consists of two chapters, 9 and 15, here placed together because they present two stages of what amounts to being the same military engagement: Nine is the first skirmish: Fifteen is the final assault. During much of the narrative in the five intervening chapters, Julien is away from the battlefield—that is, the Rênals' big country house—although in Sixteen he draws up a plan of operations, then makes the gross tactical error of stealing a kiss. The military terms are appropriate to the subject matter, for the truth is that Julien's effort to rise in French society, inspired by the example of Napoleon, is undertaken like a military campaign.

Stendhal himself, a veteran of the Napoleonic wars, makes wide use of military language. In the first sentence of Chapter Nine, Julien looks at Mme. de Rênal "as if she were an enemy with whom he would soon have to do battle." She is the enemy because she is the first woman he has set himself to subjugate; in Napoleonic terms, the first country he has chosen to invade. But this disciple of the upstart emperor is a twenty-year-old soldier undergoing his baptism of fire, and hence his struggle in the beginning is not with the enemy, but with his own fright. He wonders, "Will I shake like this and feel so wretched the first time I have to fight a duel?" "The frightful combat going on in his breast, waged by duty against timidity, was so painful that he was in no condition to observe anything outside himself." Yes, "duty" is the word, that is, fidelity to his picture of himself as a conqueror. If he holds the hand of Mme. de Rênal, he will have gained "a decided victory," but only if he holds it long enough for her to acknowledge defeat. "Almost by chance, he had found the blind courage it takes for action." "He had done *his duty, a heroic duty*." The military metaphors continue through Chapter Fifteen, which recounts the actual seduction. When Julien steps into the corridor leading to Mme. Rênal's bedroom, he suffers "a thousand times more than if he were walking to his death . . . he could think of nothing but his *duty*." Afterward he reviews every detail of his conduct "Like the soldier who comes back from a parade."

One is reminded of *Dangerous Liaisons*, which also uses military metaphors (together with those of the chase; Mme. de Tourvel is a stag that must be brought to bay) and which also deals with a planned campaign of seduction. There is, however, a difference in the two protagonists. Valmont in *Liaisons* is an old mercenary soldier, hopelessly corrupt and even satanistic, but astute; when he lays plans he carries them through, and usually with success. Julien is a new character in fiction: the outsider, the upstart, who remains at heart a romantic idealist; he tries to be as cynical as Valmont, but he makes his conquest of Mme. de Rênal only when he forgets his plans and reveals his warmth of spirit by falling at her feet. It was "a conquest," Stendhal says, offering one of his many commentaries on the action, "that all his clumsy maneuvering could never have brought off."

Another new element in *The Red and the Black*, as compared with *Dangerous Liaisons*, is politics. We are never allowed to forget that the action takes place under the restored Bourbon monarchy, when peasants were treated with contempt and a young man of talent had to forget his scruples if he hoped to rise. Another revolution grumbles on the horizon. Even in this episode concerned with a seduction, politics intrudes into the garden and the bedroom. ("Politics in the novel," Stendhal had said on various occasions, "is like a pistol shot at a concert.") Here M. de Rênal, the husband, represents the new class of manufacturers who prospered under the Bourbons. He has pretensions to aristocracy, but he stuffs the mattresses in his château with corn husks and throws stones at a little peasant girl who trespasses on his land. Julien, though a peasant's son, has more of the aristocratic spirit than his employer. Still, he does not forget his origin, and another reason why he looks at Mme. de Rênal as "an enemy" is that she represents for him a hostile class. "That's the rich for you," he mutters while she is strolling in the garden on his arm. At the moment he is identifying her with her husband, who has just berated him in coarse terms. "It is, no doubt, such moments of humiliation that have produced our Robespierres," the author says in another of his editorial comments.

Stendhal's technique, as opposed to his subject matter, is generally old-fashioned. The point of view he adopts, that of the omniscient narrator, is as old as the *Iliad*. It gives him the privilege of reading the mind of any character, but there will be degrees of thoroughness in what he reveals about them. Julien is revealed completely and judged at all times, but with indulgence; he is the sort of young man the author might have wished to be. Mme. de Rênal is depicted with sympathy, not empathy, and is less fully revealed; one might say that the author sees *into* her, as he sees *through* her husband and other disagreeable characters. Lately it has become a doctrine that novelists are obliged to *show* characters in action instead of merely *telling* about them. Stendhal has so many actions to report that he can't take the time to dramatize or "show" each one of them. Except in the case of significant actions—as when Julien seizes Mme. de Rênal's hand in the darkness, a fully dramatized scene—he merely "tells" what happened, while carrying along the reader by the speed of his narrative. He breaks another of the rules imposed on fiction since his time by making editorial comments on his characters and sometimes on the world in which they live. We forgive him because the comments are so candid and based on such a wide experience of the world. The story of Julien Sorel without Stendhal's gloss on it would be like a dinner without salt.

To read him quickly, as one can read Balzac or Dickens, is to miss the moments when he lets drop an unexpected phrase or has a character think or feel in a fashion we could not have foreseen. In Chapter 9 there is Julien's reaction when he squeezes Mme. de Rênal's hand a second time: "happiness . . . because a horrible torture had come to an end." There is her sudden desire "to be revenged against her husband," who will later snore contentedly while he is being cuckolded. In Chapter 15 there is Julien's unpremeditated remark: "Madam, tonight, at two o'clock, I am coming to your room." Best of all, there is the terse and understated paragraph that begins with the sentence: "When Julien left Mme. de Rênal's bedroom some hours later, it might be said, in the style of the novel, that he had nothing more to desire." We have been led up to the decisive moment, and another author might have taken us at least to the bed. Stendhal does not "show"; he briefly tells what happened and then stops. The sentence, not at all what we expect, was his admission that the novel, brilliantly equipped to explore the contours of human experience, sometimes works best by suggestion, not representation.

Eugénie Grandet (1833)

Like so many of his fictional heroes, HONORÉ DE BALZAC
(1799-1850) came from the provinces to make his fortune in Paris.
An unsuccessful law student, he turned to writing potboilers under
such incredible pseudonyms as "Lord R'Hoone" and "Horace de St.-
Aubin." *Les Chouans* (1829), a historical novel after the manner of
Scott and Cooper, was his first important work. A series of liaisons with
titled women culminated in his stormy affair with the Polish countess
Evalina Hanska, whom he finally married five months before his death.

It is hard to believe that Balzac could have enjoyed any private life.
Normally writing from fourteen to eighteen hours a day, he once
stayed writing in one room for twenty-six days. These literary labors
gradually took the form of the *Human Comedy*, no doubt the most
grandiose literary scheme ever conceived. Of the projected one hundred
and forty-four titles, some ninety-two were actually written—and those
in a period of only twenty years. Balzac intended to create four thousand characters, and managed to fashion about half this number. His own
comments underscore his hyperbolic aim. "I shall have borne an entire
society in my head. Hail me! I am about to become a genius. . . . What
Napoleon began with the sword, I shall complete with the pen."

The vast undertaking fell into three major categories: *Studies of
Morals and Manners*, *Philosophical Studies*, and *Analytical Studies*.
Most of the novels came under the first heading, which was in turn
subdivided into "Scenes from Private Life," "Scenes from Provincial
Life"—*Eugénie Grandet* is the second book in this group—"Life in
Paris," "Political Life," "Military Life," and "Life in the Country."

Balzac's mania for systems was also reflected in his enthusiasm for certain zoological concepts, especially those advanced by Étienne Geoffroy Saint-Hilaire in his *Philosophie anatomique* (1808-1822). In the "Foreword to the *Human Comedy*" (1842), Balzac makes much of the need for the novelist to compare "Humanity and Animality"; he draws the analogy that "Society is similar to Nature" and cites the "existence of Social as well as Zoological Species." This insistence on capital letters (rarely used with French substantives) hints at a kind of genial amateurism: zoology for Balzac was as exciting as phrenology and Mesmerism, to name two contemporary popular fields of intellectual speculation.

In the *Human Comedy*, a number of novels (chiefly those in the *Philosophical Studies* category) hark back to the Middle Ages and the Renaissance, but the majority take place from the late eighteenth to the mid-nineteenth century; for Balzac's stated intention was to demonstrate a Legitimist thesis: that the venality and decline of modern morality could be attributed to the loss of "Throne and Altar," for which the constitutional monarchies of Charles X and Louis Philippe were shabby replacements. "The people who have forty-thousand laws have no law," he said. "God and the King. These two principles are the only ones that can keep the ignorant part of the nation inside the boundaries of its patient and resigned life."

Old Grandet is the personification of all that Balzac manifestly despised in the new France that emerged after 1789, whose mercenary standards were neatly caught up in two *dicta* pronounced by Louis Philippe's Minister, Guizot: "Get rich," and "Everyone for himself, everyone in his own house." Ironically, Balzac himself was a product of this same rapacious age. Despite his protestations against the unbridled scramble for wealth, few writers have ever coveted money more and handled it worse. His craving for luxury kept him in debt throughout his life, and his writing was in part motivated by a frantic desire for the financial solvency he never attained.

THE STORY

While the following scene has Balzac's unmistakable signature written all over it, *Eugénie Grandet* seems slightly atypical when placed against most of his novels. Compared with *Père Goriot* (1835) or *Lost Illusions* (1837), it has relatively few characters; and its rigid dramatic structure, like that of a three- or five-act play, is rare for Balzac: a summary at the start, then a climactic scene with Eugénie and her beloved cousin Charles, with the rest of the novel a slow falling-action. The characters display the single-minded and relatively uncomplex pas-

sions we associate with the *personae* of French classical comedy and
tragedy; although in all truth this might be said for most of Balzac's
creations throughout the *Human Comedy*.

The town is Saumur, made to be the epitome of all that is bourgeois
and provincial: a world of gossip and spying and making money. A
humble cooper before 1789, Grandet makes a rich marriage; and slowly
he buys up the confiscated vineyards, abbeys, and chateaux of the
émigrés. His daughter Eugénie is eagerly pursued by two young men
from Saumur's leading families, the Cruchots and the Grassins. Then
Grandet's nephew Charles arrives from Paris, bearing a letter saying that
his father is bankrupt. The next morning the newspaper reports his
father's suicide, and the young dandy and boulevardier Charles is now
destitute. After a short stay, he leaves to make his fortune in the Indies,
but not before he and Eugénie confide their mutual love. She gives
him the gold that her father annually increases for her, and for which
he demands an accounting each New Year's Day.

On the New Year's Day after Charles' departure, then, there is
a terrible confrontation between father and daughter. That spring
Mme. Grandet dies. Grandet finally "forgives" Eugénie, though swindling
her out of any share in her mother's legacy. He dies in 1827, leaving
Eugénie heiress to a fortune of seventeen million francs. She finally
hears from Charles, who has married, and she realizes his worthlessness.
She then marries M. Cruchot, solely that he may become an agent in
extracting Charles from bankruptcy. In six months Eugénie is a widow at
thirty-three, a recluse known for her pious good works. Balzac con-
cludes by taking the reader up to the present (September 1833), when
the book was published. He informs us that all of Saumur is speculating
whether the heroine will become the wife of the Marquis de Froidfond,
whose family "has begun to lay siege to the rich widow."

The following episode is the confrontation between father and
daughter that takes place on New Year's Day, 1820, two months after
Charles' departure. The modern translation is by Lowell Bair for Bantam
Books (1959).

[*New Year's Day*]

"Oh, oh, where's Old Man Grandet going so early in the
morning, running as though his house were on fire?" asked the
tradesmen as they opened their shops. Then, when they saw him

coming back from the waterfront followed by a porter from the stagecoach office pushing a wheelbarrow laden with full sacks, one of them said, "Water always flows toward the river: the old man was going after his money."

"It comes in to him from Paris, Froidfond and Holland," said another.

"He'll end up by buying the whole town of Saumur!" cried a third.

"He doesn't even notice the cold, his mind is always on his business," said a wife to her husband.

"Look, Monsieur Grandet, if those bags are too heavy for you, I'll be glad to take them off your hands," said a clothier, his nearest neighbor.

"Oh, there's nothing but copper coins in them," said the wine-grower.

"He means silver," said the porter in a low voice.

"If you want me to treat you right, you'd better learn to keep your mouth shut," the old man said to the porter as he opened his front door.

"Oh, the old fox!" thought the porter. "I thought he was hard of hearing. There doesn't seem to be anything wrong with his ears when it's cold."

"Here's twenty sous as a New Year's present, and hold your tongue," said Grandet. "You can leave now, Nanon will bring back the wheelbarrow. . . . Nanon, have the two little birds gone off to mass?"

"Yes, monsieur."

"Come, get a move on! Let's go to work!" he cried, loading her up with bags. A few moments later the money had been carried up to his room, where he locked himself in. "Knock on the wall when breakfast is ready. Take the wheelbarrow back to the stage-coach office."

The family did not have breakfast until ten o'clock.

"Your father won't ask to see your gold here, and you can pretend to be very cold," said Madame Grandet to her daughter when they returned from mass. "Then we'll have time to replace your treasure before your birthday. . . ."

As Grandet came down the stairs he was planning to turn his Parisian silver coins into good, solid gold without delay and thinking of his admirable speculation in government bonds. He had decided to invest his income in them until they rose to one hundred. His meditations were to have disastrous consequences for Eugénie.

As soon as he came in the two women wished him a happy New Year, his daughter by affectionately hugging him, his wife gravely and with dignity.

"Listen, my child," he said as he kissed his daughter on both cheeks, "I'm working for you . . . I want you to be happy. It takes money to be happy. Without money, you might as well give up. Look, here's a brand-new napoleon I sent for from Paris. I swear I don't have one ounce of gold! You're the only one that has any. Show me your gold, sweetie."

"Oh, it's too cold; let's have breakfast," replied Eugénie.

"After breakfast, then, all right? It will help us digest better. . . . Look what good old des Grassins sent us! Go on, eat, children, it's free. Des Grassins is doing well and I'm satisfied with him; the old fish is doing a lot of good for Charles, and that's free too. He's straightening out the poor deceased Grandet's affairs very well. . . . Oh! This is good!" he said with his mouth full, after a pause. "Eat some of it, my dear! It will keep you fed for at least two days."

"I'm not hungry. I'm not feeling well, you know that."

"Come, come! You can stuff yourself all you like and nothing will go wrong with you. You're a La Bertellière, a solid woman. Your skin is a bit yellow, it's true, but I like yellow."

A condemned man awaiting an ignominious and public death feels less horror, perhaps, than Madame Grandet and her daughter felt as they awaited the events that were to follow this family breakfast. The more cheerfully the old winegrower talked as he ate, the heavier grew the hearts of the two women. But Eugénie had something to support her in this crisis: she drew strength from her love. "For him, for him," she said to herself, "I'd suffer a thousand deaths." At this thought she looked at her mother with courage flashing from her eyes.

"Take all this away," Grandet said to Nanon when breakfast was over, toward eleven o'clock, "but leave us the table. We'll be able to look at your little treasure more comfortably," he said, looking at Eugénie. "Little? What am I saying? You have gold worth five thousand nine hundred and fifty-nine francs by weight, plus forty more this morning: that makes you just one franc short of six thousand. Well, I'll give you the franc you need to make an even six thousand, because you see, sweetie . . . Well? Why are you listening to us, Nanon? Get out of here, get back to your work!"

Nanon disappeared.

"Listen, Eugénie, you must give me your gold. You won't refuse your old daddy, will you, sweetie?" The two women were silent. "I have no more gold. I had some, but it's gone. I'll give you six thousand francs in *livres* and tell you how to invest it. You must forget about your marriage dozen. When you marry, which will be soon, I'll find you a husband who'll give you the finest dozen anyone ever heard of in the whole province, so listen to me, sweetie, here's a wonderful opportunity for you: you can invest your six thousand francs with the government and every six months you'll get nearly two hundred francs in interest, with no worry about taxes, repairs, hail, frost or any of the other things that plague property owners. Perhaps you don't like the idea of parting with your gold, eh, sweetie? Bring it to me just the same. I'll collect more gold for you—Dutch and Portuguese coins, Mogul rupees, genovines—and, with the coins I'll give you for your birthdays and name days, within three years you'll have made up half of your pretty little golden treasure again. What do you say to that, sweetie? Come on, look up at me. Go get your precious little treasure. You ought to kiss me on the eyes for telling you these secrets and mysteries of the life and death of money. Really, coins live and move like people; they come and go, they sweat, they reproduce. . . ."

Eugénie stood up, but after taking several steps toward the door she abruptly turned around, looked at her father and said, "I no longer have *my* gold."

"You no longer have your gold?" cried Grandet, starting up like a horse which has heard a cannon fired ten paces away.

"No, I no longer have it."

"You're mistaken, Eugénie."

"No."

"By my father's pruning knife!"

When the cooper uttered this oath the rafters trembled.

"Good God and all the saints in heaven!" cried Nanon. "Look how pale madame is!"

"Grandet, your anger will kill me," said the poor woman.

"Nonsense! People in your family live forever! Eugénie, what have you done with your gold coins?" he shouted, rushing toward her.

"Monsieur," she said, falling at Madame Grandet's knees, "my mother is suffering terribly. . . . Look at her. . . . Don't kill her. . . ."

Grandet was alarmed by the pallor spread over his wife's face, which was usually so yellow.

"Nanon, help me go upstairs to bed," she said weakly. "I'm dying."

Nanon immediately gave her arm to her mistress; Eugénie did the same, and it was only with great difficulty that they succeeded in getting her up to her room, for she fainted at every step. Grandet was left alone. Nevertheless, he walked up seven or eight steps a few moments later and called out, "Eugénie, come downstairs as soon as your mother's in bed."

"Yes, father."

She came down a short time later, after reassuring her mother.

"Daughter," said Grandet, "you are going to tell me where your treasure is."

"Father, if you give me presents that aren't entirely at my disposal, you can take them back," replied Eugénie coldly, taking the napoleon from the mantelpiece and handing it to him.

Grandet eagerly seized the napoleon and slipped it into his vest pocket. "I'll certainly never give you anything again, not even this much!" he said, clicking his thumbnail under his front tooth. "So you despise your father! You don't trust him! Don't you know what a father is? If he's not everything to you, then he's nothing. Where's your gold?"

"Father, I love and respect you, in spite of your anger, but let me humbly point out to you that I'm twenty-three years old. You've told me I'm of age so often that I can't forget it now. I've done as I pleased with my money, and you can be sure it's well invested."

"Where?"

"That's an inviolable secret," she said. "Don't you have your secrets too?"

"I'm the head of the family—can't I have my own affairs?"

"This is *my* affair."

"It must be a bad one, then, if you can't tell your father about it, Mademoiselle Grandet."

"It's an excellent one, and I can't tell my father about it."

"At least you can tell me when you gave away your gold." Eugénie shook her head. "You still had it on your birthday, didn't you?" Eugénie, whom love had made as crafty as avarice had made her father, shook her head again. "Who ever heard of such stubbornness, or such a theft?" continued Grandet in a voice which gradually rose to a crescendo and reverberated through the whole house. "What! Here, in my own house, my own home, someone has taken your gold, the only gold there was, and I'll never know who it was? Gold is a precious thing. The most honorable girls may make mistakes and give away I don't know what; it sometimes happens in great noble families, and even in middle-class families. But to give away gold! . . . Because you did give it to someone, didn't you?" Eugénie remained impassive. "Was there ever such a daughter before? Am I really your father? If you've invested it, then you must have a receipt. . . ."

"Was I free to do with it as I saw fit or not? Did it belong to me or not?"

"But you're still a child!"

"I'm of age."

Dumbfounded by his daughter's logic, Grandet turned pale, stamped his foot and swore; then, finally finding words, he cried out, "Cursed serpent of a daughter! Oh, ungrateful child, you know I love you and you take advantage of it! You're torturing your own father! By God, I'll bet you've thrown our fortune at the feet of that worthless pauper in morocco boots! By my father's pruning knife! I can't disinherit you, damn it, but I curse you, your cousin and your children! Nothing good will come of this, do you hear me? If it was Charles that . . . But no, that's impossible. What! Can that malicious young fop have robbed me?" He looked at his daughter, who still remained cold and silent. "She doesn't move, she doesn't flinch! She's more of a Grandet than I am! At least you didn't give your gold away for nothing, did you? Come on, tell me!"

Eugénie looked at her father with an ironical expression which offended him. "Eugénie, you're in my house, in your father's house," he said. "To stay here, you must submit to his orders. The priests order you to obey me." Eugénie bowed her head. "You've offended me in what I hold most dear," he went on. "I don't want to see you again until you're obedient. Go to your room. You will stay there until I allow you to come out. Nanon will bring you bread and water. You heard me, go!"

Eugénie burst into tears and fled to her mother's room. After walking around his garden a few times in the snow, without no-ticing the cold, Grandet began to suspect that his daughter was in his wife's room. Delighted at the thought of catching her disobeying his orders, he climbed the stairs with the agility of a cat and walked into Madame Grandet's room as she was stroking her daughter's hair. Eugénie's face was pressed against her mother's bosom.

"Don't be too upset, my poor child, your father will calm down. . . ."

"She no longer has a father!" said the cooper. "Can it be you and I, Madame Grandet, who produced such a disobedient daughter? A fine upbringing, and so religious, too! Well, why aren't you in your room? Go on, to prison, mademoiselle, to prison!"

"Are you trying to deprive me of my daughter, monsieur?" said Madame Grandet, her face flushed with fever.

"If you want to keep her, take her away with you—you can both clear out of my house. My God, where's the gold? What's become of the gold?"

Eugénie stood up, cast a haughty glance at her father and went into her room. The old man turned the key in the lock.

"Nanon," he called out, "put out the fire in the living room." Then he sat down in an armchair beside the fireplace in his wife's room and said to her, "She probably gave it to that wretched seducer Charles, who was only after our money."

From the danger threatening her daughter and from her feeling for her, Madame Grandet drew enough strength to remain outwardly cold, silent and deaf.

"I didn't know anything about all this," she said, turning her face toward the wall to avoid her husband's glowing eyes. "Your violence is making me suffer so much that, if my premonitions are right, I'll never leave this room alive. You should have spared me at this time, monsieur; I've never caused you any pain, at least I don't think I have. Your daughter loves you and I believe she's as innocent as a newborn babe, so don't torment her: revoke your sentence. It's terribly cold now; you might be the cause of a serious illness."

"I won't see her or speak to her. She'll stay in her room on bread and water until she's satisfied her father. What the devil! The head of a family ought to know what happens to the gold in his house! She had what may have been the only rupees in France, and genovines, and Dutch ducats. . . ."

"Monsieur, Eugénie is our only child, and even if she'd thrown them into the river . . ."

"Thrown them into the river!" shouted the old man. "Into the river! You're mad, Madame Grandet. I mean what I say, you know that. If you want to have peace in this house, make your daughter confess, get the truth out of her; women are better at that kind of thing among themselves than men are. No matter what she's done, I won't eat her. Is she afraid of me? Even if she covered her cousin with gold from head to foot, he's at sea now, so we can't very well run after him. . . ."

"Well, monsieur . . ." Made more perceptive by her nervous state, or by her daughter's misfortune, which heightened her tenderness and intelligence, Madame Grandet became aware of something sinister in the way her husband's wen twitched as she began to reply; she changed her mind without changing her tone. "Well, monsieur, do you think I have more control over her than you do? She's told me nothing; she takes after you."

"My God, how your tongue keeps wagging this morning! Ta, ta, ta, ta! I think you're trying to defy me! You're probably in league with her."

His wife stared at him intently and said, "Really, Monsieur Grandet, if you want to kill me, all you have to do is go on like this. I'm telling you, monsieur, and even if it costs me my life I'll go on repeating it, that you're treating your daughter unjustly. She's more reasonable than you are. That money belonged to her; she can only have put it to a good use, and God alone has the right to know our good deeds. I beg you, monsieur, bring Eugénie back into your good graces! . . . You'll lessen the effect of the blow your anger has dealt me and you may save my life. My daughter, monsieur, give me back my daughter!"

"I'm getting out of here," he said. "I can't bear to stay in my own house. My wife and daughter talk as if . . . Ugh! Pooh! You've given me a cruel New Year's gift, Eugénie!" he shouted. "That's right, cry! You'll be sorry for what you're doing, do you hear me? What good does it do you to eat the consecrated wafer six times every three months if you secretly give your father's gold to a lazy good-for-nothing who'll devour your heart when you have nothing else to lend him? You'll see what kind of a man your Charles is, with his morocco boots and his disdainful airs. He has neither heart nor soul, because he dares to carry off a poor girl's treasure without her parents' consent."

When the front door closed, Eugénie left her room, came back to her mother and said to her, "You were very brave for your daughter's sake."

"Now you see where improper conduct can lead us, my child. . . . You've made me tell a lie."

"Oh! I'll ask God to give me all the punishment for it!"

"Is it true, mademoiselle," asked Nanon in alarm as she entered the room, "that you've been put on bread and water for the rest of your life?"

"What does it matter, Nanon?" said Eugénie calmly.

"Oh, how could I eat jam when the daughter of the house is eating only dry bread? No, no!"

"Not a word about all this, Nanon," said Eugénie.

"I'll keep quiet; but you'll see!"

That evening Grandet had dinner alone for the first time in twenty-four years.

"Well, you're a widower now, monsieur," said Nanon. "It's very unpleasant to be a widower with two women in the house."

"I'm not talking to you, Nanon. Keep your mouth shut or I'll dismiss you. What's in that saucepan I hear simmering on the stove?"

"It's some fat I'm melting. . . ."

"I'm having company tonight, light the fire."

The Cruchots, Madame des Grassins and her son arrived at eight o'clock and were surprised to see neither Madame Grandet nor her daughter.

"My wife is feeling a little indisposed and Eugénie is staying with her," said the old winegrower, whose face betrayed no emotion.

After an hour had been spent in insignificant conversation, Madame des Grassins, who had gone up to pay a visit to Madame Grandet, came back downstairs and everyone asked her, "How's Madame Grandet feeling?"

"Not well at all," she replied. "Her condition seems quite alarming to me. . . . At her age, you ought to take every precaution, Papa Grandet."

"We'll see about that," replied the winegrower absentmindedly.

Everyone bade him good night. When the Cruchots were outside in the street, Madame des Grassins said to them, "Something's happened in the Grandet family. The mother is very ill, but she doesn't seem to know it. The daughter's eyes are red, as though she'd been crying for a long time. Can it be that they're trying to marry her to someone against her will?"

When Grandet was in bed, Nanon came silently in her slippers to Eugénie's room and showed her a pâté made in a saucepan. "Here, mademoiselle," said the kindly old maid. "Cornoiller gave me a hare. You eat so little that this pâté will last you at least a week, and in this cold weather it's sure not to spoil. At least you won't have to live on dry bread. That's not healthy at all."

"Poor Nanon!" said Eugénie, pressing her hand.

"I made it very good, just right; and *he* didn't notice anything. I paid for the lard, the bay leaves and everything else out of my six francs. After all, it's my money."

Then the servant hurried away, thinking she had heard Grandet.

AFTERWORD

"Money is the most general element of Balzac's novels," said Henry James, who admired the novels unwillingly; "other things come and go, but money is always there. . . . Each particular episode of the *Comédie Humaine* has its own hero and heroine, but the great general protagonist is the twenty-franc piece." The scene we have just read is one of those that concentrate on money with hyperbolic intensity. Old Grandet comes back from the stagecoach office followed by a porter pushing a wheelbarrow loaded with heavy sacks; from the preceding scene we know that the sacks contain thirty thousand francs in silver. The choric comments of the townspeople at the start refer to Grandet's avarice with tradesmen's humor. In another of the preceding scenes, however, Balzac had spoken directly to the reader and prepared him for grimmer events. "In three days," he had said—and this is the third day—"a terrible drama would begin, a drama undignified by poison, dagger, or bloodshed, but fate dealt scarcely more cruelly with the princely house of Atreus than with the actors in this bourgeois tragedy."

Balzac's narrative point of view, like Stendhal's, is the old and easy one of the ominscient author who sets no limits on himself. He follows one character, then another; he sees into their hearts, if only so far as is necessary for the story; he takes the reader into his confidence by telling him what is going to happen; and very often he interrupts the story with philosophical digressions that are merely ostentatious. There are no such digressions in the present scene. It is the other and greater side of Balzac: all drama, all energy, all concentration on the results of a single ruling passion.

Grandet's first rendered thoughts have to do with financial schemes, and his opening speech to Eugénie is a request for her gold. In the long statement that precedes her plaintive reply, "I no longer have *my* gold," every sentence uttered by the father has to do with money. "There is life in Balzac's hats and neckties," George Moore once said. In this scene Grandet makes us feel that there is even more life in coins. "Really, coins live and move like people," he says; "they come and go, they sweat, they reproduce." When he transmutes the franc into crowns, silver, gold, consols, napoleons, Eugénie's marriage portion, ducats, genovines, moidores, and rupees, the names suggest that money has a human complexity.

"Of all the great novelists, [Balzac] is weakest in talk," said Henry James. It is true that the dialogue in this scene is flat and lacking in verbal surprise. On the other hand, it is accompanied by violent physical action. When Grandet utters his oath, "By my father's pruning knife!" the rafters tremble. He shouts, he stamps, he curses; his voice reverberates through the house. Eugénie by contrast is as laconic as Cordelia, but she falls at her mother's knee. There is probably some connection between such actions and the popular theater of the nineteenth century. Dickens too was fond of scenes in which characters "act" like those in a popular melodrama.

In describing people, Balzac uses few similes, and nearly all of them are animalian—perhaps as a result of his home-brewed theories about the zoological nature of society. Grandet, for instance, is described as an "old fox"; he starts up "like a horse which has heard a cannon fired" after Eugénie's startling declaration; he calls her a "cursed serpent"; and he climbs upstairs to spy on mother and daughter "with the agility of a cat." Des Grassins is described as an "old fish." The wen on Grandet's face reflects a tendency on Balzac's part to identify physical ugliness with moral defects, physical beauty with virtue. Other novelists have used this convenient device, but few have used it as much as Balzac, who may have been influenced in this direction by his fondness for the phrenological theories of Gall and Lavater.

A last remark might concern Balzac's choice of proper names, a special problem for the novelist. Ian Watt has noted in *The Rise of the Novel* that Defoe and Richardson were departing from an earlier tradition when they gave their characters nonsymbolic names (while still making some effort, however, to keep the names appropriate). Dickens is beyond a doubt the English novelist who devoted the greatest care to finding names that suggest some trait of personality; as witness Fagin, Uriah Heep, Pumblechook, Chadband, the Cheerible brothers, and dozens more. Balzac *seems* less prone to use canting names (the phrase is from heraldry and is used when the coat of arms contains a pictorial reference to its bearer), yet the four families mentioned in this scene are each named for some representative quality. Grandet is from the verb *grandir*, to increase, an obvious allusion to his business ventures; Froidfond is a cold property or piece of land; Grassins is related to the word meaning fat or plump; and Cruchet is from *cruchon*, a little pitcher, but also colloquially a booby or simpleton.

Wuthering Heights (1847)

EMILY BRONTË's short life (1818-1848) was as outwardly uneventful as her one novel is tumultuous. Her father, born Patrick Brunty, was a North of Ireland peasant boy who put himself through Cambridge and became an Anglican clergyman. Her mother, who died when Emily was three, came from Cornwall, and this largely Celtic heredity on both sides has been seized upon to explain the most un-Victorian cast of the daughter's imagination. Emily grew up with her sisters Charlotte (1816-1855) and Anne (1820-1849) and her brother Branwell, then the hope of the family. There had been two older sisters, but both had died of tuberculosis, a disease that was to carry off most of the Brontës; in these first two cases it had been contracted at a pious boarding school where the girls were ill-fed, half-frozen, and marched off to church in drenching rains. The survivors stayed at home in the parsonage at Haworth, a town in the West Riding of Yorkshire under the bleak moorland that became a setting for *Wuthering Heights*. Except for three brief and disastrous sorties into the world, it was there that Emily was to spend her life.

From earliest childhood all four children had been intensely imaginative. When their father brought home a box of wooden soldiers, they gave each of the soldiers a name and made him ruler of an imaginary country. The countries were joined in the Great Glass Town Confederacy, about which they hand-lettered stories and poems for several years; then Glass Town was destroyed by common consent. It was replaced by Angria, ruled by a dark, passionate duke—it was Charlotte's and Branwell's country—and Gondal, where the sovereign was a fierce queen. Gondal, more like Yorkshire, was the property of Emily and Anne. That was the literary apprenticeship of the family. In the end the stories, some quite long, and the poems about Angria and Gondal probably filled more pages than the published writings of the three sisters.

Branwell had decided to become a painter. With money provided by his aunt, he went to London to enroll in the school of the Royal Academy, but a week or two later he was home without the money and without having entered the school; he had spent most of his time roistering in a tavern. From that moment the young man of promise was transformed into a Victorian black sheep, making wild claims of genius and taking refuge from his failures in alcohol and opium. The sisters continued on their industrious way. Their first publication was in 1846, when, on Charlotte's initiative, they raised money to pay for printing a small volume of verse, *Poems by Currer, Ellis, and Acton Bell.* Currer was Charlotte, Ellis was Emily and incomparably the best poet of the three; Acton was Anne; and the pseudonyms were to be retained in their subsequent writing.

Although the first book went almost unnoticed and had a sale of only two copies, they were all at work on novels. Three of these were published in 1847: *Jane Eyre* by Charlotte, *Wuthering Heights* by Emily, and *Agnes Grey* by Anne. Charlotte's book was resoundingly popular from its first appearance. Thackeray gave a day from his busy life to reading *Jane Eyre*, and later Queen Victoria herself read it aloud to "dear Albert." Anne's book, however, was dismissed as insipid, and Emily's was condemned as the product of a dogged, brutal, and morose mind. "Too coarse and disagreeable to be attractive"; "This is a strange book . . . wildly disjointed and improbable"; "the characters . . . strike us as proceeding from a mind of limited experience": these were some early and appalled comments on *Wuthering Heights.* Apparently Emily read the reviews before her death by tuberculosis in December 1848, but she was "fiercely reticent," as her biographers tell us, and made no comment on them.

Branwell had died of tuberculosis, not alcoholism, in September of that same year. Anne contracted the disease from Emily, with whom she shared a room, and died in May 1849. Charlotte lived long enough to write two other successful novels, *Shirley* (1849) and *Villette* (1853). The Brontës had no issue. Only Charlotte found a husband—her father's curate and fellow Ulsterman, Arthur Bell Nichols—and she died before giving birth to their first child.

THE STORY

The Earnshaws, farmers on the same land for three hundred years, live in a bleak stone house, Wuthering Heights, on the wind-swept moor. Below them in the valley, the Lintons live cozily at Thrushcross Grange. Each family has a son and a daughter. One night Mr. Earnshaw brings home a wild swarthy boy, possibly a Gypsy, whom he had found wandering in the streets of Liverpool. Young Hindley Earnshaw hates the foundling, whom they call Heathcliff (without a Christian name), but Catherine, self-willed and lovely, roams the moors with him year after year. Mr. Earnshaw dies and Hindley, the new master, persecutes Heathcliff. Though Catherine loves him— "Nelly, I *am* Heathcliff," she says at one point—she decides to marry fair-haired, upright, rather feeble Edgar Linton; perhaps she can use Edgar's money to give her true love a start in life. At this point Heathcliff disappears.

When he returns three years later, it is with a fortune he has gained nobody knows how and with the fixed intention of ruining both families. Hindley Earnshaw has become a drunkard after losing his wife, and Heathcliff starts by winning away his land at cards; then he elopes with Edgar's sister Isabella, whom he brutally mistreats. He wants to save Catherine alone, but—a few hours after the scene reprinted here— she dies in giving birth to a daughter, also named Catherine.

The rest of the novel is concerned with the further course of Heathcliff's revenge. After Isabella, who has left him, dies in the south of England, he carries off his own son Linton, a "pale, delicate, effeminate boy." Then Edgar dies in his turn, and Heathcliff forces young Catherine to marry Linton, thus gaining effective control of Thrushcross Grange as well as Wuthering Heights. The real heir to the latter is handsome young Hareton Earnshaw, Hindley's son, whom Heathcliff permits to grow up in brutish ignorance. Indeed, he neglects or mistreats all three young people as the last representatives of two hated families. Linton pines away querulously and dies without arousing grief in his father. Morose and grasping, Heathcliff lives in communion only with the first Catherine's spirit, which, in the course of time, becomes for him her visible ghost. In the end he grows indifferent to vengeance and starves himself to death in order to join her in the churchyard. Young Cathy teaches Hareton to read, then falls in love with him; their marriage will perpetuate the two families that had come so close to being destroyed.

In the first paragraph of the chapter that follows, "I" is Mr. Lockwood, the well-meaning, rather fatuous gentleman who purports to write the story. He has heard it from the lips of the housekeeper, Nelly Dean, who serves as a "central consciousness," in Henry James's phrase, and therefore has to be present in every decisive scene, even when it is the last meeting in the flesh of two demonic lovers.

[*The Demon Lovers*]   *Chapter 15*

Another week over—and I am so many days nearer health, and spring! I have now heard all my neighbour's history, at different sittings, as the housekeeper could spare time from more important occupations. I'll continue it in her own words, only a little condensed. She is, on the whole, a very fair narrator and I don't think I could improve her style.

In the evening, she said, the evening of my visit to the Heights, I knew as well as if I saw him, that Mr. Heathcliff was about the place; and I shunned going out, because I still carried his letter in my pocket, and didn't want to be threatened, or teased any more.

I had made up my mind not to give it till my master went somewhere; as I could not guess how its receipt would affect Catherine. The consequence was, that it did not reach her before the lapse of three days. The fourth was Sunday, and I brought it into her room, after the family were gone to church.

There was a man servant left to keep the house with me, and we generally made a practice of locking the doors during the hours of service; but on that occasion, the weather was so warm and pleasant that I set them wide open; and to fulfil my engagement, as I knew who would be coming, I told my companion that the mistress wished very much for some oranges, and he must run over to the village, and get a few, to be paid for on the morrow. He departed, and I went up-stairs.

Mrs. Linton sat in a loose, white dress, with a light shawl over her shoulders, in the recess of the open window, as usual. Her thick, long hair had been partly removed at the beginning of her illness; and now, she wore it simply combed in its natural tresses over her temples and neck. Her appearance was altered, as I had told Heathcliff, but when she was calm, there seemed unearthly beauty in the change.

The flash of her eyes had been succeeded by a dreamy and melancholy softness: they no longer gave the impression of looking at the objects around her; they appeared always to gaze beyond, and far beyond—you would have said out of this world—Then, the paleness of her face, its haggard aspect having vanished as she recovered flesh, and the peculiar expression arising from her mental state, though painfully suggestive of their causes, added to the touching interest, which she awakened, and invariably to me, I know, and to any person who saw her, I should think, refuted more tangible proofs of convalescence and stamped her as one doomed to decay.

A book lay spread on the sill before her, and the scarcely perceptible wind fluttered its leaves at intervals. I believe Linton had laid it there, for she never endeavoured to divert herself with reading, or occupation of any kind; and he would spend many an hour in trying to entice her attention to some subject which had formerly been her amusement.

She was conscious of his aim, and in her better moods, endured his efforts placidly; only showing their uselessness by now and then suppressing a wearied sigh, and restraining him at last with the saddest of smiles and kisses. At other times, she would turn petulantly away, and hide her face in her hands, or even push him off angrily; and then he took care to let her alone, for he was certain of doing no good.

Gimmerton chapel bells were still ringing; and the full, mellow flow of the beck in the valley came soothingly on the ear. It was a sweet substitute for the yet absent murmur of the summer foliage which drowned that music about the Grange when the trees were in leaf. At Wuthering Heights it always sounded on quiet days, following a great thaw, or a season of steady rain—and, of Wuthering Heights, Catherine was thinking as she listened; that is, if she thought, or listened, at all; but she had the vague, distant look I mentioned before, which expressed no recognition of material things either by ear or eye.

"There's a letter for you, Mrs Linton," I said, gently inserting it in one hand that rested on her knee. "You must read it immediately, because it wants an answer. Shall I break the seal?"

"Yes," she answered, without altering the direction of her eyes.

I opened it—it was very short.

"Now," I continued, "read it."

She drew away her hand, and let it fall. I replaced it in her lap, and stood waiting till it should please her to glance down; but that movement was so long delayed that at last I resumed—

"Must I read it, ma'am? It is from Mr Heathcliff."

There was a start, and a troubled gleam of recollection, and a struggle to arrange her ideas. She lifted the letter, and seemed to peruse it; and when she came to the signature she sighed; yet still I found she had not gathered its import; for upon my desiring to hear her reply she merely pointed to the name, and gazed at me with mournful and questioning eagerness.

"Well, he wishes to see you," said I, guessing her need of an interpreter. "He's in the garden by this time, and impatient to know what answer I shall bring."

As I spoke, I observed a large dog lying on the sunny grass beneath, raise its ears, as if about to bark; and then smoothing them back, announce by a wag of the tail that someone approached whom it did not consider a stranger.

Mrs Linton bent forward, and listened breathlessly. The minute after a step traversed the hall; the open house was too tempting for Heathcliff to resist walking in: most likely he supposed that I was inclined to shirk my promise, and so resolved to trust to his own audacity.

With straining eagerness Catherine gazed towards the entrance of her chamber. He did not hit the right room directly; she motioned me to admit him; but he found it out, ere I could reach the door, and in a stride or two was at her side, and had her grasped in his arms.

He neither spoke, nor loosed his hold, for some five minutes, during which period he bestowed more kisses than ever he gave in his life before, I dare say; but then my mistress had kissed him first, and I plainly saw that he could hardly bear, for downright agony, to look into her face! The same conviction had stricken him as me, from the instant he beheld her, that there was no prospect of ultimate recovery there—she was fated, sure to die.

"Oh, Cathy! Oh my life! how can I bear it?" was the first sentence he uttered, in a tone that did not seek to disguise his despair.

And now he stared at her so earnestly that I thought the very intensity of his gaze would bring tears into his eyes; but they burned with anguish, they did not melt.

"What now?" said Catherine, leaning back, and returning his look with a suddenly clouded brow—her humour was a mere vane for constantly varying caprices. "You and Edgar have broken my heart, Heathcliff! And you both come to bewail the deed to me, as if you were the people to be pitied! I shall not pity you, not. I. You have killed me—and thriven on it, I think. How strong you are! How many years do you mean to live after I am gone?"

Heathcliff had knelt on one knee to embrace her; he attempted to rise, but she seized his hair, and kept him down.

"I wish I could hold you," she continued bitterly, "till we were both dead! I shouldn't care what you suffered. I care nothing for your sufferings. Why shouldn't you suffer? I do! Will you forget me—will you be happy when I am in the earth? Will you say twenty years hence, 'That's the grave of Catherine Earnshaw. I loved her long ago, and was wretched to lose her; but it is past. I've loved many others since—my children are dearer to me than she was, and, at death, I shall not rejoice that I am going to her, I shall be sorry that I must lose them!' Will you say so, Heathcliff?"

"Don't torture me till I am as mad as yourself," cried he, wrenching his head free, and grinding his teeth.

The two, to a cool spectator, made a strange and fearful picture. Well might Catherine deem that heaven would be a land of exile to her, unless, with her mortal body, she cast away her mortal character also. Her present countenance had a wild vindictiveness in its white cheek, and a bloodless lip, and scintillating eye; and she retained, in her closed fingers, a portion of the locks she had been grasping. As to her companion, while raising himself with one hand, he had taken her arm with the other; and so inadequate was his stock of gentleness to the requirements of her condition, that on his letting go, I saw four distinct impressions left blue in the colourless skin.

"Are you possessed with a devil," he pursued, savagely, "to talk in that manner to me, when you are dying? Do you reflect that all those words will be branded in my memory, and eating deeper eternally, after you have left me? You know you lie to say I have killed you; and, Catherine, you know that I could as soon forget you, as my existence! Is it not sufficient for your infernal selfishness, that while you are at peace I shall writhe in the torments of hell?"

"I shall not be at peace," moaned Catherine, recalled to a sense of physical weakness by the violent, unequal throbbing of her heart, which beat visibly, and audibly under this excess of agitation.

She said nothing further till the paroxysm was over; then she continued, more kindly—

"I'm not wishing you greater torment that I have, Heathcliff! I only wish us never to be parted—and should a word of mine distress you hereafter, think I feel the same distress underground, and for my own sake, forgive me! Come here and kneel down again! You never harmed me in your life. Nay, if you nurse anger, that will be worse to remember than my harsh words! Won't you come here again? Do!"

Heathcliff went to the back of her chair, and leant over, but not so far as to let her see his face, which was livid with emotion. She bent round to look at him; he would not permit it; turning abruptly, he walked to the fire-place, where he stood, silent, with his back towards us.

Mrs Linton's glance followed him suspiciously: every movement woke a new sentiment in her. After a pause, and a prolonged gaze, she resumed, addressing me in accents of indignant disappointment.

"Oh, you see, Nelly! he would not relent a moment, to keep me out of the grave! *That* is how I'm loved! Well, never mind! That is not *my* Heathcliff. I shall love mine yet; and take him with me—he's in my soul. And," added she, musingly, "the thing that irks me most is this shattered prison, after all. I'm tired, tired of being enclosed here. I'm wearying to escape into that glorious world, and to be always there; not seeing it dimly through tears, and yearning for it through the walls of an aching heart; but really with it, and in it. Nelly, you think you are better and more fortunate than I; in full health and strength—you are sorry for me —very soon that will be altered. I shall be sorry for *you*. I shall be incomparably beyond and above you all. I *wonder* he won't be near me!" She went on to herself. "I thought he wished it. Heathcliff dear! you should not be sullen now. Do come to me, Heathcliff."

In her eagerness she rose, and supported herself on the arm of the chair. At that earnest appeal, he turned to her, looking absolutely desperate. His eyes wide, and wet, at last, flashed fiercely on her; his breast heaved convulsively. An instant they held asunder; and then how they met I hardly saw, but Catherine made a spring, and he caught her, and they were locked in an embrace from which I thought my mistress would never be released alive. In fact, to my eyes, she seemed directly insensible. He flung himself into the nearest seat, and on my approaching hurriedly to ascertain if she had fainted, he gnashed at me, and foamed like a mad dog, and gathered her to him with greedy jealousy. I did not feel as if I were in the company of a creature of my own species; it appeared that he would not understand, though I spoke to him; so, I stood off, and held my tongue, in great perplexity.

A movement of Catherine's relieved me a little presently: she put up her hand to clasp his neck, and bring her cheek to his, as he held her: while he, in return, covering her with frantic caresses, said wildly—

"You teach me now how cruel you've been—cruel and false. *Why* did you despise me? *Why* did you betray your own heart, Cathy? I have not one word of comfort—you deserve this. You have killed yourself. Yes, you may kiss me, and cry; and wring out my kisses and tears. They'll blight you—they'll damn you. You loved me—then what *right* had you to leave me? What right—answer me—for the poor fancy you felt for Linton? Because misery, and degradation, and death, and nothing that God or satan could inflict would have parted us, *you*, of your own will, did it. I have not broken your heart—*you* have broken it—and in breaking it, you have broken mine. So much the worse for me, that I am strong. Do I want to live? What kind of living will it be when you—oh God! would *you* like to live with your soul in the grave?"

"Let me alone. Let me alone," sobbed Catherine. "If I have done wrong, I'm dying for it. It is enough! You left me too; but I won't upbraid you! I forgive you. Forgive me!"

"It is hard to forgive, and to look at those eyes, and feel those wasted hands," he answered. "Kiss me again; and don't let me see your eyes! I forgive what you have done to me. I love *my* murderer—but *yours!* How can I?"

They were silent—their faces hid against each other, and washed by each other's tears. At least, I suppose the weeping was on both sides; as it seemed Heathcliff *could* weep on a great occasion like this.

I grew very uncomfortable, meanwhile; for the afternoon wore fast away, the man whom I had sent off returned from his errand, and I could distinguish, by the shine of the westering sun up the valley, a concourse thickening outside Gimmerton chapel porch.

"Service is over," I announced. "My master will be here in half-an-hour."

Heathcliff groaned a curse, and strained Catherine closer—she never moved.

Ere long I perceived a group of the servants passing up the road towards the kitchen wing. Mr Linton was not far behind; he opened the gate himself, and sauntered slowly up, probably enjoying the lovely afternoon that breathed as soft as summer.

"Now he is here," I exclaimed. "For Heaven's sake, hurry down! You'll not meet any one on the front stairs. Do be quick; and stay among the trees till he is fairly in."

"I must go, Cathy," said Heathcliff, seeking to extricate himself from his companion's arms. "But, if I live, I'll see you again before you are asleep. I won't stray five yards from your window."

"You must not go!" she answered, holding him as firmly as her strength allowed. "You shall not, I tell you."

"For one hour," he pleaded earnestly.

"Not for one minute," she replied.

"I *must*—Linton will be up immediately," persisted the alarmed intruder.

He would have risen, and unfixed her fingers by the act—she clung fast gasping; there was mad resolution in her face.

"No!" she shrieked. "Oh, don't, don't go. It is the last time! Edgar will not hurt us. Heathcliff, I shall die! I shall die!"

"Damn the fool! There he is," cried Heathcliff, sinking back into his seat. "Hush, my darling! Hush, hush, Catherine! I'll stay. If he shot me so, I'd expire with a blessing on my lips."

And there they were fast again. I heard my master mounting the stairs—the cold sweat ran from my forehead; I was horrified.

"Are you going to listen to her ravings?" I said, passionately. "She does not know what she says. Will you ruin her, because she has not wit to help herself? Get up! You could be free instantly. That is the most diabolical deed that ever you did. We are all done for—master, mistress, and servant."

I wrung my hands, and cried out; and Mr Linton hastened his step at the noise. In the midst of my agitation, I was sincerely glad to observe that Catherine's arms had fallen relaxed, and her head hung down.

"She's fainted or dead," I thought, "so much the better. Far better that she should be dead, than lingering a burden, and a misery-maker to all about her."

Edgar sprang to his unbidden guest, blanched with astonishment and rage. What he meant to do, I cannot tell; however, the

other stopped all demonstrations, at once, by placing the lifeless-
looking form in his arms.

"Look there!" he said, "unless you be a fiend, help her first—
then you shall speak to me!"

He walked into the parlour, and sat down, Mr Linton summoned me, and with great difficulty, and after resorting to many
means, we managed to restore her to sensation; but she was all
bewildered; she sighed, and moaned, and knew nobody. Edgar,
in his anxiety for her, forgot her hated friend. I did not. I went,
at the earliest opportunity, and besought him to depart, affirming
that Catherine was better, and he should hear from me in the
morning, how she passed the night.

"I shall not refuse to go out of doors," he answered; "but I
shall stay in the garden; and, Nelly, mind you keep your word to-
morrow. I shall be under those larch trees, mind! or I pay another
visit, whether Linton be in or not."

He sent a rapid glance through the half-open door of the chamber, and ascertaining that what I stated was apparently true, delivered the house of his luckless presence.

AFTERWORD

Wuthering Heights is more a romance than it is, in the narrow
sense, a novel. In his preface to *The House of the Seven Gables* (1851),
Hawthorne, who called himself a romancer, was to make a distinction
between those two types of fiction. The novel, he says, "is presumed
to aim at a very minute fidelity, not merely to the possible, but to the
probable and ordinary course of man's experience." The romance, on
the other hand, "—while, as a work of art, it must rigidly subject itself
to laws, and while it sins unpardonably so far as it may swerve aside
from the truth of the human heart—has fairly a right to present that
truth under circumstances, to a great extent, of the writer's own choosing
or creation. If he thinks fit, also, he may so manage his atmospherical
medium as to bring out or mellow the lights and deepen and enrich
the shadows of the picture."

It must be added that the romance is likely to be close in spirit
to some genre of poetry, whether dramatic (*The Scarlet Letter*), epic
(*Moby-Dick*), allegorical, or pastoral (of which last a good example

is *Green Mansions*, 1904, by W. H. Hudson). *Wuthering Heights* brings back the somber, passionate mood of many old Scottish ballads. One thinks of Fair Margaret, whose ghost summoned William to join her in the grave; and again one thinks of "The Demon Lover":

> "O where have you been, my long, long love,
>   This long seven years and mair?"
> "O I'm come to seek my former vows
>   Ye granted me before."

The returned lover of the ballad is a fiend from hell who tempts and carries off a foolish wife. That might be Heathcliff, but Catherine does not have to be tempted. In some ways she brings to mind those fatal heroines whom the Romantics found ambiguously attractive: such figures as Keats's Lamia, La Belle Dame sans Merci, and even the Lorelei. She is truly a mate for Heathcliff, and their guilt is redeemed for the reader, as it obviously was for the author, by the pure intensity of their passion.

In this scene of their last meeting in the flesh, the passion becomes at moments a wish for self-annihilation, one in the other. It is also mingled, however, with resentment, even hatred (and this without swerving aside from what Hawthorne called "the truth of the human heart"). "You have killed me," Catherine says. ". . . How many years do you mean to live after I am gone?" At this point we may begin to suspect that *Wuthering Heights* has a thesis, and it is one that becomes almost explicit as the dialogue continues.

> CATHERINE. I wish I could hold you till we were both dead. . . . Will you be happy when I am in the earth?
> HEATHCLIFF. Is it not sufficient for your infernal selfishness, that while you are at peace I shall writhe in the torments of hell?
> CATHERINE. I shall not be at peace. . . . I only wish us never to be parted: and should a word of mine distress you hereafter, think I feel the same distress underground.
> HEACHCLIFF. *Stands silently by the fireplace with his back to Catherine.*
> CATHERINE. That is not *my* Heathcliff. I shall love mine yet; and take him with me—he's in my soul.

Of course the thesis—here expressed as a fierce promise—is that love can be stronger than death. This last meeting in the flesh prepares us for a final chapter in which Heathcliff takes a somber pleasure in wandering over the moors with Catherine's ghost. But is it really her ghost, or is it a phantom projected by his obsessed mind? Brontë leaves the question unanswered, as Hawthorne would have done. All we know for certain is that Heathcliff is buried at Catherine's side, like the lovers in an old ballad; presumably they are now at rest. One stormy evening, however, Mrs. Dean meets a terrified shepherd boy who blubbers, "They's Heathcliff and a woman, yonder, under t' Nab, un' Aw darnut pass 'em."

Two or three technical matters remain to be mentioned.

In the matter of style, the tragic meeting is recounted simply, but with a rhetorical excitement partly created by homely verbs of action. Thus, Heathcliff *grasps* Catherine, his eyes *burn* with anguish, she *seizes* his hair, he *wrenches* his head free, *grinds* his teeth, *gnashes* at poor Nelly Dean, and *foams* like a mad dog. "I did not feel," Nelly says, "as if I were in the company of a creature of my own species." Catherine *clings fast, grasping*, and "No!" she *shrieks*. . . . Of course the intention is to portray emotions violent enough to conquer death.

In the matter of time and setting, this *Liebestod* is played on the first pleasant Sunday of spring, with the windows open and the bells of Gimmerton chapel sounding through the still leafless trees. Those bells, and later "a concourse thickening outside Gimmerton chapel porch," provide a contrast between the pagan lovers and the stolid mass of churchgoing people, conformist, devitalized, and, in this context, essentially *wrong*.

Brontë's method of narration takes the author out of her book and dispenses her from offering editorial comments, while at the same time placing events at two removes from the reader. Mr. Lockwood, as we said, is supposed to be writing the story, but only as he hears it from the lips of the housekeeper, Nelly Dean. The function of Mr. Lockwood, a well-meaning gentleman who belongs to the world of the common reader, is to lend credibility to what might otherwise seem a bizarre and unbelievable Gothic tale. Mrs. Dean, in her short-visioned, rather officious way, has the same function, but she also serves as a central consciousness. After the first three chapters, narrated by Mr. Lockwood, nothing goes into the story unless the housekeeper has seen, has been told, or has overheard it. She therefore has to be everywhere, receive confidences from everyone—even Heathcliff—and remember conversations word for word.

Those demands on Mrs. Dean created problems for the novelist that she did not always solve without leaving questions in the reader's mind. In the present scene, for instance, why did Heathcliff and Catherine permit Mrs. Dean to linger when they were exchanging their last kisses and recriminations? Why did they tolerate her smugness and her disapproval? On the other hand, the presence of Mrs. Dean created opportunities that the author seized, perhaps unconsciously. The housekeeper's limited perception helps to make Heathcliffe and Catherine a little mysterious and unearthly. Her very disapproval of them helps to awaken the reader's sense of compassion.

Vanity Fair (1848)

WILLIAM MAKEPEACE THACKERAY (1811-1863) was born in Calcutta, where his father, like the grandfather before him, was an official in the Indian civil service. But the father died in 1816, the young mother remarried, and the boy was shipped off to England. Lonely and miserable, he was boarded at two private schools in succession, and then at eleven was sent to Charterhouse—"Slaughter House," as he called it in some of his early writings. Later he attended Trinity College, Cambridge, where he made some friends destined to become famous—Edward FitzGerald of the *Rubaiyat* was one of them—but did not complete his studies for a degree.

After a year in Germany and France, he entered the Middle Temple, but found that law was not a congenial study. When he came of age in 1832, he inherited a comfortable legacy that soon vanished; some of it was lost in the failure of an Indian bank, some at gambling tables, and some in the effort to make a success of two feeble periodicals. He then spent three years in Paris studying art; his plan was to make a career of illustrating books. When the artist who had been illustrating the first number of *Pickwick* blew out his brains, in 1836, Thackeray volunteered to continue the series, but Dickens and his publisher preferred Hablot K. Browne, or "Phiz," to the profit of two arts, caricature and fiction.

That same year Thackeray married Isabella Shawe in Paris. He returned to London in 1837 and supported his growing family by illustrating and by literary hackwork. Under a variety of pseudonyms—George Savage Fitz-Boodle, Ikey Solomons, junior, and Michael Angelo Titmarsh among others—he was soon contributing light essays and satires to the leading magazines of the day. In 1840 Mrs. Thackeray lost her mind; she was to spend the rest of her long life in asylums. The husband was left with the care of two daughters—the second of three having died in infancy—and soon with the care of his mother too, for she had returned to England. He liked the society of women and formed some platonic attachments, as notably for Jane Brookfield, the wife of a close friend, but there was an undertone of sadness in his life. Anthony Trollope was to say, in his little book on Thackeray, that he "became as it were a widower for the rest of his days."

Barry Lyndon, a satirical romance, appeared in *Fraser's Magazine* in 1844. Two years later Thackeray set to work on *Vanity Fair*, which appeared in monthly numbers from 1846 to 1848 and which earned him an international reputation. He was never to be as popular as Dickens, but until the end of the nineteenth century Thackeray was generally regarded as more "correct" and "genteel." *Vanity Fair* was followed by a series of novels, most of which were also published in monthly parts: first *Pendennis* (1848-1850), which contains a good deal of the author's early life; then *Henry Esmond* (1852), a brilliant picture of English society in the days of Queen Anne and with much of Thackeray's character in the hero—though it is true that "Esmond was a prig," as the author was to say in self-disparagement; then *The Newcomes* (1853-1854), a story purportedly told by Arthur Pendennis; and then *The Virginians* (1857-1859), a sequel to *Esmond*, sometimes as brilliant, but with moments of appalling dullness. During the same period Thackeray wrote two widely appreciated series of lectures, both of which were delivered in London, repeated on an American tour, and finally published as books: *The English Humorists* in 1853 and *The Four Georges* in 1860. Also in 1860, he became editor of the new *Cornhill Magazine*, which published his subsequent works. *The Story of Philip* (1861-1862) is the best of these, though uneven in quality. *Denis Duval*, a historical novel, promised to be better, but only three instalments were ready for publication when Thackeray died at Christmastime in 1863.

THE STORY

In her family's grand coach, Amelia Sedley is leaving Miss Pinkerton's academy for young ladies, where she has been a general favorite. She takes with her Rebecca Sharp, daughter of a drunken artist and a Frenchwoman of humble birth, who has been teaching French at the academy for her board and a few guineas a year. Becky is to be governess at Sir Pitt Crawley's after spending a week with Amelia's rich family.

These two are Thackeray's heroine and villainess, and he will divide the book between them. It has been suggested that Amelia, the good girl, was modeled after his wife. The bad girl is more vivid, and readers are likely to find that their interest flags when Becky leaves the scene.

Determined to rise in the world—a little in the fashion of Julien Sorel—Becky starts out by fascinating Jos Sedley, Amelia's fat, lazy brother. Then she wins the heart—such of it as remains—of the brutal baronet Sir Pitt Crawley. After his wife dies he proposes to her, but thereupon discovers that she has secretly married Rawdon Crawley, his dissolute but essentially decent younger son. Amelia marries handsome George Osborne, but only after her father has lost his fortune in the panic that follows Napoleon's return from Elba. It is honest Captain Dobbin, secretly in love with Amelia, who sees that the marriage is carried through.

Both couples are in Brussels on the eve of the battle of Waterloo. Osborne has been neglecting his wife for Becky, whom he asks to run away with him. Two days later he lies dead on the battlefield. Amelia is mad with grief and idealizes his memory. The young Crawleys—Becky now has a son, whom she neglects—spend three years in Paris, where Rawdon supports them by gambling, by winning at billiards, and by not paying his debts. Then they return to London, take a house in Mayfair, and move in the best society while debts accumulate. Becky is now protected by a wicked nobleman, Lord Steyne (for whom Thackeray had a model in life, the third Marquis of Hertford, one of the Regency bucks). After being arrested for debt, Rawdon is unexpectedly released from prison, and comes home to find his wife entertaining Lord Steyne. Thackeray never tells us whether she has become Steyne's mistress; "I am innocent," Becky keeps saying. But Rawdon knocks Steyne down, flings Becky's jewels at him as he lies on the floor, then leaves his wife forever. He will die as governor of a malarial island.

Becky lives meanly in Europe until she acquires Jos Sedley as a protector. (Thackeray, once again with Victorian coyness, has them occupying separate suites in a Brussels hotel.) Amelia finally marries her faithful Dobbin, after Becky has destroyed her ideal picture of George Osborne by revealing the proposal he made to her on the eve of Waterloo. Jos Sedley dies under suspicious circumstances. At the end of the novel, Becky has usurped the title of "Lady Crawley" and is maintaining herself in luxury on the money she fleeced from Jos, as well as on an allowance from her son, who refuses to see her.

The passage that follows, which recounts how Becky rose in London society and how she glittered at an evening of charades in Lord Steyne's mansion, is from Chapter 51 of the novel.

Chapter 51. In Which a Charade Is Acted Which May or May Not Puzzle the Reader

. . . .

The upshot of her visit to Lord Steyne was that His Highness the Prince of Peterwaradin took occasion to renew his acquaintance with Colonel Crawley, when they met on the next day at the Club, and to compliment Mrs. Crawley in the Ring of Hyde Park with a profound salute of the hat. She and her husband were invited immediately to one of the Prince's small parties at Levant House, then occupied by His Highness during the temporary absence from England of its noble proprietor. She sang after dinner to a very little *comité*. The Marquis of Steyne was present, paternally superintending the progress of his pupil.

At Levant House Becky met one of the finest gentlemen and greatest ministers that Europe has produced—the Duc de la Jabotière, then Ambassador from the Most Christian King, and subsequently Minister to that monarch. I declare I swell with pride as these august names are transcribed by my pen, and I think in what brilliant company my dear Becky is moving. She became a constant guest at the French Embassy, where no party was considered to be complete without the presence of the charming Madame Ravdonn Cravley.

Messieurs de Truffigny (of the Périgord family) and Champignac, both *attachés* of the Embassy, were straightway smitten by the charms of the fair Colonel's wife; and both declared, according to the wont of their nation (for who ever yet met a Frenchman, come out of England, that has not left half a dozen families miserable, and brought away as many hearts in his pocket-book?)— both, I say, declared that they were *au mieux* with the charming Madame Ravdonn.

But I doubt the correctness of the assertion. Champignac was very fond of *écarté*, and made many *parties* with the Colonel of evenings, while Becky was singing to Lord Steyne in the other room; and as for Truffigny, it is a well-known fact that he dared not go to the Travellers', where he owed money to the waiters, and if he had not had the Embassy as a dining-place, the worthy young gentleman must have starved. I doubt, I say, that Becky would have selected either of these young men as a person on whom she would bestow her special regard. They ran of her messages, purchased her gloves and flowers, went in debt for opera-boxes for her, and made themselves amiable in a thousand ways. And they talked English with adorable simplicity, and to the constant amusement of Becky and my Lord Steyne, she would mimic one or other to his face, and compliment him on his advance in the English language with a gravity which never failed to tickle the Marquis, her sardonic old patron. Truffigny gave Briggs a shawl by way of winning over Becky's confidante, and asked her to take charge of a letter, which the simple spinster handed over in public to the person to whom it was addressed, and the composition of which amused everybody who read it greatly. Lord Steyne read it—everybody but honest Rawdon, to whom it was not necessary to tell everything that passed in the little house in Mayfair.

Here, before long, Becky received not only "the best" foreigners (as the phrase is in our noble and admirable society slang), but some of the best English people too. I don't mean the most virtuous, or indeed the least virtuous, or the cleverest, or the stupidest, or the richest, or the best born, but "the best"—in a word, people about whom there is no question—such as the great Lady Fitz-Willis, that Patron Saint of Almack's, the great Lady Slowbore, the great Lady Grizzel Macbeth (she was Lady G. Glowry, daughter of Lord Grey of Glowry), and the like. When the Countess of Fitz-Willis (her Ladyship is of the King Street family, see Debrett and Burke) takes up a person, he or she is safe. There is no question about them any more. Not that my Lady Fitz-Willis is any better than anybody else, being, on the contrary, a faded person, fifty-seven years of age, and neither handsome, nor wealthy, nor entertaining; but it is agreed on all sides that she is of the "best people." Those who go to her are of the best; and from an old grudge probably to Lady Steyne (for whose coronet her Ladyship, then the youthful Georgina Frederica, daughter of the Prince of Wales's favourite, the Earl of Portansherry, had once tried), this great and famous leader of the fashion chose to acknowledge Mrs. Rawdon Crawley—made her a most marked curtsy at the assembly over which she presided, and not only encouraged her son, Sir Kitts (his Lordship got his place through Lord Steyne's interest), to frequent Mrs. Crawley's house, but asked her to her own mansion, and spoke to her twice in the most public and condescending manner during dinner. The important fact was known all over London that night. People who had been crying fie about Mrs. Crawley were silent. Wenham, the wit and lawyer, Lord Steyne's right-hand man, went about everywhere praising her; some who had hesitated came forward at once and welcomed her; little Tom Toady, who had warned Southdown about visiting such an abandoned woman, now besought to be introduced to her. In a word, she was admitted to be among the "best" people. Ah, my beloved readers and brethren, do not envy poor Becky prematurely! glory like this is said to be fugitive. It is currently reported that even in the very inmost circles they are no happier than the poor wanderers outside the zone; and Becky, who penetrated into the very centre of fashion, and saw the great George IV. face to face, has owned since that there too was Vanity.

We must be brief in descanting upon this part of her career. As I cannot describe the mysteries of Freemasonry, although I have a shrewd idea that it is a humbug, so an uninitiated man cannot take upon himself to portray the great world accurately, and had best keep his opinions to himself whatever they are.

Becky has often spoken in subsequent years of this season of her life, when she moved among the very greatest circles of the London fashion. Her success excited, elated, and then bored her. At first no occupation was more pleasant than to invent and procure (the latter a work of no small trouble and ingenuity, by the way, in a person of Mrs. Rawdon Crawley's very narrow means)— to procure, we say, the prettiest new dresses and ornaments; to drive to fine dinner parties, where she was welcomed by great people; and from the fine dinner parties to fine assemblies, whither the same people came with whom she had been dining, whom she had met the night before, and would see on the morrow—the young men faultlessly appointed, handsomely cravatted, with the neatest glossy boots and white gloves; the elders portly, brass-buttoned, noble-looking, polite, and prosy; the young ladies blonde, timid, and in pink; the mothers grand, beautiful, sumptuous, solemn, and in diamonds. They talked in English, not in bad French, as they do in the novels. They talked about each other's houses, and characters, and families, just as the Joneses do about the Smiths. Becky's former acquaintances hated and envied her; the poor woman herself was yawning in spirit. "I wish I were out of it," she said to herself. "I would rather be a parson's wife, and teach a Sunday school, than this; or a sergeant's lady, and ride in the regimental waggon; or—oh how much gayer it would be to wear spangles and trousers, and dance before a booth at a fair!"

"You would do it very well," said Lord Steyne, laughing. She used to tell the great man her *ennuis* and perplexities in her artless way; they amused him.

"Rawdon would make a very good Ecuyer—Master of the Ceremonies—what do you call him—the man in the large boots and the uniform who goes round the ring cracking the whip? He is large, heavy, and of a military figure. I recollect," Becky continued pensively, "my father took me to see a show at Brookgreen Fair when I was a child; and when we came home, I made myself a pair of stilts, and danced in the studio to the wonder of all the pupils."

"I should have liked to see it," said Lord Steyne.

"I should like to do it now," Becky continued. "How Lady Blinkey would open her eyes, and Lady Grizzel Macbeth would stare! Hush! silence! there is Pasta beginning to sing." Becky always made a point of being conspicuously polite to the professional ladies and gentlemen who attended at these aristocratic parties— of following them into the corners where they sate in silence, and shaking hands with them and smiling in the view of all persons. She was an artist herself, as she said very truly; there was a frankness and humility in the manner in which she acknowledged her origin, which provoked, or disarmed, or amused lookers-on, as the case might be. "How cool that woman is!" said one; "what airs of independence she assumes, where she ought to sit still and be thankful if anybody speaks to her!" "What an honest and good-natured soul she is!" said another. "What an artful little minx!" said a third. They were all right, very likely; but Becky went her own way, and so fascinated the professional personages that they would leave off their sore throats in order to sing at her parties, and give her lessons for nothing.

Yes, she gave parties in the little house in Curzon Street. Many scores of carriages with blazing lamps blocked up the street, to the disgust of No. 200, who could not rest for the thunder of the knocking, and of 202, who could not sleep for envy. The gigantic footmen who accompanied the vehicles were too big to be contained in Becky's little hall, and were billeted off in the neighbouring public-houses, whence, when they were wanted, call-boys summoned them from their beer. Scores of the great dandies of London squeezed and trod on each other on the little stairs, laughing to find themselves there; and many spotless and severe ladies of *ton* were seated in the little drawing-room, listening to the professional singers, who were singing according to their wont, and as if they wished to blow the windows down. And the day after, there appeared among the fashionable *réunions* in *The Morning Post* a paragraph to the following effect:—

"Yesterday Colonel and Mrs. Crawley entertained a select party at dinner at their house at Mayfair—their Excellencies the Prince and Princess of Peterwaradin, H. E. Papoosh Pasha, the Turkish Ambassador (attended by Kibob Bey, dragoman of the mission), the Marquess of Steyne, Earl of Southdown, Sir Pitt and Lady Jane Crawley, Mr. Wagg, etc. After dinner Mrs. Crawley had an assembly, which was attended by the Duchess (Dowager) of Stilton, Duc de la Gruyère, Marchioness of Cheshire, Marchese Alessandro Strachino, Comte de Brie, Baron Schapzuger, Chevalier Tosti, Countess of Slingstone, and Lady F. Macadam, Major-General and Lady G. Macbeth, and (2) Miss Macbeths; Viscount Paddington, Sir Horace Fogey, Hon. Sands Bedwin, Bobbachy Bahawder," and an etc., which the reader may fill at his pleasure through a dozen close lines of small type.

And in her commerce with the great our dear friend showed the same frankness which distinguished her transactions with the lowly in station. On one occasion, when out at a very fine house, Rebecca was (perhaps rather ostentatiously) holding a conversation in the French language with a celebrated tenor singer of that nation, while the Lady Grizzel Macbeth looked over her shoulder scowling at the pair.

"How very well you speak French!" Lady Grizzel said, who herself spoke the tongue in an Edinburgh accent most remarkable to hear.

"I ought to know it," Becky modestly said, casting down her eyes. "I taught it in a school, and my mother was a Frenchwoman."

Lady Grizzel was won by her humility, and was mollified towards the little woman. She deplored the fatal levelling tendencies of the age, which admitted persons of all classes into the society of their superiors; but her Ladyship owned that this one at least was well behaved and never forgot her place in life. She was a very good woman—good to the poor; stupid, blameless, unsuspicious. It is not her Ladyship's fault that she fancies herself better than you and me. The skirts of her ancestors' garments have been kissed for centuries; it is a thousand years, they say, since the tartans of the head of the family were embraced by the defunct Duncan's lords and councillors, when the great ancestor of the House became King of Scotland.

Lady Steyne, after the music scene, succumbed before Becky, and perhaps was not disinclined to her. The younger ladies of the House of Gaunt were also compelled into submission. Once or twice they set people at her, but they failed. The brilliant Lady Stunnington tried a passage of arms with her, but was routed with great slaughter by the intrepid little Becky. When attacked sometimes, Becky had a knack of adopting a demure, *ingénue* air, under which she was most dangerous. She said the wickedest things with the most simple, unaffected air when in this mood, and would take care artlessly to apologize for her blunders, so that all the world should know that she had made them.

Mr. Wagg, the celebrated wit, and a led-captain and trench-erman of my Lord Steyne, was caused by the ladies to charge her; and the worthy fellow, leering at his patronesses, and giving them a wink, as much as to say, "Now look out for sport," one evening began an assault upon Becky, who was unsuspiciously eating her dinner. The little woman, attacked on a sudden, but never without arms, lighted up in an instant, parried and riposted with a home-thrust which made Wagg's face tingle with shame; then she re-turned to her soup with the most perfect calm and a quiet smile on her face. Wagg's great patron, who gave him dinners and lent him a little money sometimes, and whose election, newspaper, and other jobs Wagg did, gave the luckless fellow such a savage glance with the eyes as almost made him sink under the table and burst into tears. He looked piteously at my Lord, who never spoke to him during dinner, and at the ladies, who disowned him. At last Becky herself took compassion upon him, and tried to en-gage him in talk. He was not asked to dinner again for six weeks; and Fiche, my Lord's confidential man, to whom Wagg naturally paid a good deal of court, was instructed to tell him that if he ever dared to say a rude thing to Mrs. Crawley again, or make her the butt of his stupid jokes, Milor would put every one of his notes of hand into his lawyer's hands, and sell him up without mercy. Wagg wept before Fiche, and implored his dear friend to intercede for him. He wrote a poem in favour of Mrs. R. C., which appeared in the very next number of *The Harum-scarum Maga-*

zine, which he conducted. He implored her good-will at parties where he met her. He cringed and coaxed Rawdon at the club. He was allowed to come back to Gaunt House after a while. Becky was always good to him, always amused, never angry.

His Lordship's vizier and chief confidential servant (with a seat in Parliament and at the dinner-table), Mr. Wenham, was much more prudent in his behaviour and opinions than Mr. Wagg. However much he might be disposed to hate all parvenus (Mr. Wenham himself was a stanch old True Blue Tory, and his father a small coal-merchant in the north of England), this aide-de-camp of the Marquis never showed any sort of hostility to the new favourite, but pursued her with stealthy kindness, and a sly and deferential politeness which somehow made Becky more uneasy than other people's overt hostilities.

How the Crawleys got the money which was spent upon the entertainments with which they treated the polite world was a mystery which gave rise to some conversation at the time, and probably added zest to these little festivities. Some persons averred that Sir Pitt Crawley gave his brother a handsome allowance; if he did, Becky's power over the Baronet must have been extraordinary indeed, and his character greatly changed in his advanced age. Other parties hinted that it was Becky's habit to levy contributions on all her husband's friends—going to this one in tears with an account that there was an execution in the house; falling on her knees to that one, and declaring that the whole family must go to jail or commit suicide unless such and such a bill could be paid. Lord Southdown, it was said, had been induced to give many hundreds through these pathetic representations. Young Feltham of the —th Dragoons, and son of the firm of Tiler & Feltham, hatters and army accoutrement makers, and whom the Crawleys introduced into fashionable life, was also cited as one of Becky's victims in the pecuniary way. People declared that she got money from various simply-disposed persons, under pretence of getting them confidential appointments under Government. Who knows what stories were or were not told of our dear and innocent friend? Certain it is that if she had had all the money which she was said to have begged or borrowed or stolen, she might have capitalized and been honest for life; whereas,—but this is advancing matters.

The truth is, that by economy and good management—by a sparing use of ready money and by paying scarcely anybody—people can manage, for a time at least, to make a great show with very little means; and it is our belief that Becky's much-talked-of parties, which were not, after all was said, very numerous, cost this lady very little more than the wax candles which lighted the walls. Stillbrook and Queen's Crawley supplied her with game and fruit in abundance. Lord Steyne's cellars were at her disposal, and that excellent nobleman's famous cooks presided over her little kitchen, or sent by my lord's order the rarest delicacies from their own. I protest it is quite shameful in the world to abuse a simple creature as people of her time abuse Becky, and I warn the public against believing one-tenth of the stories against her. If every person is to be banished from society who runs into debt and cannot pay—if we are to be peering into everybody's private life, speculating upon their income, and cutting them if we don't approve of their expenditure—why, what a howling wilderness and intolerable dwelling Vanity Fair would be! Every man's hand would be against his neighbour in this case, my dear sir, and the benefits of civilization would be done away with. We should be quarrelling, abusing, avoiding one another. Our houses would become caverns; and we should go in rags because we cared for nobody. Rents would go down. Parties wouldn't be given any more. All the tradesmen of the town would be bankrupt. Wine, wax-lights, comestibles, rouge, crinoline-petticoats, diamonds, wigs, Louis-Quatorze gimcracks, and old china, park hacks, and splendid high-stepping carriage horses—all the delights of life, I say—would go to the deuce if people did but act upon their silly principles, and avoid those whom they dislike and abuse. Whereas, by a little charity and mutual forbearance, things are made to go on pleasantly enough. We may abuse a man as much as we like, and call him the greatest rascal unhanged; but do we wish to hang him therefore? No; we shake hands when we meet. If his cook is good, we forgive him, and go and dine with him, and we expect he will do the same by us. Thus trade flourishes; civilization advances; peace is kept; new dresses are wanted for new assemblies every week; and the last year's vintage of Lafitte will remunerate the honest proprietor who reared it.

At the time whereof we are writing, though the Great George was on the throne and ladies wore *gigots* and large combs like tortoiseshell shovels in their hair, instead of the simple sleeves and lovely wreaths which are actually in fashion, the manners of the very polite world were not, I take it, essentially different from those of the present day, and their amusements pretty similar. To

us, from the outside, gazing over the policeman's shoulders at the
bewildering beauties as they pass into Court or ball, they may seem
beings of unearthly splendour, and in the enjoyment of an exquisite happiness by us unattainable. It is to console some of these
dissatisfied beings, that we are narrating our dear Becky's struggles, and triumphs, and disappointments, of all of which, indeed,
as is the case with all persons of merit, she had her share.

At this time the amiable amusement of acting charades had
come among us from France, and was considerably in vogue in this
country, enabling the many ladies amongst us who had beauty to
display their charms, and the fewer number who had cleverness
to exhibit their wit. My Lord Steyne was incited by Becky, who
perhaps believed herself endowed with both the above qualifications, to give an entertainment at Gaunt House which should include some of these little dramas; and we must take leave to introduce the reader to this brilliant *réunion*, and with a melancholy
welcome too, for it will be among the very last of the fashionable
entertainments to which it will be our fortune to conduct him.

A portion of that splendid room, the picture gallery of Gaunt
House, was arranged as the charade theatre. It had been so used
when George III. was king; and a picture of the Marquis of Gaunt
is still extant, with his hair in powder and a pink ribbon, in a
Roman shape, as it was called, enacting the part of Cato in Mr.
Addison's tragedy of that name, performed before their Royal High-
nesses the Prince of Wales, the Bishop of Osnaburgh, and Prince
William Henry, then children like the actor. One or two of the old
properties were drawn out of the garrets, where they had lain
ever since, and furbished up anew for the present festivities.

Young Bedwin Sands, then an elegant dandy and Eastern
traveller, was manager of the revels. An Eastern traveller was somebody in those days, and the adventurous Bedwin, who had published his quarto, and passed some months under the tents in the
desert, was a personage of no small importance. In his volume
there were several pictures of Sands in various Oriental costumes;
and he travelled about with a black attendant of most unprepos-
sessing appearance, just like another Brian de Bois Guilbert. Bedwin, his costumes, and black man were hailed at Gaunt House as
very valuable acquisitions.

He led off the first charade. A Turkish officer with an immense plume of feathers (the Janizaries were supposed to be still
in existence, and the tarboosh had not as yet displaced the ancient

and majestic head-dress of the true believers) was seen couched on a divan, and making believe to puff at a narghile, in which, however, for the sake of the ladies, only a fragrant pastille was allowed to smoke. The Turkish dignitary yawns and expresses signs of weariness and idleness. He claps his hands, and Mesrour the Nubian appears, with bare arms, bangles, yataghans, and every Eastern ornament—gaunt, tall, and hideous. He makes a salaam before my lord the Aga.

A thrill of terror and delight runs through the assembly. The ladies whisper to one another. The black slave was given to Bedwin Sands by an Egyptian Pasha in exchange for three dozen of Maraschino. He has sewn up ever so many odalisques in sacks and tilted them into the Nile.

"Bid the slave-merchant enter," says the Turkish voluptuary, with a wave of his hand. Mesrour conducts the slave-merchant into my lord's presence; he brings a veiled female with him. He removes the veil. A thrill of applause bursts through the house. It is Mrs. Winkworth (she was a Miss Absolom) with the beautiful eyes and hair. She is in a gorgeous Oriental costume; the black braided locks are twined with innumerable jewels; her dress is covered over with gold piastres. The odious Mahometan expresses himself charmed by her beauty. She falls down on her knees, and entreats him to restore her to the mountains where she was born, and where her Circassian lover is still deploring the absence of his Zuleikah. No entreaties will move the obdurate Hassan. He laughs at the notion of the Circassian bridegroom. Zuleikah covers her face with her hands, and drops down in an attitude of the most beautiful despair. There seems to be no hope for her, when—when the Kislar Aga appears.

The Kislar Aga brings a letter from the Sultan. Hassan receives and places on his head the dread firman. A ghastly terror seizes him, while on the negro's face (it is Mesrour again in another costume) appears a ghastly joy. "Mercy! mercy!" cries the Pasha; while the Kislar Aga, grinning horribly, pulls out—a *bowstring*.

The curtain draws just as he is going to use that awful weapon. Hassan from within bawls out, "First two syllables;" and Mrs. Rawdon Crawley, who is going to act in the charade, comes forward and compliments Mrs. Winkworth on the admirable taste and beauty of her costume.

The second part of the charade takes place. It is still an Eastern scene. Hassan, in another dress, is in an attitude by Zuleikah, who is perfectly reconciled to him. The Kislar Aga has become a peaceful black slave. It is sunrise on the desert, and the Turks turn their heads eastwards and bow to the sand. As there are no dromedaries at hand, the band facetiously plays "The Camels are Coming." An enormous Egyptian head figures in the scene. It is a musical one, and, to the surprise of the Oriental travellers, sings a comic song, composed by Mr. Wagg. The Eastern voyagers go off dancing, like Papageno and the Moorish King in the "Magic Flute." "Last two syllables," roars the head.

The last act opens. It is a Grecian tent this time. A tall and stalwart man reposes on a couch there. Above him hang his helmet and shield. There is no need for them now. Ilium is down; Iphigenia is slain; Cassandra is a prisoner in his outer halls. The king of men (it is Colonel Crawley, who, indeed, has no notion about the sack of Ilium or the conquest of Cassandra), the anax andrôn is asleep in his chamber at Argos. A lamp casts the broad shadow of the sleeping warrior flickering on the wall; the sword and shield of Troy glitter in its light. The band plays the awful music of "Don Juan" before the statue enters.

Ægisthus steals in pale and on tiptoe. What is that ghastly face looking out balefully after him from behind the arras? He raises his dagger to strike the sleeper, who turns in his bed, and opens his broad chest as if for the blow. He cannot strike the noble slumbering chieftain. Clytemnestra glides swiftly into the room like an apparition; her arms are bare and white, her tawny hair floats down her shoulders, her face is deadly pale, and her eyes are lighted up with a smile so ghastly that people quake as they look at her.

A tremor ran through the room. "Good God!" somebody said, "it's Mrs. Rawdon Crawley."

Scornfully she snatches the dagger out of Ægisthus's hand, and advances to the bed. You see it shining over her head in the glimmer of the lamp, and—and the lamp goes out, with a groan, and all is dark.

The darkness and the scene frightened people. Rebecca performed her part so well, and with such ghastly truth, that the spectators were all dumb, until, with a burst, all the lamps of the hall blazed out again, when everybody began to shout applause. "Brava! brava!" old Steyne's strident voice was heard roaring over all the rest. "By ——, she'd do it too," he said, between his teeth. The performers were called by the whole house, which sounded with cries of "Manager! Clytemnestra!" AGAMEMNON could not be got to show in his classical tunic, but stood in the background with Ægisthus and others of the performers of the little play. Mr. Bedwin Sands led on Zuleikah and Clytemnestra. A great personage insisted on being presented to the charming Clytemnestra. "Heigh ha? Run him through the body. Marry somebody else, hey?" was the apposite remark made by His Royal Highness.

"Mrs. Rawdon Crawley was quite killing in the part," said Lord Steyne. Becky laughed, gay, and saucy looking, and swept the prettiest little curtsy ever seen.

Servants brought in salvers covered with numerous cool dainties, and the performers disappeared to get ready for the second charade-tableau.

The three syllables of this charade were to be depicted in pantomime, and the performance took place in the following wise:—

First syllable. Colonel Rawdon Crawley, C.B., with a slouched hat and a staff, a greatcoat, and a lantern borrowed from the stables, passed across the stage, bawling out as if warning the inhabitants of the hour. In the lower window are seen two bagmen, playing apparently at the game of cribbage, over which they yawn much. To them enters one looking like Boots (the Honourable G. Ringwood, which character the young gentleman performed to perfection), and divests them of their lower coverings; and presently Chambermaid (the Right Honourable Lord Southdown), with two candlesticks and a warming-pan. She ascends to the upper apartment, and warms the bed. She uses the warming-pan as a weapon wherewith she wards off the attention of the bagmen. She exits. They put on their nightcaps and pull down the blinds. Boots comes out and closes the shutters of the ground-floor chamber. You hear him bolting and chaining the door within. All the lights go out. The music plays *Dormez, dormez, chers Amours*. A voice from behind the curtain says, "First syllable."

Second syllable. The lamps are lighted up all of a sudden. The music plays the old air from John of Paris, *Ah quel plaisir d'être en voyage*. It is the same scene. Between the first and second floors of the house represented you behold a sign on which the Steyne arms are painted. All the bells are ringing all over the house. In the lower apartment you see a man with a long slip of paper presenting it to another, who shakes his fists, threatens, and vows that it is monstrous. "Ostler, bring round my gig," cries another at the door. He chucks Chambermaid (the Right Honourable Lord Southdown) under the chin; she seems to deplore his absence, as Calypso did that of that other eminent traveller Ulysses. Boots (the Honourable G. Ringwood) passes with a wooden box containing silver flagons, and cries "Pots" with such exquisite humour and naturalness that the whole house rings with applause, and a bouquet is thrown to him. Crack, crack, crack go the whips. Landlord, chambermaid, waiter rush to the door; but just as some distinguished guest is arriving, the curtains close, and the invisible theatrical manager cries out, "Second syllable."

"I think it must be 'Hotel,'" says Captain Grigg of the Life Guards. There is a general laugh at the Captain's cleverness. He is not very far from the mark.

While the third syllable is in preparation, the band begins a nautical medley—"All in the Downs," "Cease, Rude Boreas," "Rule Britannia," "In the Bay of Biscay O!" Some maritime event is about to take place. A bell is heard ringing as the curtain draws aside. "Now, gents, for the shore!" a voice exclaims. People take leave of each other. They point anxiously as if towards the clouds, which are represented by a dark curtain, and they nod their heads in fear. Lady Squeams (the Right Honourable Lord Southdown), her lap-dog, her bags, reticules, and husband sit down, and cling hold of some ropes. It is evidently a ship.

The Captain (Colonel Crawley, c.b.), with a cocked hat and a telescope, comes in, holding his hat on his head, and looks out; his coat-tails fly about as if in the wind. When he leaves go of his hat to use his telescope, his hat flies off, with immense applause. It is blowing fresh. The music rises and whistles louder and louder; the mariners go across the stage staggering, as if the ship was in severe motion. The Steward (the Honourable G. Ringwood) passes reeling by, holding six basins. He put one rapidly by Lord Squeams. Lady Squeams, giving a pinch to her dog, which begins to howl piteously, puts her pocket-handkerchief to her face, and rushes away as for the cabin. The music rises up to the wildest pitch of stormy excitement, and the third syllable is concluded.

There was a little ballet, "Le Rossignol," in which Montessu and Noblet used to be famous in those days, and which Mr. Wagg transferred to the English stage as an opera, putting his verse, of which he was a skilful writer, to the pretty airs of the ballet. It was dressed in old French costume, and little Lord Southdown now appeared admirably attired in the disguise of an old woman hobbling about the stage with a faultless crooked stick.

Trills of melody were heard behind the scenes, and gurgling from a sweet pasteboard cottage covered with roses and trellis-work. "Philomèle, Philomèle," cries the old woman; and Philomèle comes out.

More applause: it is Mrs. Rawdon Crawley in powder and patches, the most *ravissante* little Marquise in the world.

She comes in laughing, humming, and frisks about the stage with all the innocence of theatrical youth; she makes a curtsy. Mamma says, "Why, child, you are always laughing and singing," and away she goes, with—

THE ROSE UPON MY BALCONY.

The rose upon my balcony the morning air perfuming
    Was leafless all the winter time, and pining for the spring;
You ask me why her breath is sweet and why her cheek is blooming;
    It is because the sun is out and birds begin to sing.

The nightingale, whose melody is through the greenwood ringing,
    Was silent when the boughs were bare and winds were blowing
        keen;
And if, Mamma, you ask of me the reason of his singing,
    It is because the sun is out and all the leaves are green.

Thus each performs his part, Mamma: the birds have found their
        voices,
    The blowing rose a flush, Mamma, her bonny cheek to dye;
And there's sunshine in my heart, Mamma, which wakens and
        rejoices,
    And so I sing and blush, Mamma, and that's the reason why.

During the intervals of the stanzas of this ditty, the good-natured personage addressed as mamma by the singer, and whose large whiskers appeared under her cap, seemed very anxious to exhibit her maternal affection by embracing the innocent creature who performed the daughter's part. Every caress was received with loud acclamations of laughter by the sympathizing audience. At its conclusion (while the music was performing a symphony as if ever so many birds were warbling) the whole house was unanimous for an *encore*, and applause and bouquets without end were showered upon the NIGHTINGALE of the evening. Lord Steyne's voice of applause was loudest of all. Becky, the nightingale, took the flowers which he threw to her, and pressed them to her heart with the air of a consummate comedian. Lord Steyne was frantic with delight. His guests' enthusiasm harmonized with his own. Where was the beautiful black-eyed Houri whose appearance in the first charade had caused such delight? She was twice as handsome as Becky, but the brilliancy of the latter had quite eclipsed her. All voices were for her. Stephens, Caradori, Ronzi de Begnis—people compared her to one or the other, and agreed, with good reason, very likely, that had she been an actress none on the stage could have surpassed her. She had reached her culmination; her voice rose trilling and bright over the storm of applause, and soared as high and joyful as her triumph. There was a ball after the dramatic entertainments, and everybody pressed round Becky as the great point of attraction of the evening. The Royal Personage declared, with an oath, that she was perfection, and engaged her again and again in conversation. Little Becky's soul swelled with pride and delight at these honours; she saw fortune, fame, fashion before her. Lord Steyne was her slave—followed her everywhere, and scarcely spoke to any one in the room besides, and paid her the most marked compliments and attention. She still appeared in her Marquise costume, and danced a minuet with Monsieur de Truffigny, Monsieur Le Duc de la Jabotière's *attaché;* and the Duke, who had all the traditions of the ancient Court, pronounced that Madame Crawley was worthy to have been a pupil of Vestris, or to have figured at Versailles. Only a feeling of dignity, the gout, and the strongest sense of duty and personal sacrifice prevented his Excellency from dancing with her himself; and he declared in public that a lady who could talk and dance like Mrs. Rawdon was fit to be ambassadress at any court in Eutope. He was only con-soled when he heard that she was half a Frenchwoman by birth. "None but a compatriot," his Excellency declared, "could have performed that majestic dance in such a way."

Then she figured in a waltz with Monsieur de Klingenspohr, the Prince of Peterwaradin's cousin and *attaché.* The delighted Prince, having less *retenue* than his French diplomatic colleague, insisted on taking a turn with the charming creature, and twirled round the ball-room with her, scattering the diamonds out of his boot-tassels and hussar jacket until His Highness was fairly out of breath. Papoosh Pasha himself would have liked to dance with her if that amusement had been the custom of his country. The com-pany made a circle round her, and applauded as wildly as if she had been a Noblet or a Taglioni. Everybody was in ecstasy; and Becky too, you may be sure. She passed by Lady Stunnington with a look of scorn. She patronized Lady Gaunt and her astonished and mortified sister-in-law—she *écraséd* all rival charmers. As for poor Mrs. Winkworth, and her long hair and great eyes, which had made such an effect at the commencement of the evening, where was she now? Nowhere in the race. She might tear her long hair and cry her great eyes out, but there was not a person to heed or to deplore the discomfiture.

The greatest triumph of all was at supper-time. She was placed at the grand exclusive table with his Royal Highness, the exalted personage before-mentioned, and the rest of the great guests. She was served on gold plate. She might have had pearls melted into her champagne if she liked—another Cleopatra; and the potentate of Peterwaradin would have given half the brilliants off his jacket for a kind glance from those dazzling eyes. Jabotière wrote home about her to his government. The ladies at the other tables, who supped off mere silver, and marked Lord Steyne's constant attention to her, vowed it was a monstrous infatuation, a gross insult to ladies of rank. If sarcasm could have killed, Lady Stunnington would have slain her on the spot.

Rawdon Crawley was scared at these triumphs. They seemed to separate his wife farther than ever from him somehow. He thought, with a feeling very like pain, how immeasurably she was his superior.

When the hour of departure came, a crowd of young men followed her to her carriage, for which the people without bawled, the cry being caught up by the linkmen who were stationed outside the tall gates of Gaunt House, congratulating each person who issued from the gate and hoping his Lordship had enjoyed this noble party.

Mrs. Rawdon Crawley's carriage, coming up to the gate after due shouting, rattled into the illuminated courtyard, and drove up to the covered way. Rawdon put his wife into the carriage, which drove off. Mr. Wenham had proposed to him to walk home, and offered the Colonel the refreshment of a cigar.

They lighted their cigars by the lamp of one of the many link-boys outside, and Rawdon walked on with his friend Wenham. Two persons separated from the crowd and followed the two gentlemen; and when they had walked down Gaunt Square a few score of paces, one of the men came up, and touching Rawdon on the shoulder, said, "Beg your pardon, Colonel, I vish to speak to you most particular." This gentleman's acquaintance gave a loud whistle as the latter spoke, at which signal a cab came clattering up from those stationed at the gate of Gaunt House, and the aide-de-camp ran round and placed himself in front of Colonel Crawley.

That gallant officer at once knew what had befallen him. He was in the hands of the bailiffs. He started back, falling against the man who had first touched him.

"We're three on us; it's no use bolting," the man behind said.

"It's you, Moss, is it?" said the Colonel, who appeared to know his interlocutor. "How much is it?"

"Only a small thing," whispered Mr. Moss, of Cursitor Street, Chancery Lane, and assistant officer to the Sheriff of Middlesex—"one hundred and thirty-six, six and eightpence, at the suit of Mr. Nathan."

"Lend me a hundred, Wenham, for God's sake," poor Rawdon said; "I've got seventy at home."

"I've not got ten pounds in the world," said poor Mr. Wenham. "Good-night, my dear fellow."

"Good-night," said Rawdon ruefully. And Wenham walked away, and Rawdon Crawley finished his cigar as the cab drove under Temple Bar.

AFTERWORD

"Then I saw in my dream that when they were got out of the wilderness, they presently saw a town before them, and the name of that Town is Vanity; and at the town there is a fair kept called Vanity Fair. It is kept all the year long; it beareth the name of Vanity Fair, because the town where 'tis kept is lighter than vanity, and also because all that is there sold or that cometh thither is Vanity."

—The Pilgrim's Progress.

Those lines from John Bunyan provide the novel with a title, with part of its subject matter—insofar as Thackeray transposes the dream into his own century—and with one of its two controlling metaphors. Thackeray is telling us that the whole fashionable world, whether in London or Paris or at some German princeling's court, is merely a fair at which worthless things are bought and sold. He is also preaching with some of Bunyan's moral earnestness, but he is not writing an allegory like *The Pilgrim's Progress*. The characters in his story are presented as typical persons, but not, in most cases, as embodiments of vices or virtues. The vicious are sometimes punished, but not always; the virtuous are sometimes rewarded, as are patient Amelia and her faithful Dobbin, but in other cases they end as doddering bankrupts, like Amelia's father; and Thackeray does not promise that they will be recompensed in the Celestial City. The story has a literal but not a figurative meaning, and it points no moral except that we had better stay out of the chaffering for what Bunyan listed as "houses, lands, trades, places, honours, preferments, titles, countries, kingdoms, lusts, pleasures, and delights of all sorts." "Vanity of vanities, saith the preacher, vanity of vanities; all is vanity."

The second controlling metaphor, not inconsistent with the first, is that of the fashionable world as a stage or a puppet theatre. It is a stage because everyone is acting a part and everything presents an illusion. It is a puppet theatre because the characters have no freedom of movement, but are pulled about by their lusts and vanities or even—so the author pretends—by his own whimiscal notions of what they should do. The author compares himself to a stage manager or a puppet master. He insists on being permitted not only to introduce his characters,

> but occasionally to step down from the platform, and talk about them; if they are good and kindly, to love them and shake them by the hand; if they are silly, to laugh at them confidentially in the reader's sleeve; if they are wicked and heartless, to abuse them in the strongest terms which politeness permits of. [See the final paragraphs of Chapter VIII.]

The same privilege is claimed by puppet masters, who also address remarks to the audience. We shall see that, in *Vanity Fair*, the author's remarks—and his assumed character as well—are an essential part of the performance.

The entertainment at Gaunt House, with the events that lead up to it, is not the climax of the novel; that will come two chapters later, when Rawdon Crawley surprises his wife with Lord Steyne. The present chapter, however, is close to the heart of Thackeray's subject and illustrates both of his controlling metaphors. Becky rises in the fashionable world by pretending to qualities she does not possess—in other words, by selling false merchandise in Vanity Fair—and she achieves her moment of triumph on a stage, by acting in two charades.

In the novel as a whole, the point of view is usually that of an omniscient narrator, but sometimes the author himself takes over the story in the first person singular. The present chapter uses both methods. In the first half of it, Thackeray addresses the reader directly: "I declare

I swell with pride," he says, "as those august names are transcribed by my pen." This device enables him to give a rapid summary, as from a distance, of "my dear Becky's" rise in the fashionable world, and also to step down from the platform and make a number of ironic comments. The second half of the chapter begins with the sentence, "A portion of that splendid room, the picture gallery of Gaunt House, was arranged as a charade theatre." What follows is a brilliant scene presented— that is, "shown," not told about—by an omniscient narrator, the "I" having receded into the background. At the end of the chapter, Rawdon Crawley's arrest for debt—a briefer scene, but fully dramatized—serves as an effective curtain.

Thackeray's comments on the action, as in the first half of the chapter, have been severely condemned. One of the most scathing critics is Ford Madox Ford, who says, "No author would, like Thackeray, to-day intrude his broken nose and myopic spectacles into the middle of the most thrilling scene he ever wrote, in order to tell you that, though his heroine was a wrong 'un, his own heart was in his right place." It is true that some of Thackeray's comments impress one as being arch or priggish or unnecessary. We have omitted one of the longer ones, at the very beginning of the chapter; not only could it be spared, but also it would require historical footnotes to be fully understood by readers today. There is much to be said, however, in defense of his other comments and of the role that Thackeray plays in his own novel.

The "I" of the narrative is not the author as he was in life. Rather he is another of the created characters, more innocent than Thackeray himself, more tolerant of Becky, more conventional, and closer to his middle-class readers. He is not invited to splendid entertainments like those at Gaunt House. Instead he gets his information from newspapers and from the gossip, sometimes false, that he heard about Becky. He learns more about her as the reader also learns. In other words, he is a character with whom the reader can identify himself and one who sets the tone of the story. He plays the part, in some degree, of what Henry James was later to call "the central consciousness," that is, of a character like Lambert Strether in *The Ambassadors*.

In the second half of the chapter, Becky, the villainess, reveals more of herself on the stage than she has ever revealed in life. The same statement applies to some of the other persons who figure in the scene. Thus, the Honourable G. Ringwood takes the part of Boots, "which character the young gentleman performed to perfection," for the reason, we infer, that he is really a sort of underservant. Little, effeminate Lord

Southdown is convincing in the role of a flirtatious chambermaid. Rawdon Crawley is the bluff warrior who will undergo almost the same fate in life as in the charade of Agamemnon. When Becky leans over him with a dagger gleaming in her hand, there is "a ghastly truth" in her performance; "By God, she'd do it too," Lord Steyne mutters between his teeth. Soon we shall learn, by her betrayal of Rawdon and by the mysterious death of Jos Sedley, that Becky in life is Clytemnestra.

The Scarlet Letter (1850)

NATHANIEL HAWTHORNE (1804-1864) was born in Salem, Massachusetts, where one of his ancestors had been a judge in the witchcraft trials of 1692. The boy's father, a sea captain, died of yellow fever at Surinam in 1808, and the little family—there were two girls marked for spinsterhood—was left dependent on Mrs. Hawthorne's brothers. At fourteen, the boy went to Maine with the family and spent a year wandering in the woods or, in winter, skating alone by moonlight on Sebago Lake; "it was there," he said later, "I first got my cursed habits of solitude." Having returned to Salem, he prepared for college and entered Bowdoin with the class of 1825.

Among his Bowdoin contemporaries were Longfellow, Horatio Bridge, later a naval officer, Jonathan Cilley, later a congressman, and future President Franklin Pierce. Hawthorne's college years were moderately social, but after graduation he went back to Salem and disappeared from sight. He used to say that he doubted whether twenty persons in the town so much as knew of his existence. The remark exaggerates the degree of his physical isolation. He did have some Salem friends besides his two adoring sisters; he sometimes played cards, and he took a certain interest in Democratic party politics. Psychologically, however, he felt shipwrecked from the world. He often spent the whole day in his room, writing, reading—he preferred Colonial records and the novels of Sir Walter Scott—or letting his fancies wander.

After twelve years he began making efforts to emerge from his solitude. His stories had been appearing anonymously, mostly in "gift books"— annual publications designed for the Christmas trade—and in 1837

Hawthorne collected them in *Twice-Told Tales*. His friend Horatio Bridge guaranteed the publisher against loss and Longfellow reviewed the book enthusiastically. Hawthorne began to appear in a few Salem houses, including that of his neighbors the Peabodys. There were three Peabody sisters, and he fell in love with the youngest, Sophia, then an invalid. The engagement lasted four years; they were waiting for Sophia to recover her health and for Hawthorne to find means of supporting a wife. He received his first political appointment, as weigher and gauger at the Boston custom house, but resigned it after the Democrats were turned out of office. Then he invested his savings in Brook Farm, a utopian community, but the experiment was a failure for him before it was for others. In 1842 he and Sophia decided to risk getting married and to depend for a livelihood on Providence and Hawthorne's pen.

At the Old Manse in Concord, they lived happily on almost nothing a year. Hawthorne became a good friend of young Henry Thoreau and a respectful but distant friend of Emerson. In 1846 he published another collection of stories, *Mosses from an Old Manse*, which was widely praised. Debts were piling up, however, and that same year he was glad to accept a second political appointment, as surveyor of the custom house in Salem. The post was almost a sinecure, but he did no writing for publication until he lost it in the summer of 1849, after another Whig administration was installed in Washington. Immediately he set to work on the first and greatest of his novels.

The Scarlet Letter was recognized as a powerful book from the moment it appeared. But Salem hated it, and Hawthorne left his native town without regret. While living for two years in the Berkshires, he saw a good deal of Herman Melville; then in 1852 he bought a house in Concord, "The Wayside." It was a period of intense literary activity during which he published two more novels—*The House of the Seven Gables* (1851) and *The Blithedale Romance* (1852)—a third collection of stories, two books for boys and girls, and a campaign biography of Franklin Pierce. After Pierce took office, Hawthorne received the last and most lucrative of his political appointments: as consul at Liverpool, then the busiest port in the world. Once again he did not write for publication while employed by the government; but after he resigned his post in 1857, he spent two years in Italy and then wrote *The Marble Faun* (1860), the most admired in its time of his four novels.

That same year he returned to Concord. His health was failing, he was disheartened by the Civil War, and he found himself unable to finish any of the new novels he started one after another. The only book that came out of his last years, *Our Old Home* (1863), was based on notebooks he had kept in England. He insisted on dedicating the book to his old friend Franklin Pierce, who was then being reviled as a Copperhead. The following spring, Pierce took him on a carriage trip, hoping that his health would revive in the New Hampshire hills, but he died in his sleep before catching a last glimpse of the White Mountains.

THE STORY

Hester Prynne, a young woman of great beauty, is married to an old, rich, misshapen scholar. He sends her to Boston, then newly settled, to prepare for his arrival in the Colony, but he fails to appear. Hester falls in love with her pastor, the Reverend Arthur Dimmesdale, and bears him a child—in prison, for she has been charged with adultery. Having refused to divulge the name of her lover, she is condemned to wear a scarlet A on her breast during her lifetime; but first she must do public penance by standing for three hours, her baby in her arms, on the scaffold of the pillory.

The first scene of *The Scarlet Letter* is played—the proper word, for the book is constructed like a drama—in the Boston marketplace, on and around the scaffold. In the crowd, Hester recognizes her husband, who has been released from captivity among the Indians. He lays a finger on his lips. From the balcony of the meeting house, Dimmesdale adjures her to reveal the name of her fellow sinner and thus remove a burden from his heart. Hester shakes her head. The scene has introduced the four principal characters, and the action that follows will be an *interaction* among these four: Hester, the child—called Pearl, as being of great price—the wronged husband, who has assumed the name of Chillingworth, and the guilty minister.

Before they are released from prison, Hester and the child need medical attention. The physician summoned by the jailer turns out to be Chillingworth. He says that he is determined to have revenge on the guilty man, whoever that man may be, and he extracts the promise from Hester that she will keep his own identity secret. Three years pass, during which Hester supports herself by needlework. Pearl is an "elvish" child, and there is talk of taking her away from the mother to give her a Christian education; but Dimmesdale makes an eloquent plea that changes the minds of the magistrates. The minister's health has been weakened by his feeling of guilt, and Chillingworth volunteers to live in the same house with him and be his physician. Suspecting that the minister is Pearl's father, Chillingworth probes his mind relentlessly and discovers the truth by accident. While still concealing his own identity, he punishes the former lover day after day by playing on his conscience.

It is now seven years since Hester stood on the scaffold of the pillory. Driven half-insane, Dimmesdale tries to lighten the burden of his guilt by a private mimicry of public confession. He climbs on the scaffold at midnight and shrieks aloud to the sleeping town, but nobody listens. Hester comes by with little Pearl on her way home from the deathbed of Governor Winthrop. (It is the scene reprinted in this volume.) A few days later Hester meets her former husband alone and begs him to release her from her promise not to tell Dimmesdale who he is. Chillingworth consents; but still he refuses to forgo his search for revenge, which is turning him into a fiend. "It has all been a dark necessity," he says. "Let the black flower blossom as it may."

Hester—with Pearl at her side, as always—goes into the forest to meet Dimmesdale on his return from a visit to Indian converts. She warns him against Chillingworth; then she is so disturbed by the minister's condition that she offers to run away with him; a ship is sailing for Bristol in four days. Dimmesdale accepts what seems to be his only hope of release. Hester unfastens the scarlet letter from her breast and suddenly the forest is flooded with sunlight. But little Pearl, who has been playing at a distance, will not return to her side until Hester has replaced the emblem; and when the minister kisses Pearl on the forehead, she washes off the kiss.

The day before the ship is to sail for Bristol is Election Sunday, when the Colony installs its magistrates. Dimmesdale has been chosen to deliver the Election sermon. Hester, as she stands with the crowd in the marketplace, learns that Chillingworth has engaged passage on the same vessel; there will be no escape. Dimmesdale's sermon is the most eloquent that Boston has ever heard. But later, as he totters out of the meeting house in a procession of dignitaries, he begs Hester and Pearl to help him climb the steps of the scaffold. "Is not this better," he murmurs, "than what we dreamed of in the forest?" Tearing away the ministerial band from his breast, he reveals a scarlet letter burned into his flesh; then he sinks to the platform.

Chillingworth stands over the dying man. "Thou hast escaped me!" he says more than once. Having lost his reason for living, the old scholar loses his vigor too, and he dies within the year, leaving his fortune to little Pearl. Hester, after a long sojourn in Europe—Pearl is married there—comes back to Boston and again pins the scarlet letter on her breast. Many years later she is buried beside Dimmesdale, and the letter is inscribed on the headstone that serves for both graves.

The scene that follows is Chapter 12, a turning point in the tightly constructed book of twenty-four chapters. The text is that of the first edition, which is more to be trusted than the second or the third.

Chapter 12. The Minister's Vigil

Walking in the shadow of a dream, as it were, and perhaps actually under the influence of a species of somnambulism, Mr. Dimmesdale reached the spot, where, now so long since, Hester Prynne had lived through her first hour of public ignominy. The same platform or scaffold, black and weather-stained with the storm or sunshine of seven long years, and foot-worn, too, with the tread of many culprits who had since ascended it, remained standing beneath the balcony of the meeting-house. The minister went up the steps.

It was an obscure night of early May. An unvaried pall of cloud muffled the whole expanse of sky from zenith to horizon. If the same multitude which had stood as eyewitnesses while Hester Prynne sustained her punishment could now have been summoned forth, they would have discerned no face above the platform, nor hardly the outline of a human shape, in the dark gray of the midnight. But the town was all asleep. There was no peril of discovery. The minister might stand there, if it so pleased him, until morning should redden in the east, without other risk than that the dank and chill night-air would creep into his frame, and stiffen his joints with rheumatism, and clog his throat with catarrh and cough; thereby defrauding the expectant audience of to-morrow's prayer and sermon. No eye could see him, save that ever-wakeful one which had seen him in his closet, wielding the bloody scourge. Why, then, had he come hither? Was it but the mockery of penitence? A mockery, indeed, but in which his soul trifled with itself! A mockery at which angels blushed and wept, while fiends rejoiced, with jeering laughter! He had been driven hither by the impulse of that Remorse which dogged him everywhere, and whose own sister and closely linked companion was that Cowardice which invariably drew him back, with her tremulous gripe, just when the other impulse had hurried him to the verge of a disclosure. Poor, miserable man! what right had infirmity like his to burden itself with crime? Crime is for the iron-nerved, who have their choice either to endure it, or, if it press too hard, to exert their fierce and savage strength for a good purpose, and fling it off at once! This feeble and most sensitive of spirits could do neither, yet continually did one thing or another, which intertwined, in the same inextricable knot, the agony of heaven-defying guilt and vain repentance.

And thus, while standing on the scaffold, in this vain show of expiation, Mr. Dimmesdale was overcome with a great horror of mind, as if the universe were gazing at a scarlet token on his naked breast, right over his heart. On that spot, in very truth, there was, and there had long been, the gnawing and poisonous tooth of bodily pain. Without any effort of his will, or power to restrain himself, he shrieked aloud; an outcry that went pealing through the night, and was beaten back from one house to another, and reverberated from the hills in the background; as if a company of devils, detecting so much misery and terror in it, had made a plaything of the sound, and were bandying it to and fro.

"It is done!" muttered the minister, covering his face with his hands. "The whole town will awake, and hurry forth, and find me here!"

But it was not so. The shriek had perhaps sounded with a far greater power, to his own startled ears, than it actually possessed. The town did not awake; or, if it did, the drowsy slumberers mistook the cry either for something frightful in a dream, or for the noise of witches; whose voices, at that period, were often heard to pass over the settlements or lonely cottages, as they rode with Satan through the air. The clergyman, therefore, hearing no symptoms of disturbance, uncovered his eyes and looked about him. At one of the chamber-windows of Governor Bellingham's mansion, which stood at some distance, on the line of another street, he beheld the appearance of the old magistrate himself, with a lamp in his hand, a white night-cap on his head, and a long white gown enveloping his figure. He looked like a ghost, evoked unseasonably from the grave. The cry had evidently startled him. At another window of the same house, moreover, appeared old Mistress Hibbins, the Governor's sister, also with a lamp, which, even thus far off, revealed the expression of her sour and discontented face. She thrust forth her head from the lattice, and looked anxiously upward. Beyond the shadow of a doubt, this venerable witch-lady had heard Mr. Dimmesdale's outcry, and interpreted it, with its multitudinous echoes and reverberations, as the clamor of the fiends and nighthags, with whom she was well known to make excursions into the forest.

Detecting the gleam of Governor Bellingham's lamp, the old lady quickly extinguished her own, and vanished. Possibly, she went up among the clouds. The minister saw nothing further of her motions. The magistrate, after a wary observation of the darkness —into which, nevertheless, he could see but little farther than he might into a mill-stone—retired from the window.

The minister grew comparatively calm. His eyes, however, were soon greeted by a little, glimmering light, which, at first a long way off, was approaching up the street. It threw a gleam of recognition on here a post, and there a garden-fence, and here a latticed window-pane, and there a pump, with its full trough of water, and here, again, an arched door of oak, with an iron knocker, and a rough log for the door-step. The Reverend Mr. Dimmesdale noted all these minute particulars, even while firmly convinced that the doom of his existence was stealing onward, in the footsteps which he now heard; and that the gleam of the lantern would fall upon him, in a few moments more, and reveal his long-hidden secret. As the light drew nearer, he beheld, within its illuminated circle, his brother clergyman,—or, to speak more accurately, his professional father, as well as highly valued friend,—the Reverend Mr. Wilson; who, as Mr. Dimmesdale now conjectured, had been praying at the bedside of some dying man. And so he had. The good old minister came freshly from the death-chamber of Governor Winthrop, who had passed from earth to heaven within that very hour. And now, surrounded, like the saint-like personages of olden times, with a radiant halo, that glorified him amid this gloomy night of sin,—as if the departed Governor had left him an inheritance of his glory, or as if he had caught upon himself the distant shine of the celestial city, while looking thitherward to see the triumphant pilgrim pass within its gates,—now, in short, good Father Wilson was moving homeward, aiding his footsteps with a lighted lantern! The glimmer of this luminary suggested the above conceits to Mr. Dimmesdale, who smiled,—nay, almost laughed at them,— and then wondered if he were going mad.

As the Reverend Mr. Wilson passed beside the scaffold, closely muffling his Geneva cloak about him with one arm, and holding the lantern before his breast with the other, the minister could hardly restrain himself from speaking.

"A good evening to you, venerable Father Wilson! Come up hither, I pray you, and pass a pleasant hour with me!"

Good heavens! Had Mr. Dimmesdale actually spoken? For one instant, he believed that these words had passed his lips. But they were uttered only within his imagination. The venerable Father Wilson continued to step slowly onward, looking carefully at the muddy pathway before his feet, and never once turning his head towards the guilty platform. When the light of the glimmering lantern had faded quite away, the minister discovered, by the faintness which came over him, that the last few moments had been a crisis of terrible anxiety; although his mind had made an involuntary effort to relieve itself by a kind of lurid playfulness.

Shortly afterwards, the like grisly sense of the humorous again stole in among the solemn phantoms of his thought. He felt his limbs growing stiff with the unaccustomed chilliness of the night, and doubted whether he should be able to descend the steps of the scaffold. Morning would break, and find him there. The neighbourhood would begin to rouse itself. The earliest riser, coming forth in the dim twilight, would perceive a vaguely defined figure aloft on the place of shame; and, half crazed betwixt alarm and curiosity, would go, knocking from door to door, summoning all the people to behold the ghost—as he needs must think it—of some defunct transgressor. A dusky tumult would flap its wings from one house to another. Then—the morning light still waxing stronger— old patriarchs would rise up in great haste, each in his flannel gown, and matronly dames, without pausing to put off their night-gear. The whole tribe of decorous personages, who had never heretofore been seen with a single hair of their heads awry, would start into public view, with the disorder of a nightmare in their aspects. Old Governor Bellingham would come grimly forth, with his King James's ruff fastened askew; and Mistress Hibbins, with some twigs of the forest clinging to her skirts, and looking sourer than ever, as having hardly got a wink of sleep after her night ride; and good Father Wilson, too, after spending half the night at a death-bed, and liking ill to be disturbed, thus early, out of his dreams about the glorified saints. Hither, likewise, would come the elders and deacons of Mr. Dimmesdale's church, and the young virgins who so idolized their minister, and had made a shrine for him in their white bosoms; which, now, by the by, in their hurry and confusion, they would scantly have given themselves time to cover with their kerchiefs. All people, in a word, would come stumbling over their thresholds, and turning up their amazed and horror-stricken visages around the scaffold. Whom would they discern there, with the red eastern light upon his brow? Whom, but the Reverend Arthur Dimmesdale, half frozen to death, overwhelmed with shame, and standing where Hester Prynne had stood!

Carried away by the grotesque horror of this picture, the minister, unawares, and to his own infinite alarm, burst into a great peal of laughter. It was immediately responded to by a light, airy, childish laugh, in which, with a thrill of the heart,—but he knew not whether of exquisite pain, or pleasure as acute,—he recognized the tones of little Pearl.

"Pearl! Little Pearl!" cried he, after a moment's pause; then, suppressing his voice,—"Hester! Hester Prynne! Are you there?"

"Yes; it is Hester Prynne!" she replied, in a tone of surprise; and the minister heard her footsteps approaching from the sidewalk, along which she had been passing.—"It is I, and my little Pearl."

"Whence come you, Hester?" asked the minister. "What sent you hither?"

"I have been watching at a death-bed," answered Hester Prynne;—"at Governor Winthrop's death-bed, and have taken his measure for a robe, and am now going homeward to my dwelling."

"Come up hither, Hester, thou and little Pearl," said the Reverend Mr. Dimmesdale. "Ye have both been here before, but I was not with you. Come up hither once again, and we will stand all three together!"

She silently ascended the steps, and stood on the platform, holding little Pearl by the hand. The minister felt for the child's other hand, and took it. The moment that he did so, there came what seemed a tumultuous rush of new life, other life than his own, pouring like a torrent into his heart, and hurrying through all his veins, as if the mother and the child were communicating their vital warmth to his half-torpid system. The three formed an electric chain.

"Minister!" whispered little Pearl.

"What wouldst thou say, child?" asked Mr. Dimmesdale.

"Wilt thou stand here with mother and me, to-morrow noon-tide?" inquired Pearl.

"Nay; not so, my little Pearl!" answered the minister; for, with the new energy of the moment, all the dread of public exposure, that had so long been the anguish of his life, had returned upon him; and he was already trembling at the conjunction in which— with a strange joy, nevertheless—he now found himself. "Not so, my child. I shall, indeed, stand with thy mother and thee one other day, but not to-morrow!"

Pearl laughed, and attempted to pull away her hand. But the minister held it fast.

"A moment longer, my child!" said he.

"But wilt thou promise," asked Pearl, "to take my hand, and mother's hand, to-morrow noontide?"

"Not then, Pearl," said the minister, "but another time!"

"And what other time?" persisted the child.

"At the great judgment day!" whispered the minister,—and, strangely enough, the sense that he was a professional teacher of the truth impelled him to answer the child so. "Then, and there, before the judgment-seat, thy mother, and thou, and I, must stand together! But the daylight of this world shall not see our meeting!"

Pearl laughed again.

But, before Mr. Dimmesdale had done speaking, a light gleamed far and wide over all the muffled sky. It was doubtless caused by one of those meteors, which the night-watcher may so often observe burning out to waste, in the vacant regions of the atmosphere. So powerful was its radiance, that it thoroughly illuminated the dense medium of cloud betwixt the sky and earth. The great vault brightened, like the dome of an immense lamp. It showed the familiar scene of the street, with the distinctness of midday, but also with the awfulness that is always imparted to familiar objects by an unaccustomed light. The wooden houses, with their jutting stories and quaint gable-peaks; the door-steps and the thresholds, with the early grass springing up about them; the garden-plots, black with freshly turned earth; the wheel-track, little worn, and, even in the market-place, margined with green on either side; —all were visible, but with a singularity of aspect that seemed to give another moral interpretation to the things of this world than they had ever borne before. And there stood the minister, with his hand over his heart; and Hester Prynne, with the embroidered letter glimmering on her bosom; and little Pearl, herself a symbol, and the connecting link between those two. They stood in the noon of that strange and solemn splendor, as if it were the light that is to reveal all secrets, and the daybreak that shall unite all who belong to one another.

There was witchcraft in little Pearl's eyes; and her face, as she glanced upward at the minister, wore that naughty smile which made its expression frequently so elvish. She withdrew her hand from Mr. Dimmesdale's, and pointed across the street. But he clasped both his hands over his breast, and cast his eyes towards the zenith.

Nothing was more common, in those days, than to interpret all meteoric appearances, and other natural phenomena, that occurred with less regularity than the rise and set of sun and moon, as so many revelations from a supernatural source. Thus, a blazing spear, a sword of flame, a bow, or a sheaf of arrows, seen in the midnight sky, prefigured Indian warfare. Pestilence was known to have been foreboded by a shower of crimson light. We doubt whether any marked event, for good or evil, ever befell New England, from its settlement down to Revolutionary times, of which the inhabitants had not been previously warned by some spectacle of this nature. Not seldom, it had been seen by multitudes. Oftener, however, its credibility rested on the faith of some lonely eyewitness, who beheld the wonder through the colored, magnifying, and distorting medium of his imagination, and shaped it more distinctly in his after-thought. It was, indeed, a majestic idea, that the destiny of nations should be revealed, in these awful hieroglyphics, on the cope of heaven. A scroll so wide might not be deemed too expansive for Providence to write a people's doom upon. The belief was a favorite one with our forefathers, as betokening that their infant commonwealth was under a celestial guardianship of peculiar intimacy and strictness. But what shall we say, when an individual discovers a revelation, addressed to himself alone, on the same vast sheet of record! In such a case, it could only be the symptom of a highly disordered mental state, when a man, rendered morbidly self-contemplative by long, intense, and secret pain, had extended his egotism over the whole expanse of nature, until the firmament itself should appear no more than a fitting page for his soul's history and fate.

We impute it, therefore, solely to the disease in his own eye and heart, that the minister, looking upward to the zenith, beheld there the appearance of an immense letter,—the letter A,—marked out in lines of dull red light. Not but the meteor may have shown itself at that point, burning duskily through a veil of cloud; but with no such shape as his guilty imagination gave it; or, at least, with so little definiteness, that another's guilt might have seen another symbol in it.

There was a singular circumstance that characterized Mr. Dimmesdale's psychological state, at this moment. All the time that he gazed upward to the zenith, he was, nevertheless, perfectly aware that little Pearl was pointing her finger towards old Roger Chillingworth, who stood at no great distance from the scaffold. The minister appeared to see him, with the same glance that discerned the miraculous letter. To his features, as to all other objects, the meteoric light imparted a new expression; or it might well be that the physician was not careful then, as at all other times, to hide the malevolence with which he looked upon his victim. Certainly, if the meteor kindled up the sky, and disclosed the earth, with an awfulness that admonished Hester Prynne and the clergyman of the day of judgment, then might Roger Chillingworth have passed with them for the arch-fiend, standing there, with a smile and scowl, to claim his own. So vivid was the expression, or so intense the minister's perception of it, that it seemed still to remain painted on the darkness, after the meteor had vanished, with an effect as if the street and all things else were at once annihilated.

"Who is that man, Hester?" gasped Mr. Dimmesdale, overcome with terror. "I shiver at him! Dost thou know the man? I hate him, Hester!"

She remembered her oath, and was silent.

"I tell thee, my soul shivers at him," muttered the minister again. "Who is he? Who is he? Canst thou do nothing for me? I have a nameless horror of the man."

"Minister," said little Pearl, "I can tell thee who he is!"

"Quickly, then, child!" said the minister, bending his ear close to her lips. "Quickly!—and as low as thou canst whisper."

Pearl mumbled something into his ear, that sounded, indeed, like human language, but was only such gibberish as children may be heard amusing themselves with, by the hour together. At all events, if it involved any secret information in regard to old Roger Chillingworth, it was in a tongue unknown to the erudite clergyman, and did but increase the bewilderment of his mind. The elvish child then laughed aloud.

"Dost thou mock me now?" said the minister.

"Thou wast not bold!—thou wast not true!" answered the child. "Thou wouldst not promise to take my hand, and mother's hand, to-morrow noontide!"

"Worthy Sir," said the physician, who had now advanced to the foot of the platform. "Pious Master Dimmesdale! can this be you? Well, well, indeed! We men of study, whose heads are in our books, have need to be straitly looked after! We dream in our waking moments, and walk in our sleep. Come, good Sir, and my dear friend, I pray you, let me lead you home!"

"How knewest thou that I was here?" asked the minister, fearfully.

"Verily, and in good faith," answered Roger Chillingworth, "I knew nothing of the matter. I had spent the better part of the night at the bedside of the worshipful Governor Winthrop, doing what my poor skill might to give him ease. He going home to a better world, I, likewise, was on my way homeward, when this strange light shone out. Come with me, I beseech you, Reverend Sir; else you will be poorly able to do Sabbath duty to-morrow. Aha! see now, how they trouble the brain,—these books!—these books! You should study less, good Sir, and take a little pastime; or these night-whimseys will grow upon you!"

"I will go home with you," said Mr. Dimmesdale.

With a chill despondency, like one awaking, all nerveless, from an ugly dream, he yielded himself to the physician, and was led away.

The next day, however, being the Sabbath, he preached a discourse which was held to be the richest and most powerful, and the most replete with heavenly influences, that had ever proceeded from his lips. Souls, it is said, more souls than one, were brought to the truth by the efficacy of that sermon, and vowed within themselves to cherish a holy gratitude towards Mr. Dimmesdale throughout the long hereafter. But, as he came down the pulpit-steps, the gray-bearded sexton met him, holding up a black glove, which the minister recognized as his own.

"It was found," said the sexton, "this morning, on the scaffold, where evil-doers are set up to public shame. Satan dropped it there, I take it, intending a scurrilous jest against your reverence. But, indeed, he was blind and foolish, as he ever and always is. A pure hand needs no glove to cover it!"

"Thank you, my good friend," said the minister gravely, but

startled at heart; for, so confused was his remembrance, that he had almost brought himself to look at the events of the past night as visionary. "Yes, it seems to be my glove indeed!"

"And, since Satan saw fit to steal it, your reverence must needs handle him without gloves, henceforward," remarked the old sexton, grimly smiling. "But did your reverence hear of the portent that was seen last night? A great red letter in the sky,—the letter A,—which we interpret to stand for Angel. For, as our good Governor Winthrop was made an angel this past night, it was doubtless held fit that there should be some notice thereof!"

"No," answered the minister. "I had not heard of it."

AFTERWORD

The first three chapters of the novel had been set in the Boston marketplace and had centered on the scaffold of the pillory. Hester had stood there with little Pearl in her arms, while Dimmesdale, from the high balcony of the meeting house, exhorted her to reveal the name of Pearl's father. "Believe me, Hester," he had said, "though he were to step down from a high place, and stand beside thee, on thy pedestal of shame, yet better were it so, than to hide a guilty heart through life." Now seven years have passed and we have reached the center of the novel, the twelfth of its twenty-four chapters (with the last of them serving as an epilogue). The setting is the same as that of the first three chapters, and Dimmesdale has obeyed his own exhortation by climbing to the platform where Hester had stood. But he has obeyed it only in part, since he stands there at midnight with no one to hear his confession. Not until a final scene, portrayed in the last chapter before the epilogue, will Dimmesdale stand there at noon, with Hester and Pearl at his side, and reveal his guilty heart to the community. The action of the novel will end where it began, on the scaffold of the pillory.

This architectural roundness was a new element in longer prose fictions. It appeared at a time when the novel was regarded as a loose and undemanding form; when it was often written and published in monthly numbers, with the author not knowing at the end of No. 5 what was going to happen in No. 6; when characters proliferated and episodes might be introduced because they were entertaining in themselves, no matter how faint their connection with a general plan. Hawthorne went to the opposite extreme by adopting a strict form close to that of classical French drama. From the beginning of his novel there is not an episode, not a speech by one of the characters or an apparently casual remark by the author, that does not contribute to the mood and foreshadow the end of the story. There are some expository chapters, but the general method is scenic: that is, the characters act their parts as if on a stage. Indeed, *The Scarlet Letter* has been described as a Racinian tragedy in five acts.

Placed as it is at the center of the book, "The Minister's Vigil" would correspond to the third act of a tragedy. It is not the climax, for that will come in the following act, when Hester and Dimmesdale have their meeting in the forest. It marks, however, a decisive change in tempo. The first half of the book has covered a space of seven years, but now events are coming fast, and the second half—before the epilogue—will cover only fifteen days. Essentially the present scene is a dramatic tableau, like the other two scenes around the scaffold; each of them presents all the named characters in the story. There are only seven of these, for Hawthorne—in contrast with the prodigality of Dickens and Thackeray—is always economical with his *dramatis personae*. Besides the four principals, there are Governor Bellingham (representing secular authority), the Reverend John Wilson (representing true piety), and Mistress Hibbins the witch-lady (representing evil and rebellion). Their silent appearance during the minister's vigil reminds us that the drama, though it seems to be played within the hearts of individuals, is also a matter of their relations with the Boston community.

Unlike many novelists and dramatists, Hawthorne makes little or no use of background music. The fact is that he showed no interest in music and could not carry a tune. There are, however, two sound effects in the present chapter: Dimmesdale's shriek of agony that does not awaken the town, and his peal of sardonic laughter that is unexpectedly answered by little Pearl. More characteristic are the lighting effects in which Hawthorne seems to delight, as if his dramas were acted on a stage. In the present chapter there is Father Wilson's lantern, which reveals the Boston houses in their "minute particulars" while casting a halo round his saintly head; and there is the meteor which, as it gleams through the clouds, reveals the whole town in a new aspect, perhaps closer to the truth than its look by day. Chillingworth, for example, loses his daytime benignity and scowls like a fiend.

The author's point of view is that of the so-called "omniscient narrator," but, as we have found in other cases, there are limits to his omniscience. He sees deeply into the minister's heart; he sees into Hester's too, though not quite so deeply (and not at all in the present chapter); and he has some inner knowledge of Chillingworth. On the other hand, he is puzzled as well as fascinated by little Pearl and merely reports her actions, as he does those of the minor characters. His story deals with Boston in the seventeenth century (the actual years are 1642-1649), but he does not let us forget that he is a man of modern times and that his knowledge of the Bay Colony comes from brooding over documents. Sometimes he throws in a historical fact or explains colonial customs for the reader's benefit. Sometimes he confesses to being in doubt; "perhaps," he says, and "possibly," and "doubtless" (in the sense of "we might as well believe, since we can't be certain"). That is Hawthorne's famous ambiguity, which is also displayed when he wonders whether a scarlet A really appeared in the heavens or whether it was one of the minister's delusions. "We impute it . . . solely to the disease in his own eye and heart," Hawthorne says, giving a naturalistic interpretation of the miracle. At the end of the chapter, however, the reader learns that others have seen "A great red letter in the sky." Hawthorne has read and dreamed so much about the seventeenth century that he *wants* to share the colonists' belief in witchcraft and special portents—at least while he is telling the story.

Hawthorne's style, even in his own day, was regarded as graceful, correct, and a little old-fashioned. It has an eighteenth-century quality owed to his reading of Dr. Johnson, together with older touches of his favorite John Bunyan. His fictional technique includes some features that would later be condemned as awkward: for example, authorial comments, apothegms, and remarks addressed to the reader. In its use of the scenic method, however, it anticipates Henry James, and in its concern with architectural balance it anticipates more recent authors, even Joyce and Thomas Mann. As for his notion of man's fate, it was closer to the old New England Calvinism than it was to the optimism of his Concord neighbors, yet it also looked forward to such later developments as psychoanalysis and psychosomatic medicine. In retrospect Hawthorne seems a curious mixture of past and future, of the antiquarian and the revolutionary, and hence a subject for endless study.

Moby-Dick; or, The Whale (1851)

HERMAN MELVILLE (1819-1891) came of distinguished ancestry, Scottish on one side, Dutch on the other. One of his grandfathers was Major Thomas Melville of Boston, celebrated in Holmes's poem "The Last Leaf," and the other was General Peter Gansevoort, the stolid defender of Fort Stanwix, who ruled as a patroon in much of Saratoga County, New York. Allan Melville, the novelist's father, was a gentlemanly merchant who failed in business, moved from New York City to Albany, and died when the boy was twelve, leaving behind him an imperious widow, eight children—Herman was the second son— and a small factory besieged by creditors. The two oldest boys were taken out of school. Gansevoort Melville, then sixteen, tried to manage the factory, but lost it in the panic of 1837. Herman ran errands in a bank, clerked in a store, taught in a school where he was young enough to be a pupil, and finally went to sea.

In 1839 he made his first voyage before the mast, on the Liverpool packet *St. Lawrence*. He discovered during five weeks in England that industrial slums could be worse than genteel poverty in Albany, but he enjoyed life on shipboard for all its discomforts. After vain efforts to earn a living ashore, Melville became part of what was then the largest American maritime industry. Whale oil, in the years before petroleum was discovered in Pennsylvania (1859), had become one of the world's basic commodities. There were more than nine hundred whalers afloat, and five-sixths of them hailed from American ports, chiefly in New England. From the port of Fairhaven, across the harbor from New

Bedford, the whaler *Acushnet* set sail January 3, 1841, with Melville as one of the foremast hands.

The high-spirited young man tired of the voyage after eighteen months and jumped ship at Nukahiva, in the Marquesas. There he spent four weeks as guest and prisoner of the Taipi, a tribe of fierce warriors reputed to be cannibals; then he was rescued and enrolled by the Australian whaler *Lucy Ann*. When that ill-commanded vessel reached Tahiti, he took part in a mutiny and was imprisoned for some weeks in a very informal jail; "Hotel de Calabooza," the sailors called it. Soon he escaped by sea to Moorea, where he was enrolled as harpooneer on the *Charles and Henry* of Nantucket; but that was the last of his whaling voyages. Discharged in the Hawaiian Islands at his own request, he spent some months "on the beach," then enlisted as ordinary seaman on the U.S. Frigate *United States*, which cruised off Peru, rounded the Horn, and finally anchored at Boston Navy Yard October 3, 1844. Melville was paid off, after nearly four years at sea.

Having rejoined his family in a village near Albany, he recounted his adventures to neighbors and friends. "Why don't you put it all into a book?" they kept asking. He put it into a series of books, beginning with *Typee* (1846), a somewhat fictionized account of his four weeks (which he stretched into four months) among the fierce tribesmen of Nukahiva. *Typee* is the ancestor of all South Sea romances, from Pierre Loti (*Le Mariage de Loti*, 1882) to Somerset Maugham and Nordhoff and Hall (*Mutiny on the Bounty*, 1932). Next came *Omoo* (1847), based on the *Lucy Ann* mutiny and its aftermath. Melville was becoming a figure in the literary world. The famous library of Evert Duyckinck had been opened to him, and he was reading voraciously in many fields, including metaphysics.

Mardi (1849), his next romance, showed the results of that reading, and they were not to the liking of critics, who dismissed the book as "a transcendental *Gulliver*, or *Robinson Crusoe* run mad." The critics, and the public too, much preferred *Redburn*, which he published the same year; once again it was a straightforward narrative, based in this instance on Melville's first voyage to Liverpool. It contained scarcely a hint of his deeper feelings or his speculations about good and evil. "I hope I shall never write such a book again," Melville said in a letter; but he was harried by debts and had to consider what the public wanted. *White-Jacket* (1850) was another factual narrative, with only a few philosophical musings; this time he was remembering his year on an American man-of-war. It proved to be his last popular success.

Melville had married the only daughter of Chief Justice Lemuel

Shaw of Massachusetts, and in the summer of 1850 the couple moved with their first child to a farm in the Berkshires. For two years Hawthorne was one of their distant neighbors. The meeting of the two novelists— at a picnic on August 5—was an event that changed Melville's life. At the time he had almost finished a new book, "a romantic, fanciful & literal & most enjoyable presentment of the Whale Fishery," as his friend Evert Duyckinck said in a letter; apparently Duyckinck had been reading the vanished first draft of *Moby-Dick*. Now, influenced by what he called the "blackness" of Hawthorne's work and inspired by his reading of Shakespeare's tragedies, Melville spent a year reworking the novel. He said when it was finished, "I have written a very wicked book, and feel spotless as a lamb."

From the commercial point of view, the publication of *Moby-Dick*, late in 1851, was a disaster that ruined Melville's career. The critics, English and American, didn't know what to make of it and the public was completely incurious. *Pierre; or, The Ambiguities* (1852) confirmed a general impression that his writing had become wayward and in- comprehensible. His next three books—*Israel Potter* (1855), a historical novel; *The Piazza Tales* (1856), collecting the best of his shorter work; and *The Confidence Man* (1857), a bitter and confusing satire—were all commercial failures. While still in his thirties, Melville abandoned the writing of fiction for publication.

He lived on, and wrote on too, until 1891, almost totally forgotten by the American literary world (though *Typee* and *Moby-Dick* were still read in England). Instead of prose he was writing poems, often in limping meters and with flashes of genius. *Battle-Pieces*, an 1866 col- lection, had some few readers, but three subsequent books of poetry were privately printed in very small editions. During his last years, however, Melville wrote and rewrote a novelette, *Billy Budd*, which, on its publica- tion long after his death, took rank among his major productions.

THE STORY

"Call me Ishmael," the narrator says. To cure a fit of depression, he decides to ship out on a whaler as a foremast hand. He makes his way to New Bedford and there meets Queequeg, a Polynesian harpooneer —"George Washington cannibalistically developed"—whose kindness and pagan faith are more rewarding to Ishmael than the cant of preachers and the avarice of landsmen. Faring on to Nantucket by packet schooner, the new friends sign aboard a mysterious whaler, the *Pequod*, owned by two Quaker merchants, Bildad and Peleg, who quote Scripture in defense of the dollar. The *Pequod* leaves harbor on a cold Christmas day under direction of the three mates: Starbuck, a true-hearted Nantucketer, Stubb, a Cape Codder, and Flask, from Martha's Vineyard. Besides Queequeg, the harpooneers are Daggoo, a gigantic African, and Tashtego, a Gay Head Indian. It is not until the vessel is nearing the tropics that Captain Ahab comes stumping out of the cabin on his ivory leg. A few days later he has the crew summoned to the quarter-deck and announces that the purpose of the voyage is to seek out Moby Dick, the great white whale that had crippled him. Clearly the mad captain identifies the whale with "all evil," but he also hints that Moby Dick is a mask for some vision of absolute truth: "Strike through the mask!"

The voyage continues, with the narrative interrupted by scholarly and fact-filled digressions that cover the whole field of whales and whaling. After cruising fruitlessly in the South Atlantic, the *Pequod* sails eastward to the Straits of Sunda, while undergoing a series of marvels and misfortunes. It makes nine "gams" or meetings with other vessels, most of which have chased the white whale; each vessel is invested with national characteristics or is made to represent some attitude toward good and evil. At last, having emerged into the open Pacific, and having reached the whaling grounds near the equator where Ahab lost his leg, the *Pequod* sights its prey. It is Ahab himself who first shouts, "There she blows!—there she blows! A hump like a snow-hill! It is Moby Dick!"

The chase lasts three days. On the first, the whale bites Ahab's boat in two. On the second, it wrecks all three of the other whaleboats, though no one is lost but the Parsee Fedallah, Ahab's "evil shadow." Three new boats are rigged; and on the third day the chase continues with the chapter here reprinted. It ends the book, except for a brief Epilogue spoken by Ishmael, who repeats the words spoken to Job: "And I only am escaped alone to tell thee."

Chapter 135. The Chase—Third Day

The morning of the third day dawned fair and fresh, and once more the solitary night-man at the fore-mast-head was relieved by crowds of the daylight look-outs, who dotted every mast and almost every spar.

"D'ye see him?" cried Ahab; but the whale was not yet in sight.

"In his infallible wake, though; but follow that wake, that's all. Helm there; steady, as thou goest, and hast been going. What a

lovely day again! were it a new-made world, and made for a sum-
mer-house to the angels, and this morning the first of its throwing
open to them, a fairer day could not dawn upon that world. Here's
food for thought, had Ahab time to think; but Ahab never thinks;
he only feels, feels, feels; *that's* tingling enough for mortal man!
to think's audacity. God only has that right and privilege. Thinking is, or ought to be, a coolness and a calmness; and our poor
hearts throb, and our poor brains beat too much for that. And yet,
I've sometimes thought my brain was very calm—frozen calm, this
old skull cracks so, like a glass in which the contents turned to
ice, and shiver it. And still this hair is growing now; this moment
growing, and heat must breed it; but no, it's like that sort of common grass that will grow anywhere, between the earthy clefts of
Greenland ice or in Vesuvius lava. How the wild winds blow it;
they whip it about me as the torn shreds of split sails lash the
tossed ship they cling to. A vile wind that has no doubt blown ere
this through prison corridors and cells, and wards of hospitals,
and ventilated them, and now comes blowing hither as innocent
as fleeces. Out upon it!—it's tainted. Were I the wind, I'd blow
no more on such a wicked, miserable world. I'd crawl somewhere
to a cave, and slink there. And yet, 'tis a noble and heroic thing, the
wind! who ever conquered it? In every fight it has the last and
bitterest blow. Run tilting at it, and you but run through it.
Ha! a coward wind that strikes stark naked men, but will not stand
to receive a single blow. Even Ahab is a braver thing—a nobler
thing than *that*. Would now the wind but had a body; but all the
things that most exasperate and outrage mortal man, all these
things are bodiless, but only bodiless as objects, not as agents.
There's a most special, a most cunning, oh, a most malicious difference! And yet, I say again, and swear it now, that there's something
all glorious and gracious in the wind. These warm Trade Winds,
at least, that in the clear heavens blow straight on, in strong and
steadfast, vigorous mildness; and veer not from their mark, however the baser currents of the sea may turn and tack, and mightiest
Mississippies of the land swift and swerve about, uncertain
where to go at last. And by the eternal Poles! these same Trades
that so directly blow my good ship on; these Trades, or something
like them—something so unchangeable, and full as strong, blow
my keeled soul along! To it! Aloft there! What d'ye see?"

"Nothing, sir."

"Nothing! and noon at hand! The doubloon goes a-begging!

See the sun! Aye, aye, it must be so. I've oversailed him. How, got the start? Aye, he's chasing *me* now; not I, *him*—that's bad; I might have known it, too. Fool! the lines—the harpoons he's towing. Aye, aye, I have run him by last night. About! about! Come down, all of ye, but the regular look outs! Man the braces!"

Steering as she had done, the wind had been somewhat on the Pequod's quarter, so that now being pointed in the reverse direction, the braced ship sailed hard upon the breeze as she re-churned the cream in her own white wake.

"Against the wind he now steers for the open jaw," murmured Starbuck to himself, as he coiled the new-hauled main-brace upon the rail. "God keep us, but already my bones feel damp within me, and from the inside wet my flesh. I misdoubt me that I disobey my God in obeying him!"

"Stand by to sway me up!" cried Ahab, advancing to the hempen basket. "We should meet him soon."

"Aye, aye, sir," and straightway Starbuck did Ahab's bidding, and once more Ahab swung on high.

A whole hour now passed; gold-beaten out to ages. Time itself now held long breaths with keen suspense. But at last, some three points off the weather bow, Ahab descried the spout again, and instantly from the three mast-heads three shrieks went up as if the tongues of fire had voiced it.

"Forehead to forehead I meet thee, this third time, Moby Dick! On deck there!—brace sharper up; crowd her into the wind's eye. He's too far off to lower yet, Mr. Starbuck. The sails shake! Stand over that helmsman with a top-maul! So, so; he travels fast, and I must down. But let me have one more good round look aloft here at the sea; there's time for that. An old, old sight, and yet somehow so young; aye, and not changed a wink since I first saw it, a boy, from the sand-hills of Nantucket! The same!—the same!—the same to Noah as to me. There's a soft shower to leeward. Such lovely leewardings! They must lead somewhere—to something else than common land, more palmy than the palms. Leeward! the white whale goes that way; look to windward, then; the better if the bitterer quarter. But good bye, good bye, old mast-head! What's this?—green? aye, tiny mosses in these warped cracks. No such green weather stains on Ahab's head! There's the difference now between man's old age and matter's. But aye, old mast, we both grow old together; sound in our hulls, though, are we not, my ship? Aye, minus a leg, that's all. By heaven this dead wood has the better of my live flesh every way. I can't compare with it; and I've known some ships made of dead trees outlast the lives of men made of the most vital stuff of vital fathers. What's that he said? he should still go before me, my pilot; and yet to be seen again? But where? Will I have eyes at the bottom of the sea, supposing I descend those endless stairs? and all night I've been sailing from him, wherever he did sink to. Aye, aye, like many more thou told'st direful truth as touching thyself. O Parsee; but, Ahab, there thy shot fell short. Good bye, mast-head—keep a good eye upon the whale, the while I'm gone. We'll talk to-morrow, nay, to-night, when the white whale lies down there, tied by head and tail."

He gave the word; and still gazing round him, was steadily lowered through the cloven blue air to the deck.

In due time the boats were lowered; but as standing in his shallop's stern, Ahab just hovered upon the point of the descent, he waved to the mate,—who held one of the tackle-ropes on deck— and bade him pause.

"Starbuck!"

"Sir?"

"For the third time my soul's ship starts upon this voyage, Starbuck."

"Aye, sir, thou wilt have it so."

"Some ships sail from their ports, and ever afterwards are missing, Starbuck!"

"Truth, sir: saddest truth."

"Some men die at ebb tide; some at low water; some at the full of the flood;—and I feel now like a billow that's all one crested comb, Starbuck. I am old;—shake hands with me, man."

Their hands met; their eyes fastened; Starbuck's tears the glue.

"Oh, my captain, my captain!—noble heart—go not—go not!— see, it's a brave man that weeps; how great the agony of the persuasion then!"

"Lower away!"—cried Ahab, tossing the mate's arm from him. "Stand by the crew!"

In an instant the boat was pulling round close under the stern.

"The sharks! the sharks!" cried a voice from the low cabin-window there; "O master, my master, come back!"

But Ahab heard nothing; for his own voice was high-lifted then; and the boat leaped on.

Yet the voice spake true; for scarce had he pushed from the

ship, when numbers of sharks, seemingly rising from out the dark waters beneath the hull, maliciously snapped at the blades of the oars, every time they dipped in the water; and in this way accompanied the boat with their bites. It is a thing not uncommonly happening to the whale-boats in those swarming seas; the sharks at times apparently following them in the same prescient way that vultures hover over the banners of marching regiments in the east. But these were the first sharks that had been observed by the Pequod since the White Whale had been first descried; and whether it was that Ahab's crew were all such tiger-yellow barbarians, and therefore their flesh more musky to the senses of the sharks—a matter sometimes well known to affect them,—however it was, they seemed to follow that one boat without molesting the others.

"Heart of wrought steel!" murmured Starbuck gazing over the side, and following with his eyes the receding boat—"canst thou yet ring boldly to that sight?—lowering thy keel among ravening sharks, and followed by them, open-mouthed to the chase; and this the critical third day?—For when three days flow together in one continuous intense pursuit; be sure the first is the morning, the second the noon, and the third the evening and the end of that thing—be that end what it may. Oh! my God! what is this that shoots through me, and leaves me so deadly calm, yet expectant,— fixed at the top of a shudder! Future things swim before me, as in empty outlines and skeletons; all the past is somehow grown dim. Mary, girl! thou fadest in pale glories behind me; boy! I seem to see but thy eyes grown wondrous blue. Strangest problems of life seem clearing; but clouds sweep between—Is my journey's end coming? My legs feel faint; like his who has footed it all day. Feel thy heart,—beats it yet? Stir thyself, Starbuck!— stave it off—move, move! speak aloud!—Mast-head there! See ye my boy's hand on the hill?—Crazed; aloft there—keep thy keenest eye upon the boats:—mark well the whale!—Ho! again!—drive off that hawk! see! he pecks—he tears the vane"—pointing to the red flag flying at the main-truck—"Ha! he soars away with it!—Where's the old man now? see'st thou that sight, oh Ahab!—shudder, shudder!"

The boats had not gone very far, when by a signal from the mast-heads—a downward pointed arm, Ahab knew that the whale had sounded; but intending to be near him at the next rising, he held on his way a little sideways from the vessel; the becharmed crew maintaining the profoundest silence, as the head-beat waves hammered and hammered against the opposing bow.

"Drive, drive in your nails, oh ye waves! to their uttermost heads drive them in! ye but strike a thing without a lid; and no coffin and no hearse can be mine:—and hemp only can kill me! Ha ha!"

Suddenly the waters around them slowly swelled in broad circles; then quickly upheaved, as if sideways sliding from a submerged berg of ice, swiftly rising to the surface. A low rumbling sound was heard; a subterraneous hum; and then all held their breaths; as bedraggled with trailing ropes, and harpoons, and lances, a vast form shot lengthwise, but obliquely from the sea. Shrouded in a thin drooping veil of mist, it hovered for a moment in the rainbowed air; and then fell swamping back into the deep. Crushed thirty feet upwards, the waters flashed for an instant like heaps of fountains, then brokenly sank in a shower of flakes, leaving the circling surface creamed like new milk round the marble trunk of the whale.

"Give way!" cried Ahab to the oarsmen, and the boats darted forward to the attack; but maddened by yesterday's fresh irons that corroded in him, Moby Dick seemed combinedly possessed by all the angels that fell from heaven. The wide tiers of welded tendons overspreading his broad white forehead, beneath the transparent skin, looked knitted together; as head on, he came churning his tail among the boats; and once more flailed them apart; spilling out the irons and lances from the two mates' boats, and dashing in one side of the upper part of their bows, but leaving Ahab's almost without a scar.

While Daggoo and Queequeg were stopping the strained planks; and as the whale swimming out from them, turned, and showed one entire flank as he shot by them again; at that moment a quick cry went up. Lashed round and round to the fish's back; pinioned in the turns upon turns in which, during the past night, the whale had reeled the involutions of the lines around him, the half torn body of the Parsee was seen; his sable raiment frayed to shreds; his distended eyes turned full upon old Ahab.

The harpoon dropped from his hand.

"Befooled, befooled!"—drawing in a long lean breath—"Aye, Parsee! I see thee again.—Aye, and thou goest before; and this, *this* then is the hearse that thou didst promise. But I hold thee to the last letter of thy word. Where is the second hearse? Away, mates, to the ship! those boats are useless now; repair them if ye can in time, and return to me; if not, Ahab is enough to die— Down, men! the first thing that but offers to jump from this boat I stand in, that thing I harpoon. Ye are not other men, but my arms and my legs; and so obey me.—Where's the whale? gone down again?"

But he looked too nigh the boat; for as if bent upon escaping with the corpse he bore, and as if the particular place of the last encounter had been but a stage in his leeward voyage, Moby Dick was now again steadily swimming forward; and had almost passed the ship,—which thus far had been sailing in the contrary direction to him, though for the present her headway had been stopped. He seemed swimming with his utmost velocity, and now only intent upon pursuing his own straight path in the sea.

"Oh! Ahab," cried Starbuck, "not too late is it, even now, the third day, to desist. See! Moby Dick seeks thee not. It is thou, thou, that madly seekest him!"

Setting sail to the rising wind, the lonely boat was swiftly impelled to leeward, by both oars and canvas. And at last when Ahab was sliding by the vessel, so near as plainly to distinguish Starbuck's face as he leaned over the rail, he hailed him to turn the vessel about, and follow him, not too swiftly, at a judicious interval. Glancing upwards he saw Tashtego, Queequeg, and Daggoo, eagerly mounting to the three mast-heads; while the oarsmen were rocking in the two staved boats which had just been hoisted to the side, and were busily at work in repairing them. One after the other, through the port-holes, as he sped, he also caught flying glimpses of Stubb and Flask, busying themselves on deck among bundles of new irons and lances. As he saw all this; as he heard the hammers in the broken boats; far other hammers seemed driving a nail into his heart. But he rallied. And now marking that the vane or flag was gone from the main-mast-head, he shouted to Tashtego, who had just gained that perch, to descend again for another flag, and a hammer and nails, and so nail it to the mast.

Whether fagged by the three days' running chase, and the resistance to his swimming in the knotted hamper he bore; or whether it was some latent deceitfulness and malice in him: whichever was true, the White Whale's way now began to abate, as it seemed, from the boat so rapidly nearing him once more; though indeed the whale's last start had not been so long a one as before. And still as Ahab glided over the waves the unpitying sharks accompanied him; and so pertinaciously stuck to the boat; and so continually bit at the plying oars, that the blades became jagged and crunched, and left small splinters in the sea, at almost every dip.

"Heed them not! those teeth but give new rowlocks to your oars. Pull on! 'tis the better rest, the shark's jaw than the yielding water."

"But at every bite, sir, the thin blades grow smaller and smaller!"

"They will last long enough! pull on!—But who can tell"—he muttered—"whether these sharks swim to feast on the whale or on Ahab?—But pull on! Aye, all alive, now—we near him. The helm! take the helm! let me pass,"—and so saying, two of the oarsmen helped him forward to the bows of the still flying boat.

At length as the craft was cast to one side, and ran ranging along with the White Whale's flank, he seemed strangely oblivious of its advance—as the whale sometimes will—and Ahab was fairly within the smoky mountain mist, which, thrown off from the whale's spout, curled round his great Monadnock[1] hump; he was even thus close to him; when, with body arched back, and both arms lengthwise high-lifted to the poise, he darted his fierce iron, and his far fiercer curse into the hated whale. As both steel and curse sank to the socket, as if sucked into a morass, Moby Dick sideways writhed; spasmodically rolled his nigh flank against the bow, and, without staving a hole in it, so suddenly canted the boat over, that had it not been for the elevated part of the gunwale to which he then clung, Ahab would once more have been tossed into the sea. As it was, three of the oarsmen—who foreknew not the precise instant of the dart, and were therefore unprepared for its effects—these were flung out; but so fell, that, in an instant two of them clutched the gunwale again, and rising to its level on a combing wave, hurled themselves bodily inboard again; the third man helplessly dropping astern, but still afloat and swimming.

Almost simultaneously, with a mighty volition of ungraduated, instantaneous swiftness, the White Whale darted through the weltering sea. But when Ahab cried out to the steersman to take new turns with the line, and hold it so; and commanded the crew to

[1 A solitary mountain in southern New Hampshire.]

turn round on their seats, and tow the boat up to the mark; the moment the treacherous line felt that double strain and tug, it snapped in the empty air!

"What breaks in me? Some sinew cracks!—'tis whole again; oars! oars! Burst in upon him!"

Hearing the tremendous rush of the sea-crashing boat, the whale wheeled round to present his blank forehead at bay; but in that evolution, catching sight of the nearing black hull of the ship; seemingly seeing in it the source of all his persecutions; bethinking it—it may be—a larger and nobler foe; of a sudden, he bore down upon its advancing prow, smiting his jaws amid fiery showers of foam.

Ahab staggered; his hand smote his forehead. "I grow blind; hands! stretch out before me that I may yet grope my way. Is't night?"

"The whale! The ship!" cried the cringing oarsmen.

"Oars! oars! Slope downwards to thy depths, O sea, that ere it be for ever too late, Ahab may slide this last, last time upon his mark! I see: the ship! the ship! Dash on, my men will ye not save my ship?"

But as the oarsmen violently forced their boat through the sledge-hammering seas, the before whale-smitten bow-ends of two planks burst through, and in an instant almost, the temporarily disabled boat lay nearly level with the waves; its half-wading, splashing crew, trying hard to stop the gap and bale out the pouring water.

Meantime, for that one beholding instant, Tashtego's masthead hammer remained suspended in his hand; and the red flag, half-wrapping him as with a plaid, then streamed itself straight out from him, as his own forward-flowing heart; while Starbuck and Stubb, standing upon the bowsprit beneath, caught sight of the down-coming monster just as soon as he.

"The whale, the whale! Up helm, up helm! Oh, all ye sweet powers of air, now hug me close! Let not Starbuck die, if die he must, in a woman's fainting fit. Up helm, I say—ye fools, the jaw—the jaw! Is this the end of all my bursting prayers? all my lifelong fidelities? Oh, Ahab, Ahab, lo, thy work. Steady! helmsman, steady. Nay, nay! Up helm again! He turns to meet us! Oh, his unappeasable brow drives on towards one, whose duty tells him he cannot depart. My God, stand by me now!"

"Stand not by me, but stand under me, whoever you are that

will now help Stubb; for Stubb, too, sticks here. I grin at thee, thou grinning whale! Who ever helped Stubb, or kept Stubb awake, but Stubb's own unwinking eye? And now poor Stubb goes to bed upon a mattrass that is all too soft; would it were stuffed with brushwood! I grin at thee, thou grinning whale! Look ye, sun, moon, and stars! I call ye assassins of as good a fellow as ever spouted up his ghost. For all that, I would yet ring glasses with thee, would ye but hand the cup! Oh, oh! oh, oh! thou grinning whale, but there'll be plenty of gulping soon! Why fly ye not, O Ahab! For me, off shoes and jacket to it; let Stubb die in his drawers! A most mouldy and oversalted death, though;—cherries! cherries! cherries! Oh, Flask, for one red cherry ere we die!"

"Cherries? I only wish that we were where they grow. Oh, Stubb, I hope my poor mother's drawn my part-pay ere this; if not, few coppers will now come to her, for the voyage is up."

From the ship's bows, nearly all the seamen now hung inactive; hammers, bits of plank, lances, and harpoons, mechanically retained in their hands, just as they had darted from their various employments; all their enchanted eyes intent upon the whale, which from side to side strangely vibrating his predestinating head, sent a broad band of overspreading semicircular foam before him as he rushed. Retribution, swift vengeance, eternal malice were in his whole aspect, and spite of all that mortal man could do, the solid white buttress of his forehead smote the ship's starboard bow, till men and timbers reeled. Some fell flat upon their faces. Like dislodged trucks, the heads of the harpooneers aloft shook on their bull-like necks. Through the breach, they heard the waters pour, as mountain torrents down a flume.

"The ship! The hearse!—the second hearse!" cried Ahab from the boat; "its wood could only be American!"

Diving beneath the settling ship, the whale ran quivering along its keel; but turning under water, swiftly shot to the surface again, far off the other bow, but within a few yards of Ahab's boat, where, for a time, he lay quiescent.

"I turn my body from the sun. What ho, Tashtego! let me hear thy hammer. Oh! ye three unsurrendered spires of mine; thou uncracked keel; and only god-bullied hull; thou firm deck, and haughty helm, and Pole-pointed prow,—death-glorious ship! must ye then perish, and without me? Am I cut off from the last fond pride of meanest shipwrecked captains? Oh, lonely death on lonely life! Oh, now I feel my topmost greatness lies in my topmost grief. Ho, ho! from all your furthest bounds, pour ye now in, ye bold billows of my whole foregone life, and top this one piled comber of my death! Towards thee I roll, thou all-destroying but unconquering whale; to the last I grapple with thee; from hell's heart I stab at thee; for hate's sake I spit my last breath at thee. Sink all coffins and all hearses to one common pool! and since neither can be mine, let me then tow to pieces, while still chasing thee, though tied to thee, thou damned whale! *Thus,* I give up the spear!"

The harpoon was darted; the stricken whale flew forward; with igniting velocity the line ran through the groove;—ran foul. Ahab stooped to clear it; he did clear it; but the flying turn caught him round the neck, and voicelessly as Turkish mutes bowstring their victim, he was shot out of the boat, ere the crew knew he was gone. Next instant, the heavy eye-splice in the rope's final end flew out of the stark-empty tub, knocked down an oarsman, and smiting the sea, disappeared in its depths.

For an instant, the tranced boat's crew stood still; then turned. "The ship? Great God, where is the ship?" Soon they through dim, bewildering mediums saw her sidelong fading phantom, as in the gaseous Fata Morgana; only the uppermost masts out of water; while fixed by infatuation, or fidelity, or fate, to their once lofty perches, the pagan harpooners still maintained their sinking lookouts on the sea. And now, concentric circles seized the lone boat itself, and all its crew, and each floating oar, and every lance-pole, and spinning, animate and inanimate, all round and round in one vortex, carried the smallest chip of the Pequod out of sight.

But as the last whelmings intermixingly poured themselves over the sunken head of the Indian at the mainmast, leaving a few inches of the erect spar yet visible, together with long streaming yards of the flag, which calmly undulated, with ironical coincidings, over the destroying billows they almost touched;—at that instant, a red arm and a hammer hovered backwardly uplifted in the open air, in the act of nailing the flag faster and yet faster to the subsiding spar. A sky-hawk that tauntingly had followed the maintruck downwards from its natural home among the stars, pecking at the flag, and incommoding Tashtego there; this bird now chanced to intercept its broad fluttering wing between the hammer and the wood; and simultaneously feeling that etherial thrill, the submerged savage beneath, in his death-gasp, kept his hammer frozen there; and so the bird of heaven, with archangelic shrieks, and his imperial beak thrust upwards, and his whole captive form folded in the flag of Ahab, went down with his ship, which, like Satan, would not sink to hell till she had dragged a living part of heaven along with her, and helmeted herself with it.

Now small fowls flew screaming over the yet yawning gulf; a sullen white surf beat against its steep sides; then all collapsed, and the great shroud of the sea rolled on as it rolled five thousand years ago.

AFTERWORD

Moby-Dick introduces into the novel another line of descent than the usual one from Cervantes to Defoe, Richardson, Fielding, and Scott. These were not Melville's favorite authors, and in fact he read comparatively little fiction, being more attracted by poetry, travel narratives, and, in a broad sense, metaphysics. His early books, except *Mardi*, were essentially "voyages" like those in Hakluyt. When he set to work on his grandest theme, the whale fishery, it seemed to demand a treatment that was completely new in prose fiction; almost all its antecedents were in poetry.

Shakespeare was the great antecedent, especially in the plays that Melville called the "black" tragedies: *Hamlet, Lear, Timon of Athens*, which he had been rereading excitedly. The Shakespearean element in *Moby-Dick* is so pervasive that some critics have interpreted the book as a five-act tragedy; but it does not lend itself to the stage—or even to the cinema, as two or three directors have found to their cost. Unlike *The Scarlet Letter*, for example, it is not essentially dramatic for all the stage devices it employs: soliloquies, asides, and stage directions ("Enter Ahab: Then, all"). It has the somewhat looser form of an epic, and on this side—as Newton Arvin was the first to point out—it has another antecedent in the great Portuguese poet Camoens, author of *The Lusiads* (1572), an epic that recounts the first voyage of Vasco da Gama. Perhaps it is because of *The Lusiads* that Captain Ahab sails eastward round the Cape of Good Hope, like Gama, instead of westward round the Horn as Melville had done in the *Acushnet*.

As the first novel (or romance) conceived on the lines of an epic poem, *Moby-Dick* was to have illustrious successors. *War and Peace* (1869) has qualities which, as we shall see, closely suggest those of the *Iliad*, though still it is a question whether Tolstoy thought of Homer

as a model. Joyce did think of him and borrowed the outline of the
Odyssey for his *Ulysses* (1922), but he was approaching another genre,
the mock-epic, when he chose a cuckold as hero. Melville is more faithful
to epic precedents, even in such minor matters as his use of Homeric—or
extended—similes. Epic poets since Homer have usually offered invocations to the Muse. Melville does not mention the Muse, but his
novel is full of invocations, usually offered at the end of chapters. The
one at the end of Chapter 26 has often been cited: "If, then, to meanest
mariners, and renegades, and castaways, I shall hereafter ascribe high
qualities, though dark; weave round them tragic graces; if even the
most mournful, perchance the most abused, among them all, shall at
times lift himself to the exalted mounts. . . . Bear me out in it, thou
great democratic God!" He is investing his characters with epic dignity.
As for the supernatural element in older epics, it is represented in the
novel by Moby Dick himself, who corresponds in some measure to
Adamastor in *The Lusiads*, wreaker of storms and malignant Spirit of
the Cape.

"A prose epic" we might call the book in short, but the prose is
often confusingly close to poetry. In this final chapter the rhythm
is heavily iambic—that is, each unstressed syllable is likely to be followed
by a stressed syllable—a pattern that departs from the usual lighter,
more rapid rhythm of prose. Ahab's soliloquies, including the one that
begins on the first page, can be scanned in large part as Shakespearean
blank verse:

God only has that right and privilege.

a coward wind that strikes stark naked men,
but will not stand to receive a single blow.

In general the language is richly emotive and adorned; it makes full
use of devices like repetition, assonance, and alliteration, which most
prose writers try to avoid. "Here's food for thought, had Ahab time
to think," the mad captain says in another blank-verse line; and "think"
is quickly followed by "thinks," "think's," and "thinking." "How the wild
winds blow it," he says; and in the next few sentences "wind" is repeated
seven times. "Mightiest Mississippies" is only one example of alliteration.
Later there will be a phrase, also in blank verse, that the author must
have relished: "*f*ixed by in*f*atuation, or *f*idelity, or *f*ate"—seven words
in a pattern of shifting vowels against repeated consonants. Melville
liked to find new forms and functions for more or less familiar words,
changing nouns into verbs and using verbal nouns in their unfamiliar

plurals: "last whelmings," for example, and "ironical coincidings," and "Such lovely leewardings!" He also liked to invent compound epithets, as, in the present chapter, "tiger-yellow barbarians," "whale-smitten bow-ends," and "god-bullied hull," among many others. In short, he was straining the resources of language to the utmost, as poets often try to do. It is no accident that the language of *Moby-Dick* has had a deeper influence on American poets—Hart Crane and Charles Olson, to mention only two—than on American novelists.

But poets writing epics or tragedies must face the same problems of narrative form that novelists face. "Form," says Kenneth Burke in a definition that applies to all the narrative arts, "is the creation of an appetite in the mind of an auditor, and the adequate satisfying of that appetite." A better word than "appetite" might be "expectations." At any rate, the preceding 134 chapters of *Moby-Dick* have created a series of expectations, and now in a final chapter they must all be satisfied. Moreover—as Burke says elsewhere in the same essay, "The Psychology of Form"—it is better if they are satisfied in an unexpected fashion, so that fulfillment can be combined with surprise.

So far this anthology of the novel has not dealt with the problem of final chapters, except in the case of *Werther*, a short and relatively uncomplicated book. Almost always the final chapter is called on to serve special purposes. In many old-fashioned novels it takes the place of an epilogue or coda, telling the reader what happened afterward and returning him to the everyday world. If the final chapter is not an epilogue, the novelist will use it to carry the action to a peak, thus avoiding anticlimax, which he regards as a capital crime. Melville, besides this problem of intensifying the action at its final moment, has to meet other conditions of a more specific nature in *Moby-Dick*. Thus, Ahab must encounter the whale for the last time. He must then die, and in a manner that accords with the prophecies made by Fedallah, whose part in the novel corresponds to that of the witches in *Macbeth*. (Fedallah has said in Chapter 117 that there will be neither hearse nor coffin for Ahab; that before death he will have seen two hearses in the sea; that only hemp can kill him; and that Fedallah himself will go before him as pilot.) The reader has been led to expect, moreover, that the *Pequod* will be lost with all its crew but one man, leaving only Ishmael to tell the story.

The chapter as written meets all those conditions, usually in a fashion that combines fulfillment with surprise. To mention only a few incidents, the *Pequod* has oversailed the whale during the night, so that Ahab exclaims, "Aye, he's chasing *me* now; not I, *him*." Ahab has himself hoisted to the masthead for a last retrospective look at the ocean. Here one notes the feeling, proper to a final chapter, of things coming to an end—as one also notes it in Starbuck's handclasp and in his soliloquy: "For when three days flow together in one continuous intense pursuit; be sure the first is the morning, the second the noon, and the third the evening and the end of the thing." When Ahab's boat is lowered after the whale, a voice from the cabin cries, "O master, my master, come back!" The voice is that of Pip, the demented cabin boy, and he is playing the part of the fool in *King Lear*, who speaks from a mad sanity. Each of Fedallah's prophecies is fulfilled, but not in a fashion the reader might have expected. Thus, Moby Dick himself is one of the two hearses, since he bears Fedallah's corpse on his back, and the *Pequod* is the other hearse, with its crew of men about to die. Each of the principal characters makes a revealing last speech or gesture. The pagan harpooneers cling to the three mastheads as the vessel goes down, Starbuck stands grimly at his post, and Stubb, in another Shakespearean touch, calls for "cherries! cherries! cherries! Oh, Flask, for one red cherry ere we die!"

For all its epic rather than dramatic structure, the book is suffused with Shakespeare from beginning to end. In Shakespeare's tragedies there is usually a final moment of self-awareness in which the hero comes to terms with his limitations and accepts the inevitability of his defeat. The corresponding moment in this chapter is Ahab's last great outburst, uttered after the *Pequod* has sunk and before he launches another harpoon into Moby Dick: "Oh, lonely death on lonely life! Oh, now I feel my topmost greatness lies in my topmost grief." Like Ahab, the author himself was seeking some ultimate truth, and—as he was to indicate in a quatrain written many years later—he thought that Shakespeare, of all writers, had come closest to finding it.

> No utter surprise can come to him
> Who reaches Shakespeare's final core;
> That which we seek and shun is there,
> Man's final lore.

Bleak House (1853)

CHARLES DICKENS (1812-1870) spent the happiest years of his childhood near the dockyard at Chatham, in the pleasant county of Kent, and he always regarded himself as a Kentishman. But he left the county and was taken from school at the age of nine, when his family removed to a shabby quarter of London. From that time he suffered the hardships that are the lot of many boys in his novels. His improvident father—the model for Mr. Micawber in *David Copperfield*—was sent to Marshalsea Prison for not paying his debts. Charles, the second of eight children, was then eleven. Most of the family moved into the prison and lived there in some comfort—they even had a maid—but Charles was put to work in a warehouse pasting labels on pots of blacking for a wage of six shillings a week, on which he lived as best he could for more than a year. The experience gave him a feeling of horror and indignation that he retained to the end of his life.

After he was released from the blacking warehouse and his father from prison, as the result of a legacy, he spent two years at a boys' academy. It was his last formal schooling, but he had been a voracious reader since his Kentish days. His father owned a little collection of works by standard novelists—Cervantes, Defoe, Lesage, Fielding, Smollett, Goldsmith—and, as Charles read them, he imagined himself in the role of each hero in turn. His favorite books were Smollett's *Roderick Random* (1748) and Goldsmith's *Vicar of Wakefield* (1766), both of which helped to shape his conception of the novel.

At the age of fifteen he became a junior law clerk, like several of the characters in *Bleak House*. He spent his nights studying shorthand, until he could take notes as rapidly as anyone in England. At nineteen, when he was hired as parliamentary reporter for a newspaper, the *True Sun*, he must have been the youngest man in the gallery of the House of Commons. He was doggedly ambitious, enterprising, full of nervous energy, and when he moved from one newspaper to another, it was at a higher salary. While on the *Morning Chronicle*, in 1836, he married Catherine Hogarth, a daughter—there were eight—of one of the chief editors. People would say much later that he had married the wrong daughter, since he got along better with two of Catherine's sisters. Also in 1836 he published his first book, *Sketches by Boz*, a collection of his magazine and newspaper pieces.

The Posthumous Papers of the Pickwick Club started as a journalistic venture. An illustrator named Seymour wanted to do a series of comic drawings, and the prospective publishers hired Dickens to write sketches that he could illustrate. Text and pictures began appearing in monthly instalments, of which the first four had no great success. To complicate matters, Seymour blew out his brains, and the publishers had to find a replacement, though they also thought of abandoning the venture. Then, in the fifth instalment, Dickens introduced Sam Weller as a foil to Pickwick, and suddenly everyone in England was reading the new serial. After it appeared as a book in 1837, when Dickens was twenty-five, he was famous all over Europe.

In the next four years he published four novels—*Oliver Twist* (1838), *Nicholas Nickleby* (1839), *The Old Curiosity Shop* (1841), and *Barnaby Rudge* (1841)—all loosely constructed, brimful of vitality, teeming with grotesque characters, and more widely read than the work of any other living English novelist. They were even more popular in the United States than at home, partly owing to the fact that they were not protected by copyright and could be sold at very low prices. *Martin Chuzzlewit* (1844) was printed like a newspaper and peddled in the streets of New York for 12½ cents a copy.

On the European continent, Balzac was Dickens' rival, and they had other points of resemblance besides their popularity and immense fecundity. Both men rose to social positions that they found more and more costly to maintain. Dickens' lecture and reading tours, made in his later years, were as exhausting as Balzac's mad schemes for becoming a millionaire. Dickens enjoyed the role of a London clubman, dreamed of having a title, and numbered among his close friends one of England's richest heiresses—even as Balzac took pride in his dubious particle (*de* Balzac) and consorted with the nobility. Dickens' liaison with the young actress, Ellen Ternan—a most un-Victorian affair that followed his estrangement from Catherine—was not dissimilar to some episodes in Balzac's complicated love life.

Bleak House, the most ambitious of Dickens' novels, belongs to the period of his major productions. (All of these are long novels plotted with greater care than his earlier books, and most of them are direct attacks on evils in society.) It was preceded by *Dombey and Son* (1848) and by his favorite among the novels, *David Copperfield* (1850); it was followed by *Hard Times* (1854), *Little Dorrit* (1857), with its scenes in debtors' prison, *A Tale of Two Cities* (1859), *Great Expectations* (1861), and *Our Mutual Friend* (1865), the last novel he finished. Worn out by the emotional strain of his public readings, Dickens died in 1870, when halfway through *The Mystery of Edwin Drood*.

THE STORY

In *Bleak House* Dickens employs two contrasting methods to tell his complicated, but, in the end, ingeniously unified story. The first, illustrated by the chapter in the present volume and about half of the other chapters, is to have an omniscient narrator recite in the present tense. "Near-omniscient" would be a more accurate term, for Dickens is curiously hesitant to go deeply into the minds of even his principal characters. The use of the present tense in these chapters produces a curiously dramatic, even cinematographic effect, since everything happens as if before our eyes. These same chapters enable Dickens to express his own opinions and notably to offer savage condemnations of social injustice.

His second method is to have the modest and virtuous young heroine, Esther Summerson, speak in the past tense. Her memories are full of childhood sentiment, stern guardians, pitiful waifs, and mysterious benefactors; and all these provided occasions for Dickens and his contemporaries to dissolve in those vicarious tears that Victorians loved to shed. Esther's half of the book was Dickens' second experiment in first-person narrative as a medium for the novel, and it was less successful than his first experiment in *David Copperfield*, which was largely autobiographical. He would return to the method in *Great Expectations*, but he would never again have his story narrated by a woman.

Bleak House was published serially in nineteen monthly numbers, from March 1852 through September 1853. The last was a double number containing Parts Nineteen and Twenty. There were three chapters in most of the numbers, which usually offered samples of both narrative methods. Of the sixty-seven chapters in the completed novel, thirty-four are told by Esther and thirty-three by the near-omniscient narrator, an almost perfect numerical balance. Each chapter is roughly the same length, rarely exceeding or falling short of the established norm by more than a page.

While writing under these stringent limitations, Dickens controlled every detail of his labyrinthine plot. John Foster, who wrote the official *Life of Charles Dickens* (1872-1874), has given the best summary of *Bleak House*, and we quote it here instead of attempting a summary of our own:

> The heart of the story is a Chancery suit. On this the plot hinges; and on incidents connected with it, trivial or important, the passion and suffering turn exclusively. . . . Even the fits of the little law-stationer's servant help directly in the chain of small things that lead indirectly to Lady Dedlock's death. One strong chain of interest holds together Chesney Wold and its inmates, Bleak House and the Jarndyce group, Chancery with its sorry and sordid neighborhood. The characters multiply as the tale advances, but in each the drift is the same. "There's no great odds betwixt my learned and noble brother and myself," says the grotesque proprietor of the rag and bottle shop under the wall of Lincoln's Inn; "they call me Lord Chancellor and my shop Chancery, and we both of us grub on in a muddle." *Edax rerum* [devourer of things] the motto of both, but with a difference. Out of the lumber of the shop emerge slowly some fragments of evidence by which the chief actors in the story are sensibly affected, and to which Chancery itself might have succumbed if its devouring capacities had been less complete. But by the time there is found among the lumber the will which puts all to rights in the Jarndyce suit, it is found to be too late to put anything to rights. The costs have swallowed up the estate, and there is an end of the matter.

The first chapter, which follows, states the theme and sets the tone that will be maintained, though with many variations, to the end of *Bleak House*.

Chapter 1. In Chancery

London. Michaelmas Term lately over, and the Lord Chancellor sitting in Lincoln's Inn Hall. Implacable November weather. As much mud in the streets, as if the waters had but newly retired from the face of the earth, and it would not be wonderful to meet a Megalosaurus, forty feet long or so, waddling like an elephantine lizard up Holborn Hill. Smoke lowering down from chimney-pots, making a soft black drizzle, with flakes of soot in it as big as full-grown snow-flakes—gone into mourning, one might imagine, for the death of the sun. Dogs, undistinguishable in mire. Horses, scarcely better; splashed to their very blinkers. Foot passengers, jostling one another's umbrellas, in a general infection of ill-temper, and losing their foothold at street-corners, where tens of thousands of other foot passengers have been slipping and sliding since the day broke (if this day ever broke), adding new deposits to the crust upon crust of mud, sticking at those points tenaciously to the pavement, and accumulating at compound interest.

Fog everywhere. Fog up the river, where it flows among green aits[1] and meadows; fog down the river, where it rolls defiled among the tiers of shipping, and the waterside pollutions of a great (and dirty) city. Fog on the Essex marshes, fog on the Kentish heights. Fog creeping into the cabooses of collier-brigs; fog lying out on the yards, and hovering in the rigging of great ships; fog drooping on the gunwales of barges and small boats. Fog in the eyes and throats of ancient Greenwich pensioners, wheezing by the firesides of their wards; fog in the stem and bowl of the afternoon pipe of the wrathful skipper, down in his close cabin; fog cruelly pinching the toes and fingers of his shivering little 'prentice boy on deck. Chance people on the bridges peeping over the parapets into a nether sky of fog, with fog all round them, as if they were up in a balloon, and hanging in the misty clouds.

Gas looming through the fog in divers places in the streets, much as the sun may, from the spongy fields, be seen to loom by husbandman and ploughboy. Most of the shops lighted two hours before their time—as the gas seems to know, for it has a haggard and unwilling look.

The raw afternoon is rawest, and the dense fog is densest, and the muddy streets are muddiest, near the leaden-headed old obstruction, appropriate ornament for the threshold of a leaden-headed old corporation: Temple Bar. And hard by Temple Bar, in Lincoln's Inn Hall, at the very heart of the fog, sits the Lord High Chancellor in his High Court of Chancery.

Never can there come fog too thick, never can there come mud and mire too deep, to assort with the groping and floundering condition which this High Court of Chancery, most pestilent of hoary sinners, holds, this day, in the sight of heaven and earth.

On such an afternoon, if ever, the Lord High Chancellor ought

[1 Aits: small islands.]

to be sitting here—as here he is—with a foggy glory round his head, softly fenced in with crimson cloth and curtains, addressed by a large advocate with great whiskers, a little voice, and an interminable brief, and outwardly directing his contemplation to the lantern in the roof, where he can see nothing but fog. On such an afternoon, some score of members of the High Court of Chancery bar ought to be—as here they are—mistily engaged in one of the ten thousand stages of an endless cause, tripping one another up on slippery precedents, groping knee-deep in technicalities, running their goat-hair and horse-hair warded heads against walls of words, and making a pretence of equity with serious faces, as players might. On such an afternoon, the various solicitors in the cause, some two or three of whom have inherited it from their fathers, who made a fortune by it, ought to be—as are they not?—ranged in a line, in a long matted well (but you might look in vain for Truth at the bottom of it), between the registrar's red table and the silk gowns, with bills, cross-bills, answers, rejoinders, injunctions, affidavits, issues, references to masters, masters' reports, mountains of costly nonsense, piled before them. Well may the court be dim, with wasting candles here and there; well may the fog hang heavy in it, as if it would never get out; well may the stained glass windows lose their colour, and admit no light of day into the place; well may the uninitiated from the streets, who peep in through the glass panes in the door, be deterred from entrance by its owlish aspect, and by the drawl languidly echoing to the roof from the padded dais where the Lord High Chancellor looks into the lantern that has no light in it, and where the attendant wigs are all stuck in a fog-bank! This is the Court of Chancery; which has its decaying houses and its blighted lands in every shire; which has its worn-out lunatic in every madhouse, and its dead in every churchyard; which has its ruined suitor, with his slipshod heels and threadbare dress, borrowing and begging through the round of every man's acquaintance; which gives to monied might the means abundantly of wearying out the right; which so exhausts finances, patience, courage, hope; so overthrows the brain and breaks the heart; that there is not an honourable man among its practitioners who would not give—who does not often give—the warning, "Suffer any wrong that can be done you rather than come here!"

Who happen to be in the Lord Chancellor's court this murky afternoon besides the Lord Chancellor, the counsel in the cause, two or three counsel who are never in any cause, and the well of solicitors before mentioned? There is the registrar below the Judge, in wig and gown; and there are two or three maces, or petty-bags, or privy purses, or whatever they may be, in legal court suits. These are all yawning; for no crumb of amusement ever falls from JARNDYCE AND JARNDYCE (the cause in hand), which was squeezed dry years upon years ago. The short-hand writers, the reporters of the court, and the reporters of the newspapers, invariably decamp with the rest of the regulars when Jarndyce and Jarndyce comes on. Their places are a blank. Standing on a seat at the side of the hall, the better to peer into the curtained sanctuary, is a little mad old woman in a squeezed bonnet, who is always in court, from its sitting to its rising, and always expecting some incomprehensible judgment to be given in her favour. Some say she really is, or was, a party to a suit; but no one knows for certain, because no one cares. She carries some small litter in a reticule which she calls her documents; principally consisting of paper matches and dry lavender. A sallow prisoner has come up, in custody, for the half-dozenth time, to make a personal application "to purge himself of his contempt;" which, being a solitary surviving executor who has fallen into a state of conglomeration about accounts of which it is not pretended that he had ever any knowledge, he is not at all likely ever to do. In the meantime his prospects in life are ended. Another ruined suitor, who periodically appears from Shropshire, and breaks out into efforts to address the Chancellor at the close of the day's business, and who can by no means be made to understand that the Chancellor is legally ignorant of his existence after making it desolate for a quarter of a century, plants himself in a good place and keeps an eye on the Judge, ready to call out "My Lord!" in a voice of sonorous complaint, on the instant of his rising. A few lawyers' clerks and others who know this suitor by sight, linger, on the chance of his furnishing some fun, and enlivening the dismal weather a little.

Jarndyce and Jarndyce drones on. This scarecrow of a suit has, in course of time, become so complicated, that no man alive knows what it means. The parties to it understand it least; but it has been observed that no two Chancery lawyers can talk about it for five minutes, without coming to a total disagreement as to all the premises. Innumerable children have been born into the cause; innumerable young people have married into it; innumerable old people have died out of it. Scores of persons have deliriously found themselves made parties in Jarndyce and Jarndyce, without knowing how or why; whole families have inherited legendary hatreds with the suit. The little plaintiff or defendant, who was promised a new rocking-horse when Jarndyce and Jarndyce should be settled, has grown up, possessed himself of a real horse, and trotted away into the other world. Fair wards of court have faded into mothers and grandmothers; a long procession of Chancellors has come in and gone out; the legion of bills in the suit have been transformed into mere bills of mortality; there are not three Jarndyces left upon the earth perhaps, since old Tom Jarndyce in despair blew his brains out at a coffeehouse in Chancery Lane; but Jarndyce and Jarndyce still drags its dreary length before the Court, perennially hopeless.

Jarndyce and Jarndyce has passed into a joke. That is the only good that has ever come of it. It has been death to many, but it is a joke in the profession. Every master in Chancery has had a reference out of it. Every Chancellor was "in it," for somebody or other, when he was counsel at the bar. Good things have been said about it by blue-nosed, bulbous-shoed old benchers, in select port-wine committee after dinner in hall. Articled clerks have been in the habit of fleshing their legal wit upon it. The last Lord Chancellor handled it neatly, when, correcting Mr. Blowers the eminent silk gown who said that such a thing might happen when the sky rained potatoes, he observed, "or when we get through Jarndyce and Jarndyce, Mr. Blowers;"—a pleasantry that particularly tickled the maces, bags, and purses.

How many people out of the suit, Jarndyce and Jarndyce has stretched forth its unwholesome hand to spoil and corrupt, would be a very wide question. From the master, upon whose impaling files reams of dusty warrants in Jarndyce and Jarndyce have grimly writhed into many shapes; down to the copying-clerk in the Six Clerks' Office, who has copied his tens of thousands of Chancery-folio-pages under that eternal heading; no man's nature has been made better by it. In trickery, evasion, procrastination, spoliation, botheration, under false pretences of all sorts, there are influences that can never come to good. The very solicitors' boys who have kept the wretched suitors at bay, by protesting time out of mind that Mr. Chizzle, Mizzle, or otherwise, was particularly engaged and had appointments until dinner, may have got an extra moral twist and shuffle into themselves out of Jarndyce and Jarndyce. The receiver in the cause has acquired a goodly sum of money by it, but has acquired too a distrust of his own mother, and a contempt for his own kind. Chizzle, Mizzle, and otherwise, have lapsed into a habit of vaguely promising themselves that they will look into that outstanding little matter, and see what can be done for Drizzle—who was not well used—when Jarndyce and Jarndyce shall be got out of the office. Shirking and sharking, in all their many varieties, have been sown broadcast by the ill-fated cause; and even those who have contemplated its history from the outermost circle of such evil, have been insensibly tempted into a loose way of letting bad things alone to take their own bad course, and a loose belief that if the world go wrong, it was, in some off-hand manner, never meant to go right.

Thus, in the midst of the mud and the heart of the fog, sits the Lord High Chancellor in his High Court of Chancery.

"Mr. Tangle," says the Lord High Chancellor, latterly something restless under the eloquence of that learned gentleman.

"Mlud," says Mr. Tangle. Mr. Tangle knows more of Jarndyce and Jarndyce than anybody. He is famous for it—supposed never to have read anything else since he left school.

"Have you nearly concluded your argument?"

"Mlud, no—variety of points—feel it my duty tsubmit—ludship," is the reply that slides out of Mr. Tangle.

"Several members of the bar are still to be heard, I believe?" says the Chancellor, with a slight smile.

Eighteen of Mr. Tangle's learned friends, each armed with a little summary of eighteen hundred sheets, bob up like eighteen hammers in a pianoforte, make eighteen bows, and drop into their eighteen places of obscurity.

"We will proceed with the hearing on Wednesday fortnight," says the Chancellor. For, the question at issue is only a question of costs, a mere bud on the forest tree of the parent suit, and really will come to a settlement one of these days.

The Chancellor rises; the bar rises; the prisoner is brought forward in a hurry; the man from Shropshire cries, "My lord!" Maces, bags, and purses, indignantly proclaim silence, and frown at the man from Shropshire.

"In reference," proceeds the Chancellor, still on Jarndyce and Jarndyce, "to the young girl——"

"Begludship's pardon—boy," says Mr. Tangle, prematurely.

"In reference," proceeds the Chancellor, with extra distinctness, "to the young girl and boy, the two young people,"

(Mr. Tangle crushed.)

"Whom I directed to be in attendance to-day, and who are now in my private room, I will see them and satisfy myself as to the expediency of making the order for their residing with their uncle."

"Begludship's pardon—dead."

"With their," Chancellor looking through his double eye-glass at the papers on his desk, "grandfather."

"Begludship's pardon—victim of rash action—brains."

Suddenly a very little counsel, with a terrific bass voice, arises, fully inflated, in the back settlements of the fog, and says, "Will your lordship allow me? I appear for him. He is a cousin, several times removed. I am not at the moment prepared to inform the Court in what exact remove he is a cousin; but he *is* a cousin."

Leaving this address (delivered like a sepulchral message) ringing in the rafters of the roof, the very little counsel drops, and the fog knows him no more. Everybody looks for him. Nobody can see him.

"I will speak with both the young people," says the Chancellor anew, "and satisfy myself on the subject of their residing with their cousin. I will mention the matter to-morrow morning when I take my seat."

The Chancellor is about to bow to the bar, when the prisoner is presented. Nothing can possibly come of the prisoner's conglomeration, but his being sent back to prison; which is soon done. The man from Shropshire ventures another demonstrative "My lord!" but the Chancellor, being aware of him, has dexterously vanished. Everybody else quickly vanishes too. A battery of blue bags is loaded with heavy charges of papers and carried off by clerks; the little mad old woman marches off with her documents; the empty court is locked up. If all the injustice it has committed, and all the misery it has caused, could only be locked up with it, and the whole burnt away in a great funeral pyre,—why so much the better for other parties than the parties in Jarndyce and Jarndyce!

AFTERWORD

This first chapter of *Bleak House* is like the overture of an opera, presenting the grand theme that the author intends to develop, and in terms of massive orchestration it is unique even among Dickens' novels. It stands in marked contrast to a London scene by another author—the beginning of Virginia Woolf's *Mrs. Dalloway*, also in the present volume—which seems more like chamber music. Shifting the comparison, one can say that the immediate effect of the Dickens scene is that of a high-angle motion-picture camera gradually closing in on Lincoln's Inn Hall, where, "at the very heart of the fog, sits the Lord High Chancellor in his High Court of Chancery." The long descriptive passage (six paragraphs) with which the chapter opens imperceptibly moves into exposition (the account of the Jarndyce suit), which in turn leads into dramatic dialogue.

Dickens has a special fondness for figures of speech (to use the term in its broad sense as covering all sorts of rhetorical devices). Thus, in the first three paragraphs of the chapter, verbs are completely lacking, except for a series of present participles. Grammatically speaking, there are no complete sentences. Instead we are given subjects without predicates, as a catalogue of inert things over which the fog plays. By metaphorical extension, fog in the air and mud in the streets become the hateful elements that Dickens equates with Chancery. In the sixth and last of the paragraphs, he makes a triple use of *anaphora* (the repetition of a word or phrase at the beginning of successive clauses or sentences). "On such an afternoon" is repeated three times, and "Well may" four times. When we reach the climactic sentence that begins "This is the Court of Chancery," five clauses, each introduced by "which," precede the final statement in quotation marks, and the statement itself is a grim warning like the inscription over the gates to Dante's *Inferno*.

The chapter illustrates a double process of personalization and depersonalization that is often to be found in Dickens' work. On the one hand, the fog acquires a quasi-human personality as it creeps through the city; on the other hand, Dickens' people tend to become objects. The officials of the court, for instance, are twice presented as "maces, bags, and purses." Mr. Tangle's eighteen learned friends, "each armed with a little summary of eighteen hundred sheets, bob up like eighteen hammers in a pianoforte." The laughter aroused by many of Dickens' comic characters is caused by this transformation of persons into automatons, of the organically human into something rigid and repetitive. Later in *Bleak House*, Smallweed *always* throws a pillow at his wife, Turveydrop is *never* anything but "false complexion, false teeth, false whiskers, and a wig," and Chadband keeps asking rhetorical questions that transform him into a verbal machine. They are all mechanisms, though each of a different type, and perhaps it was this quality that inspired Taine to say, "The imagination of Dickens is like that of monomaniacs." The same French critic commented on a hallucinatory quality in the world created by the novelist, and recent critics have suggested that Dickens' "reality" is close to the reality of our dreams.

Three other features of his writing are illustrated in this opening chapter of *Bleak House*. First there is his typical movement from the realistic to the symbolic (from fog in the London streets to mental fog in the Court of Chancery); then there is his blending of the comic with the melodramatic and potentially tragic ("Begludship's pardon," Mr. Tangle says, "—victim of rash action—brains," referring to Tom Jarndyce's suicide); and finally there is the feeling he conveys of hidden signs and portents, of mysteries later to be revealed. Who are the two young people? Who is the unnamed cousin who will take care of them? And the mad little old lady? We can be certain that all these questions, introduced at the beginning, will be answered before the end.

Madame Bovary (1857)

GUSTAVE FLAUBERT (1821-1880), of Norman stock, was the younger son of a doctor who may have been the model for Dr. Larivière, the eminent surgeon who arrives at the end of *Madame Bovary*, too late to save the heroine. The family lived in a wing of the Rouen municipal hospital, of which the father was head. The younger son, though a mediocre student, was already writing stories at fifteen. Such titles as "The Plague in Florence," "A Dream of Hell," and "Memories of a Madman" reveal that they were in the Gothic vein of what the French call "low" or "black" romanticism. The older brother had already taken a medical degree and a wife, but the boy had one close friend, Louis Le Poittevin, remembered as the uncle of the novelist Guy de Maupassant (1850-1893). After passing his baccalaureate in 1840, Flaubert studied law in Paris, an activity he found revolting. His formal studies ended in 1844, when he had something that resembled an epileptic seizure and came home to his family.

In 1846 his father died, then his beloved sister Caroline, and the family—consisting now of the novelist, his mother, and his orphaned niece, also named Caroline—moved to their villa on the Seine, which was to be Flaubert's home for the rest of his life. Also in 1846 he became the intermittent lover of a minor poetess, Louise Colet, to whom he wrote marvelous letters, and the lifelong friend of Louis Bouilhet, a local poet of some talent. Family and friends were always more important to him than mistresses. In 1848 Flaubert and Bouilhet went to Paris for a look at the revolution "from the artistic point of view," but they returned to Normandy after two days. Their friend Le Poittevin died about this time; he had been the guardian spirit of the first book that Flaubert finished, a five-hundred-page version of *The Temptation of Saint Anthony*. Beginning in September 1849, Flaubert read the book aloud to Bouilhet and another friend, Maxime du Camp, a literary careerist who was to end in the French Academy. The friends told Flaubert that he should throw it into the fire and never speak of it again.

He traveled to the Near East with Du Camp and spent some twenty months in Egypt, Syria, and Greece. Shortly after his return he started *Madame Bovary*—at the insistence of Bouilhet, who gave him the subject—and toiled at the manuscript for nearly five years. He reported his agonizingly slow progress in letters to Louise Colet, of whom he was again the intermittent lover, but he broke with her before the book was finished in April 1856. Du Camp, then editor of the *Revue de Paris*, persuaded him to let it be published serially, then violated a promise to Flaubert and blue-penciled some of the scenes in the final instalments. The highly moral government of Napoleon III was not appeased by his omissions and indicted the author, the editor, and the printer for offenses against morality and religion. They were acquitted at a famous trial and released with a stern reprimand. *Madame Bovary*, unexpurgated, was published in April 1857 and had the large sale for the time of fifteen thousand copies.

Still toiling assiduously, Flaubert completed only four other books during the rest of his life. *Salammbô* (1862) displays the romantic side of his talent; it is a historical novel full of lush descriptions partly inspired by his travels in the Near East. *Sentimental Education* (1869) is "the moral history of the man of my generation, sentimental might be a truer word." It is a longer novel than *Bovary* and has always been less admired. Henry James, for example, described it as "large, labored, immensely 'written,' with beautiful passages and a general emptiness, with a kind of leak in its stored sadness, moreover, by which its moral dignity escapes." *The Temptation of Saint Anthony*, after being completely reworked, was published in 1874 as a long play reminiscent of Goethe's *Faust* and, like the second part of that drama, meant chiefly to be read, not performed. *Three Tales* (1877) includes the most famous of his shorter works, "A Simple Heart." During his later years Flaubert was the patron and mentor of the younger Naturalistic writers and especially of Maupassant, the most popular at the time and the nephew of his boyhood friend. He also carried on a brilliant correspondence with George Sand (1804-1876), then an old benevolent woman retired to her château of Nohant after a stormy life, but still adding to her immense shelf of novels; her complete works were soon to be published in 105 volumes. Flaubert envied her fecundity while undertaking what was to have been his sixth book, *Bouvard and Pécuchet*; it was to deal with two ludicrously commonplace bachelors who undertake an investigation into all areas of experience and knowledge. He was still far from completing the novel when he died.

Madame Bovary, his first published book, was still his masterpiece. It was unique for its time in at least two fashions: first, as being born out of genuine hatred for its subject, and second, as being the first long novel consciously wrought in every detail. In regard to the first point, Flaubert has always been admired for his "realism" or "fidelity to his subject matter," yet here is a quotation from one of his letters. "Do you think," he says, "that this ignoble reality, so disgusting to you in reproduction, does not oppress my heart as it does yours? . . . Everyone thinks I am in love with reality, when the truth is that I despise it. It was in hatred of realism that I undertook this book." Once he remarked that the subject "stinks in my nose."

To this subject, however, he devoted his enormous patience and his mania for style, architectural form, *le mot juste* ("the right word"), and aesthetic perfection. In *Madame Bovary*, as Allen Tate has said, "the novel has at last caught up with poetry." Although the book appears to be concerned with "ignoble reality" and the accurate depiction of life in French provincial towns, nothing in it is left to mere photography or chance; the artist is always in control as he manipulates characters, episodes, images, and the rhythm of his prose. His cult of style is best expressed in a letter to Louise Colet. "What I should like to do," he says, "is to write a book about nothing, a book with no reference to anything outside itself, which would stand on its own by the inner strength of its style." That he venerated his craft so highly as to make it a sacred calling, a priesthood devoted to the religion of art, is evident in a statement to one of his readers.

> There is nothing true about *Madame Bovary* [he told her]. It is a story of *pure invention*. I have put none of my own feelings into it, nor anything of my own life. . . . It is one of my principles that one must not write oneself into one's work. The artist must be in his work as God is in creation, invisible yet all-powerful; we must sense him everywhere but never see him.

THE STORY

Call it the successive disillusionments of Emma Bovary. In the first part of the novel, she becomes disillusioned with marital love and domesticity; in the second part, with romantic love; in the third and last part, with pure sexual passion. What drives her to suicide, however, is not so much disillusionment as the debts she has incurred to satisfy her craving for luxuries.

Emma is the daughter of a well-to-do farmer. Sent to a convent school, she becomes infatuated with the romantic world of Scott, Lamartine, and Chateaubriand; in this respect she comes close to being a latter-day Don Quixote. She marries the local health officer, Charles Bovary, a young widower whose previous marriage to an older woman had been sterile and bleak. Soon Emma is bored by her wellmeaning husband, whose conversation is "flat as a sidewalk." The Bovarys are invited to a ball at La Vaubyessard given by the local nobility, and here Emma is transported by her first glimpse of wealth and fashion. At the end of Part One, she persuades Charles to leave the drab town of Tostes, but first she burns her bridal bouquet.

Yonville-l'Abbaye, scene of the other two parts, is no improvement over Tostes; indeed, it is monumental in its middle-class provincial dreariness. Here the principal background figures are Father Bournisien, the narrow-minded priest, and Homais, the local pharmacist and freethinker, on whom Flaubert lavishes his contempt for the arrogant, self-educated intellectual. Urged on by Homais, Charles performs an operation for clubfoot that reveals his utter incompetence. Emma gives birth to a daughter; then she falls in love with Léon Dupuis, a notary's clerk with romantic dreams much like her own; but he goes away to study law in Paris. After the big agricultural show at Yonville—the admirable scene that we have chosen—Emma is seduced by the local Don Juan, a wealthy bachelor named Rodolphe Boulanger. He rejects her after a time, and she finds that religion as expounded by Father Bournisien does nothing to assuage her grief. Charles, who is blind to her infidelity, tries to distract her by taking her to the opera in Rouen. There she meets Léon again, and they have a passionate love affair that continues till Emma has plunged the household into hopeless debt. She begs for money everywhere—even from Rodolphe, who says he has none to spare—then steals a lethal dose of arsenic from Homais' pharmacy. Charles dies of discouragement not long after the funeral. Her little daughter Berthe is taken in by a poor relative, then sent to work in a cotton mill. As a final touch of bitterness, Homais the hateful is awarded the Legion of Honor.

The chapter on the agricultural show is one that Flaubert researched with even more than his usual care, then wrote with full control of its multiple elements. The modern translation—brilliant in conveying the nuances of Flaubert's style—was made by Francis Steegmuller for the Modern Library.

[*The Agricultural Show*]

The great day arrived at last.

The morning of the Agricultural Show all the Yonvillians were standing on their doorsteps discussing the preparations. The pediment of the town hall had been looped with ivy; a marquee had been set up for the banquet in one of the meadows; and in the middle of the square, in front of the church, stood an antiquated fieldpiece that was to be fired as a signal announcing the arrival of the prefect and the proclamation of the prize winners. The Buchy national guard (Yonville had none) had come to join forces with the fire brigade, commanded by Binet. Today he wore a collar even higher than usual; and his bust, tightly encased in his tunic, was so stiff and inflexible that all his animal fluids seemed to be concentrated in his legs, which rose and fell with the music in rhythmic jerks. Since the tax collector and the colonel were rivals, each showed off his talents by drilling his men separately. First the red epaulettes would march up and down, and then the black breastplates. And then it would begin all over again: there was no end to it. Never had there been such a display of pomp! A number of citizens had washed their housefronts the day before; tricolor flags were hanging from half-open windows; all the cafés were full; and in the perfect weather the headdresses of the women seemed whiter than snow, their gold crosses glittered in the bright sun, and their multicolored neckcloths relieved the somber monotony of the men's frock coats and blue smocks. As the farm women dismounted from their horses they undid the big pins that had held their skirts tucked up away from splashing. The men's concern was for their hats: to protect them they had covered them with large pocket handkerchiefs, holding the corners between their teeth as they rode.

The crowd converged on the main street from both ends of the village, from the paths between the houses, from the lanes, and from the houses themselves; knockers could be heard falling against doors as housewives in cotton gloves emerged to watch the festivities. Particularly admired were the two large illumination frames laden with colored glass lamps that flanked the official grandstand; and against the four columns of the town hall stood four poles, each with a little banner bearing a legend in gold letters on a greenish ground. One said "Commerce," another "Agriculture," the third "Industry," and the fourth "Fine Arts."

But the jubilation brightening all faces seemed to cast a gloom over Madame Lefrançois, the hotel-keeper. She was standing on her kitchen steps muttering to herself:

"It's a crime—a crime, that canvas shack! Do they really think the prefect will enjoy eating his dinner in a tent, like a circus performer? They pretend the whole thing's for the good of this village —so why bring a third-class cook over from Neufchâtel? And who's it all for, anyway? A lot of cowherds and riffraff."

The apothecary came by. He was wearing a black tail coat, yellow nankeen trousers, reverse-calf shoes, and—most exceptionally—a hat: a stiff, low-crowned hat.

"Good morning!" he said. "Forgive me for being in such a hurry."

And as the buxom widow asked him where he was going:

"I imagine it must seem funny to you, doesn't it? Considering that most of the time I can't be pried loose from my laboratory any more than the old man's rat from his cheese."

"What cheese is that?" asked the landlady.

"Oh, nothing, nothing," said Homais. "I was merely referring to the fact, Madame Lefrançois, that I usually stay at home, like a recluse. But today things are different. I must absolutely . . ."

"You don't mean you're going *there?*" she said with a scornful look.

"Of course I'm going there," the apothecary replied, surprised. "Don't you know I'm on the advisory committee?"

Madame Lefrançois looked at him for a moment or two and then answered with a smile:

"That's all right, then. But what have you got to do with farming? Do you know anything about it?"

"Certainly I know something about it, being a pharmacist! A pharmacist is a chemist, Madame Lefrançois; and since the aim of chemistry is to discover the laws governing the reciprocal and molecular action of all natural bodies, it follows that agriculture falls within its domain! Take the composition of manures, the fermentation of liquids, the analysis of gasses, the effects of noxious effluvia—what's all that, I ask you, if it isn't chemistry in the strictest sense of the word?"

The landlady made no reply. Homais went on:

"Do you think that to be an agronomist you must till the soil or fatten chickens with your own hands? No: you have to study the composition of various substances—geological strata, atmospheric phenomena, the properties of the various soils, minerals, types of water, the density of different bodies, their capillary attraction. And a hundred other things. You have to be thoroughly versed in all the principles of hygiene—that's an absolute prerequisite if you're going to serve in a supervisory or consultant capacity in anything relating to the construction of farm buildings, the feeding of livestock, the preparation of meals for hired men. And then you've got to know botany, Madame Lefrançois: be able to tell one plant from another—you know what I mean? Which ones are benign and which ones are poisonous, which ones are unproductive and which ones are nutritive; whether it's a good thing to pull them out here and resow them there, propagate some and destroy others. In short, you've got to keep abreast of science by reading pamphlets and publications; you've got to be always on the alert, always on the lookout for possible improvements. . . ."

All this time the landlady never took her eyes off the door of the Café Français. The pharmacist continued:

"Would to God our farmers were chemists, or at least that they listened more carefully to what science has to say. I myself recently wrote a rather considerable little treatise—a monograph of over seventy-two pages, entitled: *Cider: Its Manufacture and Its Effects; Followed by Certain New Observations on This Subject.* I sent it to the Agronomical Society of Rouen, and it even brought me the honor of being admitted to membership in that body— Agricultural Section, Pomology Division. Now if this work of mine had been made available to the public . . ."

The apothecary broke off: Madame Lefrançois' attention was obviously elsewhere.

"Just look at them," she said. "How can they patronize such a filthy place?"

And with shrugs that stretched her sweater tight over her bosom, she pointed with both hands to her competitor's café, out of which came the sound of singing.

"Anyway, it won't be there much longer," she said. "Just a few days more, and then—*finis.*"

Homais drew back in amazement, and she came down her three steps and put her lips to his ear:

"What! Haven't you heard? They're padlocking it this week. It's Lheureux who's forcing the sale; all those notes Tellier signed were murder."

"What an unutterable catastrophe!" The apothecary always had the proper expression ready, whatever the occasion.

The landlady proceeded to tell him the story, which she had from Théodore, Maître Gullaumin's servant; and although she detested Tellier she had nothing but harsh words for Lheureux. He was a wheedler, a cringer.

"Look—there he is now, in the market," she said. "He's greeting Madame Bovary. She's wearing a green hat. In fact, she's on Monsieur Boulanger's arm."

"Madame Bovary!" cried Homais. "I must go and pay her my respects. She might like to have a seat in the enclosure, under the portico."

And ignoring Madame Lefrançois' attempts to detain him with further details, he hurried off, smiling and with springy step, bestowing innumerable salutations right and left, and taking up a good deal of room with his long black coat tails that streamed in the wind behind him.

Rodolphe had seen him coming and had quickened his pace; but Madame Bovary was out of breath, and he slowed and smiled at her. "I was trying to avoid that bore," he said savagely. "You know, the apothecary."

She nudged him with her elbow.

"What does that mean?" he wondered, glancing at her out of the corner of his eye as they moved on.

Her face, seen in profile, was so calm that it gave him no hint. It stood out against the light, framed in the oval of her bonnet, whose pale ribbons were like streaming reeds. Her eyes with their long curving lashes looked straight ahead: they were fully open, but seemed a little narrowed because of the blood that was pulsing gently under the fine skin of her cheekbones. The rosy flesh between her nostrils was all but transparent in the light. She was inclining her head to one side, and the pearly tips of her white teeth showed between her lips.

"Is she laughing at me?" Rodolphe wondered.

But Emma's nudge had been no more than a warning, for

Monsieur Lheureux was walking along beside them, now and then addressing them as though to begin conversation.

"What a marvelous day! Everybody's out! The wind is from the east."

Neither Madame Bovary nor Rodolphe made any reply, though at their slightest movement he edged up to them saying, "Beg your pardon?" and touching his hat.

When they were in front of the blacksmith's, instead of following the road as far as the gate Rodolphe turned abruptly into a side path, drawing Madame Bovary with him.

"Good-bye, Monsieur Lheureux!" he called out. "We'll be seeing you!"

"You certainly got rid of him!" she said, laughing.

"Why should we put up with intruders?" he said. "Today I'm lucky enough to be with you, so . . ."

Emma blushed. He left his sentence unfinished, and talked instead about the fine weather and how pleasant it was to be walking on the grass. A few late daisies were blooming around them.

"They're pretty, aren't they?" he said. "If any of the village girls are in love they can come here for their oracles." And he added: "Maybe I should pick one. What do you think?"

"Are you in love?" she asked, coughing a little.

"Ah, ah! Who knows?" answered Rodolphe.

The meadow was beginning to fill up, and housewives laden with big umbrellas, picnic baskets and babies were bumping into everyone. It was constantly necessary to turn aside, out of the way of long lines of girls—servants from farms, wearing blue stockings, low-heeled shoes and silver rings and smelling of the dairy when they came close. They walked holding hands, forming chains the whole length of the meadow, from the row of aspens to the banquet tent. It was time for the judging, and one after another the farmers were filing into a kind of hippodrome marked off by a long rope hung on stakes.

Here stood the livestock, noses to the rope, rumps of all shapes and sizes forming a ragged line. Lethargic pigs were nuzzling the earth with their snouts; calves were lowing and sheep bleating; cows with their legs folded under them lay on the grass, slowly chewing their cud and blinking their heavy eyelids under the midges buzzing around them. Bare-armed teamsters were holding rearing stallions by the halter: these were neighing loudly in the direction of the mares, who stood there quietly, necks outstretched and manes drooping, as their foals rested in their shadow or came now and again to suck. Above the long undulating line of these massed bodies a white mane would occasionally surge up like a wave in the wind, or a pair of sharp horns would stick out, or men's heads would bob up as they ran. Quite apart, outside the arena, a hundred yards off, was a big black bull with a strap harness and an iron ring through its nose, motionless as a brazen image. A ragged little boy held it by a rope.

Meanwhile a group of gentlemen were solemnly advancing between the two rows, inspecting each animal and then conferring in an undertone. One, who seemed the most important, was writing details in a notebook as he walked. This was the chairman of the jury, Monsieur Derozerays de la Panville. As soon as he recognized Rodolphe he quickly stepped forward and addressed him with a cordial smile: "What's this, Monsieur Boulanger? You've deserted us?"

Rodolphe assured him that he was coming directly. But when the chairman had passed:

"I'll certainly *not* be going," he said to Emma. "I like your company better than his."

And though he kept making fun of the show, Rodolphe displayed his blue pass to the guard so that they could walk about unmolested, and he even stopped from time to time in front of some particularly fine exhibit. It was never anything that Madame Bovary cared about: he noticed this, and began to make jokes about the Yonville ladies and the way they dressed; then he apologized for the carelessness of his own costume. This was a mixture of the casual and the refined—the kind of thing that both fascinates and exasperates the common herd, hinting as it does at an eccentric way of life, indulgence in wild passions and "artistic" affectations, and a contempt for social conventions. His batiste shirt (it had pleated cuffs) puffed out from the opening of his gray twill vest at each gust of wind; and his broad-striped trousers ended at nankeen shoes trimmed with patent leather so shiny that the grass was reflected in it. He tramped unconcernedly through horse dung, one thumb in his vest pocket, his straw hat tilted over one ear.

"Anyway," he said, "when you live in the country . . ."

"Any trouble you take is wasted," said Emma.

"Completely," replied Rodolphe. "Think of it: there isn't a single person here today capable of appreciating the cut of a coat."

And they talked about the mediocrity of provincial life, so suffocating, so fatal to all noble dreams.

"So," said Rodolphe, "I just get more and more engulfed in gloom as time goes on. . . ."

"You do!" she cried, in surprise. "I thought of you as being very jolly."

"Of course—that's the impression I give: I've learned to wear a mask of mockery when I'm with other people. But many's the time I've passed a cemetery in the moonlight and asked myself if I wouldn't be better off lying there with the rest. . . ."

"Oh! And what about your friends?" she asked. "Have you no thought for them?"

"My friends? What friends? Have I any? Who cares anything about me?"

And he accompanied those last words with a kind of desperate whistle.

But they had to draw apart to make way for a tall tower of chairs borne by a man coming up behind them. He was so excessively laden that the only parts of him visible were the tips of his wooden shoes and his two outstretched hands. It was Lestiboudois, the gravedigger, who was renting out church seats to the crowd. He was highly inventive where his own interests were concerned, and had thought up this way of profiting from the show. It was a good idea: everyone was hailing him at once. The villagers were hot; they clamored for the straw-seated chairs that gave off a smell of incense, and they leaned back with a certain veneration against the heavy slats stained with candlewax.

Then once again Madame Bovary took Rodolphe's arm, and he went on as though talking to himself:

"Yes, so many things have passed me by! I've always been so alone! Ah! If I'd had a purpose in life, if I'd met anyone with true affection, if I'd found somebody who . . . Oh! Then I wouldn't have spared any effort; I'd have surmounted every obstacle, let nothing stand in my way . . . !"

"It seems to me, though," said Emma, "that you're scarcely to be pitied."

"Oh? You think that?" said Rodolphe.

"Yes," she answered, "because after all you're free"—she hesitated—"rich . . ."

"Don't make fun of me," he begged.

And she was swearing that she was doing nothing of the kind, when a cannon shot resounded and everyone began to hurry toward the village.

It was a false alarm: the prefect wasn't even in sight, and the members of the jury were in a quandary, not knowing whether to begin the proceedings or wait a while longer.

Finally at the far end of the square appeared a big hired landau drawn by two skinny horses who were being furiously whipped on by a white-hatted coachman. Binet had just time to shout, "Fall in!" and the colonel to echo him; there was a rush for the stacked rifles; and in the confusion some of the men forgot to button their collars. But the official coach-and-pair seemed to sense the difficulty, and the emaciated beasts, dawdling on their chain, drew up at a slow trot in front of the portico of the town hall just at the moment when the national guard and the fire brigade were deploying into line to the beating of the drums.

"Mark time!" cried Binet.

"Halt!" cried the colonel. "Left, turn!"

And after a present-arms during which the rattle of the metal bands as they slid down the stocks and barrels sounded like a copper cauldron rolling down a flight of stairs, all the rifles were lowered.

Then there emerged from the carriage a gentleman clad in a short, silver-embroidered coat, his forehead high and bald, the back of his head tufted, his complexion wan and his expression remarkably benign. His eyes, very large and heavy-lidded, half shut as he peered at the multitude; and at the same time he lifted his sharp nose and curved his sunken mouth into a smile. He recognized the mayor by his sash, and explained that the prefect had been unable to come. He himself was a prefectural councilor, and he added a few words of apology. Tuvache replied with compliments, the emissary declared himself unworthy of them; and the two officials stood there face to face, their foreheads almost touching, all about them the members of the jury, the village council, the local elite, the national guard and the crowd. Holding his little black three-cornered hat against his chest, the prefectural councilor reiterated his greetings; and Tuvache, bent like a bow, returned his smiles, stammered, clutched uncertainly for words, protested his devotion to the monarchy and his awareness of the honor that was being bestowed on Yonville.

Hippolyte, the stable-boy at the hotel, came to take the horses from the coachman; and limping on his clubfoot he led them through the gateway of the Lion d'Or, where a crowd of peasants gathered to stare at the carriage. There was a roll of the drums, the howitzer thundered, and the gentlemen filed up and took their seats on the platform in red plush armchairs loaned by Madame Tuvache.

All in this group looked alike. Their flabby, fair-skinned, slightly sun-tanned faces were the color of new cider, and their bushy side whiskers stuck out over high, stiff collars that were held in place by white cravats tied in wide bows. Every vest was of velvet, with a shawl collar; every watch had an oval carnelian seal at the end of a long ribbon; and every one of the gentlemen sat with his hands planted on his thighs, his legs carefully apart, the hard-finished broadcloth of his trousers shining more brightly than the leather of his heavy shoes.

The invited ladies were seated to the rear, under the portico between the columns, while the ordinary citizens faced the platform, either standing, or sitting on chairs. Lestiboudois had re-transported to this new location all those that he had previously taken to the meadow; now he kept bringing still more from the church; and he was crowding the place so with his chair-rental business that it was almost impossible for anyone to reach the few steps leading to the platform.

"In my opinion," said Monsieur Lheureux, addressing the pharmacist, who was passing by on his way to take his seat, "they should have set up a pair of Venetian flagstaffs: trimmed with something rich and not too showy they'd have made a very pretty sight."

"Certainly," said Homais. "But what can you expect? The mayor took everything into his own hands. He hasn't much taste, poor Tuvache: in fact, he's completely devoid of what is known as the artistic sense."

Meanwhile Rodolphe, with Madame Bovary, had gone up to the second floor of the town hall, into the "council chamber": it was quite empty—a perfect place, he said, from which to have a comfortable view of the ceremonies. He took three of the stools that stood around the oval table under the king's bust and moved them over to one of the windows; and there they sat down close together.

There was a certain agitation on the platform—prolonged whisperings and consultations. Finally the prefectural councilor rose to his feet. It had become known that he was called Lieuvain, and

his name was repeated from one to another in the crowd. H
made sure that his sheets of paper were in proper order, peered
at them closely, and began:

"Gentlemen: I should like, with your permission (before speak
ing to you about the object of today's meeting—and this sentiment
I am sure, will be shared by all of you), I should like, with you
permission, to pay tribute to the national administration, to the
government, to the monarch, gentlemen, to our sovereign, to the
beloved king to whom no branch of public or private prosperity i
indifferent, and who, with so firm and yet so wise a hand, guide
the chariot of state amidst the constant perils of a stormy sea
maintaining at the same time public respect for peace as well a
for war—for industry, for commerce, for agriculture, for the fin
arts."

"I ought to move a little further back," said Rodolphe.

"Why?" said Emma.

But at that moment the councilor's voice rose to an extraor
dinary pitch. He was declaiming:

"Gone forever, gentlemen, are the days when civil discor
drenched our streets with blood; when the landlord, the busines
man, nay, the worker, sank at night into a peaceful slumber trem
bling lest they be brutally awakened by the sound of inflamma
tory tocsins; when the most subversive principles were audaciousl
undermining the foundations . . ."

"It's just that I might be caught sight of from below," sai
Rodolphe. "If I were, I'd have to spend the next two week
apologizing; and what with my bad reputation . . ."

"Oh! You're slandering yourself," said Emma.

"No, no, my reputation's execrable, I assure you."

"But, gentlemen," continued the councilor, "if I dismiss thos
depressing evocations and turn my eyes to the present situation o
our cherished fatherland, what do I see before me? Commerc
and the arts are thriving everywhere; everywhere new channels o
communication, like so many new arteries in the body politic
are multiplying contacts between its various parts; our great manu
facturing centers have resumed their activity; religion, its founda
tions strengthened, appeals to every heart; shipping fills our ports
confidence returns; at long last, France breathes again!"

"Moreover, from the point of view of society it's probably de
served," Rodolphe said.

"What do you mean?" she asked.

"Do you really not know," he said, "that there exist souls that are ceaselessly in torment? That are driven now to dreams, now to action, driven from the purest passions to the most orgiastic pleasures? No wonder we fling ourselves into all kinds of fantasies and follies!"

She stared at him as if he were a traveler from mythical lands. "We poor women," she said, "don't have even that escape."

"A poor escape," he said, "since it doesn't bring happiness."

"But do we ever find happiness?" she asked.

"Yes, it comes along one day," he answered.

"And the point has not been lost on you," the councilor was saying. "Not on you, farmers and workers in the fields! Not on you, champions of progress and morality! The point has not been lost on you, I say, that the storms of political strife are truly more to be dreaded than the disorders of the elements!"

"Yes, it comes along one day," Rodolphe repeated. "All of a sudden, just when we've given up hope. Then new horizons open before us: it's like a voice crying, 'Look! It's here!' We feel the need to pour out our hearts to a given person, to surrender, to sacrifice everything. In such a meeting no words are necessary: each senses the other's thoughts. Each is the answer to the other's dreams." He kept staring at her. "There it is, the treasure so long sought for—there before us: it gleams, it sparkles. But still we doubt; we daren't believe; we stand there dazzled, as though we'd come from darkness into light."

As he ended, Rodolphe enhanced his words with pantomime. He passed his hand over his face, like someone dazed; then he let it fall on Emma's hand. She withdrew hers. The councilor read on:

"And who is there who would wonder at such a statement, gentlemen? Only one so blind, so sunk (I use the word advisedly), so sunk in the prejudices of another age as to persist in his misconceptions concerning the spirit of our farming population. Where, I ask you, is there to be found greater patriotism than in rural areas, greater devotion to the common weal, greater—in one word—intelligence? And by intelligence, gentlemen, I do not mean that superficial intelligence that is a futile ornament of idle minds, but rather that profound and moderate intelligence that applies itself above all to useful ends, contributing in this manner to the good of all, to public improvement and the upholding of the state —that intelligence that is the fruit of respect for law and the performance of duty!"

"Ah, there they go again!" said Rodolphe. "Duty, duty, always duty—I'm sick of that word. Listen to them! They're a bunch of doddering old morons and bigoted old church mice with foot warmers and rosaries, always squeaking, 'Duty! Duty!' at us. I have my own idea of duty. Our duty is to feel what is great and love what is beautiful—not to accept all the social conventions and the infamies they impose on us."

"Still . . . still . . ." objected Madame Bovary.

"No! Why preach against the passions? Aren't they the only beautiful thing in this world, the source of heroism, enthusiasm, poetry, music, the arts, everything?"

"But still," said Emma, "we have to be guided a little by society's opinions; we have to follow its standards of morality."

"Ah! But there are two moralities," he replied. "The petty one, the conventional one, the one invented by man, the one that keeps changing and screaming its head off—that one's noisy and vulgar, like that crowd of fools you see out there. But the other one, the eternal one . . . Ah! This one's all around us and above us, like the landscape that surrounds us and the blue sky that gives us light."

Monsieur Lieuvain had just wiped his mouth with his pocket handkerchief. He resumed:

"Why should I presume, gentlemen, to prove to you who are here today the usefulness of agriculture? Who is it that supplies our needs, who is it that provisions us, if not the farmer? The farmer, gentlemen, sowing with laborious hand the fertile furrows of our countryside, brings forth the wheat which, having been ground and reduced to powder by means of ingenious machinery, emerges in the form of flour, and from thence, transported to our cities, is presently delivered to the baker, who fashions from it a food for the poor man as well as for the rich. Is it not the farmer, once again, who fattens his plentiful flocks in the pastures to provide us with our clothing? For how would we be clothed, for how would we be nourished, without agriculture? Indeed, gentlemen— is there need to seek so far afield for examples? Who among you has not often given thought to the immense benefit we derive from that modest creature—adornment of our kitchen yards—which provides at one and the same time a downy pillow for our beds, its succulent meat for our tables, and eggs? But I should never end, had I to enumerate one after another the different products which properly cultivated soil lavishes on its children like a generous mother. Here, the grape; there, the cider apple; yonder, the colza; elsewhere, a thousand kinds of cheese. And flax, gentlemen, do not forget flax!—an area in which within the past few years there has been considerable development, and one to which I particularly call your attention."

There was no need for him to "call their attention": every mouth in the crowd was open, as though to drink in his words. Tuvache, sitting beside him, listened wide-eyed; Monsieur Derozerays' lids now and again gently shut; and further along the pharmacist, holding his son Napoléon between his knees, cupped his hand to his ear lest he miss a single syllable. The other members of the jury kept slowly nodding their chins against their vests to express their approval. The fire brigade, at the foot of the platform, leaned on their bayonets; and Binet stood motionless, elbow bent, the tip of his sword in the air. He could hear, perhaps, but he certainly could not see, for the visor of his helmet had fallen forward onto his nose. His lieutenant, who was Monsieur Tuvache's younger son, had gone him one better: the helmet he was wearing was far too big for him and kept teetering on his head and showing a corner of the calico nightcap he had on under it. He was smiling from beneath his headgear as sweetly as a baby; and his small pale face, dripping with sweat, wore an expression of enjoyment, exhaustion and drowsiness.

The square was packed solidly with people as far as the houses. Spectators were leaning out of every window and standing on every doorstep; and Justin, in front of the pharmacy show window, seemed nailed to the spot in contemplation of the spectacle. Despite the crowd's silence, Monsieur Lieuvain's voice didn't carry too well in the open air. What came was fragmentary bits of sentences interrupted here and there by the scraping of chairs; then all at once from behind there would resound the prolonged lowing of an ox, and lambs bleated to one another on the street corners. For the cowherds and shepherds had driven their animals in that close, and from time to time a cow would bellow as her tongue tore off some bit of foliage hanging down over her muzzle.

Rodolphe had come close to Emma and was speaking rapidly in a low voice:

"Don't you think it's disgusting, the way they conspire to ruin everything? Is there a single sentiment that society doesn't condemn? The noblest instincts, the purest sympathies are persecuted and dragged in the mud; and if two poor souls do find one another, everything is organized to keep them apart. They'll try, just the same; they'll beat their wings, they'll call to each other. Oh! Never fear! Sooner or later, in six months or ten years, they'll come together and love one another, because they can't go against fate and because they were born for each other."

He was leaning forward with his arms crossed on his knees, and lifting his face to Emma's he looked at her fixedly from very near. In his eyes she could see tiny golden lines radiating out all around his black pupils, and she could even smell the perfume of the pomade that lent a gloss to his hair. Then a languor came over her; she remembered the vicomte who had waltzed with her at La Vaubyessard and whose beard had given off this same odor of vanilla and lemon; and automatically she half closed her eyes to breathe it more deeply. But as she did this, sitting up straight in her chair, she saw in the distance, on the farthest horizon, the old stagecoach, the Hirondelle, slowly descending the hill of Les Leux, trailing a long plume of dust behind it. It was in this yellow carriage that Léon had so often returned to her; and that was the road he had taken when he had left forever. For a moment she thought she saw him across the square, at his window; then everything became confused, and clouds passed before her eyes; it seemed to her that she was still whirling in the waltz, under the blaze of the chandeliers, in the vicomte's arms, and that Léon was not far off, that he was coming. . . . And yet all the while she was smelling the perfume of Rodolphe's hair beside her. The sweetness of this sensation permeated her earlier desires, and like grains of sand in the wind these whirled about in the subtle fragrance that was filling her soul. She opened her nostrils wide to breathe in the freshness of the ivy festooning the capitals outside the window. She took off her gloves and wiped her hands; then she fanned herself with her handkerchief, hearing above the beating of the pulse in her temples the murmur of the crowd and the councilor's voice as he intoned his periods.

"Persist!" he was saying. "Persevere! Follow neither the beaten tracks of routine nor the rash counsels of reckless empiricism. Apply yourselves above all to the improvement of the soil, to rich fertilizers, to the development of fine breeds—equine, bovine, ovine and porcine. May this exhibition be for you a peaceful arena where the winner, as he leaves, will stretch out his hand to the loser and fraternize with him, wishing him better luck another time! And you, venerable servants, humblest members of the household, whose painful labors have by no government up until today been given the slightest consideration: present yourselves now, and receive the reward of your silent heroism! And rest assured that the state henceforth has its eyes upon you, that it encourages you, that it protects you, that it will honor your just demands, and lighten, to the best of its ability, the burden of your painful sacrifices!"

Monsieur Lieuvain sat down.

Monsieur Derozerays stood up, and began another speech. His was perhaps not quite so flowery as the councilor's; but it had the advantage of being characterized by a more positive style—by a more specialized knowledge, that is, and more pertinent arguments. There was less praise of the government, and more mention of religion and agriculture. He showed the relation between the two and how they had always worked together for the good of civilization. Rodolphe was talking to Madame Bovary about dreams, forebodings, magnetism. Going back to the cradle of human society, the orator depicted the savage ages when men lived off acorns in the depths of the forest. Then they had cast off their animal skins, garbed themselves in cloth, dug the ground and planted the vine. Was this an advance? Didn't this discovery entail more disadvantages than benefits? That was the problem Monsieur Derozerays set himself. From magnetism Rodolphe gradually moved on to affinities; and as the chairman cited Cincinnatus and his plow, Diogenes planting his cabbages and the Chinese emperors celebrating the New Year by sowing seed, the young man was explaining to the young woman that these irresistible attractions had their roots in some earlier existence.

"Take us, for example," he said. "Why should we have met? How did it happen? It can only be that something in our particular inclinations made us come closer and closer across the distance that separated us, the way two rivers flow together."

He took her hand, and this time she did not withdraw it.

"First prize for all-round farming!" cried the chairman.

"Just this morning, for example, when I came to your house . . ."

"To Monsieur Bizet, of Quincampoix."

"Did I have any idea that I'd be coming with you to the show?"

"Seventy francs!"

"A hundred times I was on the point of leaving, and yet I followed you and stayed with you . . ."

"For the best manures."

". . . as I'd stay with you tonight, tomorrow, every day, all my life!"

"To Monsieur Caron, of Argueil, a gold medal!"

"Never have I been so utterly charmed by anyone . . ."

"To Monsieur Bain, of Givry-Saint-Martin!"

". . . so that I'll carry the memory of you with me. . . ."

"For a merino ram . . ."

"Whereas you'll forget me: I'll vanish like a shadow."

"To Monsieur Belot, of Notre-Dame . . ."

"No, though! Tell me it isn't so! Tell me I'll have a place in your thoughts, in your life!"

"Hogs: a tie! To Messieurs Lehérissé and Cullembourg, sixty francs!"

Rodolphe squeezed her hand, and he felt it all warm and trembling in his, like a captive dove that longs to fly away; but then, whether in an effort to free it, or in response to his pressure, she moved her fingers.

"Oh! Thank God! You don't repulse me! How sweet, how kind! I'm yours: you know that now! Let me see you! Let me look at you!"

A gust of wind coming in the windows ruffled the cloth on the table; and down in the square all the tall headdresses of the peasant women rose up like fluttering white butterfly wings.

"Use of oil-cakes!" continued the chairman.

He was going faster now.

"Flemish fertilizer . . . flax-raising . . . drainage, long-term leases . . . domestic service!"

Rodolphe had stopped speaking. They were staring at each other. As their desire rose to a peak their dry lips quivered; and, languidly, of their own accord, their fingers intertwined.

"Catherine-Nicaise-Elizabeth Leroux, of Sassetot-la-Guerrière, for fifty-four years of service on the same farm, a silver medal, value twenty-five francs!"

"Where is Catherine Leroux?" repeated the councilor.

There was no sign of her, but there was the sound of whispering voices:

"Go ahead!"

"No!"

"To the left!"

"Don't be scared!"

"Stupid old thing!"

"Is she there or isn't she?" cried Tuvache.

"Yes! Here she is!"

"Then send her up!"

Everyone watched her as she climbed to the platform: a fright-ened-looking little old woman who seemed to have shriveled inside her shabby clothes. On her feet were heavy wooden clogs, and she wore a long blue apron. Her thin face, framed in a simple coif, was more wrinkled than a withered russet, and out of the sleeves of her red blouse hung her large, gnarled hands. Years of barn dust, washing soda and wool grease had left them so crusted and rough and hard that they looked dirty despite all the clear water they'd been rinsed in; and from long habit of service they hung half open, as though offering their own humble testimony to the hard-ships they had endured. A kind of monklike rigidity gave a certain dignity to her face, but her pale stare was softened by no hint of sadness or human kindness. Living among animals, she had taken on their muteness and placidity. This was the first time she had ever been in the midst of so great a crowd; and inwardly terrified by the flags and the drums, by the gentlemen in tail coats and by the decoration worn by the councilor, she stood still, uncertain whether to move ahead or to turn and run, comprehending neither the urgings of the crowd nor the smiles of the jury. Thus did half a century of servitude stand before these beaming bourgeois.

"Step forward, venerable Catherine-Nicaise-Elizabeth Leroux!" cried the councilor, who had taken the list of prize winners from the chairman.

Looking at the sheet of paper and at the old woman in turn, he kept urging her forward like a father: "Come right here, come ahead!"

"Are you deaf?" cried Tuvache, jumping up from his chair.

And he proceeded to shout into her ear: "Fifty-four years of service! A silver medal! Twenty-five francs! For you!"

She took the medal and stared at it. Then a beatific smile spread over her face, and as she left the platform those nearby could hear her mumble: "I'll give it to our priest and he'll say some Masses for me."

"Such fanaticism!" hissed the pharmacist, bending toward the notary.

The ceremonies were ended; the crowd dispersed; and now that the speeches had been read everyone resumed his rank and every-thing reverted to normal. Masters bullied their servants, the servants beat their cows and their sheep, and the cows and the sheep —indolent in their triumph—moved slowly back to their sheds, their horns decked with the green wreaths that were their trophies.

Meanwhile the national guard had gone up to the second floor of the town hall: brioches were impaled on their bayonets, and their drummer bore a basketful of bottles. Madame Bovary took Rodolphe's arm; he escorted her home; they said good-bye at her door; and then he went for a stroll in the meadow until it was time for the banquet.

The feast was long, noisy, clumsily served: the guests were so crowded that they could scarcely move their elbows; and the narrow planks that were used for benches threatened to snap under their weight. They ate enormously, each piling his plate high to get full value for his assessment. Sweat poured off every forehead; and over the table, between the hanging lamps, hovered a whitish vapor, like a river mist on an autumn morning. Rodolphe, his back against the cloth side of the tent, was thinking so much about Emma that he was aware of nothing going on around him. Out on the grass behind him servants were stacking dirty plates; his tablemates spoke to him and he didn't answer; someone kept filling his glass, and his mind was filled with stillness despite the growing noise. He was thinking of the things she had said and of the shape of her lips; her face shone out from the plaques on the shakos as from so many magic mirrors; the folds of her dress hung down the walls; and days of love-making stretched endlessly ahead in the vistas of the future.

He saw her again that evening, during the fireworks, but she was with her husband and Madame Homais and the pharmacist. The latter was very worried about stray rockets, and constantly left the others to give Binet a word of advice.

Through overprecaution, the fireworks, which had been delivered in care of Monsieur Tuvache, had been stored in his cellar, with the result that the damp powder could scarcely be got to light; and the culminating number, which was to have depicted a dragon swallowing its own tail, was a complete fiasco. Now and then some pathetic little Roman candle would go off and bring a roar from the gaping crowd—a roar amidst which could be heard the screams of women, fair game for ticklers in the darkness. Emma nestled silently against Charles's shoulder, raising her head to follow the bright trail of the rockets in the black sky. Rodolphe watched her in the glow of the colored lamps.

Gradually these went out, the stars gleamed; then came a few drops of rain, and she tied a scarf over her hair.

Just then the councilor's landau drove out of the hotel yard. The drunken coachman chose that moment to collapse; and high above the hood, between the two lamps, everyone could see the mass of his body swaying right and left with the pitching of the springs.

"There ought to be strong measures taken against drunkenness," said the apothecary. "If I had my way, there'd be a special bulletin board put up on the door of the town hall, and every week there'd be a list posted of all who had intoxicated themselves with alcoholic liquors during that period. Such a thing would be very valuable statistically, a public record that might . . . Excuse me!"

And once again he hurried off toward the captain.

The latter was homeward bound. He was looking forward to rejoining his lathe.

"It might not do any harm," said Homais, "to send one of your men, or go yourself, to . . ."

"Get away and leave me alone," replied the tax collector. "Everything's taken care of."

"You can all stop worrying," the apothecary announced when he was back with his friends. "Monsieur Binet guarantees that all necessary measures have been taken. Not a spark has fallen. The pumps are full. We can safely retire to our beds."

"I can certainly do with some sleep," said Madame Homais, with a vast yawn. "Never mind—we had a wonderfully beautiful day for the show."

Rodolphe echoed her words in a low voice, his eyes soft: "Yes, it was: wonderfully beautiful."

They exchanged good-byes and went their respective ways.

Two days later, in the *Fanal de Rouen*, there was a great article about the Agricultural Show. Homais had written it in a burst of inspiration the very next day.

"Why these festoons, these flowers, these garlands? Whither was it bound, this crowd rushing like the billows of a raging sea under a torrential tropic sun that poured its torrid rays upon our fertile meadows?"

Then he went on to speak of the condition of the peasants. The government was doing something, certainly, but not enough. "Be bold!" he cried, addressing the administration. "A thousand reforms are indispensable: let us accomplish them." Then, describing the arrival of the councilor, he didn't forget "the warlike air of our militia," or "our sprightliest village maidens," or the bald-headed old men, veritable patriarchs, "some of whom, survivors of our immortal phalanxes, felt their hearts throb once again to the manly sound of the drums." His own name came quite early in his listing of the members of the jury, and he even reminded his readers in a footnote that Monsieur Homais, the pharmacist, had sent a monograph concerning cider to the Agricultural Society. When he came to the distribution of the prizes, he depicted the joy of the winners in dithyrambic terms. Father embraced son, brother embraced brother, husband embraced wife. More than one worthy rustic proudly displayed his humble medal to the assemblage; and, returning home to his helpmeet, doubtless wept tears of joy as he hung it on the modest wall of his cot.

"About six o'clock the leading participants in the festivities forgathered at a banquet in the pasture belonging to Monsieur Liégeard. The utmost cordiality reigned throughout. A number of toasts were proposed. By Monsieur Lieuvain: 'To the king!' By Monsieur Tuvache: 'To the prefect!' By Monsieur Derozerays: 'To agriculture!' By Monsieur Homais: 'To those twin sisters, industry and the fine arts!' By Monsieur Leplichey: 'To progress!' After nightfall a brilliant display of fireworks all at once illumined the heavens. It was a veritable kaleidescope, a true stage set for an opera, and for a moment our modest village imagined itself transported into the midst of an Arabian Nights dream.

"We may mention that no untoward incidents arose to disturb this family gathering."

And he added:

"Only the clergy was conspicuous by its absence. Doubtless a totally different idea of progress obtains in the sacristies. Suit yourselves, *messieurs de Loyola!*"

AFTERWORD

Madame Bovary was a true event both in the art of fiction and in the profession of writing fiction. Not only did Flaubert amass thirty-six hundred pages of manuscript during what he called his five-year *corvée* (the word for a sentence to the galleys), but meanwhile he kept writing friends—chiefly Louise Collet—about his technical and emotional problems, which resembled those of a musician composing a symphony. Excerpts from his 1853 letters reveal some of his concerns.

> . . . I have been in fine form all this week [he says at one point]. I have written eight pages, all of which I think can remain much as they are. Tonight I have just sketched out the big scene of the Agricultural Show. It will be colossal—at least thirty pages. Against the background of this rustic-municipal celebration, with all its details (all of my minor characters will be shown in action), there will be a continuous dialogue between a gentleman and a lady he is doing his best to seduce. Furthermore, along in the middle I have a solemn speech by a councilor of the prefecture, and at the end (this I have already finished) a newspaper article written by my pharmacist, who renders an account of the celebration in fine philosophical, poetical, progressive style. You can see it is no small task. . . . If ever the effect of a symphony were to be achieved in a novel, it will be in that scene. This must resound throughout the entire concourse: we must hear at the same time the bellowing of the bulls, the sighs of love, and the speeches of the officials.

In another letter of that year, Flaubert mentions that just after composing the scene, he read an address in the Rouen *Journal* by one of the mayors in the district. He found a sentence, so he says,

> which was the very sentence I had written *word for word* one day earlier for *Madame Bovary.* . . . Not only the words and ideas were the same, but even the assonances were identical. I can't deny that this sort of coincidence pleases me.

With strange prescience, Flaubert speaks of some early drafts of *Bovary* as "scenarios"; Henry James was to use the same word about his own projects. Many critics have pointed out that Flaubert, much more than James, foreshadows cinematic techniques. In the chapter on the agricultural show, which is an especially good example, we might start with the sound effects. We hear the voices of the two speakers on the platform and the muted conversation of the soon-to-be lovers, but beneath them we are always conscious of the monotonous bleating and lowing of the livestock—as a commentary on the banalities of the councilor's exhortations, on the chairman's prize awards (with the venerable Catherine Leroux receiving, for a lifetime of service, a silver medal worth twenty-five francs, or less than half as much as had been awarded to the two prize hogs that preceded her), and on the romantic clichés uttered by Rodolphe. Earlier the stallions neighing at the mares had prefigured his verbal seduction of Emma. At the end of the evening, the fiasco of the damp fireworks that fizzed instead of exploding, but nevertheless brought roars from the crowd, is played against the silent pair: Emma following the trail of the rockets, Rodolphe gazing at her face.

Visually Flaubert's camera moves rapidly as it tracks from the decorated town to the crowd, then to individuals in the crowd (notably to the odious Homais, who will have the last word in the chapter, as in the book as a whole, and the wheedling merchant Lheureux, who has just driven an innkeeper to bankruptcy, as he will afterward drive the Bovarys), then to the lovers-to-be, then from the crowd in the meadow to the livestock. When the camera rests for a moment on Rodolphe's elegant clothes, we are meant to contrast his straw hat—then the height of dandyism—with other headgear mentioned in the chapter: Binet's helmet perched on his nose, Tuvache's son with a calico night-cap showing under his own teetering helmet, the headdresses of the peasant women, the scarf that Emma ties over her head, and finally the prize animals, their heads bedecked with green wreaths.

In a short dialogue between the principals, they discuss "the mediocrity of provincial life . . . so fatal to all noble dreams." How often in the book does Flaubert mention Emma's dreams of romance or have her gaze vacantly through a window, as if seeking some lost horizon! The critic Victor Brombert has gone so far as to call *Madame Bovary* "the tragedy of dreams" and to say that the chief impulse of Flaubert's protagonists is their "latent yearning for annihilation or nothingness." While the lovers-to-be are talking, they see the gravedigger Lestiboudois renting chairs to the onlookers; he is destined to bury Emma after her suicide.

Comedy enters with the prefectural councilor, Lieuvain, who arrives in a hired carriage drawn by two skinny horses while the national guard and the fire brigade scramble to present arms. The stage is now set on three levels. Rodolphe and Emma, from an upstairs window of the town hall, gaze down on lesser humanity. The local dignitaries are seated in red-plush armchairs on a platform behind the speakers. Beneath them are the ordinary citizens, standing in the meadow or sitting in rented chairs. Soon the councilor launches into his exordium, while the film cuts back and forth from the speaker to the lovers at their high window. This was a new device at the time, and Flaubert handles it in a masterly fashion. At first the pace is relatively slow, with a long speech by Rodolphe matched by an equally long passage from the councilor's oration. To emphasize the sense of a double verbal seduction, with the populace misled by the orator as Emma is by Rodolphe, the author pauses to survey the attentive crowd and then to enter Emma's thoughts: she smells the perfume in Rodolphe's hair and dreams of the ball at La Vaubyessard; she sees the stagecoach and remembers that it had carried Léon away. Now the prefectural councilor gives place to the chairman of the jury, Derozerays, and the tempo accelerates. There is a series of stychomythic interchanges, that is, of single lines spoken alternately by the chairman and Rodolphe; one speaks of live-stock, money, and manures, the other of romantic love. One has even more admiration for this brilliant counterpoint when one learns that Flaubert wrote the two sets of speeches separately, then pieced them together.

Besides being cinematic, the technique is novelistic in the sense that every detail in the chapter relates to the larger scheme of the book, sometimes as commentary, sometimes as concrete symbol, sometimes as a foreshadowing of events to come. There are, moreover, two final points to be made. Flaubert insisted on removing the personality of the artist from his work, as we have seen, and compared the writer to God in his universe, invisible yet omnipresent. The writer is truly invisible in this chapter, yet he is omnipresent too, and we see the events through *his* eyes, essentially, not those of the characters. If the general effect is one of drabness, that is Flaubert's judgment (though at times he comes close to agreeing with Rodolphe in that gentleman's supercilious remarks). There is also one occasion on which he breaks his own rule by making an editorial comment. At the end of a long paragraph devoted to Catherine Leroux, he loses his temper and says, "Thus did half a century of servitude stand before these beaming bourgeois."

The second of the final points has to do with Flaubert's images. Proust said that "there was not a single fine metaphor in the entire work," and suggested that the author's restricted use of metaphor and simile gave a special tone to the novel. Flaubert's comparisons are de-liberately commonplace: thus, the present-arms of the amateur soldiers sounds "like a copper cauldon rolling down a flight of stairs" and Emma's desires whirl "like grains of sand in the wind." He was trying not to be picturesque, but at the same time he wanted the book to be "a coloration, a nuance." One way of achieving that purpose was by repeating themes and images. He says, for example, that the head-dresses of the peasant women at the agricultural show were "like fluttering white butterfly wings." At the end of Part One, when Emma burns her bridal bouquet, he had said that shriveled bits of paper hovered at the back of the fireplace "like black butterflies." When

Léon seduces Emma in a cab with its curtains drawn, in Part Three, Flaubert will say that a bare hand emerged from the curtains and threw out some torn scraps of paper, which fluttered in the wind "like white butterflies, in a field of flowering red clover." Each occasion relates to one of Emma's three loves. Is it too venturesome to suggest that the writer may also have had in mind the Greek myth in which the soul—Psyche— leaves the body at the moment of death in the form of a butterfly?

Fathers and Sons (1861)

IVAN SERGEYEVICH TURGENEV (1818-1883) came of a family with estates in Orel Province, south of Moscow, but he spent most of his adult life in Germany and France. His novels are Russian in subject matter, but Western in technique, and they show a French concern for grace, precision, and clarity. Henry James seems to have regarded him as a French author; at any rate a masterly essay on Turgénieff, as the younger man called him, is included in James's collection *French Poets and Novelists* (1878). There James says of him that he "may sometimes be erratic, but he is never vague. He has a passion for distinctness, for bringing his characterization to a point, for giving you an example of his meaning." Later in the same essay James says of one novel, ". . . as always with our author, the drama is quite uncommented; the poet never plays chorus; situations speak for themselves." That was a feature of the new method already developed by Flaubert, who was to become Turgenev's friend.

The novelist's father was a colonel of cavalry who died when the boy was sixteen. His mother was an heiress, proud and vindictive, with several estates and hundreds of serfs, whom she treated despotically. She spoke Russian only to servants. Turgenev was educated by French and German tutors, and his first introduction to Russian literature was owed to a serf of the family, who read him passages from an eighteenth-century epic poem. After attending the universities of Moscow and St. Petersburg, with later studies in Berlin, he began publishing poems and sketches of no great moment; still, they were praised by Belinsky, a famous critic who also played a part in Dostoevsky's early career.

Turgenev first attracted wide attention with *A Sportsman's Notebook* (1852), in which he depicted the miserable condition of the Russian serfs. The Czar himself read the book, though it was condemned by his advisers, and later gave it credit for persuading him that the serfs should be freed.

The years that followed were the most productive ones of Turgenev's career. In 1855 he published *Rudin*, the story of a "superfluous man," one of those characters strong in yearnings but feeble in action who became a feature of Russian literature. In 1859 it was *A Nest of Gentlefolk*, about lovers kept apart by the hero's disastrous marriage. In 1860 it was *On the Eve*, with its tragic heroine, and the next year it was *Fathers and Sons*, regarded as his masterpiece. The scene reprinted here depicts a situation that recurs in many of Turgenev's books. A man and a woman in love with each other come to a confrontation. Reticence, pride, a touch of fear, and perhaps the simple inability to communicate make it impossible for them to avow their feelings, which are intensified by what a reader of our own time is likely to interpret as sexual frustration. Turgenev's biographers have suggested that his own complicated relations with the famous singer Pauline Viardot-Garcia may have provided an unconscious motive for exploiting this theme. It may also be, however, that his frustrated love for the singer was an enactment in life of the same inner need for defeat that is expressed in many of his novels.

Fathers and Sons aroused a critical tempest that raged around the figure of Bazarov, the hero or anti-hero. The younger liberals called him a caricature of everything they stood for, and Turgenev, himself a liberal, found himself in the uncomfortable position of being congratulated by the reactionaries. He had been living outside of Russia for much of the preceding decade, and he now decided to escape the hubbub by making his home in Western Europe. Most of his time was to be spent in Baden-Baden and Paris, often near the Viardot family (for he was fond of the husband and children as well as being vainly in love with the wife). Dostoevsky, whom he had befriended, attacked him noisily as being the leader of the Westernizing tendency in Russian letters. In Paris Flaubert was his closest literary friend, but he also saw a good deal of the younger Naturalists, including Zola, the brothers Goncourt, and Maupassant, who was long regarded as his disciple. The only novels of his later years were *Smoke* (1867) and *Virgin Soil* (1877), both dealing with social themes, though he also wrote a number of novellas, including the famous *Torrents of Spring*. Tired and discouraged for all his fame, Turgenev died on the outskirts of Paris near his beloved Pauline.

THE STORY

The action takes place in the spring and summer of 1859, two years before the Russian serfs were emancipated. That peaceful revolution was to be the end of an old order for which Turgenev, much as he condemned it, also felt a nostalgic affection. In *Fathers and Sons* the old order is represented by the Kirsanov brothers, Paul and Nicholas, who live on their decaying and inefficiently managed estate with their two hundred "souls." Both are types of the "superfluous man," overcome by a general faded lassitude and unable to pursue any course of action. To the estate comes Nicholas's son Arcady, down from the university at Petersburg in the company of his friend Bazarov, a medical student. Nicholas, a widower, is embarrassed by his peasant mistress Fenichka and the child she has recently borne him, but the "emancipated" young men accept the situation with equanimity. There is immediate antagonism, however, between the aristocratic older brother, Paul Kirsanov, and the self-proclaimed nihilist, Bazarov. "Our actions are governed by utility," Bazarov says. "In these days, negation is the most useful thing of all—and so we deny."

"Everything?" says Paul Kirsanov.

"Everything."

The antagonism leads to a duel in which Paul is slightly wounded, and Bazarov leaves to visit his parents. His father is a retired army surgeon, his mother is simple, affectionate, superstitious, and both of them live only in their pride and hope for their learned son. The contrast between their love and Bazarov's ruthless positivism once again underscores Turgenev's theme of generations unable to understand each other. There is a final irony. As the result of a stupid medical accident, typical of the Russian backwardness that Bazarov is trying to combat, he contracts typhus and dies shortly before the end of the novel.

Earlier in the book, the two young men meet Mme. Odintzov—Anna Sergeyevna Odintzova—a wealthy and beautiful but apparently cold widow. Arcady fancies himself in love with her, but is really in love with her younger sister Katya, whom he marries at the end of the story (as old Nicholas marries his peasant mistress). Bazarov refuses to admit to himself that he is in love with Mme. Odintzov, since that human commitment seems to him beneath the level of his scientific rationalism. The situation reaches a climax in the encounter that follows.

The translation is by George Reavey (1950) and is published by New American Library as a Signet Classic.

[*A Word Not Spoken*]   Chapter 27

Time, as we all know, is sometimes a bird on the wing, and sometimes a crawling worm; but men are happiest when oblivious of time's quick or slow pace. In this mood Arcady and Bazarov spent about a fortnight at Madame Odintzov's. Her regular life and the order she had instituted in her household were partly responsible for this. She adhered strictly to her time-table and obliged others to observe it. There was a fixed time for everything throughout the day. In the morning, at eight o'clock punctually, the company assembled for morning tea; from tea-time till lunch everyone followed his own bent; the lady of the house attended to the steward (her estate had been put on a rent basis), the servants and the head housekeeper. Before dinner the company gathered again for conversation or reading; the evening was given up to walks, card-games and music; at half-past ten Anna Sergeyevna would retire to her room, give her final instructions for the following day and go to bed.

The measured, rather dignified precision of this daily round was not to Bazarov's taste: "It's like rolling on rails," he used to declare: the footmen in livery, the decorous butlers and servants, offended his democratic sentiments. According to him, the next logical step would have been to dine in English fashion, in evening dress and white ties. One day he broached the subject to Anna Sergeyevna. Her manner disposed everyone to express his opinions frankly, and without reserve. When Bazarov had had his say, she rejoined, "You are right from your point of view, and maybe in this particular case I am too much of a 'lady'; but one cannot live in the country without routine, otherwise it would only lead to boredom." And she pursued her course. Bazarov grumbled, but the reason why Arcady and he found life so smooth at Madame Odintzov's was that everything in her house did "roll on rails." Nevertheless, since the day of their arrival at Nicolskoye's, both the young men had undergone a change. An unfamiliar anxiety had overtaken Bazarov, whom Anna Sergeyevna treated with obvious favour, even though she hardly ever saw eye to eye with him: he was easily irritated, reluctant to talk, bad-tempered in his looks and, as though impelled by an inward anguish, could hardly sit still for a moment. Arcady, who finally made up his mind that he was in love with Anna, began to suffer from subdued fits of depression. However, his depression did not prevent him from becoming more intimate with Katya; it even helped him to establish affectionate and comradely relations with her. "Anna doesn't think much of me! So be it! . . . But this good-hearted creature does not spurn me," he thought to himself, and his heart once more indulged in the sweetness of magnanimous sensations.

Katya vaguely grasped that he was seeking some consolation in her company, and she did not deny either herself or him the innocent pleasure of a half-shy, half-trusting friendship. In Anna Sergeyevna's presence they refrained from talking to one another. Katya invariably shrank into herself under her sister's probing glance, and Arcady, as befits a young man in love, had no eyes for anything but the object of his passion; but he felt happiest of all when alone with Katya. He knew that it was not in his power to hold Anna Sergeyevna's interest; when left alone with her, he grew shy and lost his pose; nor did she know what to say to him— he was too young for her. On the other hand, Arcady felt himself quite at home with Katya; he treated her indulgently, allowed her to air the impressions excited in her by the music, the reading of novels, verse and other such "trifles," without observing or, rather, failing to realize that these trifles also amused him. Katya for her part did not inhibit his feelings of melancholy. Arcady felt happy with Katya, Anna—with Bazarov; and this usually resulted in the two couples, especially when they went for a stroll, going their different ways so as to enjoy their intimacy for a while. Katya *adored* nature, and Arcady loved it too, though he did not dare to admit it; like Bazarov, Anna Sergeyevna was fairly indifferent to it. The fact that they were almost continuously separated from each other was not without its consequence for our friends: their relationship underwent a change. Bazarov stopped referring to Anna Sergeyevna when talking to Arcady; he even stopped railing at her "aristocratic ways"; he continued, it is true, to praise Katya as before, counselling his friend to tone down her sentimental inclinations, but his praise was hurried, his counsels dry, and, on the whole, he chatted with Arcady far less than was his wont . . . it looked as though he were avoiding him or felt ashamed in his presence. . . .

Arcady noted all this, but kept his observations to himself.

The real cause of all these "innovations" was the feeling inspired in Bazarov by Anna Sergeyevna—a feeling which tormented and enraged him, and which he would have at once repudiated with scoffing laughter and cynical vituperation if anyone had even distantly hinted at the possibility of what was going on in his mind. Bazarov was a great lover of women and feminine beauty, but love in the ideal sense or, as he would have put it, in the romantic sense, he called tomfoolery and unpardonable idiocy; he regarded chivalrous feelings as something in the nature of malformation or disease. On more than one occasion he had voiced his amazement at the fact that Toggenburg, with all his Minnesingers and Troubadours, had not been locked up in bedlam. "If you are attracted by a woman," he used to say, "try and gain her; but if that proves impossible—well, don't bother, drop her. A forest is not made up of one tree."

He liked Anna: the rumours about her, the freedom and independence of her mind, her undoubted penchant for him—all these seemed to argue in his favour; but he was quick to grasp that he could not "gain her." Moreover, to his amazement, he discovered that he lacked the resolution to "drop her." His blood took fire as soon as her image impinged on his mind; he could have controlled his blood easily, but something else had got into him, something he would not admit at any price, something which he had always scoffed at and which revolted his pride. In his conversations with Anna he used to indulge to an even greater extent than usual in his scathing indifference to everything savouring of romanticism; but when left to himself, he became indignantly aware of the romantic strain in his own composition. On these occasions he would set off into the forest and walk about there with large strides, breaking off any branch that barred his way and cursing both her and himself in a low voice, or he would clamber into a hayloft, into a barn, and, obstinately shutting his eyes, force himself to fall asleep, though he did not always succeed in achieving that result. Suddenly he would imagine those chaste hands one day twining themselves round his neck, those proud lips responding to his kisses, those intelligent eyes gazing lovingly—yes, lovingly—into his own; his head would go round and he would find an instant of oblivion before his indignation flared up again. As though tempted by the devil, he caught himself thinking all sorts of immodest thoughts. Sometimes, it seemed to him that a change was coming over Anna too, that there was something particular about the expression of her face, that perhaps . . . But at this point he would usually stamp his feet, grind his teeth and shake his clenched fist menacingly under his own nose.

And yet Bazarov was not entirely mistaken. He had excited Anna Sergeyevna's imagination; he had intrigued her, and she devoted much thought to him. In his absence she did not long for him, she did not yearn for him, but his presence always stimulated her; she was glad to be alone with him and glad to converse with him, even when he irritated her or shocked her taste and her refined habits of mind. She behaved as though she wished both to test him and to explore her own depths.

One day, as they were strolling in the garden, he suddenly informed her in a grim voice of his intention to depart in the near future and to visit his father. . . . Anna turned pale as though something had pricked her heart, and pricked it so painfully that she was surprised; she worried for a long time afterwards about the significance of this. Bazarov had told her of his intended departure without any idea of testing her or checking her reaction; he was not in the habit of "fabricating effects." That very morning he had seen his father's steward, Timofeyich, who was by way of being the "uncle" of his childhood. This Timofeyich, an experienced and astute old man, with faded yellow hair, red weather-beaten face and tiny teardrops in his shrunken eyes, had unexpectedly confronted Bazarov, wearing a short coat of greyish-blue cloth, belted with a leather thong, and tarred boots.

"So it's you, old Timofeyich! How goes it?" Bazarov had exclaimed.

"Greetings to you, young master," the old man had begun, smiling joyously, so that his face had suddenly dissolved into wrinkles.

"What have you come for? Were you sent to fetch me or what?"

"If it please your honour, how can that be!" Timofeyich had started to mumble (he remembered his master's strict injunctions when setting off). "I was on the way to town on the master's business when I happened to hear of your honour's being here, so I turned aside from the main road, that is—to have a peep at your honour . . . it wouldn't do to disturb you otherwise."

"Now don't tell fibs," Bazarov interrupted him: "Is this the way to town?" Timofeyich looked sheepish and made no reply. "Is my father well?"

"Yes, thank God."

"And my mother?"

"Arina Vlassyevna is very well too, the Lord be thanked."

"No doubt they are expecting me!"

Old Timofeyich hung his small head to one side.

"Ah, your honour, how could they not be expecting you! As God's my witness, my heart's grown sick with watching your parents worry."

"Well, that'll do, that'll do, don't exaggerate. Tell them I'll be coming soon."

"As you will," Timofeyich had replied with a sigh.

As he quitted the house, he had pulled his cap over his eyes with both hands. On getting into the rickety droshky, which had been left standing at the gateway, he had started off at a trot—but not in the direction of the town.

The same evening Anna Sergeyevna was sitting in her study with Bazarov, while Arcady was pacing up and down the music-room, listening to Katya as she played. The princess had retired upstairs; as a rule, she could not bear guests, especially these "new loony ones," as she had dubbed them. In the drawing-room, she merely sulked, but in her own quarters in the presence of her maid, she sometimes gave vent to such a stream of abuse as made her cap jerk up and down on her head together with her wig. Anna Sergeyevna was well aware of this.

"Why are you thinking of going away?" she began. "What about your promise?"

Bazarov stirred.

"Which promise?"

"You've forgotten then? You were going to give me a few lessons in chemistry."

"What's to be done! My father is expecting me; I can't dawdle here any longer. However, you can read Pelouse and Frémy, *Notions générales de la Chimie*; it's a good book and clearly written. You will find in it everything you need."

"But don't you remember, you tried to persuade me that a book was no substitute for . . . I forget how you put it, but you know what I want to say . . . do you remember?"

"What's to be done!" Bazarov repeated.

"Why must you go?" Anna Sergeyevna asked, lowering her voice.

He glanced at her. She had thrown her head back against the

arm-chair and folded her arms, which were bare to the elbow. She looked paler in the light of a solitary lamp, hung over with a gauze-like paper shade. She was swathed in the soft folds of a voluminous white dress; the tips of her feet, which were also crossed, were just visible.

"And why should I stay?" Bazarov replied.

Anna Sergeyevna turned her head slightly.

"What do you mean by that? Aren't you enjoying yourself here? Or do you imagine that no one here will regret your going?"

"Of that I am positive."

Anna Sergeyevna had nothing to say for a moment.

"A pity you think so. However, I don't believe you. You could not have meant it seriously." Bazarov made no move. "Why don't you speak?"

"And what am I to say to you? There's no point in having regrets about people, and even less so about me."

"Why do you say that?"

"I am a serious and uninteresting person. I'm no conversationalist."

"You're angling for a compliment, Eugene Vassilich."

"That is no habit of mine. Don't you know yourself that the refinements of life are beyond my reach—the refinements on which you set so much store?"

Anna Sergeyevna nibbled a corner of her handkerchief.

"You can think what you like, but I shall miss you when you go."

"Arcady is staying behind," Bazarov replied.

Anna Sergeyevna gave a slight shrug of her shoulders.

"I shall miss you," she said.

"Really? In any case you won't miss me for long."

"Why do you assume that?"

"Because you told me yourself that you feel bored only when your routine is upset. You have arranged your life with such blameless rectitude that there could be no place in it for boredom or grief . . . or any disturbing emotions."

"You find that I am blamelessly . . . that is, that I have arranged my life with such rectitude?"

"Exactly so! Now take this, for example: in a few minutes it will strike ten, and I already know in advance that you will send me packing."

"No, I won't. You may stay. Will you open the window? . . . It feels stuffy."

Bazarov got up and pushed at the window. It flew open at once with a rattle. . . . He had not expected it to open so easily; moreover, his hands were shaking. The dark, mild evening peeped into the room with its almost black sky, faintly rustling trees and the fresh fragrance of the pure untrammelled air.

"Draw the blind and sit down," Anna Sergeyevna said. "I'd like to have a talk with you before you depart. Tell me something about yourself; you never talk of yourself."

"I try and chat with you about useful subjects."

"How very modest of you. . . . But I should like to learn something about you, your family, your father, for whom you are forsaking us."

"Why is she talking like this?" Bazarov thought.

"It's not at all interesting," he said aloud, "especially for you; we're obscure sort of folk. . . ."

"And according to you, I am an aristocrat?"

Bazarov raised his eyes and looked at Madame Odintzov.

"Yes," he said with over-emphatic bluntness.

She smiled.

"I can see that you hardly know me, although you assure me that all people are alike and that they are not worth individual study. One day I shall tell you about my life . . . but you must tell me about yours first."

"I hardly know you," Bazarov repeated. "Maybe you are right; it may be true that every person is an enigma. Now let's take you, for instance: you shun people, you find them a nuisance, and yet here you have invited two students to come and stay with you. Why does a woman of your intelligence and your beauty live in the country?"

"What? How did you put it?" Madame Odintzov cried with animation. "With my . . . beauty?"

Bazarov frowned.

"It doesn't matter," he muttered. "I wished to say that I don't quite understand why you have settled in the country."

"You don't understand. . . . However, you must explain it in some way?"

"Yes. . . . I assume that you remain fixed in one and the same spot because you have been spoilt, you have grown too fond of comfort and all that goes with it, and are quite impervious to anything else."

Madame Odintzov smiled again.

"You are determined to disbelieve in my capacity for enthusiasm?"

Bazarov glanced at her from under his eyebrows.

"Out of curiosity, maybe; not otherwise."

"Indeed? Well, now I understand what brought us together; you are exactly like me."

"Brought us together . . ." Bazarov repeated in a hollow voice.

"Yes! . . . but I forgot that you were intending to go away."

Bazarov rose. The lamp was burning dimly in the middle of the dusky, fragrant and secluded room; the irritating freshness of the nocturnal air came pouring through the blind as it stirred occasionally, and its mysterious whispering seeped through. Anna sat perfectly still, but a secret agitation was gradually invading her. . . . It communicated itself to Bazarov. He suddenly realized that he was alone with a young and beautiful woman. . . .

"Where are you going?" she slowly asked.

Without replying he sank back into his chair.

"So you regard me as a placid, spoilt and self-indulgent creature," she went on in the same tone, without taking her eyes off the window. "But the one thing I know about myself is that I am unhappy."

"Unhappy! Why? You don't mean to say that you attach any importance to slanderous tittle-tattle?"

Madame Odintzov frowned. She felt annoyed at his interpreting her so well.

"These slanders don't even amuse me, and I am too proud to let them upset me. I am unhappy because . . . I have no desire, no longing for life. You look distrustfully at me, you think: there's an 'aristocrat,' covered in lace and seated in a velvet arm-chair. I shall not disguise the fact that I am fond of what you call comfort, but at the same time I have very little desire to live. Interpret this contradiction as you will. However, all this is romanticism in your eyes."

Bazarov shook his head.

"You are in good health, independent, rich. What more do you need? What is it you want?"

"What do I want?" Madame Odintzov repeated, sighing. "I have grown weary and old; I seem to have lived a great age. Yes, I've grown old," she added, gently drawing the ends of her mantilla over her bare arms. Her eyes met Bazarov's, and she flushed slightly. "I have behind me so many memories: my life in Petersburg, prosperity, then poverty, my father's death, my marriage, my trip abroad, it had to be . . . There are plenty of memories, but nothing to remember, and ahead, in front of me, stretches a long, long road, but I have no goal. . . . So I have no desire even to tread the path."

"You are so disillusioned?" Bazarov asked.

"No," Madame Odintzov replied with deliberation. "But I am incomplete. It seems to me that, if I were capable of becoming strongly attached to something . . ."

"You are longing to fall in love," Bazarov interrupted her, "but you are incapable of it: that is your unhappiness."

Madame Odintzov began to inspect the mantilla which covered her arms.

"Am I incapable of love?" she asked.

"Hardly! Only I was wrong to call it unhappiness. The contrary is true, people deserve pity who do fall for that."

"Fall for what?"

"Love."

"And how do you know that?"

"By hearsay," Bazarov retorted angrily.

"You're playing the coquette," he thought to himself. "You are merely bored and want to provoke me out of idleness, but I . . ." And, indeed, his heart was being torn.

"Moreover, you may be too exacting," he said, bending his whole body forward and playing with the fringe of the arm-chair.

"Perhaps. All or nothing is the way I see it. A life for a life. If you take mine, give me yours. And, if you do so, you must have no regrets or afterthoughts. Otherwise I don't want it."

"Indeed?" Bazarov remarked. "There's justice in that, and I am surprised that until now . . . you have not found what you wanted."

"And do you think it's so easy to surrender one's self completely to whatever it might be?"

"Not so easy once you start thinking, biding your time, putting a price on yourself, growing in your own estimation. That is so; but if you stop reflecting, then it's quite easy to surrender."

"But how can one fail to set a value on one's self? If I had no price, who would want my devotion?"

"That's not my affair; it's for the other person to decide on my value. What matters is to be able to surrender yourself."

Anna detached herself from the back of the arm-chair.

"You are talking as if you had experienced it all."

"It arose out of the conversation, Anna Sergeyevna. As you know, all this is not in my line."

"But would you be capable of surrendering yourself?"

"I don't know. I don't wish to boast."

Madame Odintzov did not say anything, and Bazarov fell silent. From the drawing-room came the sound of a piano being played.

"Katya is playing very late to-night," Madame Odintzov remarked.

Bazarov got up.

"Yes, it is quite late," he said. "It's time you were in bed."

"Wait. Why are you in such a hurry? . . . I want to say a word to you."

"What is it?"

"Wait," Madame Odintzov whispered. Her eyes rested on Bazarov; she seemed to be scrutinizing him with great attention.

He took a turn about the room and then, suddenly approaching her, bade her a hurried "Good night." He squeezed her hand so hard that she almost cried out and left the room. She raised her numbed fingers to her lips, blew on them and, rising brusquely and impetuously from her arm-chair, strode rapidly towards the door as though intending to call Bazarov back. . . . A maid entered with a decanter on a silver tray. Madame Odintzov stopped short, ordered her to go away and sat down again, immersed in thought. Uncoiling itself like some dark snake, her hair spread over her shoulders. For a long while yet the lamp burnt on in Anna Sergeyevna's room, and for a long while she remained sitting motionless, only occasionally with her fingers stroking her hands which were now beginning to feel the chill of the nocturnal air.

As for Bazarov, he returned some two hours later to his bedroom, his boots all wet with dew, his hair dishevelled and his expression grim. He found Arcady sitting at the writing-desk, a book in his hands and his jacket all buttoned up.

"You're not in bed yet?" Bazarov asked in a tone almost of regret.

"You were a long time with Anna Sergeyevna to-night," Arcady retorted, without replying to the question.

"Yes, I was with her all the time you and Katya were playing the piano."

"I was not playing . . ." Arcady started to say and then stopped. He felt the tears welling to his eyes, but he did not want to weep in front of his scoffing friend.

AFTERWORD

Only in the first sentence of this chapter does Turgenev make an authorial comment of the sort that Thackeray, for example, would have offered on almost every page. Elsewhere he stands at a distance, and "the drama is quite uncommented," as Henry James remarked of his work. Even that first sentence about the passage of time has a function in the story: it leads into a rapid summary of events during a fortnight when the two couples are undergoing emotional transformations.

The conflicts and contradictions are deftly introduced. Mme. Odin-tzov's orderly schedule for her household should please Bazarov, the "new" man with a passion for rational systems; instead it offends him, possibly because of the irrational emotion she has aroused in him. At the same time her rage for order seems to be a sublimation of her unruly feeling for Bazarov, of which she is not yet aware. And still another contradiction: Bazarov the realist expresses his own feelings by taking frantic walks in the woods and indulging in the daydreams of a romantic poet.

The point of view in the chapter is that of the omniscient narrator who can see into the minds of his characters, but who does not feel it necessary to look into them very far. Thus, it is enough to say of Arcady that he "finally made up his mind that he was in love with Anna," and of Katya that she "vaguely grasped that he was seeking some consolation in her company." As for Mme. Odintzov, her thoughts are not revealed, so that she retains the fascination of being to some extent a mystery. Bazarov is the only character into whose mind the narrator feels impelled to probe more deeply. The reasons for this choice may be that Turgenev found the younger generation, as represented by Bazarov, at once sympathetic and repellent. "My entire tale is directed against the gentry as a ruling class," he remarked about *Fathers and Sons*. On the other hand, he portrays the young nihilist as being arrogant, pretentious, and, in his human relations, coldly rational—in other words, as having qualities that readers were certain to regard with antipathy. Perhaps Turgenev's ambiguous attitude toward his fictional creation accounts for his giving Bazarov a rich inner life, in an effort to comprehend the actual Bazarovs he had encountered.

After the summary of events during the young men's visit to Mme. Odintzov comes a brief scene between Bazarov and his father's steward, the first dialogue in the chapter; then follows the longer and crucial scene between Bazarov and Anna Sergeyevna in her study. Here physical details are few and are chiefly seen through Bazarov's eyes: Anna's white dress, her bare arms, and the tips of her feet in the dim lamplight. Nature, officially scorned by both, intrudes twice through the opened window; it is personified by Turgenev as a beneficent force whose solace is lost on the protagonists. Their conversation gives the impression that what is unsaid is more important than what is uttered. Many remarks are questions that remain unanswered, as if to emphasize the pathetic isolation of each from the other. Physical movement in negligible: Bazarov's shaking hands, the few times he sits down or rises before his last distracted exit from the room; Anna Sergeyevna merely resting and occasionally turning her head. Once she bites her handkerchief. The noise of the crashing window at the beginning is balanced by the soft strains of Katya at the piano near the close, when music enters to amplify the emotional climate. Chekhov uses the same device in several of his plays.

The reader feels that a declaration of love is imminent; but Bazarov's brusque "Good night" cuts off Anna's statement that she wants to say a word to him. After the violent handclasp and Anna's rapid steps toward the door as if to call Bazarov back, Turgenev employs the one simile in the chapter: "Uncoiling itself like some dark snake, her hair spread over her shoulders." Her silence afterward contrasts with Bazarov's agitated two-hour walk. The very short scene between Bazarov and Arcady provides a coda. Arcady is almost weeping, though the author does not tell us why; perhaps it is from jealousy aroused by what he thinks is Bazarov's success with Mme. Odintzov. A touch of irony is that Arcady does not want to weep "in front of his scoffing friend," when we as readers know Bazarov's own despair. Analogies between the arts are risky, but might we not say that this conclusion has some of the quality of the "dying fall" to be found in music by Turgenev's near-contemporary, Tchaikowski?

War and Peace (1865-1869)

"It is hopeless to grapple with Tolstoy," T. E. Lawrence remarked in one of his letters. A big man physically, bearlike in somewhat the same fashion as Pierre Bezukhov in *War and Peace*—though not corpulent like Pierre, but simply massive—he was also hugely productive. One edition of his writings runs to ninety volumes, and it includes a six-act drama as if to prove that the customary five-act structure was not enough for such a giant. One thinks of Tolstoy (1828-1910) in connection with such disparate nineteenth-century figures as Liszt, Balzac, Hugo, and Wagner, men who carried to its apogee the Faustian will to live, love, and create works of art. Of the last activity he once said that he poured a lot of life down the inkwell.

LEV NIKOLAYEVICH TOLSTOI—to transliterate his Russian name— was born south of Moscow on the estate of Yasnaya Polyana ("Clear Meadows"), which, with its 350 serfs in four villages, had once be- longed to his mother's family, the Volkonskys; they seem to have resembled the Bolkonsky family in *War and Peace*. His father was a retired lieutenant-colonel who had fought against Napoleon at Borodino and who may have served as a model for Nikolai Rostov in the novel. The mother died before he was two years old, the father when he was nine, and Tolstoy was left to the care of his loving aunts. It was an idyllic period of his life, one which he later recorded in an autobiographical trilogy: *Childhood* (1852), *Boyhood* (1855), and *Youth* (1857).

In his sixteenth year he entered the University of Kazan with the intention of studying Oriental languages, but he changed over to the law faculty and then left the university out of disappointment with his subjects, his teachers, and his lack of progress. Having returned to Yasnaya Polyana, he entertained vague projects for scientific farming and for improving the condition of his serfs. When the projects came to nothing, he turned to the pleasures of St. Petersburg and Moscow society.

In 1851 he joined his brother Nikolai, an army officer, at a frontier post in the Caucasus, then the Wild West of Russia. Tolstoy's bravery in action against rebellious mountain tribes won him a commission. In 1855, during the Crimean War, he took part in the defense of Sevastopol against the French and the British. Out of this experience he wrote a series of magazine articles soon published as a book, *Sevastopol Sketches*. It was concerned with the horrors of warfare and the sufferings endured by the common soldier. "We must be done with lying," he said: "war is not a recreation."

As a result of *Sevastopol Sketches* and the autobiographical trilogy, he was recognized as the foremost writer of the new generation. The Tsar had him released from the army. He became a figure in literary circles and an associate of Turgenev, for example, though the two novelists were fated to quarrel. In 1857 and 1860 Tolstoy made his only visits to Western Europe. He met the exiled revolutionist Alexander Herzen in London (though he did not meet Karl Marx or read his work until much later). In France he met Proudhon, who is remembered for the phrase "Property is theft." Proudhon's book *La Guerre et la Paix* (1861) may have suggested *War and Peace* as the title finally adopted for Tolstoy's masterpiece. But in general such encounters with the West had the same effect on Tolstoy that they would later have on Dostoevsky; they reinforced his Russian nationalism.

Reestablished at Yasnaya Polyana, he started free schools for the peasants, based on theories adapted from Rousseau and Pestalozzi. The government was suspicious and sent agents to investigate for possible sedition. In 1862, at the age of thirty-four, he married Sofya Andreyevna Bers, the daughter of a prominent physician; she was then eighteen. She was to bear him thirteen children. Much later he would say, "Man survives earthquakes, epidemics, the horror of disease, and all the agonies of the soul, but for all time his most tormenting tragedy has been, is, and will be—the tragedy of the bedroom." Still, the first fifteen years of his marriage were happy ones and were also intensely productive. They were the time when he published *The Cossacks* (1863), *War and Peace* (1865-1869), and *Anna Karenina* (1875-1877).

While he was finishing this last novel, Tolstoy underwent a grave spiritual crisis; he seriously thought of committing suicide. His metaphysical sufferings are recorded in *A Confession* (1879). Rejecting as inadequate the teachings of the Russian Church and the systems propounded by philosophers, he took his departure from Matthew 5:39—"that ye resist not evil"—and evolved his own form of Christianity. God was not a personal deity, he said, but rather the symbol of the highest Good. The Kingdom of God was to be found within us, if we could love all mankind and abstain from every sort of lust, hatred, and violence. Maxim Gorky, a great admirer of Tolstoy, once said of his theology: "With God he has very suspicious relations; they sometimes remind me of the relations of two bears in one den."

For the rest of his life Tolstoy dedicated himself to the practice and preaching of his new faith, which, besides the doctrine of nonviolent resistance to evil, also included such features as vegetarianism, life without alcohol or tobacco, physical labor for the good of the soul, and the rejection of all institutions based on force. Books in which he proclaimed his doctrines include *What I Believe In* (1882) and *What Then Must We Do?* (1886). In *What Is Art?* (1897-1898) he defined art as the communication of feelings between the author and the reader and said that good art is the imaginative rendering of morally good feelings. This emphasis on moral responsibility forced him to reject almost all the artistic masterpieces of the past, including his own great novels. His later works of fiction were each written with a didactic purpose. They include "The Death of Ivan Ilyich" (1884), *The Kreutzer Sonata* (1889), *Hadji Murad* (1896-1904), and his last full-length novel, *Resurrection* (1899-1900).

THE NOVEL AND THE STORY IT TELLS

War and Peace grew out of a conception that underwent many changes before and after Tolstoy started writing the first draft. At first it was to be a book—not a novel, not a history, but a work of its own species—to be called "The Decembrists"; it was to deal with the liberalized aristocrats who planned to depose Nicholas I, a particularly autocratic ruler, and make Russia a constitutional monarchy. Their conspiracy was crushed in December 1825. It was based, however, on ideals which the liberals, mostly army officers, had acquired in France while fighting against Napoleon; and this fact, among others, led Tolstoy back to the period of the Napoleonic wars. At one time he dreamed of "The Decembrists" as a vast trilogy in which the second volume—or series of volumes —would deal with the conspiracy of 1825 and the third with Pierre Bezukhov's return, at the end of the Crimean War, from exile in Siberia.

The first volume—actually published as three—is the only one that Tolstoy wrote, except for rough drafts of a few later chapters. It deals in succession with the Austrian campaign of 1805, the Prussian campaign of 1807, and the destruction in 1812 of Napoleon's *Grande Armée* during his retreat from Moscow. Especially on its martial side, *War and Peace* is a modern *Iliad*; but it is also a novel of domestic life, one that treats the complicated interrelations of four noble families: the Rostovs, the Bezukhovs, the Bolkonskys, and the Kuragins. Finally it is a novel of spiritual regeneration as achieved in different fashions by its two heroes, Pierre Bezukhov and Prince Andrei Bolkonsky.

Throughout the novel, which is divided into fifteen parts and a double epilogue, St. Petersburg is depicted as a city of French manners and faithless hearts, in contrast with the Russian simplicity of Moscow. The Kuragins, who come closest to being the villains of the story, are a St. Petersburg family, while the open-hearted Rostovs divide their time between a country estate and Moscow. The domestic intrigue of the early parts involves the possibility that Anatol Kuragin will win the hand and fortune of Princess Marya Bolkonsky, Andrei's sister, and that Ellen Kuragin will marry the other hero, Pierre Bezukhov, an illegitimate son who is soon to inherit his father's immense estates.

Andrei leaves for the Austrian campaign of 1805, as does Nikolai Rostov, whose younger sister Natasha is the heroine of the book. At this time we are given our first glimpse of Kutuzov, the Russian commander-in-chief, a tired old man whom Tolstoy regards as the embodiment of practical wisdom; later his passivity will be contrasted with the busy arrogance of Napoleon. Andrei is severely wounded at Austerlitz. After his recovery he returns to his father's estate, Bleak Hills, in time to witness the birth of a son and the death in childbed of his wife, the "little Princess," whom he realizes that he has never truly loved. Pierre is trapped into marrying Ellen Kuragin, though later he will fight a duel with one of her lovers, then order her out of his Moscow house.

Both heroes are dissatisfied with themselves and are seeking some form of spiritual understanding. Neither of them takes part in the Prussian campaign of 1807, which is presented in Part Five through the eyes of Nikolai Rostov. Parts Six, Seven, and Eight deal with the peaceful interim that followed. They include a magnificent picture of life on the Rostovs' country estate as well as other pictures of society and politics in St. Petersburg and Moscow. Andrei becomes engaged to Natasha, but his father orders him to defer the marriage. During his absence in Western Europe, Natasha breaks off the engagement. She plans to elope with Anatol Kuragin, who does not tell her that he has a wife in Poland; but the elopement is thwarted with the help of Pierre, who buys off his brother-in-law.

Parts Nine through Fourteen are the epical story of the year 1812, when Napoleon invaded Russia. At the Battle of Borodino, Andrei is again wounded; this time the wound will prove fatal, but only after a long illness. Pierre is in Moscow when the city goes up in flames. Arrested by the French on the false charge of being an incendiary, he narrowly escapes being shot. Soon he meets another prisoner, old Platon Karataev, whose simple peasant wisdom and Christian piety suggest to him a new way of life. Andrei, while on his deathbed, undergoes a spiritual experience of the same order.

"All's Well That Ends Well" was one of Tolstoy's earlier titles for the novel. In the end the Kuragins are punished; Anatol is killed at Borodino and his sister Ellen, Pierre's wife, dies of a drug she has taken to induce an abortion. Pierre marries Natasha, and her brother Nikolai marries Princess Marya Bolkonsky. There is a passage in the otherwise happy or philosophical Epilogue that looks forward to Tolstoy's original plan for a vast trilogy. Pierre dreams of joining the men who would later be known as Decembrists in their plot to reform the government. But by this time Tolstoy's characters have taken charge of their own destinies, and the reader finds it hard to believe that Pierre, immured as he is in family life, would ever have joined a revolutionary conspiracy.

The episode that follows—the death of Petya Rostov, Natasha's younger brother—is a sequence of five short chapters from Part Fourteen. In a perceptive book, *Tolstoy and the Novel*, John Bayley calls it the true climax of *War and Peace*. The translation is a new one by Ann Dunnigan made for Signet Classics (New York: New American Library).

[*The Death of Petya*]   *Chapter 7*

Having left his parents after their departure from Moscow, Petya joined his regiment and was soon taken on as an orderly officer by a general in command of a large detachment. From the time he received his commission, and especially after joining the active army and taking part in the battle of Vyazma, Petya had been in a constant state of elation at being grown-up, and ecstatically eager not to miss any opportunity to do something really heroic. He was exceedingly delighted with what he saw and experienced in the army, but at the same time it always seemed to him that the most genuinely heroic exploits were being performed just where he did not happen to be. And he was in a hurry to get where he was not.

On the twenty-first of October, when his general expressed a wish to send someone to Denisov's detachment, Petya begged so piteously to be sent that the general could not refuse. But as he was sending him off, he recalled Petya's foolhardy action at Vyazma, where instead of keeping to the road to go where he had been sent, he had galloped to the front line under the fire of the French and there had fired two shots from his pistol; with this in mind the general explicitly forbade Petya to take part in any engagement whatever that Denisov might be planning. This is why Petya had blushed and was disconcerted when Denisov asked him whether he could stay. Until he reached the edge of the forest Petya had fully intended to carry out his instructions to the letter and return at once. But when he saw the French, saw Tikhon, and learned that there would certainly be an attack that night, he decided, with the rapidity with which young people change their views, that his general, whom he had greatly respected till then, was a rubbishy German and that Denisov was a hero, that the Esaul and Tikhon were heroes too, and that it would be shameful to desert them at a critical moment.

It was growing dark by the time Denisov, Petya, and the Esaul rode up to the watchman's hut. In the twilight they could see the saddled horses, and the Cossacks and hussars, who had rigged up rough shelters in the glade and were kindling a glowing fire in a hollow of the forest where the smoke could not be seen by the French. In the entry of the little hut a Cossack with his sleeves rolled up was cutting up a sheep. Inside the hut three of Denisov's officers were converting a door into a tabletop. Petya took off his wet clothes, gave them to be dried, and immediately set to work to help the officers arrange the dinner table.

In ten minutes the table was ready and a napkin spread on it. There was vodka, a flask of rum, white bread, roast mutton, and salt on the table.

Sitting at the table with the officers and tearing at the fat, savory mutton with greasy fingers, Petya was in an ecstatic, childish state of love for all men, and consequently convinced that others loved him in the same way.

"So then, what do you think, Vasily Dmitrich," he said to Denisov, "it won't matter my staying just one day with you, will it?" And not waiting for a reply, he answered his own question. "You see, I was told to find out, and I am finding out——Only do let me be in the very—in the chief—I don't care about rewards—but I want——"

Petya clenched his teeth and looked about him, tossing his head and waving his arm.

"In the very chief . . ." Denisov repeated with a smile.

"Only, please, do let me have absolute command of something, so that I may . . . really command," Petya continued. "What difference can it make to you? . . . Oh, you want a knife?" he said, turning to an officer who was trying to cut off a piece of mutton.

He handed him his clasp knife. The officer admired the knife.

"Please keep it. I have several like it," said Petya, blushing. "Heavens! I completely forgot," he suddenly cried, "I have some wonderful raisins—you know, the seedless ones. We have a new canteen-keeper—he gets such first-rate things. I bought ten pounds of them. I always like something sweet. Do you want some?"

And Petya ran out to his Cossack in the passage and brought back some bags which contained about five pounds of raisins.

"Have some, gentlemen, do have some. Don't you need a coffee-pot?" he said to the Esaul. "I bought a fine one from our canteen-keeper. He has first-rate things. And he's very honest. That's the great thing. I'll be sure to send it to you. Or perhaps your flints are giving out, or are worn out—that happens sometimes. I brought some with me, here they are—" and he showed them a bag, "a hundred flints. I bought them very cheap. Please take as many as you want, or all of them if you like. . . ."

And all at once, dismayed at the thought that he had let his tongue run away with him, Petya stopped and blushed.

He tried to remember whether he had been guilty of any other blunder. And recalling the events of the day, he thought of the French drummerboy.

"It's all very well for us here, but what about him? What have they done with him? Have they given him anything to eat? Have they treated him badly?" he wondered. But having caught himself saying too much about the flints, he was afraid to speak out.

"I might ask," he thought, "but they'll say: 'He's a boy himself, so he pities the other boy.' I'll show them tomorrow whether I'm a boy. . . . I wonder if I'd be embarrassed if I should ask?" Petya thought. "Oh, well, I don't care," and blushing and glancing at the officers' faces in dread of detecting their mockery, he impulsively said:

"May I call in the boy who was taken prisoner . . . and give him something to eat . . . perhaps . . . ?"

"Yes, poor little fellow," said Denisov, who evidently saw nothing shameful in this reminder. "Call him in. His name is Vincent Bosse. Have him fetched."

"I'll go," said Petya.

"Yes, poor little fellow," Denisov repeated.

Petya was standing at the door when Denisov said this. Slipping between the officers, he went up to Denisov and said:

"I must embrace you for that, my dear fellow. Ah, how splendid! How fine!"

And having embraced Denisov, he ran out to the yard.

"Bosse! Vincent!" he shouted, standing by the door.

"Who do you want, sir?" someone asked in the darkness.

Petya replied that he wanted the French boy who had been taken prisoner that day.

"Ah, Vesseny?" said a Cossack.

The name Vincent had already been changed by the Cossacks to *Vesseny*, and by the peasants and soldiers to *Visenya*. In both names there was a suggestion of spring* which seemed appropriate to the appearance of the young boy.

"He's there by the fire, warming himself. Hey, Visenya! Visenya! . . . Vesseny!" their voices rang out in the darkness, catching up the cry and laughing.

"He's a sharp little fellow," said a hussar standing near Petya. "We gave him something to eat a little while ago. He was terribly hungry."

There was the sound of footsteps in the darkness and the drummerboy came toward the door, his bare feet splashing through the mud.

"Ah, there you are!" said Petya in French. "Do you want something to eat? Don't be afraid, they won't hurt you," he added, shyly laying a friendly hand on his arm. "Come in, come in."

"*Merci, monsieur,*" said the drummerboy in a quavering, almost childish voice, and he began wiping his muddy feet on the doorsill.

* The Russian word for spring is *vesna*. TRANS.

There were a great many things Petya longed to say to the drummerboy, but he did not dare. He stood irresolutely beside him in the entry. Then in the darkness he took the boy's hand and pressed it.

"Come in, come in," he repeated in a gentle whisper.

"Oh, I wonder what I could do for him!" thought Petya, and opening the door he let the boy go in before him.

When the drummerboy was in the hut Petya sat down at some distance from him, thinking that it would not be dignified to take much notice of him. But he kept fingering the money in his pocket, wondering whether it would be humiliating to give it to the boy.

Chapter 8

The arrival of Dolokhov diverted Petya's attention from the drummerboy, who on Denisov's orders had been given some vodka and mutton, and then had been dressed in a Russian coat so that he might be kept with their band and not sent away with the other prisoners.

Petya had heard a great many stories in the army of Dolokhov's extraordinary bravery and of his cruelty to the French, so from the moment Dolokhov entered the hut he could not take his eyes off him, but held his head high, and assumed a more and more valiant air, that he might not be unworthy even of such company as Dolokhov's.

Petya was struck by the simplicity of Dolokhov's appearance.

Denisov, dressed in a Cossack coat, had a beard, wore an icon of Nikolai the Wonder-Worker on his breast, and his whole manner and way of speaking bespoke the singularity of his position. But Dolokhov, who in Moscow had affected Persian dress, now looked like the most punctilious Guards officer. He was clean-shaven, wore the padded coat of the Guards with the order of St. George in his buttonhole, and a simple forage cap set straight on his head. He took off his wet felt cloak in a corner of the room and without greeting anyone went directly to Denisov and began questioning him about the matter in hand.

Denisov told him of the designs the large detachments had on the transport, of the message Petya had brought, and his own replies to both generals. Then he told him all he knew about the position of the French detachment.

"That's all very well, but we must know what troops they are, and their numbers," said Dolokhov. "We must go and have a look. We can't start this thing without knowing for certain how many of them there are. I like doing things with precision. Come, wouldn't one of you gentlemen like to ride over to the French camp with me? I have an extra uniform with me."

"I—I—I'll come with you!" cried Petya.

"There's not the slightest need for you to go," said Denisov addressing Dolokhov, "and as for him, I won't let him go on any account."

"I like that!" exclaimed Petya. "Why shouldn't I go?"

"Because there's no weason to."

"Well, you must forgive me, because . . . because . . . I'm going and that's all. You will take me, won't you?" he cried, turning to Dolokhov.

"Why not?" replied Dolokhov absently, as he scrutinized the face of the drummerboy.

"Have you had that youngster with you long?" he asked Denisov.

"He was taken today, but he knows nothing. I'm keeping him with me."

"Oh, and what do you do with the rest?" asked Dolokhov.

"What do I do with them? Send them in and get a weceipt!" cried Denisov, suddenly flushing. "And I can say with confidence that I haven't a single man's life on my conscience. Would it be so difficult for you to send thirty, or even thwee hundwed, men to town under escort instead of sullying—I speak plainly—the honor of a soldier?"

"That kind of chivalrous talk would suit this little sixteen-year-old Count here," said Dolokhov with a cold sneer, "but it's high time you dropped it."

"Why, I haven't said anything—all I said is that I'm certainly going with you," Petya put in shyly.

"For you and me, my friend, it's time to drop these amenities," continued Dolokhov, as if deriving particular satisfaction from speaking of a subject that irritated Denisov. "Now, why have you kept this boy?" he asked, shaking his head. "Because you're sorry for him? We know these receipts of yours. You send off a hundred men and thirty get there. The rest starve or get killed. So isn't it just as well to make short work of them?"

The Esaul screwed up his light-colored eyes and nodded approvingly.

"That's not the point, and I'm not going to discuss it. I don't want to have that on my conscience. You say they die. All wight. Only it's not my doing."

Dolokhov laughed. "And don't you think they've been ordered twenty times over to catch me? And if they do catch me—or you, with all your chivalry—they'll string you up on the nearest aspen tree." He paused. "However, we must get to work. Tell my Cossack to fetch my pack. I have two French uniforms. Well, are you coming with me?" he asked Petya.

"I? Yes, yes, by all means!" cried Petya, blushing almost to tears and glancing at Denisov.

While Dolokhov had been disputing with Denisov about the disposition of prisoners, Petya again felt awkward and impatient, and again he failed to grasp what they were talking about.

"If that's what grown-up, famous men think, then it must be so, it must be right," he thought. "And the main thing is that Denisov mustn't think for a moment that I'll obey him, that he can order me about. I'll most certainly go with Dolokhov to the French camp. If he can go, so can I!"

To all Denisov's efforts to dissuade him Petya replied that he liked doing things with precision, not "just anyhow," and that he never thought of danger to himself.

"For, you must admit, if we don't know for sure how many of them there are, it might cost the lives of hundreds, and there are only two of us. Besides, I want so much to do this, and I certainly, most certainly, shall go, so don't try to stop me," he said, "it will only make things worse. . . ."

Chapter 9

Having put on French greatcoats and shakos, Petya and Dolokhov rode to the clearing from which Denisov had reconnoitered the French camp, and coming out of the forest in the pitch-darkness, descended into the hollow. When they reached the bottom of the hill Dolokhov told the Cossack accompanying him to wait there, and started off at a smart trot along the road to the bridge. Petya, almost faint with excitement, rode by his side.

"If we're caught, I won't be taken alive. I have a pistol," whispered Petya.

"Don't speak Russian," said Dolokhov in a hurried whisper, and at that moment they heard in the darkness the challenge: "Who goes there?" and the click of a musket.

The blood rushed to Petya's face and he clutched his pistol.

"Uhlans of the Sixth Regiment," answered Dolokhov in French, neither hastening nor slackening his horse's pace.

The black figure of a sentinel stood on the bridge.

"The password?"

Dolokhov reined in his horse and advanced at a walk.

"Tell me, is Colonel Gérard here?" he asked.

"The password?" repeated the sentinel, making no reply, but barring the way.

"When an officer makes a tour of the line, sentinels don't ask him for the password!" shouted Dolokhov, suddenly flaring up and riding straight at the sentinel. "I ask you, is the Colonel here?"

And without waiting for an answer from the sentinel, who had stepped aside, Dolokhov rode up the hill at a walk.

Noticing the dark form of a man crossing the road, Dolokhov stopped the man and inquired where the commander and officers were. The man, a soldier with a sack over his shoulder, stopped, came close to Dolokhov's horse, patted it, and explained in a simple, friendly way that the commander and the officers were higher up the hill on the right, in the courtyard of a farm (as he called the manor house).

After riding farther along the road, on both sides of which French talk could be heard around the campfires, Dolokhov turned in to the courtyard of the manor house. Riding through the gate, he dismounted and walked toward a big, blazing fire around which sat several men engaged in loud conversation. There was something boiling in a small kettle at the edge of the fire, and a soldier in a peaked cap and blue coat, clearly visible in the light of the fire, was kneeling beside it and stirring the contents with a ramrod.

"Oh, he's a tough nut to crack," said one of the officers who was sitting in the shadow on the opposite side of the fire.

"He'll give those fellows the slip!" said another with a laugh.

Both fell silent at the sound of Dolokhov's and Petya's footsteps and peered into the darkness as they advanced to the fire leading their horses.

"*Bonjour, messieurs!*" Dolokhov called out, loudly and distinctly.

There was a stir among the officers in the shadow on the other side of the fire, and a tall officer with a long neck walked around the fire and came toward Dolokhov.

"Is that you, Clément?" he asked. "Where the devil——" but perceiving his mistake, he broke off, and with a slight frown greeted Dolokhov as a stranger and asked him what he could do for him.

Dolokhov said that he and his companion were trying to overtake their regiment, and addressing the company in general, asked whether they knew anything of the 6th Regiment. No one could tell him anything, and Petya felt that the officers were beginning to look at them with hostility and suspicion.

No one spoke for several seconds.

"If you were counting on supper, you've come too late," said a voice from beyond the fire, with a smothered laugh.

Dolokhov replied that they were not hungry and must push on farther that night.

He handed the horses over to the soldier who was stirring the pot, and squatted down on his heels by the fire beside the officer with the long neck. The officer did not take his eyes off Dolokhov, and asked him a second time what regiment he belonged to. Dolokhov appeared not to hear the question and did not reply, but lighting a short French pipe which he took from his pocket began asking the officer how far the road ahead of them was safe from Cossacks.

"Those brigands are everywhere," replied an officer on the other side of the fire.

Dolokhov said that the Cossacks were a danger only to stragglers like himself and his comrade, and added, in a tone of inquiry, that they probably would not dare to attack a large detachment.

No one replied.

"Now surely he'll come away," Petya kept thinking every moment, as he stood by the fire listening to the talk.

But Dolokhov renewed the conversation that had been dropped and proceeded to ask point-blank how many men there were in their battalion, how many battalions they had, and how many prisoners. Inquiring about the Russian prisoners, he said:

"Nasty business, dragging these carcasses along with one. It would be better to shoot the swine," and he broke into such a strange, loud laugh that Petya thought the French must instantly see through their disguise, and involuntarily took a step back from the fire.

But Dolokhov's remark and his laughter elicited no response, and a French officer whom they could not see (he lay wrapped in a greatcoat) sat up and whispered something to a companion. Dolokhov stood up and called to the soldier who was holding their horses.

"Will they let us have our horses or not?" Petya wondered, instinctively drawing near to Dolokhov.

The horses were brought.

"Good evening, gentlemen," said Dolokhov.

Petya wished to say good night but could not utter a word. The officers were whispering together and Dolokhov was a long time mounting his horse, which would not stand still; then he rode out of the yard at a foot pace. Petya rode beside him, longing to look back and see whether the French were pursuing them, but not daring to.

When they came out onto the road Dolokhov did not turn back toward the open country, but rode through the village. At one place he stopped and listened.

"Do you hear?" he asked.

Petya recognized the sound of Russian voices, and saw the dark figures of Russian prisoners around their campfires. Descending to the bridge, Petya and Dolokhov passed the sentinel, who, without saying a word to them, morosely paced up and down; then they came out into the hollow where the Cossacks were waiting for them.

"Well, now, good-bye. Tell Denisov: at dawn, at the first shot," said Dolokhov, and was about to ride off, but Petya caught hold of his arm.

"Oh," he cried, "you are such a hero! Oh, how fine, how splendid! And how I love you!"

"All right, all right," said Dolokhov, but Petya would not let him go, and in the darkness Dolokhov perceived that he was bending toward him, and wanted to embrace him. Dolokhov kissed him, laughed, and, turning his horse, vanished into the night.

Chapter 10

On reaching the watchman's hut, Petya found Denisov in the entry. He was awaiting Petya's return in a state of agitation, anxiety, and vexation with himself for having let him go.

"Thank God!" he cried. "Well, thank God!" he repeated, listening to Petya's rapturous account. "But, damn you, I haven't slept because of you! Well, thank God! Now, go to bed. We can get a nap before morning."

"Oh, no!" said Petya. "I'm not sleepy. Besides, I know myself, if I fall asleep, I'm finished. And then, I'm accustomed to not sleeping before a battle."

Petya sat for a while in the hut, happily recalling the details of his expedition and vividly imagining what would happen the next day. Then, noticing that Denisov was asleep, he got up and went out of doors.

It was still quite dark outside. The rain was over, but drops were still falling from the trees. Not far from the watchman's hut the black outlines of the Cossacks' shanties and the tethered horses could be seen. Behind the hut loomed the dark shapes of two wagons with their horses beside them, and in the hollow the dying campfire glowed red. Not all the Cossacks and hussars were asleep: here and there, mingling with the sounds of dripping trees and munching horses, there was a low murmur as of voices whispering.

Petya came out, peered into the darkness, and went up to the wagons. Someone was snoring under the wagons, and around them stood saddled horses munching their oats. In the dark Petya recognized his own horse, which he called Karabakh,* though it was of Ukrainian breed, and went up to it.

"Well, Karabakh, we'll do service tomorrow!" he said, nuzzling and kissing the horse.

"Not sleeping, sir?" said a Cossack sitting under one of the wagons.

"No, I . . . Your name's Likhachev, isn't it? You see, I've only just come back. We've been to the French camp."

And Petya gave the Cossack a detailed account not only of his

---

* After a breed of horses from the Caucasus. TRANS.

expedition, but also of his reasons for going, and why he considered it better to risk his life than to act "just anyhow."

"Well, you should get some sleep," said the Cossack.

"No, I'm used to this," said Petya. "And how about the flints in your pistols—are they worn out? I brought some with me. Do you need any? Take some."

The Cossack poked his head out from under the wagon to get a closer look at Petya.

"Because I'm accustomed to doing things with precision," said Petya. "Some men do things haphazardly, without preparation, and regret it later. I don't like that."

"True," said the Cossack.

"Oh, yes, and another thing—please, my dear fellow, sharpen my saber for me. I got it blunted—" (but Petya could not finish the lie). "It's never been sharpened. Can you do it?"

"Of course I can."

Likhachev got up and rummaged in his pack, and soon Petya heard the martial sound of steel on whetstone. He climbed up onto the wagon and perched on the edge. The Cossack was sharpening the saber under the wagon.

"Are the men asleep?" asked Petya.

"Some are, some are awake—like us."

"And what about that boy?"

"Vesenny? He's lying over there in the hay. Fast asleep after his scare. He *was* pleased."

Petya remained silent for a long time, listening to the sounds. He heard footsteps in the darkness and a black figure appeared.

"What are you sharpening?" asked the man, coming up to the wagon.

"A saber for the gentleman here."

"A good thing," said the man, whom Petya took to be a hussar. "Was the cup left here?"

"There, by the wheel."

The hussar took the cup. "Must be getting on for daylight," he said, yawning and walking off.

Petya had every reason to know that he was in a forest, in Denisov's band, a verst from the road, sitting on a wagon captured from the French near which horses were tethered; that under it the Cossack Likhachev sat sharpening his saber for him; that the big dark patch to the right was the watchman's hut, the red spot below to the left the dying campfire; that the man who had come for the cup was a thirsty hussar; yet he neither knew nor wanted to know anything of all this. He was in an enchanted kingdom where nothing resembled reality. The big dark patch might be a hut, it is true, but then it might be a cavern leading to the very depths of the earth. The red spot might be a fire, or it might be the eye of some prodigious monster. Perhaps he really was sitting on a wagon, but it might very well be that he was not sitting on a wagon at all, but on a marvelously high tower from which, if he fell, he would go on flying for a whole day, a whole month, before he reached the earth—or he might fly forever and never reach it. Perhaps it was only the Cossack Likhachev sitting under the wagon, but it might be the kindest, bravest, most wonderful, splendid man in the whole world, whom no one knew of. It might really have been a hussar who came for water and went back into the hollow, but possibly he had simply vanished, dissolved into air, and was no more.

Nothing Petya could have seen now would have surprised him. He was in an enchanted kingdom where everything was possible.

He looked up at the sky. The sky too was an enchanted realm like the earth. It was beginning to clear, and the clouds were scudding over the treetops as though unveiling the stars. Sometimes it looked as though the clouds had been swept away and a stretch of clear black sky appeared. And sometimes these black patches seemed to be clouds. At other times the sky seemed to rise high overhead, then to sink so low that one could have reached out and touched it.

Petya's eyes began to close and he swayed slightly.

The trees were dripping. There was a low hum of talk. The horses neighed and jostled one another. Someone snored.

Ozheeg-zheeg, ozheeg-zheeg . . . hissed the saber on the whetstone, and all at once Petya heard a melodious orchestra playing some unfamiliar, sweetly solemn hymn. Petya was musical, like Natasha, and even more so than Nikolai, but he had never studied music, and never thought about it, and so the melody that came to his mind had a special freshness and charm for him. The music swelled, the melody developing and passing from one instrument to another. What was playing was a fugue—though Petya had not the slightest idea what a fugue was. Each instrument—now one resembling the violin, now one like a horn, but finer, more brilliant than either violin or horn—played its own part, and before it had finished the motif, merged with another instrument that began almost the same air, then with a third, and a fourth; and they all blended into one, and again separated, and again blended, now into solemn church music, now into some resplendent and triumphal air.

"Oh, but I must have been dreaming," Petya said to himself, as he lurched forward. "It's only in my ears. Perhaps it's music of my own making. Well, go on, my music. Now! . . ."

He closed his eyes. And on all sides, as from a distance, the notes vibrated, swelling into harmonies, dispersing and mingling again in that same sweet, solemn hymn. "Ah, this is delightful! As much as I like, and just as I like!" said Petya to himself. He tried to conduct that tremendous orchestra.

"Now softly, softly . . . die away!" And the sounds obeyed him. "Now, louder, livelier! More and more joyful!" And from unknown depths rose the swelling, exultant sounds. "Now, voices join in!" Petya commanded. At first, from afar, he heard men's, then women's voices steadily mounting in a rhapsodic crescendo. Awed and elated, Petya listened to their wondrous beauty.

The voices blended with the triumphal victory march, the dripping of the trees, the *ozheeg-zheeg-zheeg* of hissing saber . . . and again the horses jostled and neighed, not disturbing the harmony, but becoming part of it.

How long this lasted Petya could not tell; he delighted in it, wondering all the while at his delight and regretting that there was no one to share it. He was awakened by Likhachev.

"It's ready, Your Honor. You can split a Frenchman in two with it."

Petya woke up. "It's getting light—it's really getting light!" he cried.

The horses, imperceptible before, could now be seen to their very tails, and through the leafless boughs glimmered an aqueous light. Petya shook himself, jumped down, took a ruble from his pocket and gave it to Likhachev, then flourished his saber to test it before sheathing it. The Cossacks were untying their horses and tightening the saddle girths.

"Here's the commander," said Likhachev.

Denisov came out of the watchman's hut and, having called Petya, gave orders to get ready.

Chapter 11

The men rapidly picked out their horses in the semidarkness, tightened the saddle girths, and formed their units. Denisov stood by the watchman's hut giving final orders. The infantry of the detachment moved ahead on the road, hundreds of feet splashing through the mud. They quickly disappeared amid the trees and the mist of early dawn. The Esaul gave an order to the Cossacks. Petya held his horse by the bridle, impatiently awaiting the order to mount. After washing in cold water, his face, and especially his eyes, glowed; a cold chill ran down his spine and his whole body throbbed rhythmically.

"Well, is ev'wything weady?" asked Denisov. "Bwing the horses."

The horses were led up. Denisov was angry with the Cossack because the saddle girths were slack, and swore at him as he mounted. Petya put his foot in the stirrup. The horse, as was his habit, made as if to nip his leg, but Petya sprang into the saddle oblivious of his own weight, and turning to look at the hussars moving up from behind in the darkness, rode up to Denisov.

"Vasily Dmitrich, you will give me something to do, won't you? Please . . . For God's sake . . . !" he said.

Denisov seemed to have forgotten Petya's very existence. He glanced back at him.

"I ask one thing of you," he said sternly, "and that is to obey me and not plunge into anything."

He did not say another word to Petya, but rode in silence all the way. By the time they reached the edge of the forest it had grown noticeably light in the open country. Denisov said something to the Esaul in a whisper, and the Cossacks rode past Petya and Denisov. When they had all passed, Denisov touched up his horse and rode down the hill. Slipping and sinking back on their haunches, the horses descended with their riders into the hollow. Petya rode beside Denisov. The throbbing of his body increased. It was getting lighter and lighter and only distant objects were still hidden in the mist. When he reached the bottom of the hill, Denisov looked back and nodded to a Cossack near him.

"The signal," he said.

The Cossack raised his arm and a shot rang out. Instantly there was heard the thud of hoofbeats as the horses galloped forward, shouts on every side, and then more shots.

At the first sound of hoofbeats and shouting, Petya lashed his horse, gave it the rein, and galloped forward, heedless of Denisov, who shouted at him. It seemed to Petya that at the moment the shot was fired it suddenly became bright as noon. He galloped to the bridge. The Cossacks were flying along the road in front of him. On the bridge he collided with a Cossack who had fallen behind, and rode on. He saw soldiers in front of him—Frenchmen he supposed—running across the road from right to left. One of them slipped in the mud and fell under his horse's legs.

Cossacks were crowding around a hut, doing something. A fearful shriek rose from the midst of the crowd. Petya galloped up, and the first thing he saw was the white face and trembling jaw of a Frenchman, who was clutching the staff of a lance that was aimed at him.

"Hurrah! . . . Men . . . ours . . ." shouted Petya, and giving rein to his excited horse, galloped down the village street.

He could hear the shooting ahead of him. Cossacks, hussars, and tattered Russian prisoners who had come running from both sides of the road were all shouting loudly and unintelligibly. A valiant-looking Frenchman in a blue coat and no cap, his face flushed and scowling, was repulsing the hussars with his bayonet. By the time Petya galloped up, the Frenchman had fallen. "Too late again!" flashed through Petya's mind, and he rushed on to the place where rapid firing could be heard. The shots came from the yard of the manor house where he had been the night before with Dolokhov. The French were making a stand behind the wattle fence in a garden thickly overgrown with bushes, and were firing at the Cossacks crowded at the gateway. Riding up to the gate, Petya caught a glimpse of Dolokhov's pale, greenish face as he shouted to the men.

"Go around! Wait for the infantry!" he cried, just as Petya rode up to him.

"Wait? . . . Hurra-a-ah!" yelled Petya, and without pausing an instant, rushed on to where the firing and gunsmoke were thickest.

A volley rang out; the bullets whistled past and thudded into something. The Cossacks and Dolokhov galloped into the yard after Petya. In the thick, drifting smoke, some of the Frenchmen threw down their arms and ran out of the bushes to meet the Cossacks, while others fled downhill toward the pond. Petya was galloping around in the courtyard, but instead of holding the reins, he was waving his arms about in a queer, jerky way and slipping farther and farther to one side in his saddle. His horse, having run onto the ashes of a campfire that was smoldering in the morning light, stopped short, and Petya fell heavily onto the wet ground. The Cossacks saw his arms and legs twitch convulsively, though his head was motionless. A bullet had pierced his skull.

After a parley with the senior French officer, who came out of the house with a white handkerchief tied to his sword and announced that they surrendered, Dolokhov dismounted and went up to Petya who lay motionless with outstretched arms.

"Done for!" he said with a frown, and walked to the gate to meet Denisov, who was riding toward him.

"Dead?" cried Denisov, recognizing even from a distance the unmistakably lifeless attitude in which Petya's body was lying.

"Done for!" repeated Dolokhov, as if the uttering of the words afforded him some satisfaction, and he quickly went to the prisoners, whom the Cossacks were hurriedly surrounding. "We won't take them!" he called out to Denisov.

Denisov did not reply; he rode up to Petya, dismounted, and with trembling hands turned toward him the blood-stained, mud-bespattered face, which had already gone white.

"I always like something sweet. Wonderful raisins . . . Take all of them . . ." he recalled.

And the Cossacks looked around in surprise at the sound, like the yelp of a dog, that Denisov uttered as he quickly turned away, walked to the wattle fence, and gripped it.

Among the Russian prisoners rescued by Denisov and Dolokhov was Pierre Bezukhov.

AFTERWORD

"All modesty aside, it's something like the *Iliad*," Tolstoy once said of *War and Peace*. Many readers must have had the same thought, impressed as they cannot fail to be by the epic impulse in his masterpiece of prose fiction. The major theme in both works is obviously war, seen in all its horror and at the same time an occasion for deeds of bravery, generosity, and self-sacrifice. Although there is more place for peaceful elements in the later work, and notably for the domestic affairs of the Rostovs, the Bolkonskys, and the Bezukhovs, the *Iliad* too portrays the happiness of Hector, a "peaceful" warrior who fights from a sense of civic duty that bears no resemblance to Achilles' fierce pride and anger. We have such domestic scenes as the one in Book VI where Hector playfully counsels his little son Astyanax after the boy has been frightened by the great shining, horse-hair-tufted helmet.

By his metaphors and similes, Homer keeps reminding us of a world in which natural objects—stars, sky, trees, and streams—all viewed with pristine clarity, beautiful in themselves, stand in poignant contrast with the destructive passions of men. At the same time he alternates scenes on earth with others in heaven, as if to show that the gods themselves have a stake in the destiny of mortal heroes. Tolstoy's historical digressions perform much the same function as those scenes in heaven; that is, they give his narrative a metaphysical background. Beginning with Part Nine and continuing through the Epilogue, he keeps asking what really caused this tremendous military engagement, till then the greatest in modern times. By implication he also is questioning God's plan for a world in which such a cataclysmic struggle could occur.

With these general statements in mind, let us examine the foregoing scene in an effort to grasp how Tolstoy transmuted the spirit of Homer's epic into the prose world of the novel.

The entire sequence is viewed through Petya's eyes, except for a brief summary at the beginning and a single authorial comment—"with the rapidity with which young people change their views"—and except for a few short paragraphs after Petya's death. In *Four Stages of Greek Thought*, John H. Finley, Jr. has recently said that Homer possesses the special quality of presenting things exactly as they are, almost as if they were being seen for the first time through the eyes of a child, with a kind of naïve assurance in which the conscious mind does not intervene to evaluate its sense perceptions or color them with subjective emotions. The two heroes of *War and Peace*, Prince Andrei and Pierre, are "modern," mature men, and when Tolstoy delineates their inner lives he uses conventions of the modern novel that were unknown to ancient poets. Still, their responses to war have something of the naïve assurance that Finley attributes to Homer.

Sixteen-year-old Petya is a better case in point. Battle for him is a matter of *arete*, the Homeric code of honor, chivalric and outgoing, put forth most succinctly in Book XII of the *Iliad* when the Trojan Sarpedon says to his friend Glaukos that their preëminence among the people depends on their fighting in the forefront: "Forward, whether we give glory to another man, or he to us." Count Petya several times expresses the same sentiments as those earlier noblemen. Thus, he implores Denisov with exuberant incoherence, "Only do let me be in the very—in the chief—" Later he explains to a simple Cossack "why he considered is better to risk his life than to act 'just anyhow.'" Denisov's response to Petya's first declaration ("'In the very chief . . .' Denisov repeated with a smile") and the Cossack's response to the second ("Well, you should get some sleep") bring into opposition two age-old attitudes toward war. Here one is reminded of Shakespeare, who, like Homer and Tolstoy, portrays that conflict between the ideal and the real. In *Henry IV, Part I,* for instance, Hotspur's "By heaven, methinks it were an easy leap/To pluck bright honour from the pale-fac'd moon" is placed against Falstaff's "Can honour set-to a leg? no . . . what is honour? a word. What is that word, honour? What is that honour? air. A trim reckoning."

Throughout the *Iliad,* love and friendship are displayed against a background of carnage. In *War and Peace* there is Petya's impulsive generosity with his raisins, his flints, his pocket knife, and there is also his admiration for the two veterans, Denisov and Dolokhov, which at first they answer gruffly—"But, damn you, I haven't slept," Denisov says after Petya's nocturnal excursion into the enemy's camp—but which emerges in the final paragraphs with a terrible poignancy. There Tolstoy has each older man express a grief so great that it transcends his power of articulation. "'Done for!' he [Dolokhov] said with a frown, . . . 'Dead?' cried Denisov, . . . 'Done for!' Dolokhov repeated. . . . 'We won't take them!' he called out to Denisov"; and then comes the final memory of Petya and his "wonderful raisins," followed by Denisov's howling like a dog.

Other Homeric parallels abound. Although the poet is more forthright in telling us often that Achilles is destined to lead a short, glorious life, then fall in battle, Tolstoy produces the same effect by subtler devices. There are the counsels of Denisov and Dolokhov that Petya stay out of the fighting, his own exuberance, and other intimations that Petya will be killed, continuing to the moment when an anonymous French marksman picks him off. This next point may be excessive, but even Petya's brief affectionate speech to his horse—"'Well, Karabakh, we'll do service tomorrow!' he said, nuzzling and kissing the horse"—has overtones of Achilles in Book XIX of the *Iliad* addressing his own steeds just after the death of Patrokles.

Finally there is Petya's curious dream on the eve of battle, framed by the sound of his saber being sharpened (how often in the *Iliad* are weapons readied for action!). For Petya nature is irradiated into "an enchanted kingdom where everything was possible." Then he hears some gigantic piece of music, fugal at the start—though Tolstoy makes it clear that Petya has had no formal musical training—and culminating in "some resplendent and triumphal air." In Homer the gods often speak to men in dreams. Petya's vision similarly gives him a glimpse of some transcendent order above or beyond mortal understanding. It is clear that Tolstoy had in mind the last and choral movement of Beethoven's *Ninth Symphony*. In that setting of Schiller's "Ode to Joy," with the poet's exhortation that all men be brothers when at last peace and joy are brought together, there appears a brief military march—as if to remind us that peace is perhaps bought by war.

The Brothers Karamazov (1880)

Born in Moscow, FYODOR MIKHAILOVICH DOSTOEVSKY (1821-1881) was the second among eight children of a harsh military surgeon who had become a staff doctor at the Hospital for the Poor and who then acquired a country estate; in 1839 he was killed by his own serfs. The mother had died two years before. Young Fyodor was enrolled in the Military Engineering Academy in St. Petersburg, from which he was graduated in 1843. He became a draftsman in the Engineering Corps, but after a year he resigned from the civil service and turned to writing. His first publication of importance was a translation (1844) of Balzac's *Eugénie Grandet*, though he had also begun working on an epistolary novel, *Poor Folk*. Belinsky, then the leading Russian literary critic, read the manuscript and praised it for its psychological insights and its humanitarianism; he hailed the young author as the successor of Gogol, whose novel *Dead Souls* (1842) was universally admired. *Poor Folk* appeared in 1846, and Dostoevsky published a second and less successful novel that same year: it was *The Double*, concerned with the mental collapse of a clerk. Dostoevsky himself had begun to suffer from epileptic seizures that would continue through the rest of his life.

Besides moving in literary circles, he was frequenting the Petrachevsky group of young intellectuals, who discussed socialist theories and were intensely critical of the Czarist regime. Dostoevsky and the others were arrested in April 1849, during the wave of repression that spread over Europe after the failed revolutions of the previous year. Among the charges against them was that of having a secret printing press. They spent eight months in prison and then were taken out to be shot. A last-minute reprieve from Nicholas I—which the government had secretly prepared—changed the sentence from death to exile and prison in Siberia. Dostoevsky was never to forget the horror of that mock execution.

Stripped of his officer's rank, he spent four years working in fetters at a labor camp in Omsk, where the temperature sometimes dropped to forty degrees below zero. He was not allowed to communicate with friends in Russia. For reading matter he had only the New Testament, and this partly accounts for the strong religious feeling that was to color his subsequent writing. He was later to say, "Not in communism, not in mechanical forms, is the socialism of the Russian people expressed; they believe that they will finally be saved through universal communion in the name of Jesus Christ." In 1854 he was conscripted into the army for four years of service at Semipalatinsk, near the Mongolian border. In 1857 he married the widow of a customs official. The bureaucracy was coming to feel that his conduct—not to mention a number of patriotic poems dedicated to the Czar—had offered proof of his national loyalty. Dostoevsky was promoted to ensign and restored to his rank as a minor nobleman; then in July 1859 the couple received permission to return to European Russia. In December the permission was extended to St. Petersburg.

With his brother Mikhail he founded a literary review, *Vremya* (*Time*) that serialized his new book, *The Insulted and Injured* (1861-1862), and then his prison memoirs, *The House of the Dead* (1862). Dostoevsky traveled to France and England and later to Germany. In 1863, however, *Vremya* was suppressed for an article on the Polish rebellion that displeased the authorities; the suppression was ironic in the light of Dostoevsky's now fervent nationalism, his veneration for the Czar—he advocated "mutual love of the monarch for the people and also of the people for the monarch"—and his impassioned praise of the Russian Orthodox Church.

His wife, from whom he had become more and more estranged, died in 1864, and his beloved brother Mikhail soon afterward. Dostoevsky was then contributing to another short-lived magazine, *Epokha* (*The Epoch*); it published his *Notes from the Underground* (1864), in which many Existentialists find a prefiguring of their own attitudes and ideas. He returned to Western Europe in 1863 and 1865, accompanied by a young woman, Apollinaria Suslova, who had contributed to *Vremya*. Much of his time was spent at German spas, where he could indulge his ruinous passion for gambling. More frequent epileptic seizures, complicated liaisons, and an accumulation of gambling debts marked a low point in his life. He was ill when he came back from Germany in 1865 and set to work on a book that he hoped would solve his financial dilemmas; it was *Crime and Punishment* (1866), the first of his major novels.

That same year he published a short novel, *The Gambler*, based on his own experience; he dictated the book to a secretary in order to meet a deadline. The secretary was Anna Grigoryevna Snitkina, whom he married in 1867; soon afterward they left Russia to escape his creditors. Always in extreme poverty, they spent four years traveling in Germany, Austria, Switzerland, and Italy. One result of the travels was to intensify Dostoevsky's mystical belief in Russia, together with his hatred of the West and of Westernized Russians, including his great contemporary Turgenev. A famous event of 1867 was his open quarrel with Turgenev at Baden-Baden. But he also found time to write a second major novel, *The Idiot* (1868), in which the hero, Prince Myshkin, is an inspired epileptic like himself.

He had been making copious notes dealing with the problem of religious belief, "the very one which had, my whole life long, tormented my conscious or subconscious being: the question of the existence of God." His religious ideas were to be incorporated into two other major novels, *The Possessed* (1871-1872) and *The Brothers Karamazov*. In each of these a leading figure, Stavrogin in the former and Ivan Karamazov in the latter, has succumbed to Western atheism, skepticism, and socialism; their unbelief, in the author's interpretation, stems from a lack of love.

Dostoevsky returned to St. Petersburg with his family in 1871, after the first published parts of *The Possessed* had met with wide success. He went back to journalism, first as editor of the weekly *Grazhdanin* (*The Citizen*), then, after the publication of *A Raw Youth* (1875), as director and literary staff of a periodical (1876-1881) written solely by himself. *Diary of a Writer* it was called, and it contained articles on literature, politics, and society as well as stories. Meanwhile he was working intensely on *The Brothers Karamazov*, which was to be published serially in *The Russian Herald*. He was enjoying fame and a measure of financial security; he even inherited a sizable estate. At the Pushkin celebration in June 1880 he had been the main speaker; he told how the first great Russian poet had contributed to his own concept of the pure, universal Russian soul, indigenous and unsullied by Western rationalism. A dinner that evening crowned Dostoevsky's triumph. It is reported that people said, "You are our prophet; you have made us better men since we have read *The Brothers Karamazov*." Turgenev, his old antagonist, was present, and the two novelists embraced. Yet

Dostoevsky was by then in feeble health, and he died of emphysema on January 28, 1881.

THE STORY

A brutal old man, Fyodor Pavlovich Karamazov, has a son, Dmitry (or Mitya), by his first marriage and two others, Ivan and Alexey (or Alyosha), by the second. All three have been reared by others, and Dmitry and Ivan are "Westernized," in contrast with Alyosha, who has been educated in the local monastery. There is also an illegitimate son, Smerdyakov, who serves as valet to the old man. Both Dmitry and his father love Grushenka, who is one of Dostoevsky's "sacred prostitutes," and Dmitry is also deeply involved with Katerina Ivanovna, a colonel's daughter, to whom he has given money to save her father's honor. Ivan and Katerina Ivanovna feel a mutual attraction. Old Karamazov has swindled his sons, and both Ivan and Dmitry hint that they would like to kill him for his villainies.

The saintly Father Zossima, Alyosha's spiritual preceptor, dies at the monastery where the boy had been educated. This first crucial event in the novel has been preceded by two long interpolated stories. One of them is Ivan's tale of the Grand Inquisitor, a parable that on one level expresses the author's hostility toward the Roman Catholic Church and, on another level, presents his terrifying vision of a socialized society. The other is the account of his own life given by Father Zossima, who tells how he moved from sinful worldliness to love and grace. One feature of the book is this series of parables; later there will be others, of which the longest will be Ivan's hallucinated encounter with the Devil. Together they show how deeply Dostoevsky was affected by the New Testament when he read it in prison.

Dmitry tries to steal an envelope containing three thousand rubles that the old man keeps in his room. During the attempt he seriously wounds his father's servant Grigory; then he flees to the inn at Mokroye, engages in a wild carouse, and, in the midst of it, is reconciled with Grushenka. The revel is interrupted when Dmitry is arrested for murdering his father, who has been found in his room with his skull crushed in. Dmitry admits that he wanted to kill the old man, but protests his innocence of the actual crime.

There is a protracted investigation that introduces a new cast of characters, including doctors, journalists, and lawyers. On the day before the trial opens, Smerdyakov confesses to Ivan that he is the murderer but also makes it clear that he had been acting on the basis of the skeptical, amoral ideas he acquired from Ivan, his spiritual double.

Smerdyakov hangs himself that same night, thus destroying the probative value of his confession, the truth of which now rests on Ivan's unsupported word. After a trial that lasts for several days, the jury disregards Ivan's testimony and brings in a verdict based on the preponderance of evidence —as well as on an incriminating letter produced by Katerina Ivanovna, who hates and loves Dmitry at the same time. Pronounced guilty, Dmitry is sentenced to hard labor in Siberia, but Ivan has laid plans to have him rescued and sent across the Atlantic with Grushenka. Meanwhile Alyosha, carrying on the apostolic mission of Father Zossima, converts a whole group of young boys to the doctrine of Christian love.

The Brothers Karamazov is divided into twelve books and an epilogue. The scene that follows is placed near the beginning of Book Eleven, which deals with the eventful day before Dmitry is brought to trial. The central figure in the scene is poor devilish Lise, the sixteen-year-old daughter of Mme. Khokhlakov. Lise's self-hatred places her figuratively among the damned, since she is incapable of the regenerative love represented by Father Zossima and Alyosha. The new translation by David Magarshack is vastly more idiomatic than the formerly standard version by Constance Garnett. Copyright 1958 by Mr. Magarshack, it is published by Penguin Books.

The Little She-Devil

On entering Lise's room he found her half-lying in the chair in which she had been wheeled when she was still unable to walk. She did not attempt to get up to meet him, but her keen, sharp eyes were fixed on him intently. Her eyes were a little inflamed, her face was pale and sallow. Alyosha was surprised to see her so changed in three days. She even looked thinner. She did not hold out her hand to him. He touched her long, slender fingers which lay motionless on her dress, then sat down silently opposite her.

"I know," Lise said sharply, "that you are in a hurry to get to the prison, and that mother has kept you for two hours and has just been telling you about me and Julia."

"How do you know that?" asked Alyosha.

"I was eavesdropping. What are you staring at me like that for? If I want to eavesdrop, I eavesdrop. There's nothing wrong about it. I'm not sorry."

"Are you upset about something?"

"Not at all, I'm very pleased. I've just been thinking for the hundredth time how fortunate it is that I refused you and won't be your wife. You're no good as a husband: if I were to marry you and give you a note to take to the man I fell in love with after you, you'd take it and most certainly give it to him *and* bring back his answer, too. And when you were forty, you'd still be carrying such notes for me."

She suddenly laughed.

"There's something spiteful and at the same time innocent about you," Alyosha smiled at her.

"The only thing that's innocent about me is that I'm not ashamed of you. And not only am I not ashamed, but I don't want to be ashamed of you, of you in particular. Alyosha, why don't I respect you? I love you very much, but I don't respect you. If I respected you, I wouldn't have said it without being ashamed, would I?"

"You wouldn't."

"And do you believe that I'm not ashamed of you?"

"No, I don't."

Lise again laughed nervously. She was talking very rapidly.

"I sent your brother Dmitry some sweets in prison. Alyosha, you know, you're so nice! I'll love you awfully for having so quickly given me your permission not to love you."

"Why did you send for me today, Lise?"

"I wanted to tell you a certain wish of mine. I wish someone would tear me to pieces, marry me and then tear me to pieces, deceive me and leave me. I don't want to be happy."

"You love disorder?"

"Oh no, I don't want disorder. I keep wanting to set fire to the house. I keep imagining how I'd go up and set fire to it by stealth. Yes, it must be by stealth. They'll be trying to put it out, but it will go on burning. And I'll know and say nothing. Oh, what silly nonsense! And how boring it is!"

She waved her hand with disgust.

"You're too well off," Alyosha said quietly.

"Would it be better if I were poor?"

"Yes."

"That's what your deceased monk told you. It's not true. What does it matter if I'm rich and everyone else poor? I'll be eating sweets and drinking cream and give nothing to anyone. Oh, don't say anything," she waved her hand, though Alyosha never opened his mouth, "don't say anything, you've told me all before. I know it all by heart. It's boring. If I were poor, I'd kill someone, and if I'm rich, I shall probably kill someone too. What's the use of sitting about and doing nothing. And you know what I want? I want to reap, to reap rye. I'll marry you and you'll become a peasant. A real peasant. We'll keep a colt. Would you like that? Do you know Kalganov?"

"Yes."

"He's always going about and dreaming. He says: what's the use of living if you can dream? One can dream the most gay things, while to live is a bore. And yet he's going to be married soon. He has already made me a declaration of love. Can you spin tops?"

"Yes."

"Well, he's just like a top: wind him up and let him spin, and then keep lashing at him, keep lashing at him with a whip. If I marry him, I shall spin him round and round all his life. You're not ashamed to sit with me?"

"No."

"You're awfully angry because I don't talk about holy things. I don't want to be holy. What do they do to you in the next world for the greatest sin? You must know all about it."

"God will censure you," Alyosha said, looking at her closely.

"Well, that's just what I want. I'd come and I'd be censured, and I'd suddenly burst out laughing in their faces. Oh, I do so want to set fire to a house, Alyosha, to our house. You don't believe me?"

"Why not? There are children of twelve who long to set fire to something. And they do. It's a sort of illness."

"It isn't true! It isn't true! There may be such children, but I'm not talking about that."

"You take evil for good: it's a momentary crisis. Your former illness is perhaps responsible for it."

"So you do despise me, after all! I simply don't want to do good. I want to do evil. And it's nothing to do with my illness."

"Why do evil?"

"So that nothing should remain anywhere. Oh, how nice it would be if nothing remained! You know, Alyosha, sometimes I think of doing a lot of evil and everything that's bad, and I'd do it for a long time by stealth, and suddenly everyone would know about it. They would all surround me and point their fingers at me, and I'd look at them all. That would be very nice. Why would it be so nice, Alyosha?"

"Oh, I expect it's just a craving to crush something good or, as you said, to set fire to it. That, too, happens."

"I wasn't only saying it. I'm going to do it."

"I believe you."

"Oh, how I love you for saying that you believe me. And you're not lying. You're not lying at all. Or do you think perhaps that I'm saying all this to you on purpose, just to tease you?"

"No, I don't think so. Though, I daresay, there's a little of that desire, too."

"There is a little. I shall never lie to you," she said, with strangely flashing eyes.

Alyosha was more and more struck by her seriousness: there was not a trace of mockery or jesting in her face now, though before gaiety and jesting never deserted her even in her most "serious" moments.

"There are moments when people love crime," Alyosha said thoughtfully.

"Yes, yes, you've expressed my thought. They love it. They always love it, and not only at 'moments.' You know, it's as though everyone had agreed to lie about it, and they have been lying about it ever since. They all say they hate evil, but in their heart of hearts they all love it."

"And you are still reading bad books?"

"Yes, I am. Mother reads them and hides them under her pillow and I steal them."

"How aren't you ashamed to destroy yourself?"

"I want to destroy myself. There's a boy here who lay down between the railway lines and the train passed over him. Lucky boy! Listen, your brother is being tried now for murdering his father, but everyone loves his having killed his father."

"Loves his having killed his father?"

"Yes, they all love it! They all say it's horrible, but in their hearts they love it. I, for one, love it."

"There's a grain of truth in what you say about everyone," said Alyosha quietly.

"Oh, what wonderful ideas you have!" Lise shrieked in delight. "And a monk, too! You wouldn't believe how I respect you, Alyosha, for never telling a lie. Oh, I'll tell you a very funny dream I had! I sometimes dream of devils. It's night, I'm in my room, and suddenly there are devils everywhere. In all the corners and under the table, and they open doors, and behind the doors there are crowds of them, and they all want to come in and seize me. And they are already coming near and taking hold of me. But suddenly I cross myself and they all draw back, they are afraid, only they don't go away, but stand near the door and in the corners, waiting. And then I'm suddenly overcome by a desire to begin cursing God in a loud voice, and I begin cursing him and they all rush at me again in a crowd, they're so pleased, and they're again about to lay hands on me, and I cross myself again and they draw back at once. It's great fun. Oh, it takes my breath away."

"I've had the same dream, too," Alyosha said suddenly.

"Have you?" Lise cried in surprise. "Listen, Alyosha, don't laugh at me, it's awfully important: is it possible for two different people to have the same dream?"

"I suppose it is."

"Alyosha, I'm telling you this is awfully important," Lise went on with a sort of intense astonishment. "It isn't the dream that is important, but that you should have had the same dream as me. You've never lied to me, don't lie to me now. Is it true? You're not laughing?"

"It is true."

Lise was terribly struck by something and she was silent for half a minute.

"Alyosha, come and see me, come and see me more often," she said suddenly in a beseeching voice.

"I shall always come to see you, all my life," replied Alyosha firmly.

"You see, I'm telling this to you alone," Lise began again. "I'm telling it to myself and to you. To you alone in the whole world. And more readily to you than to myself. And I'm not a bit ashamed before you, not a bit. Alyosha, why am I not a bit ashamed before you, not a bit? Alyosha, is it true that Jews steal children at Easter and kill them?"

"I don't know."

"I read it in a book about a trial somewhere, and that a Jew at first cut off a four-year-old child's fingers on both hands, and then crucified him, nailed him to a wall, and then said at his trial that the boy died soon, within four hours. Soon, indeed! He said the boy kept moaning and that he stood there enjoying it. That's good."

"Good?"

"Good. I sometimes imagine that it was I who crucified him. He would hang on the wall and moan and I'd sit opposite him and eat stewed pineapples. I'm awfully fond of stewed pineapples. Are you?"

Alyosha looked at her in silence. Her pale, sallow face became suddenly distorted and her eyes glowed.

"You know, when I read about that Jew, I shook with sobs all night. I kept imagining how the little boy screamed and moaned (four-year-old boys understand, you know), and the thought of that pineapple *compote* kept hammering in my brain. Next morning I sent a letter to a man, telling him that he *must* come and see me. He came and I told him about the boy and the stewed pineapples, told him *everything, everything,* and said that it was 'good.' He suddenly laughed and said that it really was good. Then he got up and went away. He only stayed five minutes. Did he despise me? Did he? Tell me, tell me, Alyosha, did he or didn't he despise me?" she asked with flashing eyes, sitting up straight on the settee.

"Tell me," Aloyosha said agitatedly, "did you send for that man yourself?"

"Yes."

"You sent him a letter?"

"I did."

"Just to ask him about that, about the child?"

"No, not about that at all. Not at all about that. But when he came in, I asked him at once about that. He replied, laughed and went away."

"That man behaved decently to you," Alyosha said softly.

"But did he despise me? Did he laugh at me?"

"No, because I suppose he believes in the stewed pineapples himself. He, too, is very sick now, Lise."

"Yes, he does believe in it!" cried Lise with flashing eyes.

"He despises no one," Alyosha went on. "He merely doesn't believe anyone. But if he doesn't believe, he, of course, despises, too."

"So he despises me also? Me?"

"You also."

"That's good," Lise cried, grinding her teeth. "When he went out and laughed, I felt that it was good to be despised. And the boy with the cut-off fingers is good, and to be despised is good."

And she laughed in Alyosha's face with a sort of feverish malice.

"Do you know, Alyosha, do you know, I'd like. . . . Alyosha, save me!" she cried, suddenly jumping up from the settee and, rushing up to him, she flung her arms tightly around him. "Save me," she almost moaned. "Would I have said what I told you just now to anyone else in the world? And I spoke the truth, the truth, the truth! I'll kill myself because everything is so loathsome to me! I don't want to live, because everything is so loathsome to me! Everything is loathsome to me, everything! Alyosha, why don't you love me at all?" she concluded in a frenzy.

"I do love you!" Alyosha replied warmly.

"And will you cry for me? Will you?"

"I will."

"Not because I didn't want to be your wife, but simply cry for me? Simply?"

"I will."

"Thank you! All I want is your tears. Let everyone else punish me and trample me underfoot, everyone, everyone, not excepting *anyone*! Because I love no one. You hear, no one! On the contrary, I hate him! Go now, Alyosha. It's time you went to your brother!" She suddenly tore herself away from him.

"But how can I leave you like this?" Alyosha said almost in alarm.

"Go to your brother. The prison will be shut. Go! Here's your hat. Give Mitya my love. Go, go!"

And she almost pushed Alyosha out of the door by force. Alyosha looked at her in mournful perplexity, when he suddenly felt that a letter had been thrust into his hand, a little note, folded up tightly and sealed. He looked at it and instantly read the incription: "To Ivan Karamazov." He glanced at Lise. Her face looked almost stern.

"Give it to him! Be sure to give it to him!" she ordered him in a frenzy, shaking all over. "Today! At once! Or I'll poison myself! That's why I sent for you!"[1]

And she quickly slammed the door. The bolt was shot noisily. Alyosha put the letter in his pocket and went straight downstairs without going in to see Mrs Khokhlakov, forgetting all about her, in fact. And as soon as Alyosha had gone, Lise unbolted the door, opened it a little, put her finger in the crack, and slamming the door, pinched her finger with all the force at her command. Ten seconds later, releasing her finger, she went back to her chair slowly

---

[1 We never learn what was in Lise's letter, since Ivan tears it up without reading it. Obviously he was the other man to whom Lise confessed her guilty dreams.—Eds.]

and quietly, sat up erect in it, and began examining intently her blackened finger and the blood that oozed from under the nail. Her lips quivered, and she whispered rapidly to herself:

"Mean, mean, mean, mean!"

AFTERWORD

The Brothers Karamazov can be read as a detective story, and on that simplest level it has been criticized for withholding facts from the reader, as it does on the night of the crime, and for revealing the murderer too soon. But the revelation still leaves us in suspense—will the court be moved by Smerdyakov's confession as reported by Ivan?— and in any case Dostoevsky had a larger purpose in mind than writing a story of detection or even of crime and punishment. He was now writing a theodicy, that is, a treatise or narrative designed to "justify the ways of God to man." In that purpose he resembled Milton, and he adopted an epic form that was proper to the nineteenth century: the Dickensian novel with a complicated plot and a cast of vivid characters drawn from many levels of society.

For all their mixture of qualities, the characters are either essentially "good" or essentially "bad," depending on their relation to Dostoevsky's idealized notion of Christianity. In the "bad" group are those fallen figures who, in varying degrees, have been ensnared by Western liberalism, scientism, socialism, and eventual atheism. In the "good" group there is something close to an apostolic laying-on of hands: from Father Zossima, the former profligate and rake, to Alyosha Karamazov, in spite of his temporary doubt; then to characters on their way to eventual salvation, like Dmitry Karamazov and Grushenka; and finally to openhearted Kolya and the other boys who are Alyosha's disciples. These represent the future of Russia, whose real history—so Dostoevsky hoped— was to begin with the end of the novel. He predicted the coming of a Russian Christ, but in 1917 it was quite another sort of redeemer who arrived at the Finland Station.

This "good" group that accepts Father Zossima's simple credo, "Love all men, love everything!" has its dialectical counterparts in the members of a "bad" group for whom hatred of God, of others, and of themselves is a negative canon of unbelief. Such fallen creatures include old Karamazov, the brutal buffoon whose skepticism has become a self-destructive irony; his second son Ivan, who is the arch skeptic, but not quite the arch villain, since he remains capable of love after his fashion; Ivan's "double" Smerdyakov, who carries Ivan's logic into criminal action; and the journalist Rakitin, a devil figure who tries to corrupt the saintly Alyosha. Mme. Khokhlakov and her daughter Lise are also among the fallen, and Lise's pathological hatred of herself and humanity would put her low on the author's scale of theological values. In her case, however, he makes no explicit comments.

Earlier in the book, Dostoevsky has taken advantage of a privilege claimed by almost all nineteenth-century novelists (with Flaubert and James as the outstanding exceptions). That is, he has intruded into the story to offer comments on his characters. Particularly with regard to Alyosha, he addresses the reader directly to explain that this youngest brother is to be his hero. He has also used a "we" that stands for the voice of the local community and is always less sophisticated than the author's own voice. Even Flaubert had allowed himself that "we" at the beginning of *Madame Bovary*, and Dostoevsky will return to it in Book Twelve, when he comes to present Dmitry's trial for parricide. In most of his "big" scenes, however, he follows a strictly dramatic method. To make the standard distinction, he does not "tell" or "tell about"; he shows.

Dostoevsky is famous for those "big" scenes, all intensely charged with emotion: murders, suicides, sudden unpredictable confessions or revelations. His dramatic effects suggest those of Dickens, an author he greatly admired, but go beyond Dickens in subtlety, surprise, and sometimes brute power. One is not surprised to learn that when Stanislavsky was directing the Moscow Art Theatre, he not only presented dramatized versions of entire Dostoevsky novels but sometimes staged individual scenes. The one between Lise and Alyosha cries out for theatrical performance.

As one reads the text, it would seem that the drama is being enacted on a bare stage. Dostoevsky, whose imagination was not primarily visual, reveals no interest whatever in the look of a young girl's room. The only stage property he calls for is the wheel chair in which Lise is reclining as the curtain rises; much later she will jump up from it to fling her arms round Alyosha's neck. It is definitely Lise's scene, with Alyosha making brief replies to her speeches, yet we *see* very little of Lise except at the beginning, where Dostoevsky mentions her inflamed eyes, her sallow cheeks, and the long, slender fingers lying motionless on her dress. Hands and fingers recur frequently in her excited fancies, a detail for which psychoanalysts would have an interpretation. There are the people who would point fingers at her if her evil deeds were known; there are the devils who try to lay hands on her; there is the Jew of Russian legend who cuts off the fingers of a four-year-old boy;

and, as the curtain falls, there is Lise's deliberately slamming the door on her own finger.

The scene has progressed in a series of psychological shocks to the reader; one might say that these are a distinguishing feature of Dostoevsky as a novelist. Lise herself is the first shock. She is sixteen years old, but she is not the "young girl" of nineteenth-century fiction, dreaming only of hearts, goodness, and orange blossoms. Lise dreams of burning down the house, then later of blaspheming God and being assaulted by a crowd of devils. At that point the saintly Alyosha also shocks the reader: "I've had the same dream, too," he says. Then, after Lise recounts her dream of listening to the moans of a crucified little boy while eating stewed pineapples, she jumps from her wheel chair and moans—another psychological surprise—"Alyosha, save me!"

Dostoevsky likes to reveal traces of evil in the hearts of the best persons and traces of good in the wicked. "I proceed by analysis," he said in a letter to his brother Mikhail, "and not by synthesis; I plunge into the depths; and while analyzing every atom, I search out the whole." That plunge into the depths is his essential contribution to the novel. Freud, as we expected to learn, found that Dostoevsky had foreshadowed many of his ideas. The novelist foreshadows even his method in this particular scene, for Lise reclines in her chair as on a couch and recounts her dreams as if she were one of Freud's patients, while Alyosha makes the sort of brief comments that might be offered by her analyst. There is a transference—"Alyosha, why don't you love me at all?" she says—but there is no promise that Lise will come to terms with herself. "Mean, mean, mean, mean!" is her last whisper as she looks intently at her bleeding finger.

Germinal (1885)

EMILE ZOLA (1840-1902) was the founder of the international literary movement known as Naturalism, of which the central doctrine is that human beings are part of nature and are subject to the same indifferent laws. "Balzac says that he wishes to paint men, women, and things," Zola wrote in his notebook. "I count men and women the same, while admitting their natural differences, and"—he underlined the phrase—"*subject men and women to things.*" Some of the literary figures influenced by Zola's principle or his practice are Maupassant, Huysmans, George Moore, Gerhardt Hauptmann in Germany, and, in the United States, Frank Norris, Theodore Dreiser, Jack London, Eugene O'Neill (in the early plays), John Dos Passos, and John Steinbeck, among many others.

Zola was born in Paris, but grew up in Aix-en-Provence, where Cézanne was his boyhood friend. His father died when Emile was very young, leaving the family almost destitute. When he was eighteen, he went back to Paris with his mother, who hoped to receive help from her late husband's friends; enough of it was forthcoming for Emile to finish his schooling, but he failed in his final examinations. For two years he starved in the Latin Quarter; then he obtained a post in the shipping department of a publishing house. He wrote at night and managed to have a first utterly worthless book accepted for publication. Soon he was working as a literary gossip columnist. With his eye on the main chance, he wrote other books as worthless as the first. It was not until the appearance of *Thérèse Raquin* (1867), which was violently attacked in the press, that Zola began to be regarded by his fellow writers as a young man with a brilliant future.

Zola's contribution to literature was made between 1871 and 1893, when he planned and wrote a series of twenty novels under the general title of *The Rougon-Macquarts: The Natural and Social History of a Family under the Second Empire.* The plan was to have members of the family appear everywhere in French society and everywhere show the results of their disastrous heredity. The seventh novel in the series, *L'Assommoir* (1878), translated into English as *The Dram-Shop*, deals unsparingly with the Parisian lower classes; it made Zola the most controversial writer in France, and the most widely read. The ninth novel was *Nana* (1880), about a successful courtesan, and was equally successful. *Germinal,* thirteenth in the series, is a proletarian novel that set a pattern later followed in many languages; dozens of American *Germinals* were to be published during the Great Depression. *Dr. Pascal* (1893) marks the end of Zola's great enterprise, although he might have continued. He had constructed a huge genealogical chart of the Rougon-Macquarts, and on this he had noted that an "Unknown Child" was born in 1876, in the fifth generation of that blighted family. "What will become of him?" he asked himself on the chart, but he was never to answer the question.

In point of theory, Zola ascribed the same attributes to physiological determinism that had formerly been given to concepts of fate, whether human or divine. Science, he thought, had proved that our heredity—to some extent modified by social and economic forces—was indeed our fate. The chief scientific sources of his notions were Darwin, Taine—who once said that "Vice and virtue are products like vitriol and sugar"—Dr. Prosper Lucas, who wrote a *Philosophical and Physiological Treatise Concerning Natural Heredity* (1850) that now seems a preposterous work (but Zola made a summary of it for himself), and an incomparably better book that he also venerated, Claude Bernard's *Introduction to the Study of Experimental Medicine* (1865).

The chief literary source of *The Rougon-Macquarts* was of course Balzac and his scheme for a *Human Comedy*. Where Zola went beyond his predecessor was in his effort to make his fiction scientific. Balzac too had offered claims of the sort, but his scientific theories bore the stamp of a genial amateurism. Zola tried to be professional. In his manifesto *The Experimental Novel* (1880), he says that the modern novelist should emulate the physical scientist by being equally detached, dispassionate, and objective. Much as the laboratory worker measures and combines his ingredients, then steps back to observe and record, the writer selects a group of human types with known heredities, places them in a chosen environment, then documents impersonally what *must* occur. He accepts no moral responsibility for his fictional characters; he does no more than faithfully record what he sees.

One is tempted to smile at Zola's extravagant claims both for his own literary undertaking and for science itself. His statement, "We shall enter into a century when all-powerful man will have enslaved nature and used its laws to make flourish the greatest sum-total of justice and liberty possible upon this earth," rings out with gallant optimism. At the same time the quotation reminds us of a paradox implicit in Naturalism. Zola's desire to change society runs counter to his belief that everything is determined by the inexorable laws of heredity and environment.

As a public figure, Zola is best remembered for his role in the case of Alfred Dreyfus, the unfortunate army officer convicted of treason in 1894 and sent to Devil's Island. In 1898 Zola wrote his open letter "I Accuse" (*J'accuse*), denouncing the conviction as a conspiracy and demanding that the case be reopened. The government prosecuted him, found him guilty of libeling the army, fined him five thousand francs, and sentenced him to jail for six months. Friends smuggled him to England, where he remained in hiding. Largely owing to Zola's efforts, however, it was subsequently proved that the documents implicating Dreyfus were forgeries, and in 1900 a new French ministry granted amnesty to all those unjustly accused. Zola was hailed on his return to France as a champion of human rights. Two years later he died in his own bedroom, from asphyxiation caused by a defective flue.

THE STORY

A penniless young mechanic, Etienne Lantier, arrives by night at a colliery called Le Voreux ("the voracious one") for all the lives it has taken. Hired as a miner, he finds lodging with the Maheu family, all of whom—men, women, and children down to the age of eleven— work for miserable wages in the same mine. Other characters in the novel offer a social panorama of the industry. They include Hennebeau, the mine manager, caught between compassion for the miners and loyalty to the board of directors; Négrel the engineer, more interested in production than in persons; Deneulin, a mine owner driven to the edge of bankruptcy by his large competitors and hence unable to grant the miners a living wage; and the Russian anarchist Souvarine, who, after the strike is broken, destroys Le Voreux by sawing through the wooden lining of the shaft and letting the mine be flooded by an underground lake.

The first half of the novel presents the daily life of the miners as Zola had observed it during a visit of several months to one of the wretched mining towns near the Belgian frontier. Then comes the strike, with Etienne assuming its leadership, and everything explodes in violence and disaster. Etienne's love for Catherine Maheu is consummated in the mine shaft where the two of them are trapped with a dozen others by Souvarine's act of destruction. Many days have passed, and Catherine dies not long before Etienne is rescued as the only survivor. For all the bleakness of the book, it ends on a note of hope for the future. Etienne departs, looking forward to the day when the workers will triumph through collective action. "Men were springing up, a black avenging host was slowly germinating in the furrows, thrusting upwards for the harvest of future ages. And very soon their germination would crack the earth asunder." These last sentences of the book call us back to the title *Germinal*: the time of sprouting seeds and the first month of spring in the French revolutionary calendar.

The novel is divided into seven books. The chapter that follows is the last in Book 4 and marks the beginning of the violent action that will continue without intermission to the end of the novel. The modern translation was made by L.W. Tancock for Penguin Books.

[*The Mass Meeting in the Forest*]

The Plan-des-Dames was a great clearing recently opened up by tree-felling. It was on a gentle slope, girt by lofty trees, magnificent beeches whose straight, regular trunks surrounded it with a white colonnade flecked with green lichens. Some of the fallen giants still lay on the grass, while to the left a pile of sawn logs stood in a geometrical cube. With the coming of evening the cold had sharpened, and the frozen mosses crackled under foot. At ground level it was quite dark already, but the higher branches showed up against the pale sky, in which the rising full moon would soon dim the stars.

Nearly three thousand mining folk had come to the meeting-place, a milling crowd of men, women, and children gradually pouring into the clearing and overflowing into the undergrowth.

Latecomers were still arriving, and the sea of faces wrapped in shadow stretched as far as the nearby beeches. A hum of conversation rose from it like a stormy wind in the still, frozen forest.

Etienne stood at the top, looking down the slope, with Rasseneur and Maheu. A dispute had broken out and their voices could be heard in sudden bursts. Men standing near were listening, Levaque with clenched fists, Pierron turning his back to them and very worried because he had not been able to plead sickness any longer. Grandpa Bonnemort was there too, and old Mouque, side by side on a log, looking very philosophical. And behind them were the scoffers, Zacharie, Mouquet, and others who had come for fun; but the women, on the contrary, made a very serious group, as solemn as though they were in church. Maheude silently nodded while la Levaque swore under her breath. Philomène was coughing, her bronchitis having returned with the winter. The only one who frankly laughed was Mouquette, tickled by the way Ma Brûlé was carrying on about her daughter, calling her an unnatural creature who had got rid of her mother so as to guzzle rabbit, a creature who sold herself and throve on her husband's cowardice. Jeanlin had taken up his position on the pile of wood, hoisting up Lydie and making Bébert follow, all three of them up in the air and higher than anybody else.

The dispute had arisen because Rasseneur wanted to proceed constitutionally by electing officers. He was still smarting from his defeat at the Bon Joyeux, and he had sworn to have his revenge, counting on regaining his former prestige with the rank and file of the miners and not merely with the delegates. Etienne thought that a committee was outrageous and ridiculous here in the forest. Since they were hunted down like wolves they must act like revolutionaries and savages.

Seeing that the argument might go on for ever, he took control of the crowd at once by standing on a felled trunk and shouting:

'Comrades! comrades!'

The confused murmur died down like a long-drawn-out sigh. While Maheu silenced Rasseneur's protests, Etienne went on in stentorian tones:

'Comrades, since we are forbidden to speak, since they put the police on to us as though we were thieves, we have come here to thrash the matter out! We are free here, we are at home, and nobody will come and shut us up, any more than you can the birds and animals!'

He was answered by a thunder of cries and exclamations.

'Yes, yes, the forest is ours, we've a right to talk here. . . . Go on!'

Etienne stood still for a moment on his log. The moon was still too low on the horizon, and only lit the topmost branches, so that the crowd, which had gradually calmed down into complete silence, was still lost in shadow. He too looked black, and stood out above the crowd at the top of the slope like a dark pillar.

Slowly he raised one arm and began; but his voice no longer thundered, for he had adopted the frigid tones of a simple representative of the people making his report. Now at last he was able to work in the speech which the police had cut short at the Bon Joyeux. He began with a rapid history of the strike, making a point of expressing it with scientific eloquence—facts, nothing but facts. He spoke first of his dislike of strikes; the miners had not wanted this one, the directors had provoked them with their new scale of payment for timbering. Then he reminded them of the first approach made by their delegates to the manager, and of the bad faith of the Administration; and then, later, at the time of their second deputation, the tardy concession, the two centimes given back after they had tried to steal them. So now here they were: he quoted figures to show that the provident fund was exhausted, gave details of the allocation of the help that had been sent, devoted a few sentences to excusing the International, Pluchart, and the others for not having done more for them in the middle of all their preoccupations in the struggle for world conquest. So the situation was daily going from bad to worse, the Company had given them back their cards and was threatening to take on workers from Belgium, moreover they had intimidated the weaker brethren and had persuaded a number of miners to go back to work. He still spoke in a monotonous tone, as though to drive home the seriousness of his news; he told of the victory of famine and the death of hope, the struggle that had reached the culminating frenzy of courage. Then suddenly, without raising his voice, he concluded:

'It is in these circumstances, mates, that you must come to a decision tonight. Do you want the strike to go on? And if so, what do you propose to do to beat the Company?'

A great silence fell from the starry sky. In the darkness the unseen crowd held its peace at these heartbreaking words, and a sigh of despair was the only sound that could be heard through the trees.

But already Etienne was speaking again, in a different voice. He was no longer the secretary of an Association, but a leader, an apostle bringing the gospel of truth. Were there any cowards among them who would break their word? Why, they would have suffered for a whole month in vain and go back to the pits hanging their heads, back once again to face the never-ending agony! Wouldn't it be better to die at once in an attempt to destroy the tyranny of capital starving the workers? Wasn't it a stupid game that they had had quite enough of, this business of always submitting under the lash of hunger until it came to the point when once again hunger drove even the meekest of them to revolt? He showed how the miners were exploited and were the only ones to suffer from these disastrous crises, reduced to starvation whenever the exigencies of competition brought down prices. No! the timbering scale was unacceptable, it was only a disguised economy, they meant to rob each man of one hour of his working day. This time it had gone too far, and the time was coming for the downtrodden worms to turn and see justice done.

He paused, with arms outstretched. The word justice shook the crowd, and a burst of applause passed over it like the rustle of dry leaves. Voices shouted:

'Justice! it's high time. . . . Justice!'

Gradually Etienne was warming up. He lacked Rasseneur's facile stream of words. Often he was at a loss, and had to use tortuous sentences from which he emerged with an effort emphasized by a forward lunge of his shoulders. But when he was pulled up in this way he found simple, energetic images which struck home to his audience, whilst his movements, those of a workman on the job, elbows now well back and now thrust forward to strike out with his fists, his jaw suddenly jutting out as though to bite, had an extraordinary effect upon his mates. As they all said, he was not very big but he made you listen.

'The wage system is a new form of slavery,' he went on in a still more ringing voice. 'The mine should belong to the miner, like the sea to the fisherman and the earth to the peasant. . . . Do you understand? The mine is yours—yours, for you have all paid for it with a hundred years of blood and misery!'

He faced up squarely to the thorny legal question, and lost his way in the maze of special regulations on mines. The subsoil belonged to the nation just as much as the soil. It was only a hateful privilege that handed over the monopoly to the Companies, and this was all the more shameful in the case of Montsou, where the so-called legality of the concessions was complicated by agreements made ages ago with owners of ancient fiefs according to the old custom of Hainault. The mining folk had only to reconquer their own possessions, he said, as with a wave of the hand he took in the whole country, beyond the forest. Just then the moon rose clear of the topmost branches and lit him up. When the crowd, still in darkness, saw his figure standing out white, distributing fortunes with open hands, they burst out again into prolonged applause.

'Yes, yes, quite right! . . . Bravo!'

Then Etienne trotted out his favourite subject, the collectivization of the means of production, as he said more than once in a phrase the pedantic jargon of which pleased him mightily. His own evolution was not complete. He had started from the sentimental fraternity of the novice, the need to reform the wage system, and now he had reached the political theory of abolishing wages altogether. Since the Bon Joyeux meeting his collectivism, from being vague and humanitarian, had hardened into a complicated programme each point of which he could argue scientifically. As a first point he affirmed that liberty could only be gained by the destruction of the State. Then, when the people had the government in their own hands, reforms could begin: return to the primitive community, substitution of a free and equal family for the morally oppressive one, absolute civil, political, and economic equality, individual independence guaranteed thanks to the possession of the tools for work and of the whole output, and finally free technical education paid for out of collective funds. That involved a total recasting of the old corrupt society: he attacked marriage and the right to bequeath property, limited everybody's personal fortune and overthrew the iniquitous monument of dead centuries with the same repeated sweeping gesture of the harvester striking down the ripe corn with his scythe; then with the other hand he built humanity of tomorrow, an edifice of truth and justice rising in the dawn of the twentieth century. Reason tottered before this mental effort and left only the obsession of the fanatic. Gone were the scruples of his human feeling and common sense, and nothing seemed simpler than the realization of this brave new world: he had foreseen everything and he referred to it as though it were a machine he could fix up in a couple of hours, and neither fire nor blood counted.

'It is our turn now,' he yelled in a final crescendo. 'It is our turn to have power and wealth!'

Acclamations roared towards him from the depths of the forest. By now the moon lit up the whole clearing and picked out the isolated points in the sea of heads, far off into the dim recesses of the glades between the tall grey trunks. Here, in the icy winter night, was a whole people in a white heat of passion, with shining eyes and parted lips, famished men, women, and children let loose to pillage the wealth of ages, the wealth of which they had been dispossessed. They no longer felt the cold, for these burning words had warmed them to the vitals. They were uplifted in a religious ecstasy, like the feverish hope of the early Christians expecting the coming reign of justice. Many obscure phrases had baffled them, they were far from understanding these technical and abstract arguments, but their very obscurity and abstract nature broadened still further the field of promises and carried them away into hallucinations. What a wonderful dream! To be the masters and suffer no more! To enjoy life at last!

'That's right, by God! Our turn now! Death to the exploiters!'

The women were hysterical. Maheude forgot her usual calm and yielded to the intoxication of hunger, la Levaque was yelling, Ma Brûlé, beside herself, was waving her witch's arms, Philomène was shaking herself to pieces in a fit of coughing, and Mouquette was so worked up that she was shouting endearments at the speaker. Amongst the men, Maheu was quite won over and had exclaimed with impatience at Pierron trembling on one side of him and Levaque talking too much on the other, whilst the scoffers, Zacharie and Mouquet, feeling ill at ease, tried to raise a giggle by saying how amazed they were that the comrade could say so much without having a drink. But the biggest noise of all came from the wood-pile, on which Jeanlin was shouting and egging on Bébert and Lydie by brandishing the basket containing Poland.

The clamour rose again. Etienne was tasting the heady wine of popularity. This was power that he was holding in his hands, materialized in the three thousand breasts whose hearts were beating at his bidding. Had he deigned to come, Souvarine would have applauded his ideas in so far as he recognized them, and would have been pleased to see his pupil's progress towards anarchy. He would have given his approval to the programme, except in the matter of education, which was a relic of sentimental silliness, for holy, salutary ignorance must be the bath in which men would be tempered anew. As for Rasseneur, he was shrugging his shoulders in angry scorn.

'You are going to let me speak!' he shouted at Etienne.

Etienne jumped down from his tree-trunk.

'Speak away, we'll see if they listen to you!'

Rasseneur had at once jumped up in his place and was already waving his arms for silence. But the noise did not die down, for his name was being passed on from the front rows, who had recognized him, to the back rows away under the beeches; and they refused to give him a hearing, for he was a fallen idol the very sight of whom annoyed his former supporters. His facile elocution and cheery flow of words, which had charmed them so long, was now treated as lukewarm tea fit only for lulling cowards to sleep. He bellowed in vain through the din, trying to bring out once again his stock speech on appeasement: the impossibility of changing the world by acts of parliament, the necessity of allowing social evolution time to come about. But they only laughed and shushed him, and his defeat at the Bon Joyeux now worsened beyond redemption. In the end they threw bits of frozen moss at him, and a woman's shrill voice screamed: 'Down with the traitor!'

He was trying to explain that the mine could never be the miner's property in the way that the loom is the weaver's, and that he preferred profit-sharing, which made the worker an interested party, one of the family, so to speak.

'Down with the traitor!' a thousand voices repeated, and stones began to whistle.

Rasseneur turned pale and his eyes filled with tears of despair. His whole life-work was crumbling, twenty years of ambitious fraternizing crushed by the ingratitude of the mob. He stepped down from the log, cut to the heart and without the strength to go on.

'You think it's funny,' he stammered to the triumphant Etienne. 'All right, I hope it happens to you! And happen it will, make no mistake!'

And as though disclaiming any responsibility for the misfortunes he could foresee, he made one final sweeping gesture and walked off alone into the quiet and silvery countryside.

Some cat-calls were raised, and to everybody's amazement old Bonnemort could be seen standing on a log and holding forth in the midst of the uproar. Until then Mouque and he had stood there absorbed, appearing, as they always did, to be musing on far-off things. Probably he was overcome by one of those garrulous fits which suddenly came and stirred up the past so violently that his memories welled up and poured out of his mouth for hours. A deep silence had fallen, and they listened to this old man, this ghostly spectre in the moonlight, and as he was telling things with no obvious bearing on the discussion, long stories that nobody could understand, the amazement grew. He was talking about his own young days, the death of his two uncles who were crushed in a fall at Le Voreux, then he went on to the pneumonia that had carried off his wife. But through it all he clung to his point: things had never gone well in the past and they never would in the future. For example, they had had a meeting in the forest, five hundred of them, because the king would not reduce working hours; but then he stopped short and began the story of another strike— he'd seen so many of them, he had! And they all finished up under these here trees in the Plan-des-Dames, or else at the Charbonnerie, or further off still, over Saut-du-Loup way. Sometimes it was freezing, sometimes it was blazing. One night it had rained so hard that they had gone home without saying anything. And the king's soldiers arrived and it ended up with shooting.

'We put our hands up like this, and swore never to go back. Oh, I've sworn, I have. . . . oh, yes, I've sworn!'

The crowd was gaping in uncomfortable amazement when Etienne, who had been watching the scene, leaped on to the fallen tree and stood beside the old man. He had recognized Chavel among his friends in the front row, and the thought that Catherine must be there too had put new fire into him and a desire to be applauded in front of her.

'Comrades, you have just heard, here is one of our old friends and that's what he has suffered, and what our children will suffer if we don't have it out once and for all with these thieves and murderers.'

His rage was terrifying. Never had he spoken so vehemently. With one arm he supported old Bonnemort, displaying him like a flag of misery and grief, crying for vengeance. In rapid phrases he went back to the first of the Maheus, and told of the whole of this family done to death in the pit, victimized by the Company, hungrier than ever after a hundred years of toil; and then by contrast he pictured the bellies of the directors sweating money, the great crowd of shareholders kept like whores for a century, doing nothing, just enjoying their bodies. Wasn't it terrible to think of? A whole race of people dying down in the pits, sons after their fathers, so that bribes could be given to Ministers and generations of noble lords and bourgeois could give grand parties or sit and grow fat by their own firesides! He had studied miners' occupational diseases and now brought them all out with horrible details: anaemia, scrofula, black bronchitis, choking asthma, paralysing rheumatism. They, poor devils, were just machine-fodder, they were penned like cattle in housing-estates, the big Companies were gradually dominating their whole lives, regulating slavery, threatening to enlist all the nation's workers, millions of hands to increase the wealth of a thousand idlers. But the ignorant miner, the mere brute buried in the bowels of the earth, was a thing of the past. In the depths of the mine an army was springing up, a harvest of citizens germinating like seeds that would break through the earth one sunny day. And then they would know whether, after forty years' service, they could dare to offer a hundred and fifty francs as a pension to an old man of sixty, spitting coal and with legs swollen with the water of the coal-face. Yes, labour would call capital to account, capital, that impersonal god, unknown to the worker, crouching somewhere in his mysterious tabernacle whence he sucked the blood of the poor starving devils he lived on! They would go and hunt him out, and make him show his face in the glare of fires, they would drown him in blood, this disgusting hog, this monstrous idol gorged with human flesh!

He stopped, but his arms remained stretched out into space, pointing at the enemy over there, somewhere, wherever he might be in the world. This time the clamour raised by the crowd was so loud that the bourgeois of Montsou heard it and looked anxiously towards Vandame, thinking it was some terrible landslide. Night birds flew up out of the woods and soared into the moonlit sky.

He wanted an immediate decision.

'Comrades, what have you decided? Do you vote for going on with the strike?'

'Yes, yes,' roared the voices.

'Then what steps are you going to take? If any blacklegs go down the pit tomorrow we are bound to be beaten.'

The voices rose again like a hurricane:

'Death to all blacklegs!'

'Very well, then, you have decided to hold them to their duty and sworn word. This is what we could do: go to the pits, our presence will stop the blacklegs, and we could show the Company that we are all in agreement and will die rather than surrender.'

'Right-oh! to the pits, to the pits!'

All the time he had been speaking Etienne had been looking for Catherine among the pale, roaring faces down there. No, she could not be there. But Chaval he could still see, making a point of sneering and shrugging his shoulders, consumed with jealousy and ready to sell himself for a little of Etienne's popularity.

'And if there are any informers amongst our numbers, mates,' Etienne went on, 'let them look out, for we know who they are. Yes, I can see some Vandame men who haven't left their pit.'

'Is that for my benefit?' asked Chaval with a fine show of bravado.

'Yours or anybody else's. But as it's you who have spoken, you might as well understand that those who have got something to eat are quite a different thing from those who go hungry. You are working at Jean-Bart. . . .'

A mocking voice broke in:

'Oh, he works, does he? No, he's got a woman who works for him.'

Chaval went scarlet and swore.

'Christ! aren't we allowed to work, then?'

'No!' shouted Etienne, 'not when your mates are going through hell for the good of all. We are not going to let people crawl over to the bosses' side just to do themselves a good turn. If the strike had been general we should have been the masters long before this. Ought a single Vandame man to have gone down when Montsou was out? The trump card would be if the whole area stopped work —at Monsieur Deneulin's same as here. Do you see? They're all blacklegs on the coal-faces at Jean-Bart. You are all traitors!'

The crowd round Chaval was getting dangerous; fists were being brandished and cries of death were heard. He had turned pale. But in his furious determination to get the better of Etienne, he suddenly had an idea.

'Just you listen to me now! You come to Jean-Bart tomorrow and see for yourselves whether I am working! We are all on your side, and that's what I was sent here to say. The furnaces have got to be put out, and the enginemen must come out, too. And if the pumps give out, all the better! The water will bust up the pits and the whole bloody lot.'

He was wildly applauded in his turn, and from then on even Etienne was edged into the background, as speaker after speaker mounted the fallen trunk, waved his arms about in the din and threw out the wildest proposals. It was now a paroxysm of blind faith, the impatience of a religious sect, weary of waiting for a miracle and determined to provoke one itself. These people, light-headed with hunger, saw red, had visions of fire and blood in a glorious apotheosis out of which universal happiness was rising before their eyes. The peaceful moonlight bathed this surging swell, and the clamour for blood was hemmed in on all sides by the deep silence of the forest. The frozen moss crackled under foot, whilst the beeches, standing tall and strong, spreading the delicate tracery of their branches black against the sky, were blind and deaf to the poor wretches moving at their feet.

There was some pushing in the crowd, and Maheude found herself next to her husband, and both of them, crazed by the long-drawn-out exasperation of the past months, were backing up Levaque who was going one better than everybody else and demanding the heads of the engineers. Pierron had vanished. Bonnemort and Mouque, both talking at once, were saying vague and terrible things that nobody could hear. Zacharie, just for fun, was agitating for the demolition of the churches, whilst Mouquet was banging the ground with his *crosse*, just to add to the row. The women were quite off their heads: la Levaque, hands on hips, was going for Philomène, whom she accused of laughing; Mouquette talked of putting the police out of action by kicking them up the so-and-so; Ma Brûlé, who had been cuffing Lydie for being without her basket or any salad either, was aiming punches into the air, for all the bosses she would have liked to get hold of. For a moment Jeanlin had been overcome with panic, Bébert having heard from a fellow that Madame Rasseneur had seen them take Poland; but he soon decided to go back and let the rabbit loose at the door of the Avantage, and set about yelling louder than ever, opening and brandishing his new knife and proudly making the blade gleam.

'Comrades! comrades!' Etienne was repeating, at the end of his tether, hoarse with trying to get a moment's silence in order to come to some definite decision.

At last he got their attention.

'Comrades! tomorrow morning at Jean-Bart; is that settled?'

'Yes, yes, to Jean-Bart! Death to the traitors!'

The three thousand voices rose to heaven in a tempest, and died away in the pure light of the moon.

AFTERWORD

To make a fine distinction, Etienne Lantier is the hero of *Germinal*, but not really the protagonist, or principal actor, either of this chapter or of the novel as a whole. The real protagonist is a group or collectivity composed of all the thousands of miners in the country round Montsou (a name that suggests "my penny" and the struggle for bread). Especially in describing how the miners held a secret meeting, but also in the chapters that follow, Zola creates the sense of a mob in action and shows how individual feelings may coalesce into a group emotion. One might say that *Germinal*, besides being a proletarian novel, is also the first collective novel, though it was to have thousands of successors, some in every national literature. In the United States the first to appear was probably *The Octopus* (1901), by Frank Norris, which clearly made use of Zola's methods.

Among those methods are some that are usually associated with the stage (and we know from Zola's rough sketch for *Germinal* that he had thought of turning the story into a play). The curtain figuratively rises to reveal the dim clearing over which the full moon, exerting an almost tidal power over the gathering, is still to appear. The climax of Etienne's first speech exactly coincides with the moon's rising "clear of the topmost branches," while his hitherto dark figure turns white against the dark spectators. Zola's notes show a deliberate concern with color in *Germinal*. At this convocation black and white prevail, thus bearing out a remark by the author: "To obtain a big effect, the oppositions must be clear, and pushed to the highest point of intensity." Red is also used, figuratively, to describe the crowd's furious passions: "They [labor] would make him [capital] show his face in the glare of fires, they would drown him in blood," and the crowd "saw red, had visions of fire and blood."

The crowd as it assembles becomes a force of nature. Mostly it is anonymous, but a paragraph is devoted to mentioning many of the principals by name and to showing each in a characteristic act or attitude. (The next-to-last paragraph of the chapter will list those same persons in approximately the same order, thus placing the chapter in a frame.) To create the illusion of our listening to a long harangue,

Zola paraphrases the greater part of Etienne's two speeches, in such a way as to illustrate the hero's growing incoherence. Several times we hear the actual voice of the crowd making quasi-religious responses to Etienne's "sermon." The one comment by Zola himself comes at the end of the first peroration: "Reason tottered before this mental effort and left only the obsession of the fanatic."

The account of Etienne's second and shorter exhortation, after old Bonnemort has spoken, contains two metaphors, and these carry more weight because the rest of the chapter makes little use of metaphorical language. The first is "In the depths of the mine an army was springing up, a harvest of citizens germinating like seeds that would break through the earth one sunny day"; the second is "Yes, labour would call capital to account, capital, that impersonal god, unknown to the worker, crouching somewhere in his mysterious tabernacle whence he sucked the blood of the poor starving devils he lived on!" The first is an obvious allusion to the title of the book, while the second points to Zola's use of themes borrowed from mythology.

The fact is that several Graeco-Roman and Hebraic legends are suggested in the course of the novel. Among them are the Roman proletarians' dream of a new golden age, men rising from the earth after a flood, and resurrection after a symbolic death. One also finds echoes of the wars of the Titans, and the name of one mine, Le Tartaret, clearly suggests Tartarus, the prison deep under the earth from which Zeus released the hundred-armed monsters to war against their younger brother Chronos. To readers who find these mythical elements surprising by their contrast with Zola's professed realism, a letter that he wrote to his friend Céard just after the publication of *Germinal* might help to explain his purpose. "You are not stupefied to find in me a poet," he said in the letter, then added that it was "the leap to the stars from the trampoline of exact observation. With a beat of the wings, truth soars up to the symbol."

Jude the Obscure (1895)

THOMAS HARDY (1840-1928) was born near Dorchester, the county town of Dorsetshire and the "Casterbridge" of his novels. Dorset and the counties to the north and west were to become models, in topography and atmosphere, for his fictional Wessex. His hero Jude's activities as a stone mason are also based on early experience, for Hardy, at the age of sixteen, was apprenticed to a local church architect. One of his assignments was to make drawings of old Dorsetshire churches with a view to their restoration. In 1862 he went to London, where he became assistant to another architect, but he did not advance rapidly in his career. At night he taught himself Greek and pored over Greek tragedies and the Old and the New Testament. His first story was published in 1865.

At this time he was writing a great deal of verse—a medium he preferred to prose, early and late—and he was hesitating between architecture and letters as a profession. If he was to earn a living as a writer, it would have to be by fiction, not poetry, and he manfully set to work producing novels. The first was read in manuscript by George Meredith (1828-1909), who was already a famous novelist. In 1869 he advised Hardy to lay the book aside and try another with more plot. Hardy destroyed the manuscript, then followed Meredith's counsel to the unwise extent of writing a novel that was all plot: *Desperate Remedies* (1871). Published at his own expense, it received almost no attention. *Under the Greenwood Tree* (1872) and *A Pair of Blue Eyes* (1873) won the respect of some critics, but not of the public. It was not until his fourth published novel, *Far from the Madding Crowd* (1874), that his work began to be widely recognized.

The book was serialized in *Cornhill Magazine*, edited by the critic and biographer Leslie Stephen (1832-1904), the father of Virginia Woolf. The installments appeared anonymously, and many readers thought they were the work of George Eliot (1819-1880), who had published *Middlemarch* two years earlier and was then regarded as the greatest living novelist. In those days serial publication was more lucrative to many authors than book publication. Hardy now felt enough confidence in his earning power as a writer to abandon architecture and also to get married. In 1883 he designed a middle-class house for himself—Max Gate, on the outskirts of Dorchester—and there he was to spend the rest of a long and outwardly quiet life.

Among his later novels, four are widely read today: *The Return of the Native* (1878), *The Mayor of Casterbridge* (1886), *Tess of the D'Urbervilles* (1891), and *Jude the Obscure*, the last and finest. A storm had blown up over *Tess*, with its heroine who bears an illegitimate child, kills her seducer, and goes to the gallows. Hardy was said to be the English envoy of the abhorred French Naturalists, a mistaken judgment. He was indeed pessimistic and deterministic, as the Naturalists also were, but his fundamental impulse was poetic, not sociological. *Jude* raised a greater storm, one that began with its serial appearance in *Harper's Magazine* (incidentally in a bowdlerized version and under the title of "Hearts Insurgent"). When the book appeared, critics became hysterical, and a bishop burned a copy of it publicly. Knowing that he had put more of his inner thoughts into *Jude* than into his previous work, Hardy was appalled by the outcry—"the experience completely curing me of further interest in novel writing," as he was to say years later in his preface to a new edition.

His decision had been announced in 1896. After that year, to paraphrase Milton, he abandoned the cool element of prose and continued to soar in the high region of his fancies "with his garland and singing robes around him." His most ambitious undertaking in verse was *The Dynasts* (1903-1908), an "epic-drama" in three parts, nineteen acts, and a hundred and thirty scenes. Starting as an epical treatment of the Napoleonic era, it becomes a vehicle for Hardy's notions about man, nature, and the supernatural "It" that governs the universe. Most readers prefer his shorter poems, published in eight books, the last of which, *Winter Words*, appeared in 1928, not long after his death.

THE STORY

In *Jude the Obscure* Hardy is attacking three English institutions revered in his time: the great universities, the Church, and marriage, with the third attack closest to the heart of his story. Jude Fawley grows up in a Wessex village, becomes passionately enamored with learning, borrows books from a sympathetic schoolmaster, teaches himself Latin and Greek, and dreams of attending the nearby university of Christminster (for which read Oxford). The dream is thwarted not only by Jude's poverty and the social barriers he has to face but also by his entanglements with two women. The first is sensuous, vulgar, cheating Arabella. She seduces Jude, tricks him into marrying her by hinting she is pregnant, then deserts him after an unhappy brief married life. He falls in love with his cousin Sue, bright, unconventional, and also unhappily married. Leaving her husband, Sue sets up housekeeping with Jude, but refuses to marry him even after they both have been divorced. She is a frigid woman, and "though she has children," Hardy later explained in a letter, "her intimacies with Jude have never been more than occasional. . . . This has tended to keep his passion as hot at the end as at the beginning, and helps to break his heart." Of course he has been forced to relinquish his dream of attending Christminster. The lowest point of his miserable existence is reached when Arabella's child, called Father Time, hangs his half-sister, his half-brother, and himself, leaving behind the pitiful note: *Done because we are too menny.*

Sue takes refuge in religion. Having become a High Church Anglican, she leaves Jude from a feeling of duty and remarries her first husband. Arabella lures Jude back by getting him drunk. He is now a consumptive, however, and hopes only for death (while Arabella schemes to marry Vilbert, a quack doctor). One of Hardy's comments on the book is that he wished to show "the contrast between the ideal life a man wished to lead, and the squalid real life he was fated to lead." The last scene, which follows, is enacted within hearing of Christminster bells.

[*The Death of Jude*]

The last pages to which the chronicler of these lives would ask the reader's attention are concerned with the scene in and out of Jude's bedroom when leafy summer came round again.

His face was now so thin that his old friends would hardly

have known him. It was afternoon, and Arabella was at the looking-glass curling her hair, which operation she performed by heating an umbrella-stay in the flame of a candle she had lighted, and using it upon the flowing lock. When she had finished this, practised a dimple, and put on her things, she cast her eyes round upon Jude. He seemed to be sleeping, though his position was an elevated one, his malady preventing him from lying down.

Arabella, hatted, gloved, and ready, sat down and waited, as if expecting some one to come and take her place as nurse.

Certain sounds from without revealed that the town was in festivity, though little of the festival, whatever it might have been, could be seen here. Bells began to ring, and the notes came into the room through the open window, and travelled round Jude's head in a hum. They made her restless, and at last she said to herself, "Why ever doesn't father come?"

She looked again at Jude, critically gauged his ebbing life, as she had done so many times during the late months, and, glancing at his watch, which was hung up by way of timepiece, rose impatiently. Still he slept, and, coming to a resolution, she slipped from the room, closed the door noiselessly, and descended the stairs. The house was empty. The attraction which moved Arabella to go abroad had evidently drawn away the other inmates long before.

It was a warm, cloudless, enticing day. She shut the front door, and hastened round into Chief Street, and when near the Theatre could hear the notes of the organ, a rehearsal for a coming concert being in progress. She entered under the archway of Oldgate College, where men were putting up awnings round the quadrangle for a ball in the Hall that evening. People who had come up from the country for the day were picnicking on the grass, and Arabella walked along the gravel paths and under the aged limes. But finding this place rather dull, she returned to the streets, and watched the carriages drawing up for the concert, numerous Dons and their wives, and undergraduates with gay female companions, crowding up likewise. When the doors were closed, and the concert began, she moved on.

The powerful notes of that concert rolled forth through the swinging yellow blinds of the open windows, over the house-tops, and into the still air of the lanes. They reached so far as to the room in which Jude lay, and it was about this time that his cough began again and awakened him.

As soon as he could speak he murmured, his eyes still closed: "A little water, please."

Nothing but the deserted room received his appeal, and he coughed to exhaustion again—saying, still more feebly: "Water—some water—Sue—Arabella!"

The room remained still as before. Presently he gasped again: "Throat—water—Sue—darling—drop of water—please—oh, please!"

No water came, and the organ notes, faint as a bee's hum, rolled in as before.

While he remained, his face changing, shouts and hurrahs came from somewhere in the direction of the river.

"Ah—yes! The Remembrance games," he murmured. "And I here. And Sue defiled!"

The hurrahs were repeated, drowning the faint organ notes. Jude's face changed more; he whispered, slowly, his lips scarcely moving:

"Let the day perish wherein I was born, and the night in which it was said, 'There is a man child conceived.'"

("Hurrah!")

"Let that day be darkness; let not God regard it from above, neither let the light shine upon it. Lo, let that night be solitary, let no joyful voice come therein."

("Hurrah!")

"Why died I not from the womb? Why did I not give up the ghost when I came out of the belly? . . . For now should I have lain still and been quiet. I should have slept: then had I been at rest!"

("Hurrah!")

"There the prisoners rest together; they hear not the voice of the oppressor. . . . The small and the great are there; and the servant is free from his master. Wherefore is light given to him that is in misery, and life unto the bitter in soul?"

Meanwhile Arabella, on her journey to discover what was going on, took a short cut down a narrow street and through an obscure nook into the quad of Cardinal. It was full of bustle, and brilliant in the sunlight with flowers and other preparations for a ball here also. A carpenter nodded to her, one who had formerly been a fellow-workman of Jude's. A corridor was in course of erection from the entrance to the Hall staircase, of gay red-and-buff bunting. Wagon-loads of boxes containing bright plants in full bloom were being placed about, and the great staircase was covered with red cloth. She nodded to one workman and another, and ascended to the Hall on the strength of their acquaintance, where they were putting down a new floor and decorating for the dance. The cathedral bell close at hand was sounding for five-o'clock service.

"I should not mind having a spin there with a fellow's arm round my waist," she said to one of the men. "But, Lord, I must be getting home again—there's a lot to do. No dancing for me!"

When she reached home she was met at the door by Stagg and one or two other of Jude's fellow stone-workers. "We are just going down to the river," said the former, "to see the boat-bumping. But we've called round on our way to ask how your husband is."

"He's sleeping nicely, thank you," said Arabella.

"That's right. Well, now, can't you give yourself half an hour's relaxation, Mrs. Fawley, and come along with us? 'Twould do you good."

"I should like to go," said she. "I've never seen the boat-racing, and I hear it is good fun."

"Come along!"

"How I *wish* I could!" She looked longingly down the street. "Wait a minute, then. I'll just run up and see how he is now. Father is with him, I believe, so I can most likely come."

They waited, and she entered. Down-stairs the inmates were absent as before, having, in fact, gone in a body to the river, where the procession of boats was to pass. When she reached the bedroom she found that her father had not even now come.

"Why couldn't he have been here?" she said, impatiently. "He wants to see the boats himself—that's what it is!"

However, on looking round to the bed, she brightened, for she saw that Jude was apparently sleeping, though he was not in the usual half-elevated posture necessitated by his cough. He had slipped down, and lay flat. A second glance caused her to start, and she went to the bed. His face was quite white, and gradually becoming rigid. She touched his fingers; they were cold, though his body was still warm. She listened at his chest. All was still within. The bumping of near thirty years had ceased.

After her first appalled sense of what had happened, the faint notes of a military or other brass band from the river reached her ears; and in a provoked tone she exclaimed: "To think he should die just now! Why did he die just now?" Then, meditating another moment or two, she went to the door, softly closed it as before, and again descended the stairs.

"Here she is!" said one of the workmen. "We wondered if you were coming, after all. Come along; we must be quick to get a good place. . . . Well, how is he? Sleeping well still? Of course, we don't want to drag 'ee away if——"

"Oh yes—sleeping quite sound. He won't wake yet," she said, hurriedly.

They went with the crowd down Cardinal Street, where they presently reached the bridge, and the gay barges burst upon their view. Thence they passed by a narrow slit down to the river-side path—now dusty, hot, and thronged. Almost as soon as they had arrived the grand procession of boats began, the oars smacking with a loud kiss on the face of the stream as they were lowered from the perpendicular.

"Oh, I say—how jolly! I'm glad I've come," said Arabella. "And —it can't hurt my husband—my being away."

On the opposite side of the river, on the crowded barges, were gorgeous nosegays of feminine beauty, fashionably arrayed in green, pink, blue, and white. The blue flag of the boat club denoted the centre of interest, beneath which a band in red uniform gave out the notes she had already heard in the death-chamber. Collegians of all sorts, in canoes with ladies, watching keenly for "our" boat, darted up and down. While she regarded the lively scene somebody touched Arabella in the ribs, and, looking round, she saw Vilbert.

"That philter is operating, you know!" he said, with a leer. "Shame on 'ee to wreck a heart so!"

"I sha'n't talk of love to-day."

"Why not? It is a general holiday."

She did not reply. Vilbert's arm stole round her waist, which act could be performed unobserved in the crowd. An arch expression overspread Arabella's face at the feel of the arm, but she kept her eyes on the river as if she did not know of the embrace.

The crowd surged, pushing Arabella and her friends sometimes nearly into the river, and she would have laughed heartily at the horse-play that succeeded if the imprint on her mind's eye of a pale, statuesque countenance she had lately gazed upon had not sobered her a little.

The fun on the water reached the acme of excitement; there were immersions, there were shouts; the race was lost and won, the pink and blue and yellow ladies retired from the barges, and the people who had watched began to move.

"Well, it's been awfully good!" cried Arabella. "But I think I must get back to my poor man. Father is there, so far as I know; but I had better get back."

"What's your hurry?"

"Well, I must go. . . . Dear, dear, this is awkward!"

At the narrow gangway where the people ascended from the river-side path to the bridge the crowd was literally jammed into one hot mass—Arabella and Vilbert with the rest; and here they remained motionless, Arabella exclaiming, "Dear, dear!" more and more impatiently; for it had just occurred to her mind that if Jude were discovered to have died alone an inquest might be deemed necessary.

"What a fidget you are, my love," said the physician, who, being pressed close against her by the throng, had no need of personal effort for contact. "Just as well have patience; there's no getting away yet."

It was nearly ten minutes before the wedged multitude moved sufficiently to let them pass through. As soon as she got up into the street Arabella hastened on, forbidding the physician to accompany her farther that day. She did not go straight to her house, but to the abode of a woman who performed the last necessary offices for the poorer dead, where she knocked.

"My husband has just gone, poor soul," she said. "Can you come and lay him out?"

Arabella waited a few minutes; and the two women went along, elbowing their way through the stream of fashionable people pouring out of Cardinal meadow, and being nearly knocked down by the carriages.

"I must call at the sexton's about the bell, too," said Arabella. "It is just around here, isn't it? I'll meet you at my door."

By ten o'clock that night Jude was lying on the bedstead at his lodging covered with a sheet, and straight as an arrow. Through the partly opened window the joyous throb of a waltz entered from the ball-room at Cardinal.

AFTERWORD

To speak of Hardy's pessimism is to repeat what every literary history says about this author. George Meredith, his near-contemporary, described it as Hardy's "twilight view of life." In his own *The Dynasts*, Hardy cast off the "local cult they call Christianity." For him, any kind of ultimate reality seemed to be a vaguely Schopenhauerian blind force. To that deity Hardy gave capital letters ("Of It's doings if It knew/ What It does It would not do!"); but his deference to traditional typography scarcely concealed Hardy's conviction that whatever insensate and barely conscious cosmic powers there be, are less moral than mankind itself. The Greek tragic writers—Aeschylus, Sophocles, Euripides— certainly contributed to such a negative reading of existence. It is thus appropriate that Hardy chose to use passages from the Book of Job in his conclusion to *Jude the Obscure*: the one book of the Old Testament, along with Ecclesiastes, that comes closest to the attitude toward life expressed in Greek tragedy.

Save for the first paragraph, authorial comments (seized upon by Hardy's detractors as a weakness) are lacking in this scene. It is also happily devoid of the pretentious literary language in which he sometimes indulged. Excessively aware of his lack of formal schooling, he labored all his life to improve his rhetoric. ("Leafy summer," "which operation she performed," "his malady prevented him," and "the town was in festivity" seem here but mild attempts at stylistic elegance.) He excelled at conveying the nuances of rustic speech, and the dialogue of the workmen—while more polite than that of his Wessex farmers— hints at Hardy's proficiency in this respect.

There are only two similes in the entire scene ("faint as a bee's hum" and Jude laid out "straight as an arrow") and they are fittingly banal. The actions and thoughts that show Arabella's general tawdriness and duplicity are well chosen too: making up before the mirror in Jude's sickroom (from Shakespeare's *Hamlet* to Pope's *Rape of the Lock* a neat device to contrast appearance and reality); her selfish desire for her father to relieve her at Jude's bedside; her flirtation with the workmen and Vilbert; her annoyance at Jude's death; and her outright lies when she returns to her fellow spectators at the river bank—"He won't wake yet" is a phrase that must have appealed to Hardy's sense of tragic irony. Irony is also present in Hardy's counterpointing Jude's whispered lines from Job against the happy noise of the crowd on the river, reminding us of similar polyphony in the scene from *Madame Bovary*:

the double seduction of Emma by Rodolphe, and of the peasants by the glib politicians. Hardy goes even further in his use of contrast by juxtaposing Jude's death against Arabella's lust for life, *thanatos* against *eros*. Even the reference to "boat-bumping" by Stagg the stone-worker suggests a comparison between that innocent game and Arabella's listening at Jude's chest; "The bumping of nearly thirty years had ceased."

There is irony, too, in Hardy's use of coincidence. Many Victorian authors, among them Dickens, used coincidence as a device to tie together characters and events seemingly unrelated, thus imposing a form (sometimes artificial) on excessively sprawling plots. Hardy, however, wove coincidence into his novels almost as if he wished to demonstrate the workings of the universe as a colossal metaphysical and malevolent joke, in which coincidental occasions—never happy—illustrated some cosmic necessity to inflict suffering on poor humanity. Jude finally gets to the town of Christminster, seat of the university he so yearned to attend, only to die there alone.

The Ambassadors (1903)

HENRY JAMES (1843-1916), born near Washington Square in what was then the fashionable section of New York, came of a remarkable family. The grandfather, a Presbyterian immigrant from Ulster, had taken passage up the Hudson to Albany and had gone into business there. He married three times, had thirteen children, and, when he died in 1832, left the enormous fortune for the time of three million dollars, mostly in sound real estate. The father, Henry James, Sr., was an eccentric theologian and the author of intermittently brilliant books that nobody read; he lived comfortably on the income from his share of the first James's estate. He had five children, of whom the eldest was the philosopher William James (1842-1910). There were two younger boys who never amounted to much, except as conversationalists, and a daughter Alice, neurotic and perceptive. The future novelist, always called Harry, was the second son. He loved and resented William, was closely bound to his mother, the queen of the household, and stammered a little when he spoke. In a talkative family he was known as the silent James.

The father had theories about education, as about everything else. He believed that children who were being trained to become citizens of the world should not be allowed to take root in any particular region or way of life. Accordingly William and Harry were sent briefly to various schools and were placed under a succession of private tutors. In 1855 the family went abroad and wandered from city to city. Harry was most impressed by his visits to the Louvre, where masterpieces were hung in splendid salons and reflected from shining floors. Having returned to the United States in 1860, the Jameses established themselves at Newport, where Harry studied art for a few months, but showed less skill in draftsmanship than William. At a fire in Newport, he suffered an injury to his back that gave him a sound excuse for not enlisting in the Union Army like the two younger boys. He elected to become a spectator of life, "the man on whom nothing is lost."

William was studying science at Harvard. Harry followed him to Cambridge and entered the Law School, but took no interest in his studies; by then he had decided to become a great writer. Luckily he wrote like an angel almost from the beginning; it was only during his later period that the stammer got into his style. He was also pushed along by two discriminating editors, one of whom was the future art historian Charles Eliot Norton (1827-1908), then editor of *The North American Review* and associate editor of *The Nation*; the other was the novelist William Dean Howells (1837-1920), soon to become editor of *The Atlantic Monthly*. By the time Henry James, Jr.—as he signed himself for many years—had reached the age of twenty-three, his work was appearing frequently in those magazines and others.

His parents had taken a house in Cambridge, and he regarded it as his home in spite of two extended absences in Europe. But he was happier and healthier during those absences, and he decided after much hesitation—even with a perceptible sense of guilt—that he would spend the rest of his life abroad. His particular type of talent, so he often explained, could find richer subjects in European manners, though he did not advise other American writers to follow his example. In 1875 he settled in Paris, where he became a friend of Turgenev, who took him to see Flaubert, who in turn introduced him to the younger French Naturalists, including Zola, Maupassant, and Daudet. He felt, however, that he would be "an eternal outsider" in France, and a year later he moved to England, which was to be his permanent home.

As if to justify his expatriation, James was copious in works during those first years abroad. He had already finished *Roderick Hudson* (1876), the story of a young American sculptor who goes to Italy, dissipates his talent, and loses his life. Now it was followed rapidly by other novels, most of them dealing with what James called "the international theme," that is, the contrast between innocent Americans and sophisticated Europeans. Among them were *The American* (1877), *The Europeans* (1878), and *Daisy Miller* (1879), his only great popular success. *Washington Square* (1881) deals by exception with Americans at home, but before it was published James had undertaken a still more extensive treatment of the international theme. It was *The Portrait of a Lady* (1881), the last and longest work of his early period; many critics still regard it as the best of his novels.

In England James had become, not quite effortlessly, a social lion. "I think a position in society is a legitimate object of ambition," he once remarked. By his own account he dined out 107 times in the winter and spring of 1878-79 and 140 times in the following London season. He was often invited to house parties at great country houses and enjoyed them thoroughly. During his middle period, however—the years from 1882 to 1895—he was also determined to capture a wide popular audience, and this other ambition resulted in two exasperating failures.

The first failure with the public was that of his three big social novels, all dealing with contemporary questions. Inspired by Balzac and measuring himself against Turgenev, he tried to present broad pictures of American and English life. In *The Bostonians* (1886) he dealt with feminism and the decay in Boston of intellectual vitality. The book is one of his best, but it was howled down by American critics. His brother William didn't like it either, but then he never much enjoyed Harry's novels. In *The Princess Casamassima* (1886), the question is anarchism as preached in the drab quarters of London, and James "worked up" the subject as Zola might have done. The result was a complicated novel that was rejected by public and critics alike. In *The Tragic Muse* (1890) he was presenting the conflict between the worlds of politics and art; this time he had many critics on his side, but the public was not tempted to read. Never again was James to deal broadly with issues of the day.

The second and more disturbing failure was in his effort to become a successful playwright. Only two of the plays he wrote in five years were produced. One was *The American*, dramatized from his novel of the same title; it ran for two months in London. The other was *Guy Domville*, which opened on January 5, 1895, before an audience most of which was puzzled, bored, and then infuriated. Called on the stage by malice or mistake, James stood there quailing under a storm of catcalls; it was a moment of profound humiliation. Six weeks later, however, he had recovered sufficiently to write in his notebook:

> I have my head, thank God, full of visions. One has never too many—one has never enough. Ah, just to let one's self go—at last: to surrender one's self to what through all the long years one has (quite heroically, I think) hoped for and waited for—the mere potential, and relative, increase of *quantity* in the material act. . . .

That notebook entry of February 14, 1895, foreshadows James's later period, though there was still to be some fumbling before the major works of the period were under way. Of one thing James was sure from that day: those works would utilize "the divine principle of the Scenario" that he had learned from his costly experience in the theatre. They would follow the scenic method, in other words, and would be as tightly constructed as plays. They would not attempt, however, to reach an undiscriminating audience. As for the "increase of *quantity* in the material act," it soon became evident to the world. During a period of eight years, James was to publish a shelfful of books: five shorter novels, beginning in 1897 with *The Spoils of Poynton* and *What Maisie Knew*; three collections of short and long stories that included such famous ones as "The Turn of the Screw" (1898) and "The Beast in the Jungle" (1903); a very long memoir, *William Wetmore Story and His Friends* (1903); and finally three long novels that constitute what is now generally known as his "major phase." *The Ambassadors* (1903) was the first of these to be written, though it was published after *The Wings of the Dove* (1902). *The Golden Bowl* (1904) was the last novel he completed, as well as being the most difficult or Jamesian, but one does not have to agree with the critics who set it above all the others. *The Ambassadors* was the choice of the novelist himself, who called it "frankly, quite the best 'all around' of my productions."

In 1904-05 James made an extended tour of the United States after an absence of more than twenty years. He recorded part of the journey in *The American Scene* (1907), a mixture of the deeply perceptive with something close to the absurd; then he set to work on the definitive New York Edition of his novels and stories. For this he revised his earlier fiction, thickening its texture, but not always improving it, and wrote a series of magisterial prefaces. In 1910 William died, with Harry at his bedside in New Hampshire; it would be a year before the surviving brother felt strong enough for the voyage back to England. He published two volumes of memoirs in 1913 and 1914. After writing part of an American novel, *The Ivory Tower*, he abandoned it for an earlier project in fiction, *The Sense of the Past*, but work on this was interrupted by the Great War. James plunged into war work for his adopted country. Feeling ashamed that America was remaining neutral, he became a British subject in July 1915, seven months before his death.

THE STORY

Lambert Strether, fifty-five years old, the editor of a little review published in Woollett (for which read Worcester), Massachusetts, is making his second visit to Europe. In England he meets Maria Gostrey, an American who has spent most of her life in European travel. He confides to her the reason for his voyage: it was undertaken in behalf of Mrs. Newsome, the rich woman who subsidizes his review. Her son Chad has been bewitched by some creature in Paris, and Strether's task as the mother's ambassador is to rescue Chad and carry him back to the family business in Woollett. If he succeeds in his mission, Mrs. Newsome will marry him.

In Paris he finds that Chad has gone to the Riviera, leaving his grand apartment to be occupied by another young American, John Little Bilham. Strether is enchanted with everything: the apartment, its occupant, the largeness and freedom of Parisian life. Then Chad comes back and proves to be completely different from the spoiled and loutish boy whom Strether had known in Woollett. Something—or someone—has transformed him into a wholly engaging man of the world. The ambassador says, "I've come, you know, to make you break with everything . . . and take you straight home." Chad temporizes. Won't Strether wait until he has met two charming French ladies, a mother and her daughter? After that, Chad finally says, he will do whatever the ambassador thinks best.

The two ladies, Chad's closest tie with Paris, are the Countess de Vionnet and her daughter Jeanne. Strether meets them both at a reception in the garden of a famous sculptor. The scene, reprinted here, is the turning point in the novel, since it marks an immense change in Strether himself: he will be ready from this moment to abandon his mission. In his letters to Mrs. Newsome, he tries to explain his new judgment of the situation, but the only result is that she loses confidence in her ambassador and sends three others to take his place. These are the Pococks, who presently appear: prim Sarah, who is Mrs. Newsome's daughter and faithful image; fat, facetious Jim, who takes to Paris like any businessman on a spree; and Jim's lovely young sister Mamie, who is supposed to marry Chad, but who loses her heart to little Bilham. Sarah, though lavishly entertained, stands firm on her moral principles and is completely insensible to the charm of Mme. de Vionnet. Finally she lays down an ultimatum: within twenty-four hours Strether must take advantage of Chad's promise to obey him and must send the young man home. Strether tries to temporize as Chad had done, but this time Sarah marches off to her carriage with the grim words, "Then all's at an end!"—Strether's prospective marriage, his little review, everything.

Strether discovers late in the story that Chad and Mme. de Vionnet are lovers. But he accepts that too, as he has accepted so many things, and he ends by telling Chad, "You'll be a brute, you know—you'll be guilty of the last infamy—if you ever forsake her." Strether himself has sacrificed an assured future, but not his honesty of spirit. When Maria Gostrey, whose company he enjoys, makes him an offer of marriage, he gently refuses her, saying that his reward will be "Not, out of the whole affair, to have got anything for myself." But he has lived vicariously in the freedom of others, and he has also gained what James regarded as an enormous blessing: that is, a keener perception of himself and the world.

The Ambassadors is in twelve parts designed for serialization, each with a little climax at the end to whet the reader's appetite, and it appeared in twelve numbers of *The North American Review*. The scene in Gloriani's garden is the beginning of Part Fifth.

[*Gloriani's Garden*]   *Chapter 10*

The Sunday of the next week was a wonderful day, and Chad Newsome had let his friend know in advance that he had provided for it. There had already been a question of his taking him to see the great Gloriani, who was at home on Sunday afternoons and at whose house, for the most part, fewer bores were to be met than elsewhere; but the project, through some accident, had not had instant effect, and now revived in happier conditions. Chad had made the point that the celebrated sculptor had a queer old garden, for which the weather—spring at last frank and fair—was propitious; and two or three of his other allusions had confirmed for Strether the expectation of something special. He had by this time, for all introductions and adventures, let himself recklessly go, cherishing the sense that whatever the young man showed him he was showing at least himself. He could have wished indeed, so far as this went, that Chad were less of a mere cicerone; for he was not without the impression—now that the vision of his game, his plan, his deep diplomacy, did recurrently assert itself—of his taking refuge from the realities of their intercourse in profusely dispensing, as our friend mentally phrased it, *panem et circenses*. Our friend continued to feel rather smothered in flowers, though he made in his other moments the almost angry inference that this was only because of his odious ascetic suspicion of any form of beauty. He periodically assured himself—for his reactions were sharp—that he shouldn't reach the truth of anything till he had at least got rid of that.

He had known beforehand that Mme. de Vionnet and her daughter would probably be on view, an intimation to that effect having constituted the only reference again made by Chad to his good friends from the south. The effect of Strether's talk about them with Miss Gostrey had been quite to consecrate his reluctance to pry; something in the very air of Chad's silence—judged in the light of that talk—offered it to him as a reserve he could markedly match. It shrouded them about with he scarce knew what, a consideration, a distinction; he was in presence at any rate—so far as it placed him there—of ladies; and the one thing that was definite for him was that they themselves should be, to the extent of his responsibility, in presence of a gentleman. Was it because they were very beautiful, very clever, or even very good—was it for one of these reasons that Chad was, so to speak, nursing his effect? Did he wish to spring them, in the Woollett phrase, with a fuller force—to confound his critic, slight though as yet the criticism, with some form of merit exquisitely incalculable? The most the critic had at all events asked was whether the persons in question were French; and that enquiry had been but a proper comment on the sound of their name. "Yes. That is no!" had been Chad's reply; but he had immediately added that their English was the most charming in the world, so that if Strether were wanting an excuse for not getting on with them he wouldn't in the least find one. Never in fact had Strether—in the mood into which the place had quickly launched him—felt, for himself, less the need of an excuse. Those he might have found would have been, at the worst, all for the others, the people before him, in whose liberty to be as they were he was aware that he positively rejoiced. His fellow guests were multiplying, and these things, their liberty, their intensity, their variety, their conditions at large, were in fusion in the admirable medium of the scene.

The place itself was a great impression—a small pavilion, clear-faced and sequestered, an effect of polished parquet, of fine white panel and spare sallow gilt, of decoration delicate and rare, in the heart of the Faubourg Saint-Germain and on the edge of a cluster of gardens attached to old noble houses. Far back from streets and unsuspected by crowds, reached by a long passage and a quiet court, it was as striking to the unprepared mind, he immediately saw, as a treasure dug up; giving him too, more than anything yet, the note of the range of the immeasurable town and sweeping away, as by a last brave brush, his usual landmarks and terms. It was in the garden, a spacious cherished remnant, out to which a dozen persons had already passed, that Chad's host presently met them; while the tall bird-haunted trees, all of a twitter with the spring and the weather, and the high party-walls, on the other side of which grave *hôtels* stood off for privacy, spoke of survival, transmission, association, a strong indifferent persistent order. The day was so soft that the little party had practically adjourned to the open air, but the open air was in such conditions all a chamber of state. Strether had presently the sense of a great convent, a convent of missions, famous for he scarce knew what, a nursery of young priests, of scattered shade, of straight alleys and chapel-bells, that spread its mass in one quarter; he had the sense of names in the air, of ghosts at the windows, of signs and tokens, a whole range of expression, all about him, too thick for prompt discrimination.

This assult of images became for a moment, in the address of the distinguished sculptor, almost formidable: Gloriani showed him, in such perfect confidence, on Chad's introduction of him, a fine worn handsome face, a face that was like an open letter in a foreign tongue. With his genius in his eyes, his manners on his lips, his long career behind him and his honours and rewards all round, the great artist, in the course of a single sustained look and a few words of delight at receiving him, affected our friend as a dazzling prodigy of type. Strether had seen in museums—in the Luxembourg as well as, more reverently, later on, in the New York of the billionaires—the work of his hand; knowing too that after an earlier time in his native Rome he had migrated, in mid-career, to Paris, where, with a personal lustre almost violent, he shone in a constellation: all of which was more than enough to crown him, for his guest, with the light, with the romance, of glory. Strether, in contact with that element as he had never yet so intimately been, had the consciousness of opening to it, for the happy instant, all the windows of his mind, of letting this rather grey interior drink in for once the sun of a clime not marked in his old geography. He was to remember again repeatedly the medal-like Italian face, in which every line was an artist's own, in which time told only as tone and consecration; and he was to recall in especial, as the penetrating radiance, as the communication of the illustrious spirit itself, the manner in which, while they stood briefly, in welcome and response, face to face, he was held by the sculptor's eyes. He wasn't soon to forget them, was to think of them, all unconscious, unintending, preoccupied though they were, as the source of the deepest intellectual sounding to which he had ever been exposed. He was in fact quite to cherish his vision of it, to play with it in idle hours; only speaking of it to no one and quite aware he couldn't have spoken without appearing to talk nonsense. Was what it had told him or what it had asked him the greater of the mysteries? Was it the most special flare, unequalled, supreme, of the aesthetic torch, lighting that wondrous world for ever, or was it above all the long straight shaft sunk by a personal acuteness that life had seasoned to steel? Nothing on earth could have been stranger and no one doubtless more surprised than the artist himself, but it was for all the world to Strether just then as if in the matter of his accepted duty he had positively been on trial. The deep human expertness in Gloriani's charming smile—oh the terrible life behind it!—was flashed upon him as a test of his stuff.

Chad meanwhile, after having easily named his companion, had still more easily turned away and was already greeting other persons present. He was as easy, clever Chad, with the great artist as with his obscure compatriot, and as easy with every one else as with either: this fell into its place for Strether and made almost a new light, giving him, as a concatenation, something more he could enjoy. He liked Gloriani, but should never see him again; of that he was sufficiently sure. Chad accordingly, who was wonderful with both of them, was a kind of link for hopeless fancy, an implication of possibilities—oh if everything had been different! Strether noted at all events that he was thus on terms with illustrious spirits, and also that—yes, distinctly—he hadn't in the least swaggered about it. Our friend hadn't come there only for this figure of Abel Newsome's son, but that presence threatened to affect the observant mind as positively central. Gloriani indeed, remembering something and excusing himself, pursued Chad to speak to him, and Strether was left musing on many things. One of them was the question of whether, since he had been tested, he had passed. Did the artist drop him from having made out that he wouldn't do? He really felt just to-day that he might do better than usual. Hadn't he done well enough, so far as that went, in being exactly so dazzled? and in not having too, as he almost believed, wholly hidden from his host that he felt the latter's plummet? Suddenly, across the garden, he saw little Bilham approach, and it was a part of the fit that was on him that as their eyes met he guessed also *his* knowledge. If he had said to him on the instant what was uppermost he would have said: "*Have* I passed?—for of course I know one has to pass here." Little Bilham would have reassured him, have told him that he exaggerated, and have adduced happily enough the argument of little Bilham's own very presence; which, in truth, he could see, was as easy a one as Gloriani's own or as Chad's. He himself would perhaps then after a while cease to be frightened, would get the point of view for some of the faces—types tremendously alien, alien to Woollett—that he had already begun to take in. Who were they all, the dispersed groups and couples, the ladies even more unlike those of Woollett than the gentlemen?—this was the inquiry that, when his young friend had greeted him, he did find himself making.

"Oh they're every one—all sorts and sizes; of course I mean within limits, though limits down perhaps rather more than limits up. There are always artists—he's beautiful and inimitable to the *cher confrère;* and then *gros bonnets* of many kinds—ambassadors, cabinet ministers, bankers, generals, what do I know? even Jews. Above all always some awfully nice women—and not too many; sometimes an actress, an artist, a great performer—but only when they're not monsters; and in particular the right *femmes du monde.*[1] You can fancy his history on that side—I believe it's fabulous: they *never* give him up. Yet he keeps them down: no one knows how he manages; it's too beautiful and bland. Never too many—and a mighty good thing too; just a perfect choice. But there are not in any way many bores; it has always been so; he has some secret. It's extraordinary. And you don't find it out. He's the same to every one. He doesn't ask questions."

"Ah doesn't he?" Strether laughed.

Bilham met it with all his candour. "How then should *I* be here?"

"Oh for what you tell me. You're part of the perfect choice."

Well, the young man took in the scene. "It seems rather good to-day."

Strether followed the direction of his eyes. "Are they all, this time, *femmes du monde?*"

Little Bilham showed his competence. "Pretty well."

This was a category our friend had a feeling for; a light, romantic and mysterious, on the feminine element, in which he enjoyed for a little watching it. "Are there any Poles?"

[1 *Cher confrère* is "My dear colleague"; *gros bonnets* are bigwigs; *femmes du monde* are society women.]

His companion considered. "I think I make out a 'Portuguee.' But I've seen Turks."

Strether wondered, desiring justice. "They seem—all the women —very harmonious."

"Oh in closer quarters they come out!" And then, while Strether was aware of fearing closer quarters, though giving himself again to the harmonies, "Well," little Bilham went on, "it *is* at the worst rather good, you know. If you like it, you feel it, this way, that shows you're not in the least out. But you always know things," he handsomely added, "immediately."

Strether liked it and felt it only too much; so "I say, don't lay traps for me!" he rather helplessly murmured.

"Well," his companion returned, "he's wonderfully kind to *us*."

"To us Americans you mean?"

"Oh no—he doesn't know anything about *that*. That's half the battle here—that you can never hear politics. We don't talk them. I mean to poor young wretches of all sorts. And yet it's always as charming as this; it's as if, by something in the air, our squalor didn't show. It puts us all back—into the last century."

"I'm afraid," Strether said, amused, "that it puts me rather forward: oh ever so far!"

"Into the next? But isn't that only," little Bilham asked, "because you're really of the century before?"

"The century before the last? Thank you!" Strether laughed. "If I ask you about some of the ladies it can't be then that I may hope, as such a specimen of the rococo, to please them."

"On the contrary they adore—we all adore here—the rococo, and where is there a better setting for it than the whole thing, the pavilion and the garden, together? There are lots of people with collections," little Bilham smiled as he glanced round. "You'll be secured!"

It made Strether for a moment give himself again to contemplation. There were faces he scarce knew what to make of. Were they charming or were they only strange? He mightn't talk politics, yet he suspected a Pole or two. The upshot was the question at the back of his head from the moment his friend had joined them. "Have Madame de Vionnet and her daughter arrived?"

"I haven't seen them yet, but Miss Gostrey has come. She's in the pavilion looking at objects. One can see *she's* a collector," little Bilham added without offence.

"Oh yes, she's a collector, and I knew she was to come. Is Madame de Vionnet a collector?" Strether went on.

"Rather, I believe; almost celebrated." The young man met, on it, a little, his friend's eyes. "I happen to know—from Chad, whom I saw last night—that they've come back; but only yesterday. He wasn't sure—up to the last. This, accordingly," little Bilham went on, "will be—if they *are* here—their first appearance after their return."

Strether, very quickly, turned these things over. "Chad told you last night? To me, on our way here, he said nothing about it."

"But did you ask him?"

Strether did him the justice. "I dare say not."

"Well," said little Bilham, "you're not a person to whom it's easy to tell things you don't want to know. Though it *is* easy, I admit—it's quite beautiful," he benevolently added, "when you do want to."

Strether looked at him with an indulgence that matched his intelligence. "Is that the deep reasoning on which—about these ladies—you've been yourself so silent?"

Little Bilham considered the depth of the reasoning. "I haven't been silent. I spoke of them to you the other day, the day we sat together after Chad's tea-party."

Strether came round to it. "They then are the virtuous attachment?"

"I can only tell you that it's what they pass for. But isn't that enough? What more than a vain appearance does the wisest of us know? I commend you," the young man declared with a pleasant emphasis, "the vain appearance."

Strether looked more widely round, and what he saw, from face to face, deepened the effect of his young friend's words. "Is it so good?"

"Magnificent."

Strether had a pause. "The husband's dead?"

"Dear no. Alive."

"Oh!" said Strether. After which, as his companion laughed: "How then can it be so good?"

"You'll see for yourself. One does see."

"Chad's in love with the daughter?"

"That's what I mean."

Strether wondered. "Then where's the difficulty?"

"Why, aren't you and I—with our grander bolder ideas?"

"Oh mine—!" Strether said rather strangely. But then as if to attenuate: "You mean they won't hear of Woollett?"

Little Bilham smiled. "Isn't that just what you must see about?"

It had brought them, as she caught the last words, into relation with Miss Barrace, whom Strether had already observed—as he had never before seen a lady at a party—moving about alone. Coming within sound of them she had already spoken, and she took again, through her long-handled glass, all her amused and amusing possession. "How much, poor Mr. Strether, you seem to have to see about! But you can't say," she gaily declared, "that I don't do what I can to help you. Mr. Waymarsh is placed. I've left him in the house with Miss Gostrey."

"The way," little Bilham exclaimed, "Mr. Strether gets the ladies to work for him! He's just preparing to draw in another; to pounce—don't you see him?—on Madame de Vionnet."

"Madame de Vionnet? Oh, oh, oh!" Miss Barrace cried in a wonderful crescendo. There was more in it, our friend made out, than met the ear. Was it after all a joke that he should be serious about anything? He envied Miss Barrace at any rate her power of not being. She seemed, with little cries and protests and quick recognitions, movements like the darts of some fine high-feathered free-pecking bird, to stand before life as before some full shop-window. You could fairly hear, as she selected and pointed, the tap of her tortoise-shell against the glass. "It's certain that we do need seeing about; only I'm glad it's not I who have to do it. One does, no doubt, begin that way; then suddenly one finds that one has given it up. It's too much, it's too difficult. You're wonderful, you people," she continued to Strether, "for not feeling those things—by which I mean impossibilities. You never feel them. You face them with a fortitude that makes it a lesson to watch you."

"Ah but"—little Bilham put it with discouragement—"what do we achieve after all? We see about you and report—when we even go so far as reporting. But nothing's done."

"Oh you, Mr. Bilham," she replied as with an impatient rap on the glass, "you're not worth sixpence! You come over to convert the savages—for I know you verily did, I remember you—and the savages simply convert *you*."

"Not even!" the young man woefully confessed: "they haven't gone through that form. They've simply—the cannibals!—eaten me; converted me if you like, but converted me into food. I'm but the bleached bones of a Christian."

"Well then there we are! Only"—and Miss Barrace appealed again to Strether—"don't let it discourage you. You'll break down soon enough, but you'll meanwhile have had your moments. *Il faut en avoir.* I always like to see you while you last. And I'll tell you who *will* last."

"Waymarsh?"—he had already taken her up.

She laughed out as at the alarm of it. "He'll resist even Miss Gostrey: so grand is it not to understand. He's wonderful."

"He is indeed," Strether conceded. "He wouldn't tell me of this affair—only said he had an engagement; but with such a gloom, you must let me insist, as if it had been an engagement to be hanged. Then silently and secretly he turns up here with you. Do you call *that* 'lasting'?"

"Oh I hope it's lasting!" Miss Barrace said. "But he only, at the best, bears with me. He doesn't understand—not one little scrap. He's delightful. He's wonderful," she repeated.

"Michelangelesque!"—little Bilham completed her meaning. "He *is* a success. Moses, on the ceiling, brought down to the floor; overwhelming, colossal, but somehow portable."

"Certainly, if you mean by portable," she returned, "looking so well in one's carriage. He's too funny beside me in his corner; he looks like somebody, somebody foreign and famous, *en exil;* so that people wonder—it's very amusing—whom I'm taking about. I show him Paris, show him everything, and he never turns a hair. He's like the Indian chief one reads about, who, when he comes up to Washington to see the Great Father, stands wrapt in his blanket and gives no sign. *I* might be the Great Father from the way he takes everything." She was delighted at this hit of her identity with that personage—it fitted so her character; she declared it was the title she meant henceforth to adopt. "And the way he sits, too, in the corner of my room, only looking at my visitors very hard and as if he wanted to start something! They wonder what he does want to start. But he's wonderful," Miss Barrace once more insisted. "He has never started anything yet."

It presented him none the less, in truth, to her actual friends, who looked at each other in intelligence, with frank amusement on Bilham's part and a shade of sadness on Strether's. Strether's sadness sprang—for the image had its grandeur—from his thinking how little he himself was wrapt in his blanket, how little, in marble halls, all too oblivious of the Great Father, he resembled a really majestic aboriginal. But he had also another reflexion. "You've all of you here so much visual sense that you've somehow all 'run' to it. There are moments when it strikes one that you haven't any other."

"Any moral," little Bilham explained, watching serenely, across the garden, the several *femmes du monde.* "But Miss Barrace has a moral distinction," he kindly continued; speaking as if for Strether's benefit not less than for her own.

"*Have* you?" Strether, scarce knowing what he was about, asked of her almost eagerly.

"Oh not a distinction"—she was mightily amused at his tone—"Mr. Bilham's too good. But I think I may say a sufficiency. Yes, a sufficiency. Have you supposed strange things of me?"—and she fixed him again, through all her tortoise-shell, with the droll interest of it. "You *are* all indeed wonderful. I should awfully disappoint you. I do take my stand on my sufficiency. But I know, I confess," she went on, "strange people. I don't know how it happens; I don't do it on purpose; it seems to be my doom—as if I were always one of their habits: it's wonderful! I dare say, moreover," she pursued with an interested gravity, "that I do, that we all do here, run too much to mere eye. But how can it be helped? We're all looking at each other—and in the light of Paris one sees what things resemble. That's what the light of Paris seems always to show. It's the fault of the light of Paris—dear old light!"

"Dear old Paris!" little Bilham echoed.

"Everything, every one shows," Miss Barrace went on.

"But for what they really are?" Strether asked.

"Oh, I like your Boston 'reallys'! But sometimes—yes."

"Dear old Paris then!" Strether resignedly sighed while for a moment they looked at each other. Then he broke out: "Does Madame de Vionnet do that? I mean really show for what she is?"

Her answer was prompt. "She's charming. She's perfect."

"Then why did you a minute ago say, 'Oh, oh, oh!' at her name?"

She easily remembered. "Why, just because——! She's wonderful."

"Ah she too?"—Strether had almost a groan.

But Miss Barrace had meanwhile perceived relief. "Why not put your question straight to the person who can answer it best?"

"No," said little Bilham; "don't put any question; wait, rather —it will be much more fun—to judge for yourself. He has come to take you to her."

Chapter 11

On which Strether saw that Chad was again at hand, and he afterwards scarce knew, absurd as it may seem, what had then quickly occurred. The moment concerned him, he felt, more deeply than he could have explained, and he had a subsequent passage of speculation as to whether, on walking off with Chad, he hadn't looked either pale or red. The only thing he was clear about was that, luckily, nothing indiscreet had in fact been said, and that Chad himself was more than ever, in Miss Barrace's great sense, wonderful. It was one of the connexions—though really why it should be, after all, was none so apparent—in which the whole change in him came out as most striking. Strether recalled as they approached the house that he had impressed him that first night as knowing how to enter a box. Well, he impressed him scarce less now as knowing how to make a presentation. It did something for Strether's own quality—marked it as estimated; so that our poor friend, conscious and passive, really seemed to feel himself quite handed over and delivered; absolutely, as he would have said, made a present of, given away. As they reached the house a young woman, about to come forth, appeared, unaccompanied, on the steps; at the exchange with whom of a word on Chad's part Strether immediately perceived that, obligingly, kindly, she was there to meet them. Chad had left her in the house, but she had afterwards come half way and then the next moment had joined them in the garden. Her air of youth, for Strether, was at first almost disconcerning, while, his second impression was, not less sharply, a degree of relief at there not having just been, with the others, any freedom used about her. It was upon him at a touch that she was no subject for that, and meanwhile, on Chad's introducing him, she had spoken to him, very simply and gently, in an English clearly of the easiest to her, yet unlike any other he had ever heard. It wasn't as if she tried; nothing, he could see after they had been a few minutes together, was as if she tried; but her speech, charming,

correct and odd, was like a precaution against her passing for a
Pole. There were precautions, he seemed indeed to see, only when
there were really dangers.

Later on he was to feel many more of them, but by that time
he was to feel other things besides. She was dressed in black, but
in black that struck him as light and transparent; she was exceedingly fair, and, though she was as markedly slim, her face had a
roundness, with eyes far apart and a little strange. Her smile was
natural and dim; her hat not extravagant; he had only perhaps a
sense of the clink, beneath her fine black sleeves, of more gold
bracelets and bangles then he had ever seen a lady wear. Chad
was excellently free and light about their encounter; it was one of
the occasions on which Strether most wished he himself might
have arrived at such ease and such humour: "Here you are then,
face to face at last; you're made for each other—*vous allez voir*;
and I bless your union." It was indeed, after he had gone off, as if
he had been partly serious too. This latter motion had been determined by an enquiry from him about "Jeanne"; to which her
mother had replied that she was probably still in the house with
Miss Gostrey, to whom she had lately committed her. "Ah but
you know," the young man had rejoined, "he must see her"; with
which, while Strether pricked up his ears, he had started as if to
bring her, leaving the other objects of his interest together. Strether
wondered to find Miss Gostrey already involved, feeling that he
missed a link; but feeling also, with small delay, how much he
should like to talk with her of Madame de Vionnet on this basis of
evidence.

The evidence as yet in truth was meagre; which, for that matter, was perhaps a little why his expectation had had a drop. There
was somehow not quite a wealth in her; and a wealth was all that,
in his simplicity, he had definitely prefigured. Still, it was too much
to be sure already that there was but a poverty. They moved away
from the house, and, with eyes on a bench at some distance, he
proposed that they should sit down. "I've heard a great deal about
you," she said as they went; but he had an answer to it that made
her stop short. "Well, about *you*, Madame de Vionnet, I've heard,
I'm bound to say, almost nothing"—those struck him as the only
words he himself could utter with any lucidity; conscious as he was,
and as with more reason, of the determination to be in respect
to the rest of his business perfectly plain and go perfectly straight.
It hadn't at any rate been in the least his idea to spy on Chad's

proper freedom. It was possibly, however, at this very instant and under the impression of Madame de Vionnet's pause, that going straight began to announce itself as a matter for care. She had only after all to smile at him ever so gently in order to make him ask himself if he weren't already going crooked. It might be going crooked to find it of a sudden just only clear that she intended very definitely to be what he would have called nice to him. This was what passed between them while, for another instant, they stood still; he couldn't at least remember afterwards what else it might have been. The thing indeed really unmistakeable was that it rolled over him as a wave that he had been, in conditions incalculable and unimaginable, a subject of discussion. He had been, on some ground that concerned her, answered for; which gave her an advantage he should never be able to match.

"Hasn't Miss Gostrey," she asked, "said a good word for me?"

What had struck him first was the way he was bracketed with that lady; and he wondered what account Chad would have given of their acquaintance. Something not as yet traceable, at all events, had obviously happened. "I didn't even know of her knowing you."

"Well, now she'll tell you all. I'm so glad you're in relation with her."

This was one of the things—the "all" Miss Gostrey would now tell him—that, with every deference to present preoccupation, was uppermost for Strether after they had taken their seat. One of the others was, at the end of five minutes, that she—oh, incontestably, yes—*differed* less; differed, that is, scarcely at all—well, superficially speaking, from Mrs. Newsome or even from Mrs. Pocock. She was ever so much younger than the one and not so young as the other; but what *was* there in her, if anything, that would have made it impossible he should meet her at Woollett? And wherein was her talk during their moments on the bench together not the same as would have been found adequate for a Woollett garden-party?—unless perhaps truly in not being quite so bright. She observed to him that Mr. Newsome had, to her knowledge, taken extraordinary pleasure in his visit; but there was no good lady at Woollett who wouldn't have been at least up to that. Was there in Chad, by chance, after all, deep down, a principle of aboriginal loyalty that had made him, for sentimental ends, attach himself to elements, happily encountered, that would remind him most of the old air and the old soil? Why accordingly be in a flutter—Strether could even put it that way—about this unfamiliar phenomenon of the *femme du monde?* On these terms Mrs. Newsome herself was as much of one. Little Bilham verily had testified that they came out, the ladies of the type, in close quarters; but it was just in these quarters—now comparatively close—that he felt Madame de Vionnet's common humanity. She did come out, and certainly to his relief, but she came out as the usual thing. There might be motives behind, but so could there often be even at Woollett. The only thing was that if she showed him she wished to like him—as the motives behind might conceivably prompt—it would possibly have been more thrilling for him that she should have shown as more vividly alien. Ah she was neither Turk nor Pole!—which would be indeed flat once more for Mrs. Newsome and Mrs. Pocock. A lady and two gentlemen had meanwhile, however, approached their bench, and this accident stayed for the time further developments.

They presently addressed his companion, the brilliant strangers; she rose to speak to them, and Strether noted how the escorted lady, though mature and by no means beautiful, had more of the bold high look, the range of expensive reference, that he had, as might have been said, made his plans for. Madame de Vionnet greeted her as "Duchesse" and was greeted in turn, while talk started in French, as "Ma toute-belle"; little facts that had their due, their vivid interest for Strether. Madame de Vionnet didn't, none the less, introduce him—a note he was conscious of as false to the Woollett scale and the Woollett humanity; though it didn't prevent the duchess, who struck him as confident and free, very much what he had obscurely supposed duchesses, from looking at him as straight and as hard—for it *was* hard—as if she would have liked, all the same, to know him. "Oh yes, my dear, it's all right, it's *me; * and who are *you,* with your interesting wrinkles and your most effective (is it the handsomest, is it the ugliest?) of noses?"—some such loose handful of bright flowers she seemed, fragrantly enough, to fling at him. Strether almost wondered—at such a pace was he going—if some divination of the influence of either party were what determined Madame de Vionnet's abstention. One of the gentlemen, in any case, succeeded in placing himself in close relation with our friend's companion; a gentleman rather stout and importantly short, in a hat with a wonderful wide curl to its brim and a frock coat buttoned with an effect of superlative decision. His French had quickly turned to equal English, and it occurred to Strether that he might well be one of the ambassadors. His design was evidently to assert a claim to Madame de Vionnet's undivided countenance, and he made it good in the course of a minute—led her away with a trick of three words; a trick played with a social art of which Strether, looking after them as the four, whose backs were now all turned, moved off, felt himself no master.

He sank again upon his bench and, while his eyes followed the party, reflected, as he had done before, on Chad's strange communities. He sat there alone for five minutes, with plenty to think of; above all with his sense of having suddenly been dropped by a charming woman overlaid now by other impressions and in fact quite cleared and indifferent. He hadn't yet had so quiet a surrender; he didn't in the least care if nobody spoke to him more. He might have been, by his attitude, in for something of a march so broad that the want of ceremony with which he had just been used could fall into its place as but a minor incident of the procession. Besides, there would be incidents enough, as he felt when this term of contemplation was closed by the reappearance of little Bilham, who stood before him a moment with a suggestive "Well?" in which he saw himself reflected as disorganised, as possibly floored. He replied with a "Well!" intended to show that he wasn't floored in the least. No indeed; he gave it out, as the young man sat down beside him, that if, at the worst, he had been overturned at all, he had been overturned into the upper air, the sublimer element with which he had an affinity and in which he might be trusted a while to float. It wasn't a descent to earth to say after an instant in sustained response to the reference: "You're quite sure her husband's living?"

"Oh dear, yes."

"Ah then——!"

"Ah then what?"

Strether had after all to think. "Well, I'm sorry for them." But it didn't for the moment matter more than that. He assured his young friend he was quite content. They wouldn't stir; were all right as they were. He didn't want to be introduced; had been introduced already about as far as he could go. He had seen, moreover, an immensity; liked Gloriani, who, as Miss Barrace kept saying, was wonderful; had made out, he was sure, the half-dozen other men who were distinguished, the artists, the critics and oh the great dramatist—*him* it was easy to spot; but wanted—no, thanks, really—to talk with none of them; having nothing at all to say and finding it would do beautifully as it was; do beautifully because what it was—well, was just simply too late. And when after this little Bilham, submissive and responsive, but with an eye to the consolation nearest, easily threw off some "Better late than never!" all he got in return for it was a sharp "Better early than late!" This note indeed, the next thing, overflowed for Strether into a quiet stream of demonstration that, as soon as he had let himself go, he felt as the real relief. It had consciously gathered to a head, but the reservoir had filled sooner than he knew, and his companion's touch was to make the waters spread. There were some things that had to come in time if they were to come at all. If they didn't come in time they were lost for ever. It was the general sense of them that had overwhelmed him with its long, slow rush.

"It's not too late for *you*, on any side, and you don't strike me as in danger of missing the train; besides which people can be in general pretty well trusted, of course—with the clock of their freedom ticking as loud as it seems to do here—to keep an eye on the fleeting hour. All the same don't forget that you're young—blessedly young; be glad of it on the contrary and live up to it. Live all you can; it's a mistake not to. It doesn't so much matter what you do in particular, so long as you have your life. If you haven't had that what *have* you had? This place and these impressions—mild as you may find them to wind a man up so; all my impressions of Chad and of people I've seen at *his* place—well, have had their abundant message for me, have just dropped *that* into my mind. I see it now. I haven't done so enough before—and now I'm old; too old at any rate for what I see. Oh, I *do* see, at least; and more than you'd believe or I can express. It's too late. And it's as if the train had fairly waited at the station for me without my having had the gumption to know it was there. Now I hear its faint receding whistle miles and miles down the line. What one loses one loses; make no mistake about that. The affair—I mean the affair of life—couldn't, no doubt, have been different for me; for it's at the best a tin mould, either fluted and embossed, with ornamental excrescences, or else smooth and dreadfully plain, into which, a helpless jelly, one's consciousness is poured—so that one 'takes' the form, as the great cook says, and is more or less compactly held by it; one lives, in fine, as one can. Still, one has the illusion of freedom; therefore don't be, like me, without the memory of that illusion. I was either, at the right time, too stupid or too intelligent to have it; I don't quite know which. Of course at present

I'm a case of reaction against the mistake; and the voice of reaction should, no doubt, always be taken with an allowance. But that doesn't affect the point that the right time is now yours. The right time is *any* time that one is still so lucky as to have. You've plenty; that's the great thing; you're, as I say, damn you, so happily and hatefully young. Don't, at any rate, miss things out of stupidity. Of course I don't take you for a fool, or I shouldn't be addressing you thus awfully. Do what you like so long as you don't make *my* mistake. For it was a mistake. Live!" . . .

AFTERWORD

"I have my head, thank God, full of visions," James had written after the disastrous failure of *Guy Domville*. During the year that followed he transferred many of the visions into his notebooks in the form of projects for novels and stories. Thus, on October 31, 1895, he recorded that his young friend Jonathan Sturges had told him about a meeting in Paris with William Dean Howells. "It was only 10 words," James wrote, but still it gave him—as many other incidents had done that year—the subject for what he thought might be a novella. Here is part of the long notebook entry.

> [Howells] had scarcely been in Paris, ever, in former days, and he had come there to see his domiciled and initiated son, who was at the Beaux Arts. Virtually in the evening, as it were, of life, it was all new to him: all, all, all. Sturges said he seemed sad—rather brooding; and I asked him what gave him (Sturges) that impression. "Oh—somewhere—I forget, when I was with him—he laid his hand on my shoulder and said *à propos* of some remark of mine: 'Oh, you are young, you are young—be glad of it: be glad of it and live. Live all you can: it's a mistake not to. . . . This place makes it all come over me. I see it now. I haven't done so—and now I'm old. It's too late. It has gone past me—I've lost it. You have time. You are young. Live!' "

That was the "germ," as James called it, of *The Ambassadors*. In the rest of the notebook entry one can watch the germ or seed sprouting as in a test tube. The process starts with the hero, who—James reasons to himself—must be an imaginative man of Howells' age, but of course must not be a successful novelist: might he be the editor of a magazine? In any case he would have been married very young, to a straitlaced New England wife, but he has lost her some years ago and now he arrives in Paris—why? Well, there might be a rich widow to whom he is engaged, and the widow might have a son in Paris, who refuses to come home. The hero, with his New England conscience, undertakes to bring him back, but instead finds himself urging the young man to stay—even at the cost to himself of breaking his engagement to the rich widow. . . . Thus, starting with a few words repeated the night before by a younger friend, James in one morning has outlined the plot of something larger in scope than a novella, and the plot in turn has suggested other leading characters: the rich, intensely moral widow, the son who won't come home, and, by implication, the siren who is supposed to be holding him captive—all this by a process as purely logical and self-contained as the one that Edgar Poe claimed to have followed in writing "The Raven."

The plot stayed buried in James's notebook until the summer of 1900. Then, bringing it forth and once again practicing what he called "the art of *reflection*," he produced a twenty-thousand-word synopsis or scenario (which, incidentally, is printed as an appendix to that illuminating book *The Notebooks of Henry James*). By this time he had decided that the novel was to be a succession of essentially dramatic scenes as viewed by Lambert Strether. To heighten the dramatic quality, he had given Strether a confidante, Maria Gostrey, and a foil or opposite, Ned Waymark (as he is called in the scenario). To lend a necessary complication to the drama, James had brought the three Pococks to Paris and depicted them at length. There remained, however, many problems that would have to be solved in the actual writing of the novel, a process that was to require another year.

One of those problems was how to create the perfect occasion for Strether's outburst, which was to remain the center of the story. James already had the setting clearly in mind: it was to be a garden in the Faubourg Saint-Germain surrounded by ducal mansions that "spoke of survival, transmission, association," everything the novelist felt to be lacking in America. On the first perfect Sunday afternoon in spring, the garden was to be crowded—with whom? Gloriani, the famous sculptor who was holding the reception, could simply be borrowed from an earlier James novel, *Roderick Hudson*, but what about Gloriani's guests? Obviously they should be representatives of what used to be called *Tout Paris*, that is, the world of ambassadors, generals, aristocrats, society artists, actresses, and ladies of fashion. But there would also be the Americans already named in the story—not one of them would be missing, and the scene would resemble the crowded first-act curtain of a musical play.

Now let us shift from the author's problems to those of the reader (or audience).

With the stage so elaborately set and peopled, we are likely to feel that something decisive should happen before the curtain falls. We can therefore be certain that it *will* happen, since James is too skillful not to observe the first rule of narrative form: that an expectation must be created, then fully satisfied, but preferably in an unexpected fashion. Perhaps the decisive event will be the appearance of Mme. de Vionnet, which has been announced at the beginning of the second paragraph. A little later Strether inquires, during his first dialogue with little Bilham, "Have Mme. de Vionnet and her daughter arrived?" whereupon the two men fall to discussing those ladies. Miss Barrace interrupts the conversation and Strether asks her, "Does Mme. de Vionnet do that? I mean really show for what she is." The question is one that Miss Barrace would rather not answer, and she is therefore relieved when Chad appears; he has come to present Strether to the lady herself. So this might be the decisive moment—but, no, the novelist intends to lengthen our suspense. Before Mme. de Vionnet can say anything of importance, she is first accosted by a duchess, then led away by a presumed ambassador, leaving Strether alone. He is now joined on a bench by little Bilham. It is at this moment, when we are still hoping for the decisive event, but are least expecting it, that Strether delivers his surprising outburst. Fittingly he delivers it to Bilham, the "little artist-man" who had "come over to convert the savages" and then had been converted by *them*, thus prefiguring Strether's own experience.

The narrative point of view, here and elsewhere in the novel, is almost entirely that of Strether. Only at rare intervals does one overhear what must be the voice of the author. Who else than the author would know, at the time, that Strether "was not soon to forget" Gloriani's eyes, or that he "was to think of them . . . as the source of the deepest intellectual sounding to which he had ever been exposed"? For the most part, however, Strether serves as our only guide to events. We see what he sees at the moment, and usually nothing more; we hear what he hears or says, share his impressions, and speculate with him about other people's motives. No scene can be included in the novel unless Strether is present to report it. This method of telling a story, which produces an extreme unity of tone and focus, is known as that of the "central consciousness" (or "central intelligence"). Usually it is associated with Henry James. As a matter of fact, he adopted other methods when situations called for them, but this one was his favorite, and he used it with a subtlety and discretion that his followers have seldom displayed. During the scene in Gloriani's garden, for example, he is careful to stay on the surface of Strether's mind. If he had penetrated to deeper levels of feeling, he would have told us too much too soon, and the great outburst would have lost the element of surprise that is mingled with its perfect relevance to everything this most percipient hero had heard or seen.

Tonio Kröger (1903)

THOMAS MANN (1875-1955), who is nearer to being a Goethean figure than any other German of the twentieth century, was born in the ancient Hanseatic city of Lübeck. By descent he was *bürgerlich*, a word that carries more weight than "bourgeois"; the family belonged to a sort of mercantile aristocracy. His father, Johann Thomas Heinrich Mann, was a senator of the free city on the Baltic and twice served as its mayor. His mother, however, was half-Brazilian in blood and wholly Southern in temperament. The marriage explains a favorite theme in Mann: the character of children in whom the warm, outgoing, aesthetic, life-loving Mediterranean is mingled with the more restrained and "ethical" North. In *Tonio Kröger*, for example, the hero's father is Consul Kröger, "a tall, fastidiously dressed man, with his thoughtful blue eyes, and always a wild flower in his buttonhole," but the consul is married to Tonio's "beautiful, fiery mother . . . to whom nothing mattered at all," and who comes from "some place far down on the map."

Like Henry James, Mann was the second son in a family of five children. His older brother Heinrich Mann (1871-1950) was also to become a famous novelist, more political than Thomas and more involved in the defeat of German radicalism. There were two sisters who eventually committed suicide, but that was long after the happy childhood shared by all the Manns in the big house built by their father. Thomas was not a good student in the Gymnasium at Lübeck; he rebelled against the Prussian discipline and wrote poems instead of doing his homework. In 1890 his father died; there was a grand funeral and then the family business had to be liquidated. His mother went south to live in the sunnier climate of Munich, but Thomas stayed in Lübeck until he finally passed his examinations at the age of nineteen.

Having rejoined the family in Munich, he spent a year in a fire-insurance office, writing stories while pretending to copy out accounts, and another year attending courses at the university; then he followed Goethe—and how many other German writers!—southward to the land of blossoming lemon trees. In company with his brother Heinrich, he led what he judged to be a wildly irregular life, especially during their winters in Rome, but meanwhile he was working like a Hanseatic burgher. It was during those two Italian years that he finished his first book of stories, *Little Herr Friedemann* (1898)—which was accepted with enthusiam by Fischer, the leading German publishing house—and wrote the greater part of *Buddenbrooks* (1901) in first draft. (Titles here are of English translations, but dates are those of appearances in German.) *Buddenbrooks* was to trace through four generations the fortunes of a North German family not unlike the Manns. Written when the author was strongly influenced by Schopenhauer and Nietzsche, the book has a thesis, namely, the inevitable decay of a family that produces successively more self-conscious individuals. With the death at an early age of Hanno, a sickly youth and a talented musician, the Buddenbrook line comes to an end.

Mann returned to Munich in 1898 and continued to work on the huge manuscript. For a year he had a pleasant post on the staff of *Simplicissimus*, the renowned humorous weekly; then came another year of required military service. When the manuscript went off to Fischer in 1900, the publisher was appalled by its length and urged him to cut the book in half. The author, then twenty-five years old, was obstinate and finally had his way. Published complete in two expensive volumes, *Buddenbrooks* was rather peevishly reviewed by critics who thought the young man was demanding too much of their time. The first edition of a thousand copies took a year to sell; but Fischer reissued the novel in one volume at a lower price, and this time it became a sensation. More than a million copies of *Buddenbrooks* were to be sold in Germany alone before Hitler had it burned.

Mann was already "snatched up in a whirl of success" when he published *Tristan* (1903), a collection named for one of the two novellas it contained in addition to shorter stories. The title piece is about a woman who dies as a result of her sensitivity to music (with the damage compounded by a stupid man of letters); the heroine might be a sister of Hanno Buddenbrook. The other novella was *Tonio Kröger*, of which Mann later said that it had the fortune "to become a sort of symbol, to be hailed as . . . the expression in some sense, in art, of the attitude of a generation of artists." He always counted it among his major productions.

In 1905 he married Katja Pringsheim, the only daughter of a cultured mercantile family. Established in Munich—though with many lecture trips abroad—the Manns led an orderly or *bürgerliches* life that was fruitful in respect to books and children. There would be six of the latter when the family was complete, and three of them—Erika, Klaus, and Golo—were to gain some reputation as writers. The father's books, each given time to ripen, appeared at irregular intervals. In 1909 it was *Royal Highness*, which Mann described as "an attempt at comedy in the form of a novel." In 1912 it was the masterly novella *Death in Venice*, which, without a mention of politics, somehow conveyed the uneasiness that afflicted Europe before the Great War. In 1914 it was another collection of stories, published while he was working on an early draft of *The Magic Mountain*. The war, Mann said, "paralyzed my creative activities," and his chief production of the war years was a candid and profound but somewhat confused essay, *Reflections of a Non-Political Man*, which led to a quarrel with his more political brother Heinrich. Then, with the German economy in ruins, Mann went back to work on his immense novel, and it was published in 1924.

The setting of the novel, a sanitarium high in the Alps, became a powerful symbol for Western middle-class culture, existing in an unreal world and oblivious to the disasters hanging over it. Once again Mann had expressed a general mood, and *The Magic Mountain* was read and praised in many languages. In 1929 its author was awarded the Nobel Prize. That same year he published a novella, *Mario and the Magician*, which—still without mentioning politics—revealed the black magic of fascism. Mann was using his prestige to defend the Weimar Republic.

At the time of the Reichstag fire in 1933, he was lecturing abroad. Friends warned him that his life was in danger if he returned to Germany, and he settled in Switzerland, where he continued work on his Biblical tetralogy, *Joseph and His Brothers* (1933-1944). His daughter Erika had smuggled the manuscript of the first volume out of Munich in the toolbox of her Ford. In 1936 Mann denounced the Nazis in an open letter to a Zurich newspaper; he called them enemies of Christianity, of Western morality, and of civilization. He was thereupon deprived of German citizenship, and the University of Bonn took back an honorary degree it had given him after the Great War. This latter act called forth an

eloquent statement in defense of academic freedom, published in 1937
as *An Exchange of Letters.*

Mann came to the United States in 1938 and became an American
citizen in 1944, when he was living in California. During the war he
traveled over the country giving lectures against fascism, but he was
also busy at his desk. Besides the successive volumes of his Joseph
tetralogy—*Young Joseph* (1935), *Joseph in Egypt* (1938), *Joseph the
Provider* (1944)—he also published shorter novels, including *The Beloved Returns* (1939), concerned with the imagined meeting, after many
years, of Goethe and the heroine of *Werther.* He had always regarded
Goethe's life and works as a paradigm, and it was almost to be expected
that he should write a *Doctor Faustus* (1947). His twentieth-century
version of the story, with a tortured composer as hero, proved to be
the most obscure and complicated of his novels.

In 1949 Mann was invited to West Germany to receive a Goethe
prize at Frankfurt-am-Main, and he crossed the border into East Germany
for another Goethe award conferred on him at Weimar. His dialectical
mind seemed to see Russia and America as "two good-natured Colossi
in the East and the West," with a certain kinship of temperament.
After publishing a shorter novel, *The Holy Sinner* (1951), in the form
of a medieval legend, he settled again in Zurich. His last book, *The
Confessions of Felix Krull, Confidence Man* (1954), was his final portrait
of an artist, this time depicted as a genial charlatan and scoundrel. When
he died at eighty, a Danish newspaper expressed a widespread feeling
when it said, "A whole form of culture that reached its high water-
mark in Goethe, Schopenhauer, and Nietzsche goes down with him
to the grave."

THE STORY

At fourteen Tonio Kröger, son of the leading citizen of a North
German town, is a dreamer and secretly a poet. He worships his vigorous
schoolmate Hans Hansen, a "blond and blue-eyed" figure representative
of normality and health. Their relation announces the theme of the
novella, one that continued to exercise Mann's imagination. He felt that
spirit (*Geist*) and life (*Leben*) are in fundamental opposition. *Geist*
is epitomized in art, but artists yearn after the "real" world of the solid,
wholesome bourgeoisie. Thus, Tonio wants to make Hans share his
own taste for music and books, but at the same time he would like to
preserve his idol in his unreflective innocence and beauty.

At sixteen Tonio is in love with Ingeborg Holm, also blonde and
blue-eyed. He sees her every week at Herr Knaak's fashionable dancing

class and is so wrapped up in her that he makes a fool of himself in a quadrille. Everybody laughs at him except Magdalena Vermehren, who always falls down in the dances. Magdalena looks at him with her "great, dark, brilliant eyes, so serious and adoring," but Tonio would rather be scorned by blue-eyed Inge.

Tonio's father dies, his mother marries an Italian violinist, and Tonio himself, after some years of dissipation, becomes a famous writer. In Munich he has a long talk with a Russian friend, the painter Lisabeta Ivanovna. "Literature is not a calling, it is a curse," he tells her, before confessing that he feels "the gnawing, surreptitious hankering, Lisabeta, for the bliss of the commonplace." Lisabeta answers that he is "a bourgeois on the wrong track, a failed bourgeois."

Soon afterward Tonio pays a visit to his native city on the Baltic. The house where he was born is now the municipal library. After a visit there, he is nearly arrested as a swindler wanted by the police; then he continues northward to a Danish seaside resort. There is a dance one evening at the hotel—it is the scene that follows—and Tonio looks on as he sometimes did at Herr Knaak's dancing classes; he even seems to recognize Hans and Inge and dark-eyed, awkward Magdalena. The story ends with a letter to Lisabeta Ivanovna in which he sums up his feelings about art and life.

The translation, published by Knopf and reprinted as a Vintage Book, is by H. T. Lowe-Porter, who undertook the monumental task of translating almost everything Mann wrote.

[*The Blue-Eyed People*]

At second breakfast—the table was heavily laden with cold viands, roast, pickled, and smoked—Tonio Kröger inquired what was going on.

"Guests," said the fish-dealer. "Tourists and ball-guests from Helsingör. Lord help us, we shall get no sleep this night! There will be dancing and music, and I fear me it will keep up late. It is a family reunion, a sort of celebration and excursion combined; they all subscribe to it and take advantage of the good weather. They came by boat and bus and they are having breakfast. After that they go on with their drive, but at night they will all come back for a dance here in the hall. Yes, damn it, you'll see we shan't get a wink of sleep."

"Oh, it will be a pleasant change," said Tonio Kröger.

After that there was nothing more said for some time. The landlady arranged her red fingers on the cloth, the fish-dealer blew through his nostril, the Americans drank hot water and made long faces.

Then all at once a thing came to pass: *Hans Hansen and Ingeborg Holm walked through the room.*

Tonio Kröger, pleasantly fatigued after his swim and rapid walk, was leaning back in his chair and eating smoked salmon on toast; he sat facing the veranda and the ocean. All at once the door opened and the two entered hand-in-hand—calmly and unhurried, Ingeborg, blonde Inge, was dressed just as she used to be at Herr Knaak's dancing-class. The light flowered frock reached down to her ankles and it had a tulle fichu draped with a pointed opening that left her soft throat free. Her hat hung by its ribbons over her arm. She, perhaps, was a little more grown up than she used to be, and her wonderful plait of hair was wound round her head; but Hans Hansen was the same as ever. He wore his sailor overcoat with gilt buttons, and his wide blue sailor collar lay across his shoulders and back; the sailor cap with its short ribbons he was dangling carelessly in his hand. Ingeborg's narrow eyes were turned away; perhaps she felt shy before the company at table. But Hans Hansen turned his head straight towards them, and measured one after another defiantly with his steel-blue eyes; challengingly, with a sort of contempt. He even dropped Ingeborg's hand and swung his cap harder than ever, to show what manner of man he was. Thus the two, against the silent, blue-dyed sea, measured the length of the room and passed through the opposite door into the parlour.

This was at half-past eleven in the morning. While the guests of the house were still at table the company in the veranda broke up and went away by the side door. No one else came into the dining-room. The guests could hear them laughing and joking as they got into the omnibuses, which rumbled away one by one. . . .

"So they are coming back?" asked Tonio Kröger.

"That they are," said the fish-dealer. "More's the pity. They have ordered music, let me tell you—and my room is right above the dining-room."

"Oh, well, it's a pleasant change," repeated Tonio Kröger. Then he got up and went away.

That day he spent as he had the others, on the beach and in the wood, holding a book on his knee and blinking in the sun. He had but one thought; they were coming back to have a dance in the hall, the fish-dealer had promised they would; and he did nothing but be glad of this, with a sweet and timorous gladness such as he had not felt through all these long dead years. Once he happened, by some chance association, to think of his friend Adalbert, the novelist, the man who had known what he wanted and betaken himself to the café to get away from the spring. Tonio Kröger shrugged his shoulders at the thought of him.

Luncheon was served earlier than usual, also supper, which they ate in the parlour because the dining-room was being got ready for the ball, and the whole house flung in disorder for the occasion. It grew dark; Tonio Kröger sitting in his room heard on the road and in the house the sounds of approaching festivity. The picnickers were coming back; from Helsingör, by bicycle and carriage, new guests were arriving; a fiddle and a nasal clarinet might be heard practising down in the dining-room. Everything promised a brilliant ball. . . .

Now the little orchestra struck up a march; he could hear the notes, faint but lively. The dancing opened with a polonaise. Tonio Kröger sat for a while and listened. But when he heard the march-time go over into a waltz he got up and slipped noiselessly out of his room.

From his corridor it was possible to go by the side stairs to the side entrance of the hotel and thence to the veranda without passing through a room. He took this route, softly and stealthily as though on forbidden paths, feeling along through the dark, relentlessly drawn by this stupid jigging music, that now came up to him loud and clear.

The veranda was empty and dim, but the glass door stood open into the hall, where shone two large oil lamps, furnished with bright reflectors. Thither he stole on soft feet; and his skin prickled with the thievish pleasure of standing unseen in the dark and spying on the dancers there in the brightly lighted room. Quickly and eagerly he glanced about for the two whom he sought. . . .

Even though the ball was only half an hour old, the merriment seemed in full swing; however, the guests had come hither already warm and merry, after a whole day of carefree, happy companionship. By bending forward a little, Tonio Kröger could see into the parlour from where he was. Several old gentlemen sat there smoking, drinking, and playing cards; others were with their wives on the plush-upholstered chairs in the foreground watching the dance.

They sat with their knees apart and their hands resting on them, puffing out their cheeks with a prosperous air; the mothers, with bonnets perched on their parted hair, with their hands folded over their stomachs and their heads on one side, gazed into the whirl of dancers. A platform had been erected on the long side of the hall, and on it the musicians were doing their utmost. There was even a trumpet, that blew with a certain caution, as though afraid of its own voice, and yet after all kept breaking and cracking. Couples were dipping and circling about, others walked arm-in-arm up and down the room. No one wore ballroom clothes; they were dressed as for an outing in the summertime: the men in countrified suits which were obviously their Sunday wear; the girls in light-coloured frocks with bunches of field-flowers in their bodices. Even a few children were there, dancing with each other in their own way, even after the music stopped. There was a long-legged man in a coat with a little swallow-tail, a provincial lion with an eye-glass and frizzed hair, a post-office clerk or some such thing; he was like a comic figure stepped bodily out of a Danish novel; and he seemed to be the leader and manager of the ball. He was everywhere at once, bustling, perspiring, officious, utterly absorbed; setting down his feet, in shiny, pointed, military half-boots, in a very artificial and involved manner, toes first; waving his arms to issue an order, clapping his hands for the music to begin; here, there, and everywhere, and glancing over his shoulder in pride at his great bow of office, the streamers of which fluttered grandly in his rear.

Yes, there they were, those two, who had gone by Tonio Kröger in the broad light of day; he saw them again—with a joyful start he recognized them almost at the same moment. Here was Hans Hansen by the door, quite close; his legs apart, a little bent over, he was eating with circumspection a large piece of sponge-cake, holding his hand cupwise under his chin to catch the crumbs. And there by the wall sat Ingeborg Holm, Inge the fair; the post-office clerk was just mincing up to her with an exaggerated bow and asking her to dance. He laid one hand on his back and gracefully shoved the other into his bosom. But she was shaking her head in token that she was a little out of breath and must rest awhile, whereat the post-office clerk sat down by her side.

Tonio Kröger looked at them both, these two for whom he had in time past suffered love—at Hans and Ingeborg. They were Hans and Ingeborg not so much by virtue of individual traits and similarity of costume as by similarity of race and type. This was the blond, fair-haired breed of the steel-blue eyes, which stood to him for the pure, the blithe, the untroubled in life; for a virginal aloofness that was at once both simple and full of pride. . . . He looked at them. Hans Hansen was standing there in his sailor suit, lively and well built as ever, broad in the shoulders and narrow in the hips; Ingeborg was laughing and tossing her head in a certain high-spirited way she had; she carried her hand, a schoolgirl hand, not at all slender, not at all particularly aristocratic, to the back of her head in a certain manner so that the thin sleeve fell away from her elbow—and suddenly such a pang of home-sickness shook his breast that involuntarily he drew farther back into the darkness lest someone might see his features twitch.

"Had I forgotten you?" he asked. "No, never. Not thee, Hans, not thee, Inge the fair! It was always you I worked for; when I heard applause I always stole a look to see if you were there. . . . Did you read *Don Carlos*, Hans Hansen, as you promised me at the garden gate? No, don't read it! I do not ask it any more. What have you to do with a king who weeps for loneliness? You must not cloud your clear eyes or make them dreamy and dim by peering into melancholy poetry. . . . To be like you! To begin again, to grow up like you, regular like you, simple and normal and cheerful, in conformity and understanding with God and man, beloved of the innocent and happy. To take you, Ingeborg Holm, to wife, and have a son like you, Hans Hansen—to live free from the curse of knowledge and the torment of creation, live and praise God in blessed mediocrity! Begin again? But it would do no good. It would turn out the same—everything would turn out the same as it did before. For some go of necessity astray, because for them there is no such thing as a right path."

The music ceased; there was a pause in which refreshments were handed round. The post-office assistant tripped about in person with a trayful of herring salad and served the ladies; but before Ingeborg Holm he even went down on one knee as he passed her the dish, and she blushed for pleasure.

But now those within began to be aware of a spectator behind the glass door; some of the flushed and pretty faces turned to measure him with hostile glances; but he stood his ground. Ingeborg and Hans looked at him too, at almost the same time, both with that utter indifference in their eyes that looks so like contempt. And he was conscious too of a gaze resting on him from a different quarter; turned his head and met with his own the eyes that had sought him out. A girl stood not far off, with a fine, pale little face—he had already noticed her. She had not danced much, she had few partners, and he had seen her sitting there against the wall, her lips closed in a bitter line. She was standing alone now too; her dress was a thin light stuff, like the others, but beneath the transparent frock her shoulders showed angular and poor, and the thin neck was thrust down so deep between those meagre shoulders that as she stood there motionless she might almost be thought a little deformed. She was holding her hands in their thin mitts across her flat breast, with the finger-tips touching; her head was drooped, yet she was looking up at Tonio Kröger with black swimming eyes. He turned away. . . .

Here, quite close to him, were Ingeborg and Hans. He had sat down beside her—she was perhaps his sister—and they ate and drank together surrounded by other rosy-cheeked folk; they chattered and made merry, called to each other in ringing voices, and laughed aloud. Why could he not go up and speak to them? Make some trivial remark to him or her, to which they might at least answer with a smile? It would make him happy—he longed to do it; he would go back more satisfied to his room if he might feel he had established a little contact with them. He thought out what he might say; but he had not the courage to say it. Yes, this too was just as it had been: they would not understand him, they would listen like strangers to anything he was able to say. For their speech was not his speech.

It seemed the dance was about to begin again. The leader developed a comprehensive activity. He dashed hither and thither, adjuring everybody to get partners; helped the waiters to push chairs and glasses out of the way, gave orders to the musicians, even took some awkward people by the shoulders and shoved them aside. . . . What was coming? They formed squares of four couples each. . . . A frightful memory brought the colour to Tonio Kröger's cheeks. They were forming for a quadrille.

The music struck up, the couples bowed and crossed over. The leader called off; he called off—Heaven save us—in French! And pronounced the nasals with great distinction. Ingeborg Holm danced close by, in the set nearest the glass door. She moved to and fro before him, forwards and back, pacing and turning; he caught a waft from her hair or the thin stuff of her frock, and it made him close his eyes with the old, familiar feeling, the fragrance and bitter-sweet enchantment he had faintly felt in all these days, that now filled him utterly with irresistible sweetness. And what was the feeling? Longing, tenderness? Envy? Self-contempt? . . . *Moulinet des dames!* "Did you laugh, Ingeborg the blonde, did you laugh at me when I disgraced myself by dancing the *moulinet!* And would you still laugh today even after I have become something like a famous man? Yes, that you would, and you would be right to laugh. Even if I in my own person had written the nine symphonies and *The World as Will and Idea* and painted the Last Judgment, you would still be eternally right to laugh. . . ." As he looked at her he thought of a line of verse once so familiar to him, now long forgotten: "I would sleep, but thou must dance." How well he knew it, that melancholy northern mood it evoked—its heavy inarticulateness. To sleep. . . . To long to be allowed to live the life of simple feeling, to rest sweetly and passively in feeling alone, without compulsion to act and achieve—and yet to be forced to dance, dance the cruel and perilous sword-dance of art; without even being allowed to forget the melancholy conflict within oneself; to be forced to dance, the while one loved. . . .

A sudden wild extravagance had come over the scene. The sets had broken up, the quadrille was being succeeded by a galop, and all the couples were leaping and gliding about. They flew past Tonio Kröger to a maddeningly quick tempo, crossing, advancing, retreating, with quick, breathless laughter. A couple came rushing and circling towards Tonio Kröger; the girl had a pale, refined face and lean, high shoulders. Suddenly, directly in front of him, they tripped and slipped and stumbled. . . . The pale girl fell, so hard and violently it almost looked dangerous; and her partner with her. He must have hurt himself badly, for he quite forgot her, and, half rising, began to rub his knee and grimace; while she, quite dazed, it seemed, still lay on the floor. Then Tonio Kröger came forward, took her gently by the arms, and lifted her up. She looked dazed, bewildered, wretched; then suddenly her delicate face flushed pink.

"*Tak, O, mange tak!*" she said, and gazed up at him with dark, swimming eyes.

"You should not dance any more, Fräulein," he said gently. Once more he looked round at *them*, at Ingeborg and Hans, and then he went out, left the ball and the veranda and returned to his own room.

He was exhausted with jealousy, worn out with the gaiety in

which he had had no part. Just the same, just the same as it had always been. Always with burning cheeks he had stood in his dark corner and suffered for you, you blond, you living, you happy ones! And then quite simply gone away. Somebody *must* come now! Ingeborg *must* notice he had gone, must slip after him, lay a hand on his shoulder and say: "Come back and be happy. I love you!" but she came not at all. No, such things did not happen. Yes, all was as it had been, and he too was happy, just as he had been. For his heart was alive. But between that past and this present what had happened to make him become that which he now was? Icy desolation, solitude: mind, and art, forsooth!

He undressed, lay down, put out the light. Two names he whispered into his pillow, the few chaste northern syllables that meant for him his true and native way of love, of longing and happiness; that meant to him life and home, meant simple and heartfelt feeling. He looked back on the years that had passed. He thought of the dreamy adventures of the senses, nerves, and mind in which he had been involved; saw himself eaten up with intellect and introspection, ravaged and paralysed by insight, half worn out by the fevers and frosts of creation, helpless and in anguish of conscience between two extremes, flung to and fro between austerity and lust; *raffiné*, impoverished, exhausted by frigid and artificially heightened ecstasies; erring, forsaken, martyred, and ill— and sobbed with nostalgia and remorse.

Here in his room it was still and dark. But from below life's lulling, trivial waltz-rhythm came faintly to his ears.

Tonio Kröger sat up in the north, composing his promised letter to his friend Lisabeta Ivanovna.

"Dear Lisabeta down there in Arcady, whither I shall shortly return," he wrote: "Here is something like a letter, but it will probably disappoint you, for I mean to keep it rather general. Not that I have nothing to tell; for indeed, in my way, I have had experiences; for instance, in my native town they were even going to arrest me . . . but of that by word of mouth. Sometimes now I have days when I would rather state things in general terms than go on telling stories.

"You probably still remember, Lisabeta, that you called me a *bourgeois*, a *bourgeois manqué?* You called me that in an hour when, led on by other confessions I had previously let slip, I confessed to you my love of life, of what I call life. I ask myself if you were aware how very close you came to the truth, how much my love of 'life' is one and the same thing as my being a *bourgeois*. This journey of mine has given me much occasion to ponder the subject.

"My father, you know, had the temperament of the north: solid, reflective, puritanically correct, with a tendency to melancholia. My mother, of indeterminate foreign blood, was beautiful, sensuous, naïve, passionate, and careless at once, and, I think, irregular by instinct. The mixture was no doubt extraordinary and bore with it extraordinary dangers. The issue of it, a *bourgeois* who strayed off into art, a bohemian who feels nostalgic yearnings for respectability, an artist with a bad conscience. For surely it is my *bourgeois* conscience makes me see in the artist life, in all irregularity and all genius, something profoundly suspect, profoundly disreputable; that fills me with this forlorn *faiblesse* for the simple and good, the comfortably normal, the average unendowed respectable human being.

"I stand between two worlds. I am at home in neither, and I suffer in consequence. You artists call me a *bourgeois*, and the *bourgeois* try to arrest me. . . . I don't know which makes me feel worse. The *bourgeois* are stupid; but you adorers of the beautiful, who call me phlegmatic and without aspirations, you ought to realize that there is a way of being an artist that goes so deep and is such a matter of origins and destinies that no longing seems to it sweeter and more worth knowing than longing after the bliss of the commonplace.

"I admire those proud, cold beings who adventure upon the paths of great and daemonic beauty and despise 'mankind'; but I do not envy them. For if anything is capable of making a poet of a literary man, it is my *bourgeois* love of the human, the living and usual. It is the source of all warmth, goodness, and humour; I even almost think it is itself that love of which it stands written that one may speak with the tongues of men and angels and yet, having it not, be as sounding brass and tinkling cymbals.

"The work I have so far done is nothing or not much—as good as nothing. I will do better, Lisabeta—this is a promise. As I write the sea whispers to me and I close my eyes. I am looking into a world unborn and formless, that needs to be ordered and shaped; I see into a whirl of shadows of human figures who beckon to me to weave spells to redeem them: tragic and laughable figures and some that are both together—and to these I am drawn. But my deepest and secretest love belongs to the blond and blue-eyed, the fair and living, the happy, lovely, and commonplace.

"Do not chide this love, Lisabeta; it is good and fruitful. There is longing in it, and a gentle envy; a touch of contempt and no little innocent bliss."

AFTERWORD

In a book of passages from great novels, with commentaries, this is the only selection from a novella. The Italian word still sounds a little strange in English, but it seems to be driving out its equivalent— the French *nouvelle*, which Henry James preferred. Larousse defines the *nouvelle* as "a literary composition of limited extent, standing midway between the tale and the novel." That would serve for the novella in English, though we might also call it "a story or short novel of more than twenty thousand words and less than fifty thousand"; anything more specific would involve too many exceptions. But the novella *is* a distinct literary form and, in default of unbreakable rules, it has evolved a good many conventions: for instance, it has fewer characters than the average novel and tends to be more unified in mood and structure.

Henry James is the American master of the form, though many of the most admired American novellas were written by others: one thinks of *Billy Budd, Ethan Frome, A Lost Lady, The Old Man and the Sea*. Among German writers the form has been even more popular; it goes back at least as far as Novalis, who died in 1801, and continues through Hoffmann of the *Tales*, Heinrich von Kleist, Theodor Storm (once Tonio's favorite author), and Paul Heyse, who advanced a theory of the *Novelle* and compiled a vast anthology; but Thomas Mann stands high above his predecessors. Although we might have selected a scene from any of his great novels—say the duel at the end of *The Magic Mountain* or "The Painful Tongue" from *Joseph in Egypt*—it seemed important to illustrate his mastery of the shorter form.

Mies van der Rohe, the famous architect, used to praise a building in only three words: "That is built," he would say, nodding his head; *Das ist gebaut*. One feels that Mann's novels—and even more his novellas—are written, built, and in the musical sense, composed. His special contribution to the art of prose fiction was a highly developed sense of musical structure.

Mann was an ardent Wagnerian, though with reservations about the ultimate value of the composer's work. His fashion of introducing *Leitmotive*, defined as "melodic phrases that accompany the reappearance of an idea, person, or situation," has often been traced back to Wagner as the inventor of that essentially musical device. In *Tonio Kröger* there are many phrases or motifs that recur as in a Wagnerian opera; among them are the wild flower that Tonio's father wears in his buttonhole, the walnut tree that stands for Tonio's boyhood home, and the "steel-blue eyes" of Hans and Ingeborg. The Krögers always say of themselves, "After all, we are not gypsies living in a green wagon." Such repeated phrases have somewhat the same effect as rhymes in poetry. The critic Erich Heller also says of them that they become "tidy symbols of an ordered life" for an author who saw little genuine order in the daily world, who felt that the possibilities of his medium were close to being exhausted, but who still enjoyed his own efforts to impose form on chaos.

Some critics have suggested that *Tonio Kröger* has the tripartite and bithematic structure of a classical sonata, with an exposition, a development, and a recapitulation. The two themes, of course, are "life" and "art": life as represented by Hans and Ingeborg; art as represented by Tonio. The exposition, which presents the two themes, ends with Tonio's departure from his native city. The development intermingles the themes and introduces episodic material. The recapitulation is Tonio's return to the North, including his voyage to Denmark. During the final scene in the Danish hotel, themes "A" and "B" are once again contrasted; then comes the equivalent of a musical coda in the form of Tonio's letter to Lisabeta Ivanovna. As Mies van der Rohe might have said, "*Das ist gebaut.*"

The narrative method is essentially Jamesian: that is, we learn almost everything through a central intelligence, in this case Tonio himself. Once or twice we hear what must be the author's voice, as at the end of the first episode, which deals with Tonio's love for Hans Hansen. "His heart beat richly," we read; "longing was awake in it, and a gentle envy; a faint contempt, and no little innocent bliss." That statement goes beyond Tonio's boyhood capacity for self-analysis, but elsewhere the author prefers to stay within Tonio's mind. Incidentally Mann was to use the same method of the central intelligence in writing *Death in Venice*. He departs from it, however, in other famous novellas; *Tristan* has an omniscient narrator and *Mario and the Magician* is told in the first person. What seems peculiarly Mann's stamp in the technical handling of *Tonio Kröger* is that the ball at the Danish hotel is a musical recapitulation of the dancing class presented in the second episode of the story, and that the central intelligence, who was then a schoolboy of sixteen, is now a distinguished novelist.

At the dancing class, Tonio had been so entranced with blonde Ingeborg Holm that, in the quadrille, he had absentmindedly joined the ladies' windmill, *le moulinet des dames*. Herr Knaak, the pompous dancing master, had made fun of him, and everyone, even Inge, had joined in the laughter at his expense. Tonio had stolen away into the corridor and had stood there disconsolately, hoping that Inge would lay her hand on his shoulder and say, "I love you, Tonio." But nobody had looked at him except plain Magdalena Vermehren, who always fell down in the dances. Now, in Denmark, everything repeats itself as in a dream. Herr Knaak is there, in the person of a ridiculous postal clerk who acts as cotillion leader. The older relatives of the dancers are there in the old plush-covered chairs. Ingeborg Holm and Hans Hansen are there, in their Danish avatars: Inge with her blond plait and Hans in the same sailor suit. Except that Tonio does not join the ladies' windmill, everything is the same, including a reincarnation of Magdelena, who falls down as before, then looks at Tonio with dark, swimming eyes. We note, however, that the artist in growing older has become even more isolated from the ordinary life around him and even more of a furtive observer, with the change revealed by such phrases as "he slipped noiselessly out of his room," "his skin prickled with the thievish pleasure of standing unseen in the dark and spying on the dancers"; then finally, "Here in his room it was still and dark. But from below life's lulling, trivial waltz-rhythm came faintly to his ears."

Later Tonio composes his letter to Lisabeta Ivanovna, that musical coda in which he restates his feelings about life and art. "But what is the *story?*" an innocent reader might ask. Like many other well-told stories, it can be summarized in one brief sentence: "Tonio Kröger discovers and accepts a pattern in his life." The pattern is always the same, but Tonio's acceptance of it is the changed element without which there would be no story. So, at the end of his letter to Lisabeta, in defending his love for mediocre people in a mediocre world, he repeats the phrase that the author had used of him at the end of the first episode— but with a changed emphasis, for now Tonio himself recognizes and accepts the truth of it. "Do not chide this love, Lisabeta," he says; "it is good and fruitful. There is longing in it, and a gentle envy; a touch of contempt and no little innocent bliss."

Sons and Lovers (1913)

DAVID HERBERT LAWRENCE (1885-1930) was born and brought up in the English Midlands. His father, a hard-drinking and choleric miner, had married a woman socially and intellectually his superior: a schoolteacher who sang in the choir of the local Congregational chapel. She could not instill ambition into her husband and centered her affection on one after another of the five children, but especially on the frailest and most gifted of her sons. It was the family situation mirrored in Sons and Lovers, which is the most autobiographical of Lawrence's novels, though class distinction and the dominance of powerful women also appear as themes in several of the others. Lawrence himself felt that he had been wrongly born into this impoverished environment. His early life, however, accounted in part for his ability to get close to "the skin of the working people," as V. S. Pritchett once remarked.

At his mother's urging he won a scholarship to University College, Nottingham, from which he graduated with a teacher's certificate. He taught for a few years in an elementary school near London, but resigned soon after publishing his first novel, The White Peacock (1911), entertaining as he did the grandiose hope that by writing he might earn as much as £2000 a year. In spite of all the books he published— something like thirty-eight volumes of fiction, poetry, drama, travels, and essays appeared in his lifetime, not to mention several posthumous works—he was never to realize that ambition.

He met Frieda Weekly when he was twenty-seven. The daughter of Baron von Richthofen, the military governor of Metz, she was married to an English philologist and was the mother of three children. Frieda abandoned the children and fled to the Continent with Lawrence, though she could not marry him until the decree of divorce became final in 1914. Their union, though lasting, was tempestuous; friends told of noisy quarrels and dishes thrown at each other across the room. During the war, when they were living in Cornwall, Lawrence was suspected of being a spy, and his difficulties were aggravated by the fact that Manfred von Richthofen, the Red Baron, credited with shooting down eighty Allied planes, was a cousin of Frieda's.

Before the war ended, Lawrence had published four novels, besides a collection of stories (*The Prussian Officer*, 1914), a travel book, and four books of poetry. *The Trespassers* (1912) was the second novel, *Sons and Lovers* was the third, and then came *The Rainbow* (1915), which was suppressed by a magistrate with the order that all existing copies be destroyed. A fifth novel, *Women in Love*, had been finished the following year, but no English publisher would accept the manuscript; finally it was to be privately printed (1920) in the United States. Censorship, lack of acceptance of his published work, illness (tuberculosis, which he kept insisting was only the recurrence of a common cold), financial difficulties, allegations about his doubtful patriotism—all these circumstances forced the Lawrences into expatriation. Sardinia, Germany, Austria, Ceylon, Australia, Mexico, New Mexico, New Zealand: they kept traveling by land and sea partly with the aim of finding a healthy climate and partly to satisfy Lawrence's yearning for some abode removed from modern industrial civilization, which he regarded as a gigantic swindle. Near Taos, New Mexico, where he was aided by a wealthy patroness, Mabel Dodge Luhan, he dreamed of founding a Utopian community ("Rananim," he called it, adapting the name from a Hebrew song) in which a few cherished souls might gain sanctuary. That was in the middle 1920's, at a time when he could also declare, "You can have the Land of the Free—as much as I know of it. In the spring I want to come back to Europe."

The titles of Lawrence's travel books testify to his curiosity about regions far from repressive England: *Sea and Sardinia* (1921), *Mornings in Mexico* (1927), and *Etruscan Places* (posthumous, 1932). His intellectual explorations took him down strange paths into studies of Australian aborigines, the Indians of Mexico and New Mexico, the lost continent of Atlantis, Egyptian and Chaldean civilizations, and the ancient Hindus. He regarded Buddha, Christ, and the Aztec god Quetzalcoatl as prophets who pointed to some ancient wisdom, life-affirming and rooted in the earth and the body. Like Yeats, he was attracted for a time by the occult teachings of Mme. Blavatsky, the seeress; but what was central in all his writings was the theme of modern man's sexual repressions and what he called the "deep, deep life which has been denied to us, and is still denied." His essays in *Psychoanalysis and the Unconscious* (1921) and *Fantasia of the Unconscious* (1922) reveal the Freudian overtones of his thinking, though Lawrence always insisted that he had come to his conclusions independently of Freud.

Among his later novels were *Aaron's Rod* (1922), *Kangaroo* (1923), *The Plumed Serpent* (1926), and the controversial *Lady Chatterley's Lover* (published in Italy, 1928), of which he had written three complete versions. The original version, which did not contain the bad words, was published here in 1944 as *The First Lady Chatterley*, but it was not until 1959 that the uncensored text of the final version was allowed to be distributed in this country. That was twenty-nine years after Lawrence's death. Having written hard and traveled furiously almost to the end, he died in March 1930, on the French Riviera.

THE STORY

Sons and Lovers has for its setting a colliery town near Nottingham, "The Bottoms," and the surrounding countryside. Walter Morel, a drunken and brutal miner, is married to Gertrude, the daughter of an engineer. Disappointed in her own life, she seeks vicarious fulfilment first in her older son, who dies, and then in the second son (and third child) Paul, the protagonist of the novel. Paul's schooling is cut short by the poverty of the Morels, and he finds a job in a surgical-appliance factory in Nottingham, where the work is easy and where he is allowed to develop his real talent for painting. On a walk with his mother he meets Miriam Leivers, then fourteen, the daughter of a farmer. The novel follows their complicated ten-year love affair, with Miriam always trying without success to liberate the boy from bondage to his mother. (Throughout the book Lawrence contrasts Mrs. Morel's obsessive love for her sons, which poisons their relations with other women, with the violent Oedipal hatred of the sons for their father.)

Having broken away from Miriam because of his mother, Paul has a brief passionate affair with a married women, Clara Dawes, who is separated from her husband and for whom Mrs. Morel feels the same hostility she feels for Miriam. The husband, Baxter Dawes, waylays Paul and, after a wild fight, kicks him insensible. Not long afterward Mrs. Morel develops cancer, and her prolonged illness once again brings Paul under her sway, just at the moment when a reunion with Miriam had seemed possible. The end of the novel seems to point in two directions, toward death and toward life (though Lawrence said in a letter that Paul was left "with the drift towards death"):

"Mother!" he whimpered—"mother!"

. . . .

But no, . . . He would not take that direction, to the darkness, to follow her. He walked towards the faintly humming, glowing town, quickly.

The passage that follows is from Chapter 11, which occurs at a strategic point, two-thirds of the way through the novel.

The Test on Miriam

With the spring came again the old madness and battle. Now he knew he would have to go to Miriam. But what was his reluctance? He told himself it was only a sort of overstrong virginity in her and him which neither could break through. He might have married her; but his circumstances at home made it difficult, and, moreover, he did not want to marry. Marriage was for life, and because they had become close companions, he and she, he did not see that it should inevitably follow they should be man and wife. He did not feel that he wanted marriage with Miriam. He wished he did. He would have given his head to have felt a joyous desire to marry her and to have her. Then why couldn't he bring it off? There was some obstacle; and what was the obstacle? It lay in the physical bondage. He shrank from the physical contact. But why? With her he felt bound up inside himself. He could not go out to her. Something struggled in him, but he could not get to her. Why? She loved him. Clara said she even wanted him; then why couldn't he go to her, make love to her, kiss her? Why, when she put her arm in his, timidly, as they walked, did he feel he would burst forth in brutality and recoil? He owed himself to her; he wanted to belong to her. Perhaps the recoil and the shrinking from her was love in its first fierce modesty. He had no aversion for her. No, it was the opposite; it was a strong desire battling with a still stronger shyness and virginity. It seemed as if virginity were a positive force, which fought and won in both of them. And with her he felt it so hard to overcome; yet he was nearest to her, and with her alone could he deliberately break through. And he owed himself to her. Then, if they could get things right, they could marry; but he would not marry unless he could feel strong in the joy of it—never. He could not have faced his mother. It seemed to him that to sacrifice himself in a marriage he did not want would be degrading, and would undo all his life, make it a nullity. He would try what he *could* do.

And he had a great tenderness for Miriam. Always, she was sad, dreaming her religion; and he was nearly a religion to her. He could not bear to fail her. It would all come right if they tried.

He looked round. A good many of the nicest men he knew were like himself, bound in by their own virginity, which they could not break out of. They were so sensitive to their women that they would go without them for ever rather than do them a hurt, an injustice. Being the sons of mothers whose husbands had blundered rather brutally through their feminine sanctities, they were themselves too diffident and shy. They could easier deny themselves than incur any reproach from a woman; for a woman was like their mother, and they were full of the sense of their mother. They preferred themselves to suffer the misery of celibacy, rather than risk the other person.

He went back to her. Something in her, when he looked at her, brought the tears almost to his eyes. One day he stood behind her as she sang. Annie was playing a song on the piano. As Miriam sang her mouth seemed hopeless. She sang like a nun singing to heaven. It reminded him so much of the mouth and eyes of one who sings beside a Botticelli Madonna, so spiritual. Again, hot as steel, came up the pain in him. Why must he ask for the other thing? Why was there his blood battling with her? If only he could have been always gentle, tender with her, breathing with her the atmosphere of reverie and religious dreams, he would give his right hand. It was not fair to hurt her. There seemed an eternal maidenhood about her; and when he thought of her mother, he saw the great brown eyes of a maiden who was nearly scared and shocked out of her virgin maidenhood, but not quite, in spite of her seven children. They had been born almost leaving her out of count, not of her, but upon her. So she could never let them go, because she never had possessed them.

Mrs. Morel saw him going again frequently to Miriam, and was astonished. He said nothing to his mother. He did not explain nor excuse himself. If he came home late, and she reproached him, he frowned and turned on her in an overbearing way:

"I shall come home when I like," he said; "I am old enough."

"Must she keep you till this time?"

"It is I who stay," he answered.

"And she lets you? But very well," she said.

And she went to bed, leaving the door unlocked for him; but she lay listening until he came, often long after. It was a great bitterness to her that he had gone back to Miriam. She recognized, however, the uselessness of any further interference. He went to Willey Farm as a man now, not as a youth. She had no right over him. There was a coldness between him and her. He hardly told her anything. Discarded, she waited on him, cooked for him still, and loved to slave for him; but her face closed again like a mask. There was nothing for her to do now but the housework; for all the rest he had gone to Miriam. She could not forgive him. Miriam killed the joy and the warmth in him. He had been such a jolly lad, and full of the warmest affection; now he grew colder, more and more irritable and gloomy. It reminded her of William; but Paul was worse. He did things with more intensity, and more realization of what he was about. His mother knew how he was suffering for want of a woman, and she saw him going to Miriam. If he had made up his mind, nothing on earth would alter him. Mrs. Morel was tired. She began to give up at last; she had finished. She was in the way.

He went on determinedly. He realized more or less what his mother felt. It only hardened his soul. He made himself callous towards her; but it was like being callous to his own health. It undermined him quickly; yet he persisted.

He lay back in the rocking-chair at Willey Farm one evening. He had been talking to Miriam for some weeks, but had not come to the point. Now he said suddenly:

"I am twenty-four, almost."

She had been brooding. She looked up at him suddenly in surprise.

"Yes. What makes you say it?"

There was something in the charged atmosphere that she dreaded.

"Sir Thomas More says one can marry at twenty-four."

She laughed quaintly, saying:

"Does it need Sir Thomas More's sanction?"

"No; but one ought to marry about then."

"Ay," she answered broodingly; and she waited.

"I can't marry you," he continued slowly, "not now, because we've no money, and they depend on me at home."

She sat half-guessing what was coming.

"But I want to marry now—"

"You want to marry?" she repeated.

"A woman—you know what I mean."

She was silent.

"Now, at last, I must," he said.

"Ay," she answered.

"And you love me?"

She laughed bitterly.

"Why are you ashamed of it?" he answered. "You wouldn't be ashamed before your God, why are you before people?"

"Nay," she answered deeply, "I am not ashamed."

"You are," he replied bitterly; "and it's my fault. But you know I can't help being—as I am—don't you?"

"I know you can't help it," she replied.

"I love you an awful lot—then there is something short."

"Where?" she answered, looking at him.

"Oh, in me! It is I who ought to be ashamed—like a spiritual cripple. And I am ashamed. It is misery. Why is it?"

"I don't know," replied Miriam.

"And I don't know," he repeated. "Don't you think we have been too fierce in our what they call purity? Don't you think that to be so much afraid and averse is a sort of dirtiness?"

She looked at him with startled dark eyes.

"You recoiled away from anything of the sort, and I took the motion from you, and recoiled also, perhaps worse."

There was silence in the room for some time.

"Yes," she said, "it is so."

"There is between us," he said, "all these years of intimacy. I feel naked enough before you. Do you understand?"

"I think so," she answered.

"And you love me?"

She laughed.

"Don't be bitter," he pleaded.

She looked at him and was sorry for him; his eyes were dark with torture. She was sorry for him; it was worse for him to have this deflected love than for herself, who could never be properly mated. He was restless, for ever urging forward and trying to find a way out. He might do as he liked, and have what he liked of her.

"Nay," she said softly, "I am not bitter."

She felt she could bear anything for him; she would suffer for him. She put her hand on his knee as he leaned forward in his chair. He took it and kissed it; but it hurt to do so. He felt he was putting himself aside. He sat there sacrificed to her purity, which felt more like nullity. How could he kiss her hand passionately, when it would drive her away, and leave nothing but pain? Yet slowly he drew her to him and kissed her.

They knew each other too well to pretend anything. As she kissed him, she watched his eyes; they were staring across the room, with a peculiar dark blaze in them that fascinated her. He was perfectly still. She could feel his heart throbbing heavily in his breast.

"What are you thinking about?" she asked.

The blaze in his eyes shuddered, became uncertain.

"I was thinking, all the while, I love you. I have been obstinate."

She sank her head on his breast.

"Yes," she answered.

"That's all," he said, and his voice seemed sure, and his mouth was kissing her throat.

Then she raised her head and looked into his eyes with her full gaze of love. The blaze struggled, seemed to try to get away from her, and then was quenched. He turned his head quickly aside. It was a moment of anguish.

"Kiss me," she whispered.

He shut his eyes, and kissed her, and his arms folded her closer and closer.

When she walked home with him over the fields, he said:

"I am glad I came back to you. I feel so simple with you—as if there was nothing to hide. We will be happy?"

"Yes," she murmured, and the tears came to her eyes.

"Some sort of perversity in our souls," he said, "makes us not want, get away from, the very thing we want. We have to fight against that."

"Yes," she said, and she felt stunned.

As she stood under the drooping thorn-tree, in the darkness by the roadside, he kissed her, and his fingers wandered over her face. In the darkness, where he could not see her but only feel her, his passion flooded him. He clasped her very close.

"Sometime you will have me?" he murmured, hiding his face on her shoulder. It was so difficult.

"Not now," she said.

His hopes and his heart sunk. A dreariness came over him.

"No," he said.

His clasp of her slackened.

"I love to feel your arm *there!*" she said, pressing his arm against her back, where it went round her waist. "It rests me so."

He tightened the pressure of his arm upon the small of her back to rest her.

"We belong to each other," he said.

"Yes."

"Then why shouldn't we belong to each other altogether?"

"But—" she faltered.

"I know it's a lot to ask," he said; "but there's not much risk for you really—not in the Gretchen way. You can trust me there?"

"Oh, I can trust you." The answer came quick and strong. "It's not that—it's not that at all—but—"

"What?"

She hid her face in his neck with a little cry of misery.

"I don't know!" she cried.

She seemed slightly hysterical, but with a sort of horror. His heart died in him.

"You don't think it ugly?" he asked.

"No, not now. You have *taught* me it isn't."

"You are afraid?"

She calmed herself hastily.

"Yes, I am only afraid," she said.

He kissed her tenderly.

"Never mind," he said. "You shall please yourself."

Suddenly she gripped her arms round him, and clenched her body stiff.

"You *shall* have me," she said, through her shut teeth.

His heart beat up again like fire. He folded her close, and his mouth was on her throat. She could not bear it. She drew away. He disengaged her.

"Won't you be late?" she asked gently.

He sighed, scarcely hearing what she said. She waited, wishing he would go. At last he kissed her quickly and climbed the fence. Looking round he saw the pale blotch of her face down in the darkness under the hanging tree. There was no more of her but this pale blotch.

"Good-bye!" she called softly. She had no body, only a voice and a dim face. He turned away and ran down the road, his fists clenched; and when he came to the wall over the lake he leaned there, almost stunned, looking up the black water.

Miriam plunged home over the meadows. She was not afraid of people, what they might say; but she dreaded the issue with him. Yes, she would let him have her if he insisted; and then, when she thought of it afterwards, her heart went down. He would be disappointed, he would find no satisfaction, and then he would go away. Yet he was so insistent; and over this, which did not seem so all-important to her, was their love to break down. After all, he was only like other men, seeking his satisfaction. Oh, but there was something more in him, something deeper! She could trust to it, in spite of all desires. He said that possession was a great moment in life. All strong emotions concentrated there. Perhaps it was so. There was something divine in it; then she would submit, religiously, to the sacrifice. He should have her. And at the thought her whole body clenched itself involuntarily, hard, as if against something; but Life forced her through this gate of suffering, too, and she would submit. At any rate, it would give him what he wanted, which was her deepest wish. She brooded and brooded and brooded herself towards accepting him.

He courted her now like a lover. Often, when he grew hot, she put his face from her, held it between her hands, and looked in his eyes. He could not meet her gaze. Her dark eyes, full of love, earnest and searching, made him turn away. Not for an instant would she let him forget. Back again he had to torture himself into a sense of his responsibility and hers. Never any relaxing, never any leaving himself to the great hunger and impersonality of passion; he must be brought back to a deliberate, reflective creature. As if from a swoon of passion she called him back to the littleness, the personal relationship. He could not bear it. "Leave me alone—leave me alone!" he wanted to cry; but she wanted him to look at her with eyes full of love. His eyes, full of the dark, impersonal fire of desire, did not belong to her.

There was a great crop of cherries at the farm. The trees at the back of the house, very large and tall, hung thick with scarlet and crimson drops, under the dark leaves. Paul and Edgar were gathering in the fruit one evening. It had been a hot day, and now the clouds were rolling in the sky, dark and warm. Paul climbed high in the tree, above the scarlet roofs of the buildings. The wind, moaning steadily, made the whole tree rock with a subtle, thrilling motion that stirred the blood. The young man, perched insecurely in the slender branches, rocked till he felt slightly drunk, reached down the boughs, where the scarlet beady cherries hung thick underneath, and tore off handful after handful of the sleek, cool-fleshed fruit. Cherries touched his ears and his neck as he stretched forward, their chill finger-tips sending a flash down his blood. All shades of red, from a golden vermilion to a rich crimson, glowed and met his eyes under a darkness of leaves.

The sun, going down, suddenly caught the broken clouds. Immense piles of gold flared out in the southeast, heaped in soft, glowing yellow right up the sky. The world, till now dusk and grey, reflected the gold glow, astonished. Everywhere the trees, and the grass, and the far-off water, seemed roused from the twilight and shining.

Miriam came out wondering.

"Oh!" Paul heard her mellow voice call, "isn't it wonderful?"

He looked down. There was a faint gold glimmer on her face, that looked very soft, turned up to him.

"How high you are!" she said.

Beside her, on the rhubarb leaves, were four dead birds, thieves that had been shot. Paul saw some cherry-stones hanging quite bleached, like skeletons, picked clear of flesh. He looked down again to Miriam.

"Clouds are on fire," he said.

"Beautiful!" she cried.

She seemed so small, so soft, so tender, down there. He threw a handful of cherries at her. She was startled and frightened. He laughed with a low, chuckling sound, and pelted her. She ran for shelter, picking up some cherries. Two fine red pairs she hung over her ears; then she looked up again.

"Haven't you got enough?" she asked.

"Nearly. It is like being on a ship up here."

"And how long will you stay?"

"While the sunset lasts."

She went to the fence and sat there, watching the gold clouds fall to pieces, and go in immense, rose-coloured ruin towards the darkness. Gold flamed to scarlet, like pain in its intense brightness. Then the scarlet sank to rose, and rose to crimson, and quickly the passion went out of the sky. All the world was dark grey. Paul scrambled quickly down with his basket, tearing his shirt-sleeve as he did so.

"They are lovely," said Miriam, fingering the cherries.

"I've torn my sleeve," he answered.

She took the three-cornered rip, saying:

"I shall have to mend it." It was near the shoulder. She put her fingers through the tear. "How warm!" she said.

He laughed. There was a new, strange note in his voice, one that made her pant.

"Shall we stay out?" he said.

"Won't it rain?" she asked.

"No, let us walk a little way."

They went down the fields and into the thick plantation of fir-trees and pines.

"Shall we go in among the trees?" he asked.

"Do you want to?"

"Yes."

It was very dark among the firs, and the sharp spines pricked her face. She was afraid. Paul was silent and strange.

"I like the darkness," he said. "I wish it were thicker—good, thick darkness."

He seemed to be almost unaware of her as a person: she was only to him then a woman. She was afraid.

He stood against a pine-tree trunk and took her in his arms. She relinquished herself to him, but it was a sacrifice in which she felt something of horror. This thick-voiced, oblivious man was a stranger to her.

Later it began to rain. The pine-trees smelled very strong. Paul lay with his head on the ground, on the dead pine-needles, listening to the sharp hiss of the rain—a steady, keen noise. His heart was down, very heavy. Now he realized that she had not been with him all the time, that her soul had stood apart, in a sort of horror. He was physically at rest, but no more. Very dreary at heart, very sad, and very tender, his fingers wandered over her face pitifully. Now again she loved him deeply. He was tender and beautiful.

"The rain!" he said.

"Yes—is it coming on you?"

She put her hands over him, on his hair, on his shoulders, to feel if the raindrops fell on him. She loved him dearly. He, as he lay with his face on the dead pine-leaves, felt extraordinarily quiet.

He did not mind if the raindrops came on him: he would have lain and got wet through: he felt as if nothing mattered, as if his living were smeared away into the beyond, near and quite lovable. This strange, gentle reaching-out to death was new to him.

"We must go," said Miriam.

"Yes," he answered, but did not move.

To him now, life seemed a shadow, day a white shadow; night, and death, and stillness, and inaction, this seemed like *being*. To be alive, to be urgent and insistent—that was *not-to-be*. The highest of all was to melt out into the darkness and sway there, identified with the great Being.

"The rain is coming in on us," said Miriam.

He rose, and assisted her.

"It is a pity," he said.

"What?"

"To have to go. I feel so still."

"Still!" she repeated.

"Stiller than I have ever been in my life."

He was walking with his hand in hers. She pressed his fingers, feeling a slight fear. Now he seemed beyond her; she had a fear lest she should lose him.

"The fir-trees are like presences on the darkness: each one only a presence."

She was afraid, and said nothing.

"A sort of hush: the whole night wondering and asleep: I suppose that's what we do in death—sleep in wonder."

She had been afraid before of the brute in him: now of the mystic. She trod beside him in silence. The rain fell with a heavy "Hush!" on the trees. At last they gained the cartshed.

"Let us stay here awhile," he said.

There was a sound of rain everywhere, smothering everything.

"I feel so strange and still," he said; "along with everything."

"Ay," she answered patiently.

He seemed again unaware of her, though he held her hand close.

"To be rid of our individuality, which is our will, which is our effort—to live effortless, a kind of conscious sleep—that is very beautiful, I think; that is our after-life—our immortality."

"Yes?"

"Yes—and very beautiful to have."

"You don't usually say that."

"No."

In a while they went indoors. Everybody looked at them curiously. He still kept the quiet, heavy look in his eyes, the stillness in his voice. Instinctively, they all left him alone.

About this time Miriam's grandmother, who lived in a tiny cottage in Woodlinton, fell ill, and the girl was sent to keep house. It was a beautiful little place. The cottage had a big garden in front, with red brick walls, against which the plum-trees were nailed. At the back another garden was separated from the fields by a tall old hedge. It was very pretty. Miriam had not much to do, so she found time for her beloved reading, and for writing little introspective pieces which interested her.

At the holiday-time her grandmother, being better, was driven to Derby to stay with her daughter for a day or two. She was a crotchety old lady, and might return the second day or the third; so Miriam stayed alone in the cottage, which also pleased her.

Paul used often to cycle over, and they had as a rule peaceful and happy times. He did not embarrass her much; but then on the Monday of the holiday he was to spend a whole day with her.

It was perfect weather. He left his mother, telling her where he was going. She would be alone all the day. It cast a shadow over him; but he had three days that were all his own, when he was going to do as he liked. It was sweet to rush through the morning lanes on his bicycle.

He got to the cottage at about eleven o'clock. Miriam was busy preparing dinner. She looked so perfectly in keeping with the little kitchen, ruddy and busy. He kissed her and sat down to watch. The room was small and cosy. The sofa was covered all over with a sort of linen in squares of red and pale blue, old, much washed, but pretty. There was a stuffed owl in a case over a corner cupboard. The sunlight came through the leaves of the scented geraniums in the window. She was cooking a chicken in his honour. It was their cottage for the day, and they were man and wife. He beat the eggs for her and peeled the potatoes. He thought she gave a feeling of home almost like his mother; and no one could look more beautiful, with her tumbled curls, when she was flushed from the fire.

The dinner was a great success. Like a young husband, he carved. They talked all the time with unflagging zest. Then he wiped the dishes she had washed, and they went out down the fields. There was a bright little brook that ran into a bog at the foot of a very steep bank. Here they wandered, picking still a few marsh marigolds and many big blue forget-me-nots. Then she sat on the bank with her hands full of flowers, mostly golden water-blobs. As she put her face down into the marigolds, it was all overcast with a yellow shine.

"Your face is bright," he said, "like a transfiguration."

She looked at him, questioning. He laughed pleadingly to her, laying his hand on hers. Then he kissed her fingers, then her face.

The world was all steeped in sunshine, and quite still, yet not asleep, but quivering with a kind of expectancy.

"I have never seen anything more beautiful than this," he said. He held her hand fast all the time.

"And the water singing to itself as it runs—do you love it?" She looked at him full of love. His eyes were very dark, very bright.

"Don't you think it's a great day?" he asked.

She murmured her assent. She *was* happy, and he saw it.

"And our day—just between us," he said.

They lingered a little while. Then they stood up upon the sweet thyme, and he looked down at her simply.

"Will you come?" he asked.

They went back to the house, hand-in-hand, in silence. The chickens came scampering down the path to her. He locked the door, and they had the little house to themselves.

He never forgot seeing her as she lay on the bed, when he was unfastening his collar. First he saw only her beauty, and was blind with it. She had the most beautiful body he had ever imagined. He stood unable to move or speak, looking at her, his face half smiling with wonder. And then he wanted her, but as he went forward to her her hands lifted in a little pleading movement, and he looked at her face, and stopped. Her big brown eyes were watching him, still and resigned and loving; she lay as if she had given herself up to sacrifice: there was her body for him; but the look at the back of her eyes, like a creature awaiting immolation, arrested him, and all his blood fell back.

"You are sure you want me?" he asked, as if a cold shadow had come over him.

"Yes, quite sure."

She was very quiet, very calm. She only realized that she was doing something for him. He could hardly bear it. She lay to be sacrificed for him because she loved him so much. And he had to sacrifice her. For a second, he wished he were sexless or dead. Then he shut his eyes again to her, and his blood beat back again.

And afterwards he loved her—loved her to the last fibre of his being. He loved her. But he wanted, somehow, to cry. There was something he could not bear for her sake. He stayed with her till quite late at night. As he rode home he felt that he was finally initiated. He was a youth no longer. But why had he the dull pain in his soul? Why did the thought of death, the afterlife, seem so sweet and consoling?

AFTERWORD

This account of a climax in the long-standing relation of Paul Morel and Miriam Leivers is a little more than half of Chapter 11, "The Test on Miriam"—not "of Miriam." What the title implies is that Paul himself is being tested through his love. As for the selected passage, it has a unity of its own. It starts with an inner monologue of Paul's, based on a series of short questions addressed to himself ("But what was his reluctance? . . . Then why couldn't he bring it off? . . . Why was there his blood battling with her?"), questions that mirror his confusion and his groping for maturity. There follows a briefer projection of his mother's inner turmoil. Most of the passage, however, consists of three scenes between Paul and Miriam, with brief intervening summaries of events necessary to the plot. At the end Paul is still puzzled and groping, but feels "that he was finally initiated. He was a youth no longer."

The first scene with Miriam, in which she rejects his advances, is presented in a vocabulary marked by its unrelieved gloom. Words such as "bitter," bitterly," "broodingly," "ashamed," are repeated many times, along with phrases such as "eyes dark with torture," "moment of anguish," "a dreariness came over him," and others of the sort. Almost the only physical object mentioned is the drooping thorn tree by the roadside under which they stand when they kiss, a symbolically barren tree. At the end of the scene there is another dismal touch: the black water at which Paul gazes after they separate.

In the second scene, the barren thorn tree has been replaced by a cherry tree, with its richer connotations of sex and fecundity. Especially to be noted are the two paragraphs in which Paul and Miriam's brother Edgar pick the cherries. Here the cadences are close to those of Lawrence's poems in free verse, and he employs other stylistic devices that we commonly associate with verse rather than prose. One of these is assonance, as in "sk*y* . . . cl*i*mbed h*i*gh," "d*ow*n . . . b*ough*s," "gl*ow*ing yell*ow*," "r*i*ght . . . sk*y*," "g*o*ld . . . gl*ow*," "tw*i*light . . . sh*i*ning," etc. Another device is the personification of natural objects, and we note that the cherries touch Paul (not Paul the cherries) with "their chill finger-tips," while the world is "astonished" and the trees, the grass, "and the far-off water, seemed roused."

Until this moment, Lawrence has been parsimonious with color, but now he overwhelms us. The cherries are "All shades of red, from a golden vermilion to a rich crimson." The clouds that reflect the sunset are "Immense piles of gold," and in one of the succeeding paragraphs "Gold flamed to scarlet, like pain in its intense brightness." Even Miriam's face wears "a faint gold glimmer." In both East and West gold has always been the color of sanctity; hence the golden haloes about the heads of those exalted to a superior state. Lawrence's amalgam of sacred and profane love is visually amplified by the aureole of light that surrounds the pair.

In this scene as elsewhere he makes use of traditional symbols, recasting them to his own purposes. Cherries, for example, have long been associated with virginity, and one remembers the abundance of cherry trees in medieval lyrics about the Virgin Mary. But here we have four dead birds, shot for stealing cherries, and above them Paul sees cherry stones still hanging by their stems "like skeletons, picked clear of flesh." These details prefigure Paul's thoughts about dying and his later obsession with *eros* and *thanatos*, love and death, in which Lawrence uncannily paralleled his near-contemporary, Freud.

Directly afterward, as part of the same scene—indeed, as a physical reenactment of what has been presented symbolically—we are told of Miriam's and Paul's first sexual experience. A key sentence here is "He was physically at rest, but no more"; in an earlier draft Lawrence had written ". . . but not spiritually." The possessiveness of their two mothers, who "could never let them go," has prevented the spiritual union of the lovers. Nevertheless, their meeting under the fir trees is suffused with religious imagery. Miriam "sacrifices" herself to Paul, though with a feeling of horror. The rain that follows their physical union becomes a rite of baptism, to bless Paul's conversion into a new existence and his desire to be "identified with the great Being." As they walk away, Miriam's fear of him as the "brute" turns to an equal fear of him as the "mystic."

In the third and last scene, they eat an almost ritual meal together in what has become "their cottage for the day." Then Miriam picks a double handful of marigolds and, as she bends over them, her face is "all overcast with a yellow shine"; once again she wears a halo. They make love in the cottage, this time more idyllically, and the personified world itself quivers "with a kind of expectancy." The note of sexual mysticism is sounded again: Miriam's face is "like a transfiguration," and "sacrifice" (in various grammatical forms) is repeated three times. She is also "like a creature awaiting immolation." But their union is still imperfect, and Paul, as he cycles home, wonders "why had he the dull pain in his soul? Why did the thought of death, the afterlife, seem so sweet and consoling?"

One last comment, this time of a more general nature. Before Lawrence the novel both here and abroad tended to move forward with a firm sense of chronology. Events followed events in causal sequence, as dictated by a "story line." Each scene—if we remember Balzac, Stendhal, and Dickens—took place in a concrete physical environment. The novel as a genre was still bound in service to the drama and circumscribed by conventions of time and space. Lawrence, however, seems to break away from spatial and temporal considerations even in this early work. Nature, sex, mysticism, and death—not to mention the brooding spirit of Paul's mother—are poetically intertwined in this passage, thus breaking down the traditional barriers between the "realism" of the novel and the "lyricism" of poetry. With Lawrence we seem to be moving toward certain manifestations in the novel—call them anti-realistic, even anti-novelistic—that would be further developed in the latter half of the century.

Remembrance
of Things Past (1913-1927)

MARCEL PROUST (1871-1922) was the son of one of the most eminent physicians of his time. His handsome and cultured mother, born Jeanne Weill, was of a wealthy Jewish family. Her influence and his close attachment to her helped to determine the direction of his life, as well as contributing to the acute sensitivity that was a facet of his genius. From the age of nine, when he suffered his first attack of asthma, Proust's health was precarious, and his sufferings were no less real for being in part psychosomatic.

Neither his youthful contributions to little reviews nor his early volume of stories and essays, *Les Plaisirs et les Jours* (1896), for which Anatole France wrote a preface, gave any indication of his true powers. They did nothing, moreover, to dissipate the reputation he had acquired as a dilettante and a social climber. But in spite of his social aspirations, Proust broke away from his Rightist friends in 1898, when the Dreyfus Affair was at its height, and took an active part in the fight to establish Dreyfus' innocence. About this time he discovered John Ruskin's works, two of which he translated (though he had only a slight knowledge of English). It was to Ruskin's influence that he owed the lasting interest in Gothic architecture that would help to mold his own vision and style.

Proust's stature as one of the major novelists of all time rests on his only novel, *A la Recherche du Temps Perdu*[1] (literally, "in search of

[1] A volume pieced together from his discarded manuscripts in 1952 and published under the title *Jean Santeuil* is of interest for the light it casts on Proust's literary development, but by no means amounts to a novel.

lost time"). *Remembrance of Things Past*, the title of the English translation, is unfortunately misleading. All writers of fiction draw to some extent on their own remembered experience, and Proust's work has a ring of such authenticity that it may seem too "real" to be fictional. Yet it is not an autobiography, nor was it any part of Proust's purpose to recall the past, even though he sometimes introduces actual people into the narrative under their own names. His characterization of his work as one "in which there is not a single episode that is not fictitious, in which there is not a single character *à clef* [disguised from life], in which everything has been invented by me for the needs of my demonstration," is basically true. The character called "I" throughout the novel, though he greatly resembles the author, is in fact a dozen or so years younger than Proust. At the end of the novel, he is older than Proust was at his death.

We cannot fix the date when the first inspiration for his masterpiece came to Proust, but can only say that it was after the death of his mother in 1906. It is possible that the grief he felt, intensified by remorse at having done so little to fulfill the hopes she had for him, may have driven him to conceive this work to which he was to devote the rest of his life. By 1909, after much groping, he had a plan that called for a single volume of approximately 250,000 words. The novel he left at his death consisted of seven parts or "movements" divided into fifteen volumes and totaling some 1,250,000 words.

The first part, *Swann's Way*, was published at the author's expense in 1913 and attracted no attention from the general public. With the outbreak of World War I, publication of further volumes had to be suspended. The second part, *Within a Budding Grove*, appeared in 1919 and won the Prix Goncourt, an annual prize supposedly intended to encourage a budding young novelist. There were charges of political intrigue. The press objected that the author was too old and far too rich to need the encouragement. Almost overnight Proust became the most discussed living author in France.

The last years of his life were, on the whole, lonely and unhappy ones. Giving himself totally to his book, he became more and more a recluse and an eccentric. Most sounds and odors caused him acute distress. Much of his work was written in a cork-lined room which he seldom left. His habit of working all night and of taking by day the little sleep that was permitted by his chronic insomnia cut him off from most of his friends. Even the growing enthusiasm of critics in France and abroad brought him little satisfaction, since he was aware that no reader could possibly appreciate the unity and powerful structure of the work, or even guess what its fundamental message and intent would be, without having read the last half of the fifteenth volume. Only four of the seven parts or "movements" of the work had been published when Proust died. As for the last part, *The Past Recaptured*, he had worked it over so extensively and had left the manuscript in such a tattered and jumbled state that it could not be deciphered and published until five years after his death.

THE STORY AND ITS MEANING

Proust's work eludes any simple definition. For the beauty of its texture, style, construction, and imagery, it has been praised as "a great symbolist poem." Another critic sees Proust as the supreme and most hard-headed of realists. Still others have called him the Einstein of fiction. For Somerset Maugham, his most enduring quality is his vast and subtle humor, and it must be noted that Proust has few equals as a satirist and scathing critic of society.

Proust himself saw his work as concerned primarily with downfall and redemption. The hero is damned by his self-indulgence and inertia as well as by the shallowness of the society in which he has chosen to live. Through most of the book he keeps sinking deeper into a slough of monotonous futility. After spending several blank years in a nursing home where he is cut off from life, he returns to Paris resigned to living out the remainder of a sordid and meaningless existence. Suddenly he has an intimation of reality, not unlike other momentary awakenings that have come to him on several occasions. This time he heeds the call and, transformed by this mystical experience, sets about "recomposing" his wasted life, by means of art, into one of glorious achievement.

We have seen that Proust speaks of his work as a "demonstration." A central thesis is that there are two "worlds": the unreal, meaningless world that comes to us from without, whose characteristics are contingency, boredom, suffering, and death; and the *real* world within us, essential (in the metaphysical sense[2]) and extra-temporal, whose characteristics are beauty, order, and "super-terrestrial joy"—and that we are free to choose between them.

An additional aim of Proust's work is to demonstrate that the potentiality of achieving oneness with reality exists not only for a chosen few but also for humanity at large. With this intent, he takes pains not to make any of his characters supermen. A ridiculous little village music teacher becomes Vinteuil, the supreme composer. A flippant and

---

[2] In metaphysics the essence of an object is its true being as distinguished from the variable, partial, and phenomenal aspects under which we commonly see it.

vacuous hanger-on of salons rises to become Elstir, the greatest painter of his time. And the hero himself, neurotic idler and weakling that he is, thrusts aside his social ambitions and performs the task of writing this monumental work of art.

The episode of the Duchess's red shoes, reprinted here, occurs at the end of *The Guermantes Way*, which is the third part of Proust's novel. The characters are the Duke and Duchess de Guermantes, whose lineage is such that they look down on upstarts like the Bourbons, Hapsburgs, and Saxe-Gothas, and Charles Swann, son of a Jewish broker, who owes his social position to his innate elegance and distinction and to his deep understanding and love of the arts. Swann's château is near the village where the hero's family spends its summers, and he has known the hero since the latter's early childhood, but he has not seen him for a year or more.

The hero, dazzled by the glamor of the Guermantes name, which he associates with all the ancient glories of France, has managed to cultivate the acquaintance of the Duchess. But when he receives an invitation to a soirée given by the even more exclusive Princesse de Guermantes, he suspects a hoax and goes to ask the Duchess, who has returned from the Riviera that day, if the invitation is genuine.

The translation is the famous one by C. K. Scott Moncrieff (New York: Random House, 1925-1930), but the paragraphing follows the authoritative Pléiade edition of the French text, which was not available in Scott Moncrieff's lifetime. A few passages referring to persons who figure elsewhere in the novel have been omitted, to avoid long explanations.

R.G.

[*The Duchess's Red Shoes*]

"You shall see Oriane in a minute," the Duke told me when I had entered the room. "As Swann is coming in presently and bringing her the proofs of his book on the coinage of the Order of Malta, and, what is worse, an immense photograph he has had taken shewing both sides of each of the coins, Oriane preferred to get dressed early so that she can stay with him until it's time to go out to dinner. We have such a heap of things in the house already that we don't know where to put them all, and I ask myself where on earth we are going to stick this photograph. But I have too good-natured a wife, who is too fond of giving people pleasure. She thought it would be polite to ask Swann to let her see side by side on one sheet the heads of all those Grand Masters of the Order whose medals he has found at Rhodes. I said Malta, didn't I, it is Rhodes, but it's all the same Order of Saint John of Jerusalem. As a matter of fact, she is interested in them only because Swann makes a hobby of it. Our family is very much mixed up in the whole story; even at the present day, my brother, whom you know, is one of the highest dignitaries in the Order of Malta. But I might have told all that to Oriane, she simply wouldn't have listened to me. On the other hand, it was quite enough that Swann's researches into the Templars (it's astonishing the passion that people of one religion have for studying others) should have led him on to the history of the Knights of Rhodes, who succeeded the Templars, for Oriane at once to insist on seeing the heads of these Knights. They were very small fry indeed compared with the Lusignans, Kings of Cyprus, from whom we descend in a direct line. But so far, as Swann hasn't taken them up, Oriane doesn't care to hear anything about the Lusignans."

I could not at once explain to the Duke why I had come. What happened was that several relatives or friends, including Mme. de Silistrie and the Duchesse de Montrose, came to pay a call on the Duchess, who was often at home before dinner, and not finding her there stayed for a short while with the Duke. The first of these ladies (the Princesse de Silistrie), simply dressed, with a dry but friendly manner, carried a cane in her hand. I was afraid at first that she had injured herself, or was a cripple. She was on the contrary most lovely. She spoke regretfully to the Duke of a first cousin of his own—not on the Guermantes side, but more illustrious still, were that possible—whose health, which had been in a grave condition for some time past, had grown suddenly worse. But it was evident that the Duke, while full of pity for his cousin's lot, and repeating "Poor Mama! He's such a good fellow!" had formed a favourable prognosis. The fact was that the dinner at which the Duke was to be present amused him, the big party at the Princesse de Guermantes's did not bore him, but above all he was to go on at one o'clock in the morning with his wife to a great supper and costume ball, for which a costume of Louis XI for himself, and one of Isabel of Bavaria for his wife were waiting in readiness. And the Duke was determined not to be disturbed amid all these gaieties by the sufferings of the worthy Amanien d'Osmond. Two

other ladies carrying canes, Mme. de Plassac and Mme. de Tres-
mes, both daughters of the Comte de Bréquigny, came in next to
pay Basin a visit, and declared that cousin Mama's state left no
room now for hope. The Duke shrugged his shoulders, and to
change the conversation asked whether they were going that evening to Marie-Gilbert's. They replied that they were not, in view
of the state of Amanien who was in his last agony, and indeed
they had excused themselves from the dinner to which the Duke
was going, the other guests at which they proceeded to enumerate: the brother of King Theodosius, the Infanta Maria Con-
cepcion, and so forth. As the Marquis d'Osmond was less nearly
related to them than he was to Basin, their "defection" appeared
to the Duke to be a sort of indirect reproach aimed at his own
conduct. And so, although they had come down from the heights
of the Bréquigny mansion to see the Duchess (or rather to announce to her the alarming character, incompatible for his relatives with attendance at social gatherings, of their cousin's illness)
they did not stay long, and, each armed with her alpenstock,
Walpurge and Dorothée (such were the names of the two sisters)
retraced the craggy path to their citadel. . . .

The Duke appeared touched that I should have come to see
him so soon after their return to Paris. But his face grew dark
when I told him that I had come to ask his wife whether her cousin
really had invited me. I had touched upon one of those services
which M. and Mme. de Guermantes were not fond of rendering.
The Duke explained to me that it was too late, that if the Princess
had not sent me an invitation it would make him appear to be
asking her for one, that his cousins had refused him one once before, and he had no wish to appear either directly or indirectly to
be interfering with their visiting list, be "meddling"; finally, he
could not even be sure that he and his wife, who were dining out
that evening, would not come straight home afterwards, that in
that case their best excuse for not having gone to the Princess's
party would be to conceal from her the fact of their return to Paris,
instead of hastening to inform her of it, as they must do if they
sent her a note, or spoke to her over the telephone about me, and
certainly too late to be of any use, since, in all probability, the
Princess's list of guests would be closed by now. "You've not
fallen foul of her in any way?" he asked in a suspicious tone, the
Guermantes living in a constant fear of not being informed of the
latest society quarrels, and so of people's trying to climb back into

favour on their shoulders. Finally, as the Duke was in the habit of taking upon himself all decisions that might seem not very amiable: "Listen, my boy," he said to me suddenly, as though the idea had just come into his head, "I would really rather not mention at all to Oriane that you have been speaking to me about it. You know how kind-hearted she is; besides, she has an enormous regard for you, she would insist on sending to ask her cousin, in spite of anything I might say to the contrary, and if she is tired after dinner, there will be no getting out of it, she will be forced to go to the party. No, decidedly, I shall say nothing to her about it. Anyhow, you will see her yourself in a minute. But not a word about that matter, I beg of you. If you decide to go to the party, I have no need to tell you what a pleasure it will be to us to spend the evening there with you." The motives actuating humanity are too sacred for him before whom they are invoked not to bow to them, whether he believes them to be sincere or not; I did not wish to appear to be weighing in the balance for a moment the relative importance of my invitation and the possible tiredness of Mme. de Guermantes, and I promised not to speak to her of the object of my visit, exactly as though I had been taken in by the little farce which M. de Guermantes had put on for my benefit. I asked him if he thought there was any chance of my seeing Mme. de Stermaria at the Princess's. "Why, no," he replied with the air of an expert; "I know the name you mention, from having seen it in lists of club members, it is not at all the type of person who goes to Gilbert's. You will see nobody there who is not excessively proper and intensely boring, duchesses bearing titles which one thought were extinct years ago and which they have revived for the occasion, all the Ambassadors, heaps of Coburgs, foreign royalties, but you mustn't hope for the ghost of a Stermaria. Gilbert would be taken ill at the mere thought of such a thing.

"Oh, say, you're fond of painting, I must shew you a superb picture I bought from my cousin, partly in exchange for the Elstirs,[1] which frankly did not appeal to us. It was sold to me as a Philippe de Champaigne, but I believe myself that it's by some one even greater. Would you like to know what I think? I believe it to be a Velazquez, and of the best period," said the Duke, looking me in the eyes, whether to learn my impression or in the hope of enhancing it. A footman came in.

[1 Elstir is a character in the novel, presented as the greatest painter of the time.]

"Mme. la Duchesse has told me to ask M. le Duc if M. le Duc will be so good as to see M. Swann, as Mme. la Duchesse is not quite ready." "Shew M. Swann in," said the Duke, after looking at his watch and seeing that he had still a few minutes before he need go to dress. "Naturally my wife, who told him to come, is not ready. There's no use saying anything before Swann about Marie-Gilbert's party," said the Duke. "I don't know whether he's been invited. Gilbert likes him immensely, because he believes him to be the natural grandson of the Duc de Berri, but that's a long story. (Otherwise, you can imagine! My cousin, who falls in a fit if he sees a Jew a mile off.) But now, don't you see, the Dreyfus case has made things more serious. Swann ought to have realised that he more than anyone must drop all connexion with those fellows, instead of which he says the most offensive things." The Duke called back the footman to know whether the man who had been sent to inquire at cousin Osmond's had returned. His plan was as follows: as he believed, and rightly, that his cousin was dying, he was anxious to obtain news of him before his death, that is to say before he was obliged to go into mourning. Once covered by the official certainty that Amanien was still alive, he could scamper off to his dinner, to the Prince's party, to the midnight revel at which he would appear as Louis XI, and had made the most exciting assignation with a new mistress, and would make no more inquiries until the following day, when his pleasures would be at an end. Then one would put on mourning if the cousin had passed away in the night. "No, M. le Duc, he is not back yet." "For God's sake! Nothing is ever done in this house till the last minute," cried the Duke, at the thought that Amanien might still be in time to 'croak' for an evening paper, and so make him miss his revel. He sent for the *Temps,* in which there was nothing.

I had not seen Swann for a long time, and wondered at first whether in the old days he used to clip his moustache, or had worn his hair cut short, for I found in him something altered; it was simply that he was indeed greatly 'altered' because he was very ill, and illness produces in the face modifications as profound as are created by growing a beard or by changing the line of one's parting. (Swann's illness was the same that had killed his mother, who had been attacked by it at precisely the age which he had now reached. Our existences are in truth, owing to heredity, as full of cabalistic ciphers, of horoscopic castings as if there really were sorcerers in the world. And just as there is a certain duration of life for humanity in general, so there is one for families in particular, that is to say, in any one family, for the members of it who resemble one another.) Swann was dressed with an elegance which, like that of his wife, associated with what he now was what he once had been. Buttoned up in a pearl-grey frockcoat which emphasised the tallness of his figure, slender, his white gloves stitched in black, he carried a grey top hat of a specially wide shape which Delion had ceased now to make except for him, the Prince de Sagan, the Marquis de Modène, the Baron de Charlus, M. Charles Haas and Comte Louis de Turenne. I was surprised at the charming smile and affectionate handclasp with which he replied to my greeting, for I had imagined that after so long an interval he would not recognise me at once; I told him of my astonishment; he received it with a shout of laughter, a trace of indignation and a further grip of my hand, as if it were throwing doubt on the soundness of his brain or the sincerity of his affection to suppose that he did not recognise me. And yet that was what had happened; he did not identify me, as I learned long afterwards, until several minutes later when he heard my name mentioned. But no change in his face, in his speech, in the things he said to me betrayed the discovery which a chance word from M. de Guermantes had enabled him to make, with such mastery, with such absolute sureness did he play the social game. He brought to it, moreover, that spontaneity in manners and personal initiative, even in his style of dress, which characterised the Guermantes type. Thus it was that the greeting which the old clubman, without recognising me, had given me was not the cold and stiff greeting of the man of the world who was a pure formalist, but a greeting full of a real friendliness, of a true charm, such as the Duchesse de Guermantes, for instance, possessed (going so far as to smile at you first, before you had bowed to her, if she met you in the street), in contrast to the more mechanical greeting customary among the ladies of the Faubourg Saint-Germain. In the same way, again, the hat which, in conformity with a custom that was beginning to disappear, he laid on the floor by his feet, was lined with green leather, a thing not usually done, because, according to him, this kept the hat much cleaner, in reality because it was highly becoming.

"Say, Charles, you're a great expert, come and see what I've got to shew you, after which, my boys, I'm going to ask your permission to leave you together for a moment while I go and change my clothes, besides, I expect Oriane won't be long now." And he shewed his "Velazquez" to Swann. "But it seems to me that I know this," said Swann with the grimace of a sick man for whom the mere act of speaking requires an effort. "Yes," said the Duke, turned serious by the time which the expert took in expressing his admiration. "You have probably seen it at Gilbert's."

"Oh, yes, of course, I remember."

"What do you suppose it is?"

"Oh, well, if it comes from Gilbert's, it is probably one of your *ancestors*," said Swann with a blend of irony and deference towards a form of greatness which he would have felt it impolite and absurd to despise, but to which for reasons of good taste he preferred to make only a playful reference.

"To be sure, it is," said the Duke bluntly. "It's Boson, the I forget how manieth de Guermantes. Not that I care a damn about that. You know I'm not as feudal as my cousin. I've heard the names mentioned of Rigaud, Mignard, Velazquez even!" he went on, fastening on Swann the gaze of an inquisitor and executioner in an attempt at once to read into his mind and to influence his response. "Well," he concluded, for when he was led to provoke artificially an opinion which he desired to hear, he had the faculty, after a few moments, of believing that it had been spontaneously uttered; "come, now, none of your flattery, do you think it's by one of those big masters I've mentioned?"

"Nnnnno," said Swann.

"But after all, I know nothing about these things, it's not for me to decide who daubed the canvas. But you're a dilettante, a master of the subject, to whom do you attribute it? You're enough of an expert to have some idea. What would you put it down as?"

Swann hesitated for a moment before the picture, which obviously he thought atrocious. "Sheer spite!" he replied, with a smile at the Duke who could not check an impulsive movement of rage. When this had subsided: "Be good fellows, both of you, wait a moment for Oriane, I must go and put on my swallow-tails and then I'll join you. I shall send word to my good woman that you're both waiting for her."

I talked for a minute or two with Swann about the Dreyfus case, and asked him how it was that all the Guermantes were anti-Dreyfusards. "In the first place because at heart all these people are anti-Semites," replied Swann, who, all the same, knew very well from experience that certain of them were not, but like everyone who supports any cause with ardour, preferred, to explain the fact that other people did not share his opinion, to suppose in them a preconceived reason, a prejudice against which there was nothing to be done, rather than reasons which might permit of discussion. Besides, having come to the premature term of his life, like a weary animal that is goaded on, he cried out against these persecutions and was returning to the spiritual fold of his fathers.

"Yes, the Prince de Guermantes," I said, "it is true, I've heard that he was antisemitic."

"Oh, that fellow! I wasn't even thinking about him. He carries it to such a point that when he was in the army and had a frightful toothache he preferred to grin and bear it rather than go to the only dentist in the district, who happened to be a Jew, and later on he allowed a wing of his castle which had caught fire to be burned to the ground, because he would have had to send for extinguishers to the place next door, which belongs to the Rothschilds."

"Are you going to be there this evening, by any chance?"

"Yes," Swann replied, "although I am far too tired. But he sent me a wire to tell me that he has something to say to me. I feel that I shall be too unwell in the next few days to go there or to see him at home; it would upset me, so I prefer to get it over at once."

"But the Duc de Guermantes is not anti-semitic?"

"You can see quite well that he is, since he's an anti-Dreyfusard," replied Swann, without noticing the logical fallacy. "That doesn't prevent my being very sorry that I disappointed the man— what am I saying? The Duke, I mean—by not admiring his Mignard or whatever he calls it."

"But at any rate," I went on, reverting to the Dreyfus case, "the Duchess, she, now, is intelligent."

"Yes, she is charming. To my mind, however, she was even more charming when she was still known as the Princesse des Laumes. Her mind has become somehow more angular, it was all much softer in the juvenile great lady, but after all, young or old, men or women, what can you expect, all these people belong to a different race, one can't have a thousand years of feudalism in one's blood with impunity. Naturally they imagine that it counts for nothing in their opinions." . . .

Dreyfusism had made Swann extraordinarily naïve and had imparted to his way of looking at things an impulsiveness, an inconsistency more noticeable even than had been the similar effects of his marriage to Odette; this new loss of caste would have been better described as a recasting, and was entirely to his credit, since it made him return to the ways in which his forebears had trodden and from which he had turned aside to mix with the aristocracy. But Swann, just at the very moment when with such lucidity it had been granted to him, thanks to the gifts he had inherited from his race, to perceive a truth that was still hidden from people of fashion, shewed himself quite comically blind. He subjected afresh all his admirations and all his contempts to the test of a new criterion, Dreyfusism. . . .

M. de Guermantes returned, and was presently joined by his wife, all ready now for the evening, tall and proud in a gown of red satin the skirt of which was bordered with spangles. She had in her hair a long ostrich feather dyed purple, and over her shoulder a tulle scarf of the same red as her dress. "How nice it is to have one's hat lined with leather," said the Duchess, whom nothing escaped. "However, with you, Charles, everything is always charming, whether it's what you wear or what you say, what you read or what you do." Swann meanwhile, without apparently listening, was considering the Duchess as he would have studied the canvas of a master, and then sought her gaze, making with his lips the grimace which implies: "The devil!" Mme. de Guermantes rippled with laughter. "So my clothes please you? I'm delighted. But I must say that they don't please me much," she went on with a sulking air. "Good Lord, what a bore it is to have to dress up and go out when one would ever so much rather stay at home!"

"What magnificent rubies!"

"Ah! my dear Charles, at least one can see that you know what you're talking about, you're not like that brute Monserfeuil who asked me if they were real. I must say that I've never seen anything quite like them. They were a present from the Grand Duchess. They're a little too large for my liking, a little too like claret glasses filled to the brim, but I've put them on because we shall be seeing the Grand Duchess this evening at Marie-Gilbert's," added Mme. de Guermantes, never suspecting that this assertion destroyed the force of those previously made by the Duke.

"What's on at the Princess's?" inquired Swann.

"Practically nothing," the Duke hastened to reply, the question having made him think that Swann was not invited.

"What's that, Basin? When all the highways and hedgerows have been scoured? It will be a deathly crush. What will be pretty, though," she went on, looking wistfully at Swann, "if the storm

I can feel in the air now doesn't break, will be those marvellous gardens. You know them, of course. I was there a month ago, at the time when the lilacs were in flower, you can't have any idea how lovely they were. And then the fountain, really, it's Versailles in Paris."

"What sort of person is the Princess?" I asked.

"Why, you know quite well, you've seen her here, she's as beautiful as the day, also rather an idiot. Very nice, in spite of all her Germanic high-and-mightiness, full of good nature and stupid."

Swann was too subtle not to perceive that the Duchess, in this speech, was trying to shew the "Guermantes wit," and at no great cost to herself, for she was only serving up in a less perfect form an old saying of her own. Nevertheless, to prove to the Duchess that he appreciated her intention to be, and as though she had really succeeded in being, funny, he smiled with a slightly forced air. . . .

"Come now, Oriane, what on earth are you saying?" broke in M. de Guermantes. "Marie a fool? Why, she has read everything, she's as musical as a fiddle."

"But, my poor little Basin, you're as innocent as a new-born babe. As if one could not be all that, and rather an idiot as well. Idiot is too strong a word; no, she's in the clouds, she's Hesse-Darmstadt, Holy Roman Empire, and wa-wa-wa. Her pronunciation alone makes me tired. But I quite admit that she's a charming loony. Simply the idea of stepping down from her German throne to go and marry, in the most middle-class way, a private citizen. It is true that she chose him! Yes, it's quite true," she went on, turning to me, "you don't know Gilbert. Let me give you an idea of him, he took to his bed once because I had left a card on Mme. Carnot.[2] . . . But, my little Charles," said the Duchess, changing the conversation when she saw that the story of the card left on the Carnots appeared to irritate M. de Guermantes, "you know, you've never sent me that photograph of our Knights of Rhodes, whom I've learned to love through you, and I am so anxious to make their acquaintance."

The Duke meanwhile had not taken his eyes from his wife's face. "Oriane, you might at least tell the story properly and not cut out half. I ought to explain," he corrected, addressing Swann, "that the British Ambassadress at that time, who was a very

[2 The wife of Sadi Carnot, President of the French Republic 1887-1894.]

worthy woman, but lived rather in the moon and was in the habit of making up these odd combinations, conceived the distinctly quaint idea of inviting us with the President and his wife. We were —Oriane herself was rather surprised, especially as the Ambassadress knew quite enough of the people we knew not to invite us, of all things, to so ill-assorted a gathering. There was a Minister there who is a swindler, however I pass over all that, we had not been warned in time, were caught in the trap, and, I'm bound to admit, all these people behaved most civilly to us. Only, once was enough. Mme. de Guermantes, who does not often do me the honour of consulting me, felt it incumbent upon her to leave a card in the course of the following week at the Elysée. Gilbert may perhaps have gone rather far in regarding it as a stain upon our name. But it must not be forgotten that, politics apart, M. Carnot, who for that matter filled his post quite adequately, was the grandson of a member of the Revolutionary Tribunal which caused the death of eleven of our people in a single day."

"In that case, Basin, why did you go every week to dine at Chantilly? The Duc d'Aumale was just as much the grandson of a member of the Revolutionary Tribunal, with this difference, that Carnot was a brave man and Philippe Egalité a wretched scoundrel."

"Excuse my interrupting you to explain that I did send the photograph," said Swann. "I can't understand how it hasn't reached you."

"It doesn't altogether surprise me," said the Duchess, "my servants tell me only what they think fit. They probably do not approve of the Order of Saint John." And she rang the bell.

"You, know, Oriane, that when I used to go to Chantilly it was without enthusiasm."

"Without enthusiasm, but with a nightshirt in a bag, in case the Prince asked you to stay, which for that matter he very rarely did, being a perfect cad like all the Orléans lot. Do you know who else are to be dining at Mme. de Saint-Euverte's?" Mme. de Guermantes asked her husband.

"Besides the people you know already, she's asked at the last moment King Theodosius's brother."

At these tidings the Duchess's features breathed contentment and her speech boredom. "Oh, good heavens, more princes!"

"But that one is well-mannered and intelligent," Swann suggested.

"Not altogether, though," replied the Duchess, apparently seeking for words that would give more novelty to the thought expressed. "Have you ever noticed with princes that the best-mannered among them are not really well-mannered? They must always have an opinion about everything. Then, as they have none of their own, they spend the first half of their lives asking us ours and the other half serving it up to us secondhand. They positively must be able to say that one piece has been well played and the next not so well. When there is no difference. Listen, this little Theodosius junior (I forget his name) asked me what one called an orchestral motif. I replied," said the Duchess, her eyes sparkling while a laugh broke from her beautiful red lips: " 'One calls it an orchestral motif.' I don't think he was any too well pleased, really. Oh, my dear Charles," she went on, "what a bore it can be, dining out. There are evenings when one would sooner die! It is true that dying may be perhaps just as great a bore, because we don't know what it's like."

A servant appeared. It was the young lover who used to have trouble with the porter, until the Duchess, in her kindness of heart, brought about an apparent peace between them.

"Am I to go up this evening to inquire for M. le Marquis d'Osmond?" he asked.

"Most certainly not, nothing before to-morrow morning. In fact I don't want you to remain in the house to-night. The only thing that will happen will be that his footman, who knows you, will come to you with the latest report and send you out after us. Get off, go anywhere you like, have a woman, sleep out, but I don't want to see you here before to-morrow morning."

An immense joy overflowed from the footman's face. He would at last be able to spend long hours with his ladylove, whom he had practically ceased to see ever since, after a final scene with the porter, the Duchess had considerately explained to him that it would be better, to avoid further conflicts, if he did not go out at all. He floated, at the thought of having an evening free at last, in a happiness which the Duchess saw and guessed its reason. She felt, so to speak, a tightening of the heart and an itching in all her limbs at the sight of this happiness which an amorous couple were snatching behind her back, concealing themselves from her, which left her irritated and jealous. "No, Basin, let him stay here; I say, he's not to stir out of the house."

"But, Oriane, that's absurd, the house is crammed with servants, and you have the costumer's people coming as well at twelve to dress us for this show. There's absolutely nothing for him to do, and he's the only one who's a friend of Mama's footman; I would a thousand times rather get him right away from the house."

"Listen, Basin, let me do what I want, I shall have a message for him to take in the evening, as it happens, I can't tell yet at what time. In any case you're not to go out of the house for a single instant, do you hear?" she said to the despairing footman.

If there were continual quarrels, and if servants did not stay long with the Duchess, the person to whose charge this guerrilla warfare was to be laid was indeed irremovable, but it was not the porter; no doubt for the rougher tasks, for the martyrdoms that it was more tiring to inflict, for the quarrels which ended in blows, the Duchess entrusted the heavier instruments to him; but even then he played his part without the least suspicion that he had been cast for it. Like the household servants, he admired the Duchess for her kindness of heart; and footmen of little discernment who came back, after leaving her service, to visit Françoise used to say that the Duke's house would have been the finest 'place' in Paris if it had not been for the porter's lodge. The Duchess 'played' the lodge on them, just as at different times clericalism, freemasonry, the Jewish peril have been played on the public. Another footman came into the room.

"Why have not they brought up the package that M. Swann sent here? And, by the way (you've heard, Charles, that Mama is seriously ill?), Jules went up to inquire for news of M. le Marquis d'Osmond: has he come back yet?"

"He's just come this instant, M. le Duc. They're waiting from one moment to the next for M. le Marquis to pass away."

"Ah! He's alive!" exclaimed the Duke with a sigh of relief. "That's all right, that's all right: sold again, Satan! While there's life there's hope," the Duke announced to us with a joyful air. "They've been talking about him as though he were dead and buried. In a week from now he'll be fitter than I am."

"It's the Doctors who said that he wouldn't last out the evening. One of them wanted to call again during the night. The head one said it was no use. M. le Marquis would be dead by then; they've only kept him alive by injecting him with camphorated oil."

"Hold your tongue, you damned fool," cried the Duke in a

paroxysm of rage. "Who the devil asked you to say all that? You haven't understood a word of what they told you."

"It wasn't me they told, it was Jules."

"Will you hold your tongue!" roared the Duke, and, turning to Swann, "What a blessing he's still alive! He will regain his strength gradually, don't you know. Still alive, after being in such a critical state, that in itself is an excellent sign. One mustn't expect everything at once. It can't be at all unpleasant, a little injection of camphorated oil." He rubbed his hands. "He's alive; what more could anyone want? After going through all that he's gone through, it's a great step forward. Upon my word, I envy him having such a temperament. Ah! these invalids, you know, people do all sorts of little things for them that they don't do for us. Now to-day there was a devil of a cook who sent me up a leg of mutton with *béarnaise* sauce—it was done to a turn, I must admit, but just for that very reason I took so much of it that it's still lying on my stomach. However, that doesn't make people come to inquire for me as they do for dear Amanien. We do too much inquiring. It only tires him. We must let him have room to breathe. They're killing the poor fellow by sending round to him all the time."

"Well," said the Duchess to the footman as he was leaving the room, "I gave orders for the envelope containing a photograph which M. Swann sent me to be brought up here."

"Madame la Duchesse, it is so large that I didn't know if I could get it through the door. We have left it in the hall. Does Madame la Duchesse wish me to bring it up?"

"Oh, in that case, no; they ought to have told me, but if it's so big I shall see it in a moment when I come downstairs."

"I forgot to tell Mme. la Duchesse that Mme. la Comtesse Molé left a card this morning for Mme. la Duchesse."

"What, this morning?" said the Duchess with an air of disapproval, feeling that so young a woman ought not to take the liberty of leaving cards in the morning.

"About ten o'clock, Mme. la Duchesse."

"Shew me the cards."

"In any case, Oriane, when you say that it was a funny idea on Marie's part to marry Gilbert," went on the Duke, reverting to the original topic of conversation, "it is you who have an odd way of writing history. If either of them was a fool, it was Gilbert, for having married of all people a woman so closely related to the King of the Belgians, who has usurped the name of Brabant which belongs to us. To put it briefly, we are of the same blood as the Hesses, and of the elder branch. It is always stupid to talk about oneself," he apologised to me, "but after all, whenever we have been not only at Darmstadt, but even at Cassel and all over Electoral Hesse, the Landgraves have always, all of them, been most courteous in giving us precedence as being of the elder branch."

"But really, Basin, you don't mean to tell me that a person who was a Major in every regiment in her country, who had been engaged to the King of Sweden . . ."

"Oriane, that is too much; anyone would think that you didn't know that the King of Sweden's grandfather was tilling the soil at Pau when we had been ruling the roost for nine hundred years throughout the whole of Euorpe."

"That doesn't alter the fact that if somebody were to say in the street: 'Hallo, there's the King of Sweden,' everyone would at once rush to see him as far as the Place de la Concorde, and if he said: 'There's M. de Guermantes,' nobody would know who M. de Guermantes was."

"What an argument!"

"Besides, I never can understand how, once the title of Duke of Brabant has passed to the Belgian Royal Family, you can continue to claim it."

The footman returned with the Comtesse Molé's card, or rather what she had left in place of a card. Alleging that she had none on her, she had taken from her pocket a letter addressed to herself, and keeping the contents had handed in the envelope which bore the inscription: 'La Comtesse Molé.' As the envelope was rather large, following the fashion in notepaper which prevailed that year, this manuscript 'card' was almost twice the size of an ordinary visiting card.

"That is what people call Mme. Molé's 'simplicity,' " said the Duchess ironically. "She wants to make us think that she had no cards on her, and to shew her originality. But we know all about that, don't we, my little Charles, we are quite old enough and quite original enough ourselves to see through the tricks of a little lady who has only been going about for four years. She is charming, but she doesn't seem to me, all the same, to be quite 'big' enough to imagine that she can take the world by surprise with so little effort as merely leaving an envelope instead of a card and leaving it at ten o'clock in the morning. Her old mother mouse will shew her that she knows a thing or two about that." Swann could not help smiling at the thought that the Duchess, who was, incidentally, a trifle jealous of Mme. Molé's success, would find it quite in accordance with the "Guermantes wit" to make some impertinent retort to her visitor.

"So far as the title of Duc de Brabant is concerned, I've told you a hundred times, Oriane . . ." the Duke continued, but the Duchess, without listening, cut him short.

"But, my little Charles, I'm longing to see your photograph. . . ." "Listen, Charles, let us wait downstairs till the carriage comes," said the Duke; "you can pay your call on us in the hall, because my wife won't let us have any peace until she's seen your photograph. I am less impatient, I must say," he added with a satisfied air. "I am not easily moved myself, but she would see us all dead rather than miss it."

"I am entirely of your opinion, Basin," said the Duchess, "let us go into the hall; we shall at least know why we have come down from your study, while we shall never know how we have come down from the Counts of Brabant."

"I've told you a hundred times how the title came into the House of Hesse," said the Duke (while we were going downstairs to look at the photograph, and I thought of those that Swann used to bring me at Combray), "through the marriage of a Brabant in 1241 with the daughter of the last Landgrave of Thuringia and Hesse, so that really it is the title of Prince of Hesse that came to the House of Brabant rather than that of Duke of Brabant to the House of Hesse. You will remember that our battle-cry was that of the Dukes of Brabant: 'Limbourg to her conqueror!' until we exchanged the arms of Brabant for those of Guermantes, in which I think myself that we were wrong, and the example of the Gramonts will not make me change my opinion."

"But," replied Mme. de Guermantes, "as it is the King of the Belgians who is the conqueror . . . Besides the Belgian Crown Prince calls himself Duc de Brabant."

"But, my dear child, your argument will not hold water for a moment. You know as well as I do that there are titles of pretension which can perfectly well exist even if the territory is occupied by usurpers. For instance, the King of Spain describes himself equally as Duke of Brabant, claiming in virtue of a possession less ancient than ours, but more ancient than that of the King of the

Belgians. He calls himself also Duke of Burgundy, King of the Indies Occidental and Oriental, and Duke of Milan. Well, he is no more in possession of Burgundy, the Indies or Brabant than I possess Brabant myself, or the Prince of Hesse either, for that matter. The King of Spain likewise proclaims himself King of Jerusalem, as does the Austrian Emperor, and Jerusalem belongs to neither one nor the other."

He stopped for a moment with an awkward feeling that the mention of Jerusalem might have embarrassed Swann, in view of "current events," but only went on more rapidly: "What you said just now might be said of anyone. We were at one time Dukes of Aumale, a duchy that has passed as regularly to the House of France as Joinville and Chevreuse have to the House of Albert. We make no more claim to those titles than to that of Marquis de Noirmoutiers, which was at one time ours, and became perfectly regularly the appanage of the House of La Trémoïlle, but because certain cessions are valid, it does not follow that they all are. For instance," he went on, turning to me, "my sister-in-law's son bears the title of Prince d'Agrigente, which comes to us from Joan the Mad, as that of Prince of Taranto comes to the La Trémoïlles. Well, Napoleon went and gave this title of Taranto to a soldier, who may have been admirable in the ranks, but in doing so the Emperor was disposing of what belonged to him even less than Napoleon III when he created a Duc de Montmorency, since Périgord had at least a mother who was a Montmorency, while the Taranto of Napoleon I had no more Taranto about him than Napoleon's wish that he should become so. That did not prevent Chaix d'Este-Ange, alluding to our uncle Condé, from asking the Procurer Impérial if he had picked up the title of Duc de Montmorency in the moat of Vincennes."[3]

"Listen, Basin, I ask for nothing better than to follow you to the ditches of Vincennes, or even to Taranto. And that reminds me, Charles, of what I was going to say to you when you were telling me about your Saint George at Venice. We have an idea, Basin and I, of spending next spring in Italy and Sicily. If you were to come with us, just think what a difference it would make! I'm not thinking only of the pleasure of seeing you, but imagine, after all you've told me so often about the remains of the Norman Conquest and of ancient history, imagine what a trip like that

[3 The Duc d'Enghien, last of the house of Condé, was executed by Napoleon's orders (1804) in the moat of the castle of Vincennes.]

would become if you came with us! I mean to say that even Basin—what am I saying, Gilbert—would benefit by it, because I feel that even his claims to the throne of Naples and all that sort of thing would interest me if they were explained by you in old romanesque churches in little villages perched on hills like primitive paintings. But now we're going to look at your photograph. Open the envelope," said the Duchess to a footman.

"Please, Oriane, not this evening; you can look at it to-morrow," implored the Duke, who had already been making signs of alarm to me on seeing the huge size of the photograph.

"But I like to look at it with Charles," said the Duchess, with a smile at once artificially concupiscent and psychologically subtle, for in her desire to be friendly to Swann she spoke of the pleasure which she would have in looking at the photograph as though it were the pleasure an invalid feels he would find in eating an orange, or as though she had managed to combine an escapade with her friends with giving information to a biographer as to some of her favourite pursuits.

"All right, he will come again to see you, on purpose," declared the Duke, to whom his wife was obliged to yield. "You can spend three hours in front of it, if that amuses you," he added ironically. "But where are you going to stick a toy of those dimensions?"

"Why, in my room, of course. I like to have it before my eyes."

"Oh, just as you please; if it's in your room, probably I shall never see it," said the Duke, without thinking of the revelation he was thus blindly making of the negative character of his conjugal relations.

"Very well, you will undo it with the greatest care," Mme. de Guermantes told the servant, multiplying her instructions out of politeness to Swann. "And see that you don't crumple the envelope, either." "So even the envelope has got to be respected!" the Duke murmured to me, raising his eyes to the ceiling. "But, Swann," he added, "I, who am only a poor married man and thoroughly prosaic, what I wonder at is how on earth you managed to find an envelope that size. Where did you pick it up?"

"Oh, at the photographer's; they're always sending out things like that. But the man is a fool, for I see he's written on it 'The Duchesse de Guermantes,' without putting 'Madame.' "

"I'll forgive him for that," said the Duchess carelessly; then, seeming to be struck by a sudden idea which enlivened her, checked a faint smile; but at once returning to Swann: "Well, you don't say whether you're coming to Italy with us?"

"Madame, I am really afraid that it will not be possible."

"Indeed! Mme. de Montmorency is more fortunate. You went with her to Venice and Vicenza. She told me that with you one saw things one would never see otherwise, things no one had ever thought of mentioning before, that you shewed her things she had never dreamed of, and that even in the well-known things she had been able to appreciate details which without you she might have passed by a dozen times without ever noticing. Obviously, she has been more highly favoured than we are to be. . . . You will take the big envelope from M. Swann's photograph," she said to the servant, "and you will hand it in, from me, this evening at half past ten at Mme. la Comtesse Molé's."

Swann roared with laughter.

"I should like to know, all the same," Mme. de Guermantes asked him, "how, ten months before the time, you can tell that a thing will be impossible."

"My dear Duchess, I will tell you if you insist upon it, but, first of all, you can see that I am very ill."

"Yes, my little Charles, I don't think you look at all well. I'm not pleased with your colour, but I'm not asking you to come with me next week, I ask you to come in ten months. In ten months one has time to get oneself cured, you know."

At this point a footman came in to say that the carriage was at the door. "Come, Oriane, to horse," said the Duke, already pawing the ground with impatience as though he were himself one of the horses that stood waiting outside.

"Very well, give mc in one word the reason why you can't come to Italy," the Duchess put it to Swann as she rose to say good-bye to us.

"But, my dear friend, it's because I shall then have been dead for several months. According to the doctors I consulted last winter, the thing I've got—which may, for that matter, carry me off at any moment—won't in any case leave me more than three or four months to live, and even that is a generous estimate," replied Swann with a smile, while the footman opened the glazed door of the hall to let the Duchess out.

"What's that you say?" cried the Duchess, stopping for a moment on her way to the carriage, and raising her fine eyes, their melancholy blue clouded by uncertainty. Placed for the first time in her life between two duties as incompatible as getting into her carriage to go out to dinner and shewing pity for a man who was about to die, she could find nothing in the code of conventions that indicated the right line to follow, and, not knowing which to choose, felt it better to make a show of not believing that the latter alternative need be seriously considered, so as to follow the first, which demanded of her at the moment less effort, and thought that the best way of settling the conflict would be to deny that any existed. "You're joking," she said to Swann.

"It would be a joke in charming taste," he replied ironically. "I don't know why I am telling you this; I have never said a word to you before about my illness. But as you asked me, and as now I may die at any moment . . . But whatever I do I mustn't make you late; you're dining out, remember," he added, because he knew that for other people their own social obligations took precedence of the death of a friend, and could put himself in her place by dint of his instinctive politeness. But that of the Duchess enabled her also to perceive in a vague way that the dinner to which she was going must count for less to Swann than his own death. And so, while continuing on her way towards the carriage, she let her shoulders droop, saying: "Don't worry about our dinner. It's not of any importance!" But this put the Duke in a bad humour, who exclaimed: "Come, Oriane, don't stop there chattering like that and exchanging your jeremiads with Swann; you know very well that Mme. de Saint-Euverte insists on sitting down to table at eight o'clock sharp. We must know what you propose to do; the horses have been waiting for a good five minutes. I beg your pardon, Charles," he went on, turning to Swann, "but it's ten minutes to eight already. Oriane is always late, and it will take us more than five minutes to get to old Saint-Euverte's."

Mme. de Guermantes advanced resolutely towards the carriage and uttered a last farewell to Swann. "You know, we can talk about that another time; I don't believe a word you've been saying, but we must discuss it quietly. I expect they gave you a dreadful fright, come to luncheon, whatever day you like" (with Mme. de Guermantes things always resolved themselves into luncheons), "you will let me know your day and time," and, lifting her red skirt, she set her foot on the step. She was just getting into the carriage when, seeing this foot exposed, the Duke cried in a terrifying voice: "Oriane, what have you been thinking of, you wretch? You've kept on your black shoes! With a red dress! Go upstairs quick and put on red shoes, or rather," he said to the footman, "tell the lady's maid at once to bring down a pair of red shoes."

"But, my dear," replied the Duchess gently, annoyed to see that Swann, who was leaving the house with me but had stood back to allow the carriage to pass out in front of us, could hear, "since we are late."

"No, no, we have plenty of time. It is only ten to; it won't take us ten minutes to get to the Parc Monceau. And, after all, what would it matter? If we turned up at half past eight they'd have to wait for us, but you can't possibly go there in a red dress and black shoes. Besides, we shan't be the last, I can tell you; the Sassenages are coming, and you know they never arrive before twenty to nine."

The Duchess went up to her room.

"Well," said M. de Guermantes to Swann and myself, "we poor, down-trodden husbands, people laugh at us, but we are of some use all the same. But for me, Oriane would have been going out to dinner in black shoes."

"It's not unbecoming," said Swann. "I noticed the black shoes and they didn't offend me in the least."

"I don't say you're wrong," replied the Duke, "but it looks better to have them to match the dress. Besides, you needn't worry, she would no sooner have got there than she'd have noticed them, and I should have been obliged to come home and fetch the others. I should have had my dinner at nine o'clock. Good-bye, my children," he said, thrusting us gently from the door, "get away, before Oriane comes down again. It's not that she doesn't like seeing you both. On the contrary, she's too fond of your company. If she finds you still here she will start talking again, she is tired out already, she'll reach the dinner-table quite dead. Besides, I tell you frankly, I'm dying of hunger. I had a wretched luncheon this morning when I came from the train. There was the devil of a *béarnaise* sauce, I admit, but in spite of that I shan't be at all sorry, not at all sorry to sit down to dinner. Five minutes to eight! Oh, women, women! She'll give us both indigestion before to-morrow. She is not nearly as strong as people think."

The Duke felt no compunction at speaking thus of his wife's ailments and his own to a dying man, for the former interested him more, appeared to him more important. And so it was simply from good breeding and good fellowship that, after politely shewing us out, he cried "from off stage," in a stentorian voice from the porch to Swann, who was already in the courtyard: "You, now, don't let yourself be taken in by the doctors' nonsense, damn them. They're donkeys. You're as strong as the Pont Neuf. You'll live to bury us all!"

AFTERWORD

The late Jean Cocteau, himself an inventive novelist, though not among the great, once compared the novelist's art to that of the marksman. He credited Balzac and Stendhal with hitting the bull's-eye nine times out of ten, but warned his readers to watch out for Proust, who "will make a thousand bull's-eyes while you think he is just raising the gun to his shoulder." Proust makes a score of them in the episode of the Duchess's red shoes, which is an outstanding example of his talent as a social satirist.

His method can be illuminated by the comparisons that Cocteau has chosen. Balzac and Stendhal were recognized as predecessors by Proust himself, and he pays tribute to both in the course of his work. Both were critics of the ruling classes in their own society. Though by different methods, both created great enduring characters that live in their own right. Stendhal in particular was a pioneer in the psychological novel, a medium in which Proust was to excel. But although one can single out passages in Proust that have a Balzacian or a Stendhalian flavor, his essential technique owes nothing to either man.

Like most other novelists, Balzac and Stendhal both employ what may be called a "linear" method of narration: a point or dot, so to speak, moves in a given direction, tracing a line that is the course of the story. But the Proustian narration might be called "spherical"; the dot, instead of moving, grows in all directions at once, so that it becomes a globe. Professor Germaine Brée has another comparison: she says that the development of Proust's novel is like the growth of a tree. (Incidentally, this allows her to answer the question whether the novel was actually "finished" when Proust died by asking another question: "When is a tree finished?")

As for methods of creating characters, Stendhal was guided for the most part by his shrewd, uncompromising intelligence. He explored the contradictions of men's hearts and minds as they had never been explored before. Balzac's characters were chiefly products of his vast exuberance. They were generally of heroic stature, but more or less roughly hewn out of one piece. Père Goriot is "the soul of" paternal love, just as Baron Hulot is the soul of lechery and old Grandet (see the selection in the present volume) is the soul of avarice. Proust is as far from the intellectualism of Stendhal as from the physical exuberance of Balzac. Although he does not at all reject the role of the intelligence, he arrives at an understanding of his characters by means of a deeply cultivated intuition. Even those we barely glimpse impress us with their complexity. The narrator himself does not claim to know all their facets. What his readers truly know of them is that they are as unknowable as we ourselves and that—like the Duke de Guermantes in the present episode (as in the rest of the novel)—they can be intelligent and stupid, gentle and cruel, selfish and generous, either alternately or in the same instant.

R. G.

A Portrait of the Artist
as a Young Man (1916)

JAMES JOYCE (1882-1941), born in a Dublin suburb, was the oldest of ten surviving children; still others had been stillborn or had died as infants. His mother was a good woman and a pious Catholic who held the family together in the midst of poverty, lice, and disarray. His father, John Stanislaus Joyce, was the dead spit and image of Mr. Micawber. Speaking as Stephen Dedalus, in *A Portrait of the Artist*, the son says of him that he was "A medical student, an oarsman, a tenor, an amateur actor, a shouting politician, a small landlord, a small investor, a drinker, a good fellow, a storyteller, somebody's secretary, something in a distillery, a taxgatherer, a bankrupt and at present a praiser of his own past." But the old reprobate was also a lover and praiser of his eldest son, and he wanted James to have the best education available to an Irish boy, namely, that offered by the Jesuits.

Joyce was only "half-past six," as he told his schoolmates, when he was sent as a boarder to Clongowes Wood College. He rose to the head of his class in that Jesuit school, but he had to be withdrawn from it in 1891 because John Stanislaus was on the point of losing his political sinecure in the Rates office. For more than a year the boy attended a Christian Brothers' school with children of the working class, an interlude omitted from *A Portrait*; then in 1893 he was given free tuition at Belvedere College, a Jesuit day school in Dublin. He remained there until he was graduated in 1898, once again making a brilliant academic record. He then entered University College, Dublin, another Jesuit institution and part of the Royal University. There his academic record was indifferent, but he distinguished himself by his early writing, his contentiousness, and his gift for languages. He learned Norwegian in order to read Ibsen in the original, and his first published essay, on "Ibsen's New Drama," appeared in the *Fortnightly Review* (1900). Shortly after taking his degree in the autumn of 1902, he went to Paris to study medicine.

All this is the objective background of his first twenty years, the story of which is presented subjectively in *A Portrait of the Artist.*

In Paris Joyce soon abandoned the study of medicine and began writing book reviews for a Dublin newspaper. Summoned home in the spring of 1903 by his mother's last illness—she was to die in August at the age of forty-four—he stayed in Dublin until the autumn of the following year. At this time, besides writing lyric poems, he started work on *Dubliners* and *A Portrait.* It was during the great days of the Irish literary revival, and Joyce had managed to meet most of its leaders: Yeats, Synge, Russell (AE), and Lady Gregory among others. They agreed among themselves that he was an insufferable young genius, and some of them were notably kind to him. On what was afterward to be known as Bloomsday—June 16, 1904, the date of all the events related in the 768 pages of *Ulysses*—he went out walking with Nora Barnacle. She was the tall, pert, laughing, auburn-curled, completely ignorant, but sharp-witted chambermaid from Galway with whom Joyce was to spend the rest of his life.

They left Ireland in October of that same year, traveling without money or marriage lines. Joyce obtained a position teaching English in the Berlitz School at Pola, the Austrian naval base on the Adriatic. In 1905 he moved to the Berlitz School in Trieste, a polylingual city where he was to spend most of the following ten years, though his residence there was interrupted by three visits to Dublin and a year in Rome. Poor and spendthrift, he supported himself and Nora—and soon their two children—by giving English lessons to private pupils and by displaying even more than his father's gift for borrowing money. In those same years, however, he finished his first four books—the last of them was a play, *Exiles* (1918)—and started work on *Ulysses.*

Only the first book, *Chamber Music* (1907), a collection of lyric poems, was published without incidents. *Dubliners*, an integrated group of stories, had a fantastic publishing history. In February 1906, it was accepted by the London house of Grant Richards; then there were arguments about the seemliness of Joyce's language, and the manuscript came back in September. For the next three years it made the rounds of

English publishers. In 1909 it was accepted by Maunsel and Company in Dublin, but the manager of the house found all sorts of excuses for not bringing it out. In 1912 Joyce made a trip to Dublin and pleaded for release of the book, which by then had been printed. He even offered to buy the sheets and have them bound, but the printer, calling the book unpatriotic, had all the stock destroyed. In 1913 Grant Richards changed his mind and asked to see the manuscript again. Ezra Pound had entered the scene and was writing furious letters and articles in praise of Joyce. *Dubliners* finally appeared in June 1914, after a delay of more than eight years.

A *Portrait of the Artist* also had a complicated history, but this time the difficulties were even more in the writing than in the publishing. The book started as an essay rejected by the editors of a new magazine; "I can't print what I can't understand," said one of them, John Eglinton. Joyce decided to expand the essay into a novel that would be read by his own generation as a call to arms. It was to be autobiographical, realistic, rich in episodes, and he planned to give it the ironic title of *Stephen Hero*. By 1906 he had nearly a thousand pages of manuscript, but he stuck fast in the middle of Chapter 26 and laid the project aside. When he came back to it the following year, it was with the plan of writing the shorter, more concentrated, more subjective book that we have today. This too moved slowly, however, and might have been abandoned in its turn were it not for the enthusiasm of Ezra Pound. After Pound had arranged for serial publication in a little English magazine, the *Egoist*, edited by Harriet Weaver, Joyce felt obliged to keep abreast of the printer. *A Portrait* was finished in the spring of 1915—not in 1914, the date Joyce placed on the last page—and, after being rejected by several English houses, it was published in New York (1916) by B. W. Huebsch, who was to remain on friendly terms with Joyce till the end. As for the big unfinished manuscript of *Stephen Hero*, Joyce destroyed most of it, but he saved out ten or eleven chapters and these were published after his death.

Trieste during the war years was still part of the Austrian Empire. In 1915 Joyce moved to neutral Zurich, and there he continued work on *Ulysses* while giving English lessons to support his family. Soon he was receiving subsidies from a series of remarkable women. Edith Rockefeller McCormick was the first of these; she gave him a monthly allowance, but stopped it in 1919 when he refused to let himself be psychoanalyzed by Carl Jung. Harriet Weaver came to his rescue with a considerable gift; she was later to help him at other crises. "Her benefaction did not make Joyce rich," says his biographer Richard Ellmann; "no amount of money could have done that; but it made it possible for him to be poor only through determined extravagance."

In July 1920, at the insistence of Ezra Pound, he went to Paris for a week's visit; he was to stay there for nineteen years. He made some trips to other countries, but, after the printed stock of *Dubliners* was destroyed, he would never go back to Ireland. On a visit to London in 1931, he was married to Nora at the Registry Office; he signed his name as James Augustine Aloysius Joyce. In Paris he spent the first two years rounding out *Ulysses*, with its eighteen chapters each restating an episode from the *Odyssey* in terms of Dublin life on Bloomsday. The chapters had been appearing serially in the *Little Review*, but the magazine was suppressed by the American postal authorities after the issue of October 1920. No English printer dared to set the work in type. Finally it was published in Paris by another remarkable woman, Sylvia Beach, who owned an American bookstore on the Left Bank. The first copies reached Joyce on his fortieth birthday, February 2, 1922.

By this time he was a world figure revered by younger writers, and everybody wondered what his next book would be. It was already planned, and sections of it were to appear during the interwar years under the general title of "Work in Progress." Gradually Joyce revealed that the book was to represent one-third of human existence, the sleeping third, and that it was to embody what Jung had called the racial unconscious. As for the style, in which words from several languages are broken apart and recomposed, "It's pure music," Joyce said. The final title, *Finnegans Wake*, was kept a secret until the book was published in 1939.

It was Joyce's last undertaking. World War II drove him out of Paris, and he spent a year in the south of France. In December 1940 the family again sought refuge in Zurich, but Joyce was already ill and he died the following month.

THE STORY

There are five chapters in *A Portrait of the Artist as a Young Man*. The first of them takes us through the early boyhood of the hero, Stephen Dedalus, in a series of scenes. Stephen is bright, weak-eyed, and sensitive, and he feels his isolation from the world of his schoolmates. The chapter ends with his being whipped by the sadistic Father Dolan for breaking his glasses, then making his way to the Rector to demand exoneration. As for the name Dedalus, it is that of the great artificer who went to Crete and designed the labyrinth for the dreaded Minotaur. Imprisoned by King Minos, he made wings for himself and for his son Icarus. Dedalus escaped on them to Sicily, but Icarus flew too close to the sun, the wax on his wings melted, and he fell into the sea. Stephen identifies himself sometimes with the father and sometimes with the son.

Chapter 2 takes us through Stephen's sixteenth year. Exhorted by everyone to be a good son, a good patriot, a good Catholic, and a good athlete, he falls into increasing doubts. The end of the chapter is his first sexual experience, with a Dublin prostitute. Chapter 3 is devoted to Stephen's repentance. During a retreat in honor of St. Francis Xavier, founder of the Jesuit order, Father Arnall preaches a series of sermons each of which is more terrifying to the boy, now convinced of his utter sinfulness. In one sermon the preacher tells of Lucifer's defiantly saying *"Non serviam"*—"I will not serve," a motto that Stephen himself will take over at the end of the book. After a nightmare, Stephen goes to confessional and feels the sense of a whole new life, "of grace and virtue and happiness."

Chapter 4 begins with Stephen in a state of grace. After a scene with the director of the school, who suggests that he might have a vocation for the priesthood, he goes home and is appalled by the "disorder, the misrule and confusion of his father's house." The breaking of his ties with family, church, and nation, then his rebirth as a priest of art, are suggested in a famous scene at the seashore that ends the chapter. In Chapter 5, Stephen propounds his theories of art to his bemused companions at the university. He sees his beloved, then wakes before dawn to address her in an ecstatic poem. (It is not a very good poem, and it has led to a critical controversy about whether Joyce intended to portray the hero as a potentially great artist or as a confused and posturing young man.) Later he confesses himself to his friend Cranly and says that the tools he will use are "silence, exile, and cunning." The last few pages of the book are extracts from a journal that Stephen keeps before he leaves for France, and the last words are an apostrophe to his namesake: "Old father, old artificer, stand me now and ever in good stead."

The scene that follows is the end of Chapter 4 and marks the climax of the book (with Chapter 5 as a long epilogue). The text is that of the Viking Compass edition, which was corrected (1964) from the Joyce papers by Chester G. Anderson and edited by Richard Ellmann.

[*The Birth of an Artist*]

He could wait no longer.

From the door of Byron's publichouse to the gate of Clontarf Chapel, from the gate of Clontarf Chapel to the door of Byron's publichouse and then back again to the chapel and then back again to the publichouse he had paced slowly at first, planting his steps scrupulously in the spaces of the patchwork of the footpath, then timing their fall to the fall of verses. A full hour had passed since his father had gone in with Dan Crosby, the tutor, to find out for him something about the university. For a full hour he had paced up and down, waiting: but he could wait no longer.

He set off abruptly for the Bull, walking rapidly lest his father's shrill whistle might call him back; and in a few moments he had rounded the curve at the police barrack and was safe.

Yes, his mother was hostile to the idea, as he had read from her listless silence. Yet her mistrust pricked him more keenly than his father's pride and he thought coldly how he had watched the faith which was fading down in his soul aging and strengthening in her eyes. A dim antagonism gathered force within him and darkened his mind as a cloud against her disloyalty: and when it passed, cloudlike, leaving his mind serene and dutiful towards her again, he was made aware dimly and without regret of a first noiseless sundering of their lives.

The university! So he had passed beyond the challenge of the sentries who had stood as guardians of his boyhood and had sought to keep him among them that he might be subject to them and serve their ends. Pride after satisfaction uplifted him like long slow waves. The end he had been born to serve yet did not see had led him to escape by an unseen path: and now it beckoned to him once more and a new adventure was about to be opened to him. It seemed to him that he heard notes of fitful music leaping upwards a tone and downwards a diminished fourth, upwards a tone and downwards a major third, like triplebranching flames leaping fitfully, flame after flame, out of a midnight wood. It was an elfin prelude, endless and formless; and, as it grew wilder and faster, the flames leaping out of time, he seemed to hear from under the boughs and grasses wild creatures racing, their feet pattering like rain upon the leaves. Their feet passed in pattering tumult over his mind, the feet of hares and rabbits, the feet of harts and hinds and antelopes, until he heard them no more and remembered only a proud cadence from Newman: *Whose feet are as the feet of harts and underneath the everlasting arms.*

The pride of that dim image brought back to his mind the dignity of the office he had refused. All through his boyhood he had mused upon that which he had so often thought to be his destiny and when the moment had come for him to obey the call he had turned aside, obeying a wayward instinct. Now time lay between: the oils of ordination would never anoint his body. He had refused. Why?

He turned seaward from the road at Dollymount and as he passed on to the thin wooden bridge he felt the planks shaking with the tramp of heavily shod feet. A squad of christian brothers was on its way back from the Bull and had begun to pass, two by two, across the bridge. Soon the whole bridge was trembling and resounding. The uncouth faces passed him two by two, stained yellow or red or livid by the sea, and as he strove to look at them with ease and indifference, a faint stain of personal shame and commiseration rose to his own face. Angry with himself he tried to hide his face from their eyes by gazing down sideways into the shallow swirling water under the bridge but he still saw a reflection therein of their topheavy silk hats, and humble tapelike collars and loosely hanging clerical clothes.

—Brother Hickey.

Brother Quaid.

Brother MacArdle.

Brother Keogh.

Their piety would be like their names, like their faces, like their clothes, and it was idle for him to tell himself that their humble and contrite hearts, it might be, paid a far richer tribute of devotion than his had ever been, a gift tenfold more acceptable than his elaborate adoration. It was idle for him to move himself to be generous towards them, to tell himself that if he ever came to their gates, stripped of his pride, beaten and in beggar's weeds, that they would be generous towards him, loving him as themselves. Idle and embittering, finally, to argue, against his own dispassionate certitude, that the commandment of love bade us not to love our neighbour as ourselves with the same amount and intensity of love but to love him as ourselves with the same kind of love.

He drew forth a phrase from his treasure and spoke it softly to himself:

—A day of dappled seaborne clouds.

The phrase and the day and the scene harmonised in a chord. Words. Was it their colours? He allowed them to glow and fade, hue after hue: sunrise gold, the russet and green of apple orchards, azure of waves, the greyfringed fleece of clouds. No, it was not their colours: it was the poise and balance of the period itself. Did he then love the rhythmic rise and fall of words better than their associations of legend and colour? Or was it that, being as weak of sight as he was shy of mind, he drew less pleasure from the reflection of the glowing sensible world through the prism of a language manycoloured and richly storied than from the contemplation of an inner world of individual emotions mirrored perfectly in a lucid supple periodic prose?

He passed from the trembling bridge on to firm land again. At that instant, as it seemed to him, the air was chilled and looking askance towards the water he saw a flying squall darkening and crisping suddenly the tide. A faint click at his heart, a faint throb in his throat told him once more of how his flesh dreaded the cold infrahuman odour of the sea: yet he did not strike across the downs on his left but held straight on along the spine of rocks that pointed against the river's mouth.

A veiled sunlight lit up faintly the grey sheet of water where the river was embayed. In the distance along the course of the slow-flowing Liffey slender masts flecked the sky and, more distant still, the dim fabric of the city lay prone in haze. Like a scene on some vague arras, old as man's weariness, the image of the seventh city of christendom was visible to him across the timeless air, no older nor more weary nor less patient of subjection than in the days of the thingmote.

Disheartened, he raised his eyes towards the slowdrifting clouds, dappled and seaborne. They were voyaging across the deserts of the sky, a host of nomads on the march, voyaging high over Ireland, westward bound. The Europe they had come from lay out there beyond the Irish Sea, Europe of strange tongues and valleyed and woodbegirt and citadelled and of entrenched and marshalled races. He heard a confused music within him as of memories and names which he was almost conscious of but could not capture even for an instant; then the music seemed to recede, to recede, to recede: and from each receding trail of nebulous

music there fell always one longdrawn calling note, piercing like
a star the dusk of silence. Again! Again! Again! A voice from beyond the world was calling.

—Hello, Stephanos!

—Here comes The Dedalus!

—Ao! . . . Eh, give it over, Dwyer, I'm telling you or I'll give
you a stuff in the kisser for yourself. . . . Ao!

—Good man, Towser! Duck him!

—Come along, Dedalus! Bous Stephanoumenos! Bous Stephaneforos!

—Duck him! Guzzle him now, Towser!

—Help! Help! . . . Ao!

He recognised their speech collectively before he distinguished
their faces. The mere sight of that medley of wet nakedness chilled
him to the bone. Their bodies, corpsewhite or suffused with a
pallid golden light or rawly tanned by the suns, gleamed with the
wet of the sea. Their divingstone, poised on its rude supports and
rocking under their plunges, and the roughhewn stones of the
sloping breakwater over which they scrambled in their horseplay,
gleamed with cold wet lustre. The towels with which they smacked
their bodies were heavy with cold seawater: and drenched with
cold brine was their matted hair.

He stood still in deference to their calls and parried their banter
with easy words. How characterless they looked: Shuley without
his deep unbuttoned collar, Ennis without his scarlet belt with the
snaky clasp, and Connolly without his Norfolk coat with the flap-
less sidepockets! It was a pain to see them and a swordlike pain
to see the signs of adolescence that made repellent their pitiable
nakedness. Perhaps they had taken refuge in number and noise
from the secret dread in their souls. But he, apart from them and
in silence, remembered in what dread he stood of the mystery of his
own body.

—Stephanos Dedalos! Bous Stephanoumenos! Bous Stephaneforos!

Their banter was not new to him and now it flattered his mild
proud sovereignty. Now, as never before, his strange name seemed
to him a prophecy. So timeless seemed the grey warm air, so fluid
and impersonal his own mood, that all ages were as one to him.
A moment before the ghost of the ancient kingdom of the Danes
had looked forth through the vesture of the hazewrapped city.
Now, at the name of the fabulous artificer, he seemed to hear

the noise of dim waves and to see a winged form flying above the waves and slowly climbing the air. What did it mean? Was it a quaint device opening a page of some medieval book of prophecies and symbols, a hawklike man flying sunward above the sea, a prophecy of the end he had been born to serve and had been following through the mists of childhood and boyhood, a symbol of the artist forging anew in his workshop out of the sluggish matter of the earth a new soaring impalpable imperishable being?

His heart trembled; his breath came faster and a wild spirit passed over his limbs as though he were soaring sunward. His heart trembled in an ecstasy of fear and his soul was in flight. His soul was soaring in an air beyond the world and the body he knew was purified in a breath and delivered of incertitude and made radiant and commingled with the element of the spirit. An ecstasy of flight made radiant his eyes and wild his breath and tremulous and wild and radiant his windswept limbs.

—One! Two! . . . Look out!

—O, cripes, I'm drownded!

—One! Two! Three and away!

—Me next! Me next!

—One! . . . Uk!

—Stephaneforos!

His throat arched with a desire to cry aloud, the cry of a hawk or eagle on high, to cry piercingly of his deliverance to the winds. This was the call of life to his soul not the dull gross voice of the world of duties and despair, not the inhuman voice that had called him to the pale service of the altar. An instant of wild flight had delivered him and the cry of triumph which his lips withheld cleft his brain.

—Stephaneforos!

What were they now but cerements shaken from the body of death—the fear he had walked in night and day, the incertitude that had ringed him round, the shame that had abased him within and without—cerements, the linens of the grave?

His soul had arisen from the grave of boyhood, spurning her graveclothes. Yes! Yes! Yes! He would create proudly out of the freedom and power of his soul, as the great artificer whose name he bore, a living thing, new and soaring and beautiful, impalpable, imperishable.

He started up nervously from the stoneblock for he could no longer quench the flame in his blood. He felt his cheeks aflame and his throat throbbing with song. There was a lust of wandering in his feet that burned to set out for the ends of the earth. On! On! his heart seemed to cry. Evening would deepen above the sea, night fall upon the plains, dawn glimmer before the wanderer and show him strange fields and hills and faces. Where?

He looked northward towards Howth. The sea had fallen below the line of seawrack on the shallow side of the breakwater and already the tide was running out fast along the foreshore. Already one long oval bank of sand lay warm and dry amid the wavelets. Here and there warm isles of sand gleamed above the shallow tide, and about the isles and around the long bank and amid the shallow currents of the beach were lightclad gayclad figures, wading and delving.

In a few moments he was barefoot, his stockings folded in his pockets and his canvas shoes dangling by their knotted laces over his shoulders: and, picking a pointed salteaten stick out of the jetsam among the rocks, he clambered down the slope of the breakwater.

There was a long rivulet in the strand: and, as he waded slowly up its course, he wondered at the endless drift of seaweed. Emerald and black and russet and olive, it moved beneath the current, swaying and turning. The water of the rivulet was dark with endless drift and mirrored the high-drifting clouds. The clouds were drifting above him silently and silently the seatangle was drifting below him; and the grey warm air was still: and a new wild life was singing in his veins.

Where was his boyhood now? Where was the soul that had hung back from her destiny, to brood alone upon the shame of her wounds and in her house of squalor and subterfuge to queen it in faded cerements and in wreaths that withered at the touch? Or where was he?

He was alone. He was unheeded, happy and near to the wild heart of life. He was alone and young and wilful and wildhearted, alone amid a waste of wild air and brackish waters and the seaharvest of shells and tangle and veiled grey sunlight and gayclad lightclad figures, of children and girls and voices childish and girlish in the air.

A girl stood before him in midstream, alone and still, gazing out to sea. She seemed like one whom magic had changed into the likeness of a strange and beautiful seabird. Her long slender bare legs were delicate as a crane's and pure save where an emerald trail of seaweed had fashioned itself as a sign upon the flesh. Her thighs, fuller and softhued as ivory, were bared almost to the hips where the white fringes of her drawers were like featherings of soft white down. Her slateblue skirts were kilted boldly about her waist and dovetailed behind her. Her bosom was as a bird's soft and slight, slight and soft as the breast of some darkplumaged dove. But her long fair hair was girlish: and girlish, and touched with the wonder of mortal beauty, her face.

She was alone and still, gazing out to sea; and when she felt his presence and the worship of his eyes her eyes turned to him in quiet sufferance of his gaze, without shame or wantonness. Long, long she suffered his gaze and then quietly withdrew her eyes from his and bent them towards the stream, gently stirring the water with her foot hither and thither. The first faint noise of gently moving water broke the silence, low and faint and whispering, faint as the bells of sleep; hither and thither, hither and thither: and a faint flame trembled on her cheek.

—Heavenly God! cried Stephen's soul, in an outburst of profane joy.

He turned away from her suddenly and set off across the strand. His cheeks were aflame; his body was aglow; his limbs were trembling. On and on and on and on he strode, far out over the sands, singing wildly to the sea, crying to greet the advent of the life that had cried to him.

Her image had passed into his soul for ever and no word had broken the holy silence of his ecstasy. Her eyes had called him and his soul had leaped at the call. To live, to err, to fall, to triumph, to recreate life out of life! A wild angel had appeared to him, the angel of mortal youth and beauty, an envoy from the fair courts of life, to throw open before him in an instant of ecstasy the gates of all the ways of error and glory. On and on and on and on!

He halted suddenly and heard his heart in the silence. How far had he walked? What hour was it?

There was no human figure near him nor any sound borne to him over the air. But the tide was near the turn and already the day was on the wane. He turned landward and ran towards the shore and, running up the sloping beach, reckless of the sharp shingle, found a sandy nook amid a ring of tufted sandknolls and lay down there that the peace and silence of the evening might still the riot of his blood.

He felt above him the vast indifferent dome and the calm

processes of the heavenly bodies; and the earth beneath him, the earth that had borne him, had taken him to her breast.

He closed his eyes in the languor of sleep. His eyelids trembled as if they felt the vast cyclic movement of the earth and her watchers, trembled as if they felt the strange light of some new world. His soul was swooning into some new world, fantastic, dim, uncertain as under sea, traversed by cloudy shapes and beings. A world, a glimmer, or a flower? Glimmering and trembling, trembling and unfolding, a breaking light, an opening flower, it spread in endless succession to itself, breaking in full crimson and unfolding and fading to palest rose, leaf by leaf and wave of light by wave of light, flooding all the heavens with its soft flushes, every flush deeper than other.

Evening had fallen when he woke and the sand and arid grasses of his bed glowed no longer. He rose slowly and, recalling the rapture of his sleep, sighed at its joy.

He climbed to the crest of the sandhill and gazed about him. Evening had fallen. A rim of the young moon cleft the pale waste of sky like the rim of a silver hoop embedded in grey sand; and the tide was flowing in fast to the land with a low whisper of her waves, islanding a few last figures in distant pools.

AFTERWORD

In a novel called *A Portrait of the Artist as a Young Man*, one expects to find a moment or an occasion that transforms the "young man" into the "artist." The occasion is Stephen's ramble on the seashore at the end of Chapter 4. In the course of that afternoon he changes completely, not in substance, but in form, as if crystals had taken shape in a saturate solution. To use another figure, it is as if he buried his past, underwent the rite of baptism, and was reborn into a new life. The word "rite" suggests the religious feeling that underlies the scene. "Have you ever felt that you had a vocation?" the director of his school had asked him a few pages before. Stephen had answered noncommittally, but soon his mind rejected the flattering notion that he might enter a seminary: "the oils of ordination would never anoint his body." Neither, one might add, would his mind ever lose the stamp of his Jesuit education, so that even his rejection of the priesthood is expressed in sacerdotal terms. He is about to feel, moreover, that he has a new vocation, also priestly in its fashion, but not Christian.

The scene on the seashore begins with other rejections, first of his father ("walking rapidly lest his father's shrill whistle might call him back"), then of his mother ("he was made aware dimly and without regret of a first noiseless sundering of their lives"). At the bridge to North Bull Island, he passes a squad of Christian Brothers with "uncouth faces" and rejects their humble piety, which, he says, "would be like their names, like their faces, like their clothes." On a spine of rocks at the river's mouth, he sees a group of his schoolmates, a "medley of wet nakedness." They call to him in schoolboy Greek, "Bous Stephanoumenos! Bous Stephaneforos!" (Ox wreathed! Ox garlanded!) and he joins in their banter; but soon he rejects them too. Meanwhile their mention of his last name, Dedalus, has seemed to him a "prophecy of the end he had been born to serve."

> His soul had arisen from the grave of boyhood, spurning her grave-clothes. Yes! Yes! Yes! He would create proudly out of the freedom and power of his soul, as the great artificer whose name he bore, a living thing, new and soaring and beautiful, impalpable, imperishable.

The past has been buried now, and Stephen has received a prophecy of his new vocation. The prophecy must be confirmed, however, by something that corresponds to the rite of baptism. We read in John III, 5, "Except a man be born of water and of the Spirit, he cannot enter into the kingdom of God." The baptism by water is a homely matter here: Stephen takes off his canvas shoes and wades into a long rivulet that crosses the strand at low tide. Then he has what seems to him the supernal vision of a girl standing alone in the water and gazing out to sea:

> Her thighs, fuller and softhued as ivory, were bared almost to the hips where the white fringes of her drawers were like the featherings of soft white down. Her slateblue skirts were kilted boldly about her waist and dovetailed behind her. Her bosom was as a bird's soft and slight, slight and soft as the breast of some darkplumaged dove. But her long fair hair was girlish: and girlish, and touched with the wonder of mortal beauty, her face.

There are intimations of the Virgin in the words "ivory" ("tower of ivory") and "-blue," since blue is the Virgin's color (or blue over white). But even more the girl suggests the Holy Spirit, the Dove, with the fringes of her drawers "like the featherings of soft white down"—trust Joyce to mix the sacramental and the mildly scatological—with her skirts "dovetailed behind her," and with her bosom "slight and soft as the breast of some darkplumaged dove." Her eyes rest on Stephen's as if in benediction, and "Heavenly God!" cries his soul, not his body, "in an outburst of profane joy." After striding away ecstatically, he finds a sandy nook, and there, as in earth's bosom, he is reborn into the kingdom of art. We read:

> His soul was swooning into some new world, fantastic, dim, uncertain as under sea, traversed by cloudy shapes and beings. A world, a glimmer, or a flower? Glimmering and trembling, trembling and unfolding, a breaking light, an opening flower, it spread in endless succession to itself, breaking in full crimson and unfolding and fading to palest rose. . . .

One cannot help feeling that Joyce had in mind that greatest of Christian poems *The Divine Comedy*, and specifically Cantos XXX and XXXI of the *Paradiso*, in which Dante the pilgrim is vouchsafed an ultimate vision and in which the abode of the blessed is seen as a great white rose. But we turn the page—if we have the complete novel before us—and read at the beginning of Chapter 5: "He drained his third cup of watery tea to the dregs and set to chewing the crusts of fried bread that were scattered near him. . . ." Let us not be misled by the sordidness of breakfast in the Dedalus kitchen. Joyce *wants* the sordidness as a contrast to the heavens unfolding like a flower, but he also wants to suggest that the watery tea and the crusts of fried bread are the wine and wafers of a new sacrament, a communion after confirmation.

The contemporary reader is likely to be less impressed by those religious images than puzzled by the prose in which they are presented. Grave, heavily cadenced, and incantatory, it sounds like something chanted before an altar. It is rich in rhetorical devices that appeal to the ears rather than the eyes: alliteration, assonance, words repeated in intricate patterns. There are examples of all three in the quoted passage about the world's unfolding like a flower. Alliteration: "soul . . . swooning . . . some . . . uncertain . . . sea"; or again, "unfolding . . . flower . . . full . . . unfolding . . . fading." Assonance (there is more of it in other paragraphs): "breaking . . . fading . . . palest." As for repetitions, note the last two of the quoted sentences, with the repeated words italicized: "A world, a *glimmer*, or a *flower*? *Glimmering* and *trembling*, *trembling* and *unfolding*, a *breaking* light, an opening *flower* . . . *breaking* in full crimson and *unfolding* to palest rose." Note also that the repeated "and's" and the short phrases followed by commas give a scriptural tone to the passage.

This auditory rather than visual style came naturally to an author who was "weak of sight," as Stephen says of himself, but keen of hearing and retentive in his memory of spoken words and phrases. Stephen is Joyce himself as a young man. In the new world into which he is reborn, the colors are such as might be seen by a short-sighted person, while the shapes are "fantastic, dim, uncertain as under sea," or as if Stephen had lost his glasses. Essentially both shapes and colors matter much less to the hero, and to the author, than do tones, accents, tempos, pauses, vowel qualities, and verbal patterns. Stephen's new world of art is one in which words have almost completely taken the place of objects and serve as the true events.

All this helps to explain Joyce's style in this crucial scene. Elsewhere he is more prosaic, but here, when he invokes a solemn emotion, this comparatively early writing seems to us "poetic," even purple, and a little outmoded. By contrast with the more colloquial style that later came into fashion, it looks back to Walter Pater (1839-1894), who was one of Joyce's early masters—Cardinal Newman was the other—and perhaps it looks back even farther, to the chants of the Irish harpers. It also looks forward, however, to Joyce's later style and the verbal music of *Finnegans Wake*. In that novel Anna Livia Plurabelle is his personification of the River Liffey, and she passes the scene of Stephen's ramble on her way to consummation in the sea. Perhaps we can hear the echo of Stephen's voice as she utters her lament:

And it's old it's sad and old it's sad and weary I go back to you, my cold father, my cold mad father, my cold mad feary father, till the near sight of the mere size of him, the moyles and moyles of it, moananoaning, makes me seasilt saltsick and I rush, my only, into your arms.

Mrs. Dalloway (1925)

VIRGINIA WOOLF's life (1882-1941) and background make her the most literary of the novelists represented here. She was the daughter of the formidable Sir Leslie Stephen, who edited *The Dictionary of National Biography*, and the goddaughter of James Russell Lowell. As a child she met the Victorian eminences, Meredith, Hardy, Stevenson, Ruskin, and others. Nevertheless she was a shy and lonely girl, especially after her mother died in 1895, and she haunted her father's library.

The father died in 1904 after a long illness, and Virginia, with her sister Vanessa and her two brothers, took a house in Gordon Square that soon became the headquarters of the Bloomsbury group. The novelist E. M. Forster (1879-1970) was a member of the group, and it also included the biographer Lytton Strachey, the economist John Maynard Keynes, and the art critic Clive Bell, who soon married Vanessa. They were all brilliant people, scathing in conversation, and with a weakness for writing favorable reviews of one another's books. Outsiders rather feared them and called them "the Bloomsberries." Relations within the group were close—one might almost say incestuous, since it formed an extended family. Virginia was briefly engaged to Lytton Strachey, till both thought better of it; then in 1912 she married Leonard Woolf, also a member of the group and later known for his writing on international affairs.

In 1915 Mrs. Woolf published her first novel, *The Voyage Out*, faultlessly written in the genre of E. M. Forster (who paid more attention to events in the external world than she was to pay in her later novels). In 1917 the Woolfs founded the Hogarth Press by printing *Two Stories* by L. and V. Woolf on an old handpress. The edition quickly sold out, and the following year they published *Prelude* by Katherine Mansfield, then unknown, and *Poems* by T. S. Eliot. The Hogarth Press showed such discrimination in its choice of authors that it became an established commercial venture. Mrs. Woolf, after recovering from what seems to have been a serious breakdown, went back to writing novels. *Night and Day* (1919) still shows the influence of Forster and is taken to be her least successful book. She found her own voice in *Jacob's Room* (1922), which is the story of a young man's life as revealed obliquely, for the most part, by the impressions of those who knew him. The next two novels are essentially inner monologues (though they shift from one character to another), and the method is admirably suited to her sensitive perception and her introspective temperament. The books are *Mrs. Dalloway*, the most widely read of her novels, and *To the Lighthouse* (1927), preferred by Woolf enthusiasts. She was also writing critical essays, including those collected in *Mr. Bennett and Mrs. Brown* (1924). Here after repudiating the sociological novels of Bennett, Wells, and Galsworthy, she insisted that the novel must be self-contained and not an incitement to actions such as "joining a society or writing a check." That works of art should have no practical consequences was a doctrine accepted by the whole Bloomsbury group.

Virginia Woolf's last four novels—*Orlando* (1928), *The Waves* (1931), *The Years* (1937), and *Between the Acts* (1941)—are all experiments, each in a different direction, and their readers complained that "nothing happened" (except in *Orlando*, which is a historical fantasy); that the drama, if any, was all in the consciousness of her protagonists; and that she seemed to take no interest in the objective world. She became depressed, not by her critics, but by World War II and chiefly by fears of another nervous breakdown. In March 1941 she committed suicide. After her death Leonard Woolf edited collections of her stories and essays, as well as a more personal book, *Writer's Diary* (1953).

THE STORY

"What is it about?" people ask when first hearing of a novel. The question is hard to answer in this case. Essentially, one might say, *Mrs. Dalloway* is *about* the progress of a charming middle-aged woman toward a moment of vision in which, after hearing about the suicide of a young veteran, she perceives the inner emptiness of her life. The progress takes place in her stream of consciousness, which consists partly of memories, partly of immediate perceptions and what they suggest to the heroine. It is explained and illuminated by other streams of consciousness, notably those of the young veteran and of her old friend Peter Walsh. Obviously such streams are inclined to wander over the landscape, but the author controls them here—and gives form to her novel—by having it observe the three classical unities: time, place, action. The setting of *Mrs. Dalloway* is London, or rather, a circumscribed and elegant part of London. The temporal span is less than the twenty-four hours permitted by neoclassical critics of the drama: it is a morning and an afternoon in the city, followed by a party that evening which Clarissa Dalloway has planned with all the care of an artist executing a masterpiece. The end of the party, at three o'clock the following morning, is also the end of the novel.

There is, however, another story suggested by *Mrs. Dalloway*, and it is more like the plot of a novel by John Galsworthy, extending as it does over more than thirty years. The reader pieces it together from Clarissa's and Peter Walsh's memories. When Clarissa was a girl at Bourton, in the English countryside, she had been in love with Peter, a bright young man sent down in disgrace from Oxford. He was not a conventional match for her, and at a given moment—"The death of the soul," Peter called it—she had thrown him over for Richard Dalloway, a right-thinking young man certain to rise in government service. Peter had gone out to India and married a young woman he met on the boat. Years later she died, and he is now involved with the wife of an Anglo-Indian major; he plans to marry her and has come back to London to arrange for her divorce. Meanwhile Clarissa has become a fashionable hostess and something of a snob, though without losing her charm. When Peter pays her an unexpected visit and she invites him to her party, she thinks what her life might have been if she had married him instead of a rather stuffy bureaucrat. At the end of the party (and of the novel), Peter is terrified and ecstatic because Clarissa— after her moment of vision, which she nurses as a secret—is at last coming to exchange a few words with him.

Mrs. Dalloway also has a subplot that raises a puzzling question. An emotionally disturbed veteran, Septimus Warren Smith, has returned to London with his Italian bride Lucrezia. Depressed by people and their actions, he kills himself by jumping from a window. ("He did not want to die. Life was good. The sun was hot. Only human beings—what did *they* want?") Peter has seen him once, and later sees the ambulance that carries away his body; Clarissa never sees him. The two stories are linked, however, by the presence of Septimus's doctor, Sir William Bradshaw, at the Dalloway party. Clarissa is told about the suicide as a piece of social chitchat: "Just as we were starting, my husband was called up on the telephone, a very sad case. A young man (that is what Sir William is telling Mr. Dalloway) had killed himself. He had been in the army." Clarissa keeps thinking about the young man, and she says to herself during her moment of vision, "She felt somehow very like him." But why? Mrs. Woolf untangles many complicated relations, but she does not make it clear to the reader why Clarissa and Septimus are—as she was later to say in a preface—"one and the same person."

What follows is the opening scene of the novel, and it brings to mind the opening chapter of *Bleak House.* Winter/summer, foggy/sunlit, masculine/feminine: there are many contrasts in the two passages, but they resemble each other in one respect. In their pictures of London, Dickens and Mrs. Woolf are both able to introduce a number of themes that will take on significance later in their respective novels.

[*Mrs. Dalloway's London*]

Mrs. Dalloway said she would buy the flowers herself.

For Lucy had her work cut out for her. The doors would be taken off their hinges; Rumpelmayer's men were coming. And then, thought Clarissa Dalloway, what a morning—fresh as if issued to children on a beach.

What a lark! What a plunge! For so it had always seemed to her, when, with a little squeak of the hinges, which she could hear now, she had burst open the French windows and plunged at Bourton into the open air. How fresh, how calm, stiller than this of course, the air was in the early morning; like the flap of a wave; the kiss of a wave; chill and sharp and yet (for a girl of eighteen as she then was) solemn, feeling as she did, standing there at the open window, that something awful was about to happen; looking at the flowers, at the trees with the smoke winding off them and the rooks rising, falling; standing and looking until Peter Walsh said, "Musing among the vegetables?"—was that it?—"I prefer men to cauliflowers"—was that it? He must have said it at breakfast one morning when she had gone out on to the terrace—Peter Walsh. He would be back from India one of these days, June or July, she forgot which, for his letters were awfully dull; it was his sayings one remembered; his eyes, his pocket-knife, his smile, his grumpiness and, when millions of things had utterly vanished—how strange it was!—a few sayings like this about cabbages.

She stiffened a little on the kerb, waiting for Durtnall's van to pass. A charming woman, Scrope Purvis thought her (knowing her as one does know people who live next door to one in Westminster); a touch of the bird about her, of the jay, blue-green, light, vivacious, though she was over fifty, and grown very white since her illness. There she perched, never seeing him, waiting to cross, very upright.

For having lived in Westminster—how many years now? over twenty,—one feels even in the midst of the traffic, or waking at night, Clarissa was positive, a particular hush, or solemnity; an indescribable pause; a suspense (but that might be her heart, affected, they said, by influenza) before Big Ben strikes. There! Out it boomed. First a warning, musical; then the hour, irrevocable. The leaden circles dissolved in the air. Such fools we are, she thought, crossing Victoria Street. For Heaven only knows why one loves it so, how one sees it so, making it up, building it round one, tumbling it, creating it every moment afresh; but the veriest frumps, the most dejected of miseries sitting on doorsteps (drink their downfall) do the same; can't be dealt with, she felt positive, by Acts of Parliament for that very reason: they love life. In people's eyes, in the swing, tramp, and trudge; in the bellow and the uproar; the carriages, motor cars, omnibuses, vans, sandwich men shuffling and swinging; brass bands; barrel organs; in the triumph and the jingle and the strange high singing of some aeroplane overhead was what she loved; life; London; this moment of June.

For it was the middle of June. The War was over, except for some one like Mrs. Foxcroft at the Embassy last night eating her heart out because that nice boy was killed and now the old Manor House must go to a cousin; or Lady Bexborough who opened a bazaar, they said, with the telegram in her hand, John, her favourite, killed; but it was over; thank Heaven—over. It was June. The King and Queen were at the Palace. And everywhere, though it was still so early, there was a beating, a stirring of galloping ponies, tapping of cricket bats; Lords, Ascot, Ranelagh and all the rest of it; wrapped in the soft mesh of the grey-blue morning air, which, as the day wore on, would unwind them, and set down on their lawns and pitches the bouncing ponies, whose forefeet just struck the ground and up they sprung, the whirling young men, and laughing girls in their transparent muslins who, even now, after dancing all night, were taking their absurd woolly dogs for a run; and even now, at this hour, discreet old dowagers were shooting out in their motor cars on errands of mystery; and the shopkeepers were fidgeting in their windows with their paste and diamonds, their lovely old sea-green brooches in eighteenth-century settings to tempt Americans (but one must economise, not buy things rashly for Elizabeth), and she, too, loving it as she did with an absurd and faithful passion, being part of it, since her people were courtiers once in the time of the Georges, she, too, was going that very night to kindle and illuminate; to give her party. But how strange, on entering the Park, the silence; the mist; the hum; the slow-swimming happy ducks; the pouched birds waddling; and who should be coming along with his back against the Government buildings, most appropriately, carrying a despatch box stamped with the Royal Arms, who but Hugh Whitbread; her old friend Hugh—the admirable Hugh!

"Good-morning to you, Clarissa!" said Hugh, rather extravagantly, for they had known each other as children. "Where are you off to?"

"I love walking in London," said Mrs. Dalloway. "Really it's better than walking in the country."

They had just come up—unfortunately—to see doctors. Other people came to see pictures; go to the opera; take their daughters out; the Whitbreads came "to see doctors." Times without number Clarissa had visited Evelyn Whitbread in a nursing home. Was Evelyn ill again? Eveyln was a good deal out of sorts, said Hugh, intimating by a kind of pout or swell of his very well-covered, manly, extremely handsome, perfectly upholstered body (he was almost too well dressed always, but presumably had to be, with his little job at Court) that his wife had some internal ailment, nothing serious, which, as an old friend, Clarissa Dalloway would quite understand without requiring him to specify. Ah yes, she did of course; what a nuisance; and felt very sisterly and oddly conscious at the same time of her hat. Not the right hat for the early morning, was that it? For Hugh always made her feel, as he bustled on, raising his hat rather extravagantly and assuring her that she might be a girl of eighteen, and of course he was coming to her party to-night, Evelyn absolutely insisted, only a little late he might be after the party at the Palace to which he had to take one of Jim's boys,—she always felt a little skimpy beside Hugh; schoolgirlish; but attached to him, partly from having known him always, but she did think him a good sort in his own way, though Richard was nearly driven mad by him, and as for Peter Walsh, he had never to this day forgiven her for liking him.

She could remember scene after scene at Bourton—Peter furious; Hugh not, of course, his match in any way, but still not a positive imbecile as Peter made out; not a mere barber's block. When his old mother wanted him to give up shooting or to take her to Bath he did it, without a word; he was really unselfish, and as for saying, as Peter did, that he had no heart, no brain, nothing but the manners and breeding of an English gentleman, that was only her dear Peter at his worst; and he could be intolerable; he could be impossible; but adorable to walk with on a morning like this.

(June had drawn out every leaf on the trees. The mothers of Pimlico gave suck to their young. Messages were passing from the Fleet to the Admiralty. Arlington Street and Piccadilly seemed to chafe the very air in the Park and lift its leaves hotly, brilliantly, on waves of that divine vitality which Clarissa loved. To dance, to ride, she had adored all that.)

For they might be parted for hundreds of years, she and Peter; she never wrote a letter and his were dry sticks; but suddenly it would come over her, If he were with me now what would he say? —some days, some sights bringing him back to her calmly, without the old bitterness; which perhaps was the reward of having cared for people; they came back in the middle of St. James's Park on a fine morning—indeed they did. But Peter—however beautiful the day might be, and the trees and the grass, and the little girl in pink—Peter never saw a thing of all that. He would put on his spectacles, if she told him to; he would look. It was the state of the world that interested him; Wagner, Pope's poetry, people's characters eternally, and the defects of her own soul. How he scolded her! How they argued! She would marry a Prime Minister and stand at the top of a staircase; the perfect hostess he called her (she had cried over it in her bedroom), she had the makings of the perfect hostess, he said.

So she would still find herself arguing in St. James's Park, still making out that she had been right—and she had too—not to marry him. For in marriage a little license, a little independence there must be between people living together day in day out in the same house; which Richard gave her, and she him. (Where was he this morning for instance? Some committee, she never asked what.)

But with Peter everything had to be shared; everything gone into. And it was intolerable, and when it came to that scene in the little garden by the fountain, she had to break with him or they would have been destroyed, both of them ruined, she was convinced; though she had borne about with her for years like an arrow sticking in her heart the grief, the anguish; and then the horror of the moment when some one told her at a concert that he had married a woman met on the boat going to India! Never should she forget all that! Cold, heartless, a prude, he called her. Never could she understand how he cared. But those Indian women did presumably—silly, pretty, flimsy nincompoops. And she wasted her pity. For he was quite happy, he assured her—perfectly happy, though he had never done a thing that they talked of; his whole life had been a failure. It made her angry still.

She had reached the Park gates. She stood for a moment, looking at the omnibuses in Piccadilly.

She would not say of any one in the world now that they were this or were that. She felt very young; at the same time unspeakably aged. She sliced like a knife through everything; at the same time was outside, looking on. She had a perpetual sense, as she watched the taxi cabs, of being out, out, far out to sea and alone; she always had the feeling that it was very, very dangerous to live even one day. Not that she thought herself clever, or much out of the ordinary. How she had got through life on the few twigs of knowledge Fräulein Daniels gave them she could not think. She knew nothing; no language, no history; she scarcely read a book now, except memoirs in bed; and yet to her it was absolutely absorbing; all this; the cabs passing; and she would not say of Peter, she would not say of herself, I am this, I am that.

Her only gift was knowing people almost by instinct, she thought, walking on. If you put her in a room with some one, up went her back like a cat's; or she purred. Devonshire House, Bath House, the house with the china cockatoo, she had seen them all lit up once; and remembered Sylvia, Fred, Sally Seton—such hosts of people; and dancing all night; and the waggons plodding past to market; and driving home across the Park. She remembered once throwing a shilling into the Serpentine. But every one remembered; what she loved was this, here, now, in front of her; the fat lady in the cab. Did it matter then, she asked herself, walking towards Bond Street, did it matter that she must inevitably cease completely; all this must go on without her; did she resent it; or did it not become consoling to believe that death ended absolutely? but that somehow in the streets of London, on the ebb and flow of things, here, there, she survived, Peter survived, lived in each other, she being part, she was positive, of the trees at home; of the house there, ugly, rambling all to bits and pieces as it was; part of people she had never met; being laid out like a mist between the people she knew best, who lifted her on their branches as she had seen the trees lift the mist, but it spread ever so far, her life, herself. But what was she dreaming as she looked into Hatchards' shop window? What was she trying to recover? What image of white dawn in the country, as she read in the book spread open:

> Fear no more the heat o' the sun
>> Nor the furious winter's rages.

This late age of the world's experience had bred in them all, all men and women, a well of tears. Tears and sorrows; courage and endurance; a perfectly upright and stoical bearing. Think, for example, of the woman she admired most, Lady Bexborough, opening the bazaar.

There were Jorrocks' *Jaunts and Jollities*; there were *Soapy Sponge* and Mrs. Asquith's *Memoirs* and *Big Game Shooting in Nigeria*, all spread open. Ever so many books there were; but none that seemed exactly right to take to Evelyn Whitbread in her nursing home. Nothing that would serve to amuse her and make that indescribably dried-up little woman look, as Clarissa came in, just for a moment cordial; before they settled down for the usual interminable talk of women's ailments. How much she wanted it— that people should look pleased as she came in, Clarissa thought and turned and walked back towards Bond Street, annoyed, because it was silly to have other reasons for doing things. Much rather would she have been one of those people like Richard who did things for themselves, whereas, she thought, waiting to cross, half the time she did things not simply, not for themselves; but to make people think this or that; perfect idiocy she knew (and now the policeman held up his hand) for no one was ever for a second taken in. Oh if she could have had her life over again! she thought, stepping on to the pavement, could have looked even differently!

She would have been, in the first place, dark like Lady Bexborough, with a skin of crumpled leather and beautiful eyes. She would have been, like Lady Bexborough, slow and stately; rather

large; interested in politics like a man; with a country house; very
dignified, very sincere. Instead of which she had a narrow pea-
stick figure; a ridiculous little face, beaked like a bird's. That she
held herself well was true; and had nice hands and feet; and
dressed well, considering that she spent little. But often now
this body she wore (she stopped to look at a Dutch picture), this
body, with all its capacities, seemed nothing—nothing at all. She
had the oddest sense of being herself invisible; unseen; unknown; there being no more marrying, no more having of children now, but only this astonishing and rather solemn progress
with the rest of them, up Bond Street, this being Mrs. Dalloway;
not even Clarissa any more; this being Mrs. Richard Dalloway.

Bond Street fascinated her; Bond Street early in the morning
in the season; its flags flying: its shops; no splash; no glitter; one
roll of tweed in the shop where her father had bought his suits for
fifty years; a few pearls; salmon on an iceblock.

"That is all," she said, looking at the fishmonger's. "That is
all," she repeated, pausing for a moment at the window of a glove
shop where, before the War, you could buy almost perfect gloves.
And her old Uncle William used to say a lady is known by her
shoes and her gloves. He had turned on his bed one morning in
the middle of the War. He had said, "I have had enough." Gloves
and shoes; she had a passion for gloves; but her own daughter, her
Elizabeth, cared not a straw for either of them.

Not a straw, she thought, going on up Bond Street to a shop
where they kept flowers for her when she gave a party. Elizabeth
really cared for her dog most of all. The whole house this morning smelt of tar. Still, better poor Grizzle than Miss Kilman; better distemper and tar and all the rest of it than sitting mewed in a
stuffy bedroom with a prayer book! Better anything, she was inclined to say. But it might be only a phase, as Richard said, such
as all girls go through. It might be falling in love. But why with
Miss Kilman? who had been badly treated of course; one must
make allowances for that, and Richard said she was very able,
had a really historical mind. Anyhow they were inseparable, and
Elizabeth, her own daughter, went to Communion; and how she
dressed, how she treated people who came to lunch she did not
care a bit, it being her experience that the religious ecstasy made
people callous (so did causes); dulled their feelings, for Miss Kilman would do anything for the Russians, starved herself for the

Austrians, but in private inflicted positive torture, so insensitive was she, dressed in a green mackintosh coat. Year in year out she wore that coat; she perspired; she was never in the room five minutes without making you feel her superiority, your inferiority; how poor she was; how rich you were; how she lived in a slum without a cushion or a bed or a rug or whatever it might be, all her soul rusted with that grievance sticking in it, her dismissal from school during the War—poor embittered unfortunate creature! For it was not her one hated but the idea of her, which undoubtedly had gathered in to itself a great deal that was not Miss Kilman; had become one of those spectres with which one battles in the night; one of those spectres who stand astride us and suck up half our life-blood, dominators and tyrants; for no doubt with another throw of the dice, had the black been uppermost and not the white, she would have loved Miss Kilman! But not in this world. No.

It rasped her, though, to have stirring about in her this brutal monster! to hear twigs cracking and feel hooves planted down in the depths of that leaf-encumbered forest, the soul; never to be content quite, or quite secure, for at any moment the brute would be stirring, this hatred, which, especially since her illness, had power to make her feel scraped, hurt in her spine; gave her physical pain, and made all pleasure in beauty, in friendship, in being well, in being loved and making her home delightful rock, quiver, and bend as if indeed there were a monster grubbing at the roots, as if the whole panoply of content were nothing but self love! this hatred!

Nonsense, nonsense! she cried to herself, pushing through the swing doors of Mulberry's the florists.

She advanced, light, tall, very upright, to be greeted at once by button-faced Miss Pym, whose hands were always bright red, as if they had been stood in cold water with the flowers.

There were flowers: delphiniums, sweet peas, bunches of lilac; and carnations, masses of carnations. There were roses; there were irises. Ah yes—so she breathed in the earthy garden sweet smell as she stood talking to Miss Pym who owed her help, and thought her kind, for kind she had been years ago; very kind, but she looked older, this year, turning her head from side to side among the irises and roses and nodding tufts of lilac with her eyes half closed, snuffing in, after the street uproar, the delicious scent, the exquisite coolness. And then, opening her eyes, how fresh like frilled linen clean from a laundry laid in wicker trays the roses looked; and dark and prim the red carnations, holding their heads up; and all the sweet peas spreading in their bowls, tinged violet, snow white, pale—as if it were the evening and girls in muslin frocks came out to pick sweet peas and roses after the superb summer's day, with its almost blue-black sky, its delphiniums, its carnations, its arum lilies was over; and it was the moment between six and seven when every flower—roses, carnations, irises, lilac—glows; white, violet, red, deep orange; every flower seems to burn by itself, softly, purely in the misty beds; and how she loved the grey-white moths spinning in and out, over the cherry pie, over the evening primroses!

And as she began to go with Miss Pym from jar to jar, choosing, nonsense, nonsense, she said to herself, more and more gently, as if this beauty, this scent, this colour, and Miss Pym liking her, trusting her, were a wave which she let flow over her and surmount that hatred, that monster, surmount it all; and it lifted her up and up when—oh! a pistol shot in the street outside!

"Dear, those motor cars," said Miss Pym, going to the window to look, and coming back and smiling apologetically with her hands full of sweet peas, as if those motor cars, those tyres of motor cars, were all *her* fault.

AFTERWORD

Since this scene is a brilliant example, the first in this volume, of what is known as the stream-of-consciousness method or genre, a few general remarks would seem to be indicated.

The phrase "stream of consciousness" was coined by William James (see his *Principles of Psychology*, 1890) to describe the amorphous flow of psychic activity. In his context James was referring to life itself, and it is not on record who first applied the phrase to a fictional method. In that connection it acquires a somewhat different meaning. It might be defined as an effort to present the most private impressions and feelings of a character, including those on a level beneath that of spoken discourse.

Novelists have always tried to depict their characters as not only doing and speaking but also thinking and feeling. The musings of

Stendhal's characters, for example, are masterly revelations of the mind at work. Tolstoy came closer to the stream-of-consciousness method in presenting the disordered thoughts of Anna Karenina before her suicide. The first novel wholly written by the method was published in 1888: *Les Lauriers sont coupés* by Edouard Dujardin (1861-1949). In England the precursor was Dorothy Richardson (1882-1957), who started publishing her twelve-volume novel *Pilgrimage* in 1915. Joyce, of course, used the method in parts of *A Portrait of the Artist*, carried it further in *Ulysses* (especially in Molly Bloom's soliloquy at the end of the novel), and developed it beyond hope of imitation in *Finnegans Wake*.

Novelists using the method—and many other names might be mentioned—have labored toward a more immediate presentation of the psyche. In the deepest level of the personality, so they insist, reason, sequence, and rhetoric are put to flight by vagrant onslaughts of free association. When we read stream-of-consciousness prose, we seem to be entering a prelogical world in which the naked image takes the place of concepts and abstractions. "That's how we really are," the novelist seems to be saying; and one of his aims is to make the novel appear less of an intellectual exercise; in short, to make it more like "life."

Is his novel indeed more "real" than others that follow conventional modes of narration? It is a question that leads to others and will not be settled for a long time. There is no doubt, however, that the method can be tremendously effective in the hands of a master. But *is* it a method, strictly speaking, or is it rather a choice of subject matter? The stream-of-consciousness novelist is dealing with the psyche, which becomes for him a mirror in which external events are reflected, sometimes rather dimly. The mirror, not the events, serves as his real and distinguishing subject. He can approach it by any one of several methods or techniques. Thus, Dorothy Richardson writes as an omniscient author who has stationed herself inside the mind of the heroine. From that post she narrates and describes in a rather conventional fashion. Joyce effaces himself as author and writes direct interior monologue. The broken phrases we overhear are those of the character speaking in the first person. In *The Sound and the Fury* and *As I Lay Dying*, Faulkner identifies himself with each of several characters in turn and uses their sharply different idioms.

Virgina Woolf adopts still another method, one that Robert Humphrey describes (in *Stream of Consciousness in the Modern Novel*, 1954) as indirect interior monologue. That is, she reports the impressions and memories of her characters in the third person, always using the same voice, which is really that of the author. The method allows her a great deal of freedom. She can pass easily from the mind of one character to that of another, she can make remarks that are clearly her own, and she can give us more of the external scene—and of Clarissa Dalloway's appearance—than if she were speaking only for Clarissa and only in the first person.

In this opening scene of the novel, expository material is introduced as needed, and it is conveyed to the reader in bits and pieces, in a fashion that makes it resemble our own fleeting memories of the past. How deft this seems as compared with the old method of presenting information in stereotyped exposition, with the immediate action halted while the author enlightens us about earlier events! There is no halt in the present scene, yet unobtrusively we are told about Clarissa's relations with Peter, about her coming party, her illness, her daughter, and everything else we need to know.

While her random memories predominate, they are punctuated with reminders of London on the present June morning. We hear Big Ben striking the hour—it will continue to mark time through the book— and four curious nouns describe Clarissa's reaction: "hush, solemnity, pause, suspense." As contrasted with the description of London at the beginning of *Bleak House*, which concentrates on visual details, there is an appeal to all the senses in this account of Clarissa's morning walk. Especially in the paragraph near the end that describes the flowers in Miss Pym's shop, there is a sense of light, color, and texture that reminds us of the Post-Impressionist painters and how Mrs. Woolf admired them.

At intervals in the scene, motifs are introduced that will be repeated later. There is the shilling thrown in the Serpentine. There are the lines from Shakespeare: "Fear no more the heat o' the sun/Nor the furious winter's rages." There are Clarissa's thoughts about death, Lady Bexborough's son killed, Mrs. Whitbread's illness and that of the heroine; then finally there is the backfire that sounds like a pistol shot. Soon we shall find that most of these motifs point to poor Septimus, whom we are yet to see. The care with which the author arranges all the seemingly random impressions attests to what she regarded as her artistic accomplishment: "Certain emotions have been placed in the right relations to each other."

In the matter of style, Clarissa's sensations are given to us in long sentences usually consisting of short parallel phrases, as if to convey the feeling of breathless exhilaration and wonder manifested by Clarissa at that "moment," so intense amid the city's apparent banality. Present participles abound, suggesting action. In her notebooks Woolf herself wonders whether she overemployed this form of the verb ("old dowagers were shooting out . . . shopkeepers were fidgeting . . . she, too, loving it . . . she too, was going.") One happy effect of the construction is that it enhances our feeling of continuous, flowing, and rhythmical action in the heroine's mind.

The Sound and the Fury (1929)

WILLIAM FAULKNER (1897-1962) was born in New Albany, Mississippi, but was still a child when the family moved thirty-five miles westward to Oxford, which was to become the "Jefferson" of his novels in the Yoknapatawpha County cycle. The family looked back with something like veneration to the novelist's hot-tempered great-grandfather, Colonel William Falkner, who had commanded the Seventh Mississippi Cavalry under General Forrest, who had then built a narrow-gauge railroad into Tennessee, and who had been shot dead by his former business partner. "Old Colonel," as he was called to distinguish him from his less energetic son "the Young Colonel," even found time to write a romantic novel, *The White Rose of Memphis* (1880), which used to be hawked on Southern railroad trains. When little Billy Falkner —he added the "u" to his name later—was in the third grade, he was asked more than once what he wanted to do when he grew up. He would rise in his seat and answer, "I want to be a writer like my great-grandaddy."

Billy was an imaginative boy, always making up stories and often getting his three brothers into scrapes (as when he persuaded Dean that he could fly with wings made of corn shucks). He was a constant but desultory reader, not much interested in his studies, and he dropped out of high school. At the time he was in love with the girl next door, Estelle Oldham. A young Oxford lawyer, Philip Stone, took on the unpaid job of directing his reading and kept him supplied with books, mostly in the Symbolist tradition; Joyce, Baudelaire, Verlaine, and Conrad Aiken were among his favorite authors. Later Stone was to pay for the publication of Faulkner's first book, a sequence of poems, *The Marble Faun* (1924).

In the last summer of the Great War, Faulkner enlisted in the Royal Canadian Air Force, not being tall enough for American aviation. He "didn't get over," in the phrase of the time, and was still in training when the war ended. His life for the next few years would be a rather disjointed series of adventures. Thus, he attended the University of Mississippi (in Oxford) for two terms and part of a third and earned the title of Count No 'Count . . . traveled around the country with a friend and drinking companion who had been appointed receiver of a big bankrupt lumber company . . . went to New York and clerked in a bookstore for $11 a week . . . was called back to Oxford as postmaster at the Univeristy—"the damndest postmaster the World has ever seen," Phil Stone wrote of him . . . became a close friend of Sherwood Anderson in New Orleans (1925) and there wrote his first novel, *Soldiers' Pay* . . . went to Italy on a freighter, then made his way to Paris, partly on foot . . . spent some months on the Left Bank, where he heard that the novel had been accepted for publication in 1926 . . . returned to Oxford with the fixed intention of becoming a professional writer . . . and more, more: house painting, palling around with barnstorming aviators, shrimp trawling in the Gulf of Mexico, smuggling rum on a speedboat in the Louisiana bayous, all of which would be imaginatively projected and magnified in his fiction.

Writing mostly at night, he was enormously productive and earned very little money. He submitted stories to Phil Stone, which were typed by Stone's secretary and submitted to magazines—but they always came back, until they nearly filled a drawer of a filing cabinet. He wrote a second novel, *Mosquitoes* (1927), which was less favorably received than the first had been; then a third novel, *Sartoris* (1928), which was the first to deal with Yoknapatawpha County. While the manuscript was making the rounds of New York publishers, Faulkner became convinced that his work would never again appear between hard covers. He said to himself, "Now I can write," and, with a feeling of joyful release, set to work on *The Sound and the Fury*. It was published after some delay, as *Sartoris* had been, and proved to be the first of his major novels.

There were events in his private life. Estelle Oldham came back from China after the failure of her first marriage, and she and Faulkner were married in the summer of 1929. He had written *Sanctuary* that spring, but his publisher had rejected it—"Good God, I can't publish this," he said. "We'd both be in jail." After a honeymoon on the Gulf Coast, Faulkner started *As I Lay Dying*, which he wrote on the back of a shovel, so he says, while working as night fireman at the University power station. Meanwhile the enthusiastic reviews of *The Sound and the Fury* had persuaded editors to take a second look at his short stories. Enough of these were being accepted for Faulkner to take the risk of buying a dilapidated pre-war mansion in Oxford, which he repaired with his own hammer and saw.

He had entered what has since been called his major phase. In the following years—besides two collections of stories and a second book of poems—he was to publish nine novels: *As I Lay Dying* (1930); *Sanctuary* (1931), about which the publisher had changed his mind and which Faulkner had rewritten in proof without softening its violence; *Light in August* (1932); *Pylon* (1935), published in the year when his brother Dean was killed in piloting Faulkner's plane; *Absalom, Absalom!* (1936), one of his best books and the most derisively reviewed, so that it lost him readers; *The Unvanquished* (1938), about the Sartoris family in and after the Civil War; *The Wild Palms* (1939), two separate stories counterpointed in alternate chapters; *The Hamlet* (1940), first volume of a projected trilogy about the Snopes family; and *Go Down, Moses* (1942), about the white and the black descendants of old Carothers McCaslin. In these books, all but one of which contribute to the history of his mythical Yoknapatawpha County, he had performed a labor of the imagination unparalleled among the major novelists of our time. In some ways it suggests the Brontë children and their creation of Angria and Gondal. Faulkner's creation, however, is also a fable of the real South, and beyond it of human destinies everywhere. The last two books contain some of his best writing, including a magnificent story "The Bear," but they went almost unnoticed at the time of publication. By 1945 all of Faulkner's books were out of print (except for a few unsold copies of *Mosquitoes*). No longer able to earn a living as a writer, he had accepted a long-term contract in Hollywood at a low salary.

His second and steeper rise to fame is a long story that begins with the publication of *The Portable Faulkner* in 1946. This presented a picture of his work as a whole, it was widely reviewed, and it led to the reissue of his earlier books one after another. In 1948 he published a new novel, *Intruder in the Dust*, about the debated question of the Negroes in Mississippi. His *Collected Stories* appeared in 1950 and later won the National Book Award. In Europe his reputation had never declined, and, also in 1950, he was awarded the Nobel Prize (as of 1949). Now the critics went to work on his characters, his narrative method, his metaphysics, his symbolism, until the novels themselves were buried under a tumulus of treatises.

Much against his inclination, Faulkner became a public figure, traveling for the State Department and talking to students in Japan, Brazil, Greece, Italy, and other countries. He was happier in his appointment as writer in residence at the University of Virginia, since his only daughter, Jill Summers, was living nearby with her husband and children. His later novels lacked the demonic fire of his early ones; they expressed faith in human nature and the future of mankind. The most important of them are *A Fable* (1954), about Christ reincarnated in a French corporal during World War I; *The Town* (1957) and *The Mansion* (1959), two volumes that completed the Snopes trilogy; and a nostalgic comedy of innocence, *The Reivers*, which appeared to great acclaim in June 1962, only a month before his death in Oxford.

THE STORY

What Faulkner gives us in *The Sound and the Fury* is not so much a story—that is, a sequence of events leading to something changed—as a *situation* presented from different angles in widening circles of comprehension. The situation is the collapse of the Compson family. First we see it from the angle of a feeble-minded son who has no sense of sequential time and confuses the past with the present; then from the angle of a time-obsessed son on the day of his suicide; then from that of a third son who thinks clearly, but is mean and short-sighted. Finally we have the view of an objective narrator, not quite omniscient, but able to bring events at the Compsons' back into daylight. There is also an "Appendix," written many years after the rest of the novel, that records the earlier history of the family and the fate of the survivors.

Once the family had included a governor of Mississippi and a general in the Confederate Army. Once the Compson Domain had been a square mile in the heart of Jefferson, but by 1909 it has been reduced to a rotting mansion, its grounds, and a big pasture. The family now consists of Mr. Compson, a hard-drinking lawyer without briefs; Mrs. Compson, proud, stupid, whining; and their four children. The oldest of these, Quentin, is in love with his sister, but more in love with death. Candace or Caddy is a warm-hearted young woman bent on her own damnation. Jason is calculating and spiteful, and Benjy, the idiot son, loves only three things: the pasture, his sister Caddy who is good to him, and firelight.

If the situation were a conventional plot, it might be further summarized in this fashion:

After several love affairs, Caddy becomes engaged to a rich Northerner, although she is two months pregnant by another man. Quentin tells his father that he has committed incest. It is a false confession, but he wants to be joined to Caddy in proud isolation. Not believing the confession, Mr. Compson sells the pasture to a golf club in order to give Caddy a fine wedding and Quentin a year at Harvard. Quentin studies dutifully during the year, then, on June 2, 1910, he commits suicide. The Northerner divorces Caddy after refusing to acknowledge paternity of her child. Though the child is a girl, Caddy has named it Quentin after her brother. Mr. Compson quietly drinks himself to death. Caddy leaves the child with her mother and promises Jason, now head of the household, to send a monthly sum for its support. In 1913 Benjy awkwardly molests a little girl and Jason has him castrated.

Everything goes to pieces in three days beginning with Good Friday, 1928. Jason mistreats the girl Quentin, now seventeen years old. Quentin retaliates by climbing along the rain gutter, breaking the window of Jason's room, prizing open his strongbox, and taking his hoard (most of which was really hers, since it was the money that Caddy had sent for her support). She climbs down a pear tree in blossom (or down a rainpipe in the "Appendix") and runs off with a pitchman in the circus. On the next morning, which is Easter Sunday, Jason pursues her vainly, while Mrs. Compson lies in a state of collapse and the Negro servant Dilsey—Benjy's only protector now—takes him to hear a sermon in a Negro church. "I seed de first en de last," Dilsey says when she returns to the spectrally quiet house.

[*Dilsey*]

APRIL 8, 1928

The day dawned bleak and chill. A moving wall of grey light out of the northeast which, instead of dissolving into moisture, seemed to disintegrate into minute and venomous particles, like dust that, when Dilsey opened the door of the cabin and emerged, needled laterally into her flesh, precipitating not so much a moisture as a substance partaking of the quality of thin, not quite congealed oil. She wore a stiff black straw hat perched upon her turban, and a maroon velvet cape with a border of mangy and anonymous fur above a dress of purple silk, and she stood in the door for awhile with her myriad and sunken face lifted to the weather, and one gaunt hand flac-soled as the belly of a fish, then she moved the cape aside and examined the bosom of her gown.

The gown fell gauntly from her shoulders, across her fallen breasts, then tightened upon her paunch and fell again, ballooning a little above the nether garments which she would remove layer by layer as the spring accomplished and the warm days, in colour regal and moribund. She had been a big woman once but now her skeleton rose, draped loosely in unpadded skin that tightened again upon a paunch almost dropsical, as though muscle and tissue had been courage or fortitude which the days or the years had consumed until only the indomitable skeleton was left rising like a ruin or a landmark above the somnolent and impervious guts, and above that the collapsed face that gave the impression of the bones themselves being outside the flesh, lifted into the driving day with an expression at once fatalistic and of a child's astonished disappointment, until she turned and entered the house again and closed the door.

The earth immediately about the door was bare. It had a patina, as though from the soles of bare feet in generations, like old silver or the walls of Mexican houses which have been plastered by hand. Beside the house, shading it in summer, stood three mulberry trees, the fledged leaves that would later be broad and placid as the palms of hands streaming flatly undulant upon the driving air. A pair of jaybirds came up from nowhere, whirled up on the blast like gaudy scraps of cloth or paper and lodged in the mulberries, where they swung in raucous tilt and recover, screaming into the wind that ripped their harsh cries onward and away like scraps of paper or of cloth in turn. Then three more joined them and they swung and tilted in the wrung branches for a time, screaming. The door of the cabin opened and Dilsey emerged once more, this time in a man's felt hat and an army overcoat, beneath the frayed skirts of which her blue gingham dress fell in uneven balloonings, streaming too about her as she crossed the yard and mounted the steps to the kitchen door.

A moment later she emerged, carrying an open umbrella now, which she slanted ahead into the wind, and crossed to the woodpile and laid the umbrella down, still open. Immediately she caught at it and arrested it and held to it for a while, looking about her. Then she closed it and laid it down and stacked stove-wood into her crooked arm, against her breast, and picked up the umbrella and got it open at last and returned to the steps and held the wood precariously balanced while she contrived to close the umbrella, which she propped in the corner just within the door. She dumped the wood into the box behind the stove. Then she removed the overcoat and hat and took a soiled apron down from the wall and put it on and built a fire in the stove. While she was doing so, rattling the grate bars and clattering the lids, Mrs Compson began to call her from the head of the stairs.

She wore a dressing gown of quilted black satin, holding it close under her chin. In the other hand she held a red rubber hot water bottle and she stood at the head of the back stairway, calling "Dilsey" at steady and inflectionless intervals into the quiet stair-well that descended into complete darkness, then opened again where a grey window fell across it. "Dilsey," she called, without inflection or emphasis or haste, as though she were not listening for a reply at all. "Dilsey."

Dilsey answered and ceased clattering the stove, but before she could cross the kitchen Mrs Compson called her again, and before she crossed the diningroom and brought her head into relief against the grey splash of the window, still again.

"All right," Dilsey said, "All right, here I is. I'll fill hit soon ez I git some hot water." She gathered up her skirts and mounted the stairs, wholly blotting the grey light. "Put hit down dar en g'awn back to bed."

"I couldn't understand what was the matter," Mrs Compson said. "I've been lying awake for an hour at least, without hearing a sound from the kitchen."

"You put hit down and g'awn back to bed," Dilsey said. She toiled painfully up the steps, shapeless, breathing heavily. "I'll have de fire gwine in a minute, en de water hot in two mo."

"I've been lying there for an hour, at least," Mrs Compson said. "I thought maybe you were waiting for me to come down and start the fire."

Dilsey reached the top of the stairs and took the water bottle. "I'll fix hit in a minute," she said. "Luster overslep dis mawnin, up half de night at dat show. I gwine build de fire myself. Go on now, so you wont wake de others twell I ready."

"If you permit Luster to do things that interfere with his work, you'll have to suffer for it yourself," Mrs Compson said. "Jason wont like this if he hears about it. You know he wont."

"Twusn't none of Jason's money he went on," Dilsey said. "Dat's one thing sho." She went on down the stairs. Mrs Compson returned to her room. As she got into bed again she could hear Dilsey yet descending the stairs with a sort of painful and terrific slowness that would have become maddening had it not presently ceased beyond the flapping diminishment of the pantry door.

She entered the kitchen and built up the fire and began to prepare breakfast. In the midst of this she ceased and went to the window and looked out toward her cabin, then she went to the door and opened it and shouted into the driving weather.

"Luster!" she shouted, standing to listen, tilting her face from the wind, "You, Luster?" She listened, then as she prepared to shout again Luster appeared around the corner of the kitchen.

"Ma'am?" he said innocently, so innocently that Dilsey looked down at him, for a moment motionless with something more than mere surprise.

"Whar you at?" she said.

"Nowhere," he said. "Jes in de cellar."

"Whut you doin in de cellar?" she said. "Dont stand dar in de rain, fool," she said.

"Aint doin nothin," he said. He came up the steps.

"Dont you dare come in dis do widout a armful of wood," she said. "Here I done had to tote yo wood en build yo fire bofe. Didn't I tole you not to leave dis place last night befo dat woodbox wus full to de top?"

"I did," Luster said, "I filled hit."

"Whar hit gone to, den?"

"I dont know'm. I aint teched hit."

"Well, you git hit full up now," she said. "And git on up den en see bout Benjy."

She shut the door. Luster went to the woodpile. The five jaybirds whirled over the house, screaming, and into the mulberries again. He watched them. He picked up a rock and threw it. "Whoo," he said, "Git on back to hell, whar you belong at. 'Taint Monday yit."

He loaded himself mountainously with stove wood. He could not see over it, and he staggered to the steps and up them and blundered crashing against the door, shedding billets. Then Dilsey came and opened the door for him and he blundered across the kitchen. "You, Luster!" she shouted, but he had already hurled the wood into the box with a thunderous crash. "H'h!" he said.

"Is you tryin to wake up de whole house?" Dilsey said. She hit him on the back of his head with the flat of her hand. "Go on up dar and git Benjy dressed, now."

"Yessum," he said. He went toward the outer door.

"Whar you gwine?" Dilsey said.

"I thought I better go round de house en in by de front, so I wont wake up Miss Cahline en dem."

"You go on up dem backstairs like I tole you en git Benjy's clothes on him," Dilsey said. "Go on, now."

"Yessum," Luster said. He returned and left by the dining-room door. After awhile it ceased to flap. Dilsey prepared to make biscuit. As she ground the sifter steadily above the bread board, she sang, to herself at first, something without particular tune or words, repetitive, mournful and plaintive, austere, as she ground a faint, steady snowing of flour onto the breadboard. The stove had begun to heat the room and to fill it with murmurous minors of the fire, and presently she was singing louder, as if her voice too had been thawed out by the growing warmth, and then Mrs Compson called her name again from within the house. Dilsey raised her face as if her eyes could and did penetrate the walls and ceiling and saw the old woman in her quilted dressing gown at the head of the stairs, calling her name with machinelike regularity.

"Oh, Lawd," Dilsey said. She set the sifter down and swept up the hem of her apron and wiped her hands and caught up the bottle from the chair on which she had laid it and gathered her apron about the handle of the kettle which was now jetting faintly. "Jes a minute," she called, "De water jes dis minute got hot."

It was not the bottle which Mrs Compson wanted however, and clutching it by the neck like a dead hen Dilsey went to the foot of the stairs and looked upward.

"Aint Luster up dar wid him?" she said.

"Luster hasn't been in the house. I've been lying here listening for him. I knew he would be late, but I did hope he'd come in time to keep Benjamin from disturbing Jason on Jason's one day in the week to sleep in the morning."

"I dont see how you expect anybody to sleep, wid you standin in de hall, holl'in at folks fum de crack of dawn," Dilsey said.

She began to mount the stairs, toiling heavily. "I sont dat boy up dar half hour ago."

Mrs Compson watched her, holding the dressing gown under her chin. "What are you going to do?" she said.

"Gwine git Benjy dressed en bring him down to de kitchen, whar he wont wake Jason en Quentin," Dilsey said.

"Haven't you started breakfast yet?"

"I'll tend to dat too," Dilsey said. "You better git back in bed twell Luster make yo fire. Hit cold dis mawnin."

"I know it," Mrs Compson said. "My feet are like ice. They were so cold they waked me up." She watched Dilsey mount the stairs. It took her a long while. "You know how it frets Jason when breakfast is late," Mrs Compson said.

"I cant do but one thing at a time," Dilsey said. "You git on back to bed, fo I has you on my hands dis mawnin too."

"If you're going to drop everything to dress Benjamin, I'd better come down and get breakfast. You know as well as I do how Jason acts when it's late."

"En who gwine eat yo messin?" Dilsey said. "Tell me dat. Go on now," she said, toiling upward. Mrs Compson stood watching her as she mounted, steadying herself against the wall with one hand, holding her skirts up with the other.

"Are you going to wake him up just to dress him?" she said.

Dilsey stopped. With her foot lifted to the next step she stood there, her hand against the wall and the grey splash of the window behind her, motionless and shapeless she loomed.

"He aint awake den?" she said.

"He wasn't when I looked in," Mrs Compson said. "But it's past his time. He never does sleep after half past seven. You know he doesn't."

Dilsey said nothing. She made no further move, but though she could not see her save as a blobby shape without depth, Mrs Compson knew that she had lowered her face a little and that she stood now like a cow in the rain, as she held the empty water bottle by its neck.

"You're not the one who has to bear it," Mrs Compson said. "It's not your responsibility. You can go away. You dont have to bear the brunt of it day in and day out. You owe nothing to them, to Mr Compson's memory. I know you have never had any tenderness for Jason. You've never tried to conceal it."

Dilsey said nothing. She turned slowly and descended, lowering her body from step to step, as a small child does, her hand against the wall. "You go on and let him alone," she said. "Dont go in dar no mo, now. I'll send Luster up soon as I find him. Let him alone, now."

She returned to the kitchen. She looked into the stove, then she drew her apron over her head and donned the overcoat and opened the outer door and looked up and down the yard. The weather drove upon her flesh, harsh and minute, but the scene was empty of all else that moved. She descended the steps, gingerly, as if for silence, and went around the corner of the kitchen. As she did so Luster emerged quickly and innocently from the cellar door.

Dilsey stopped. "Whut you up to?" she said.

"Nothin," Luster said, "Mr Jason say fer me to find out what dat water leak in de cellar fum."

"En when wus hit he say fer you to do dat?" Dilsey said. "Last New Year's day, wasn't hit?"

"I thought I jes be lookin whiles dey sleep," Luster said. Dilsey went to the cellar door. He stood aside and she peered down into the obscurity odorous of dank earth and mould and rubber.

"Huh," Dilsey said. She looked at Luster again. He met her gaze blandly, innocent and open. "I dont know whut you up to, but you aint got no business doin hit. You jes tryin me too dis mawnin cause de others is, aint you? You git on up dar en see to Benjy, you hear?"

"Yessum," Luster said. He went on toward the kitchen steps, swiftly.

"Here," Dilsey said, "You git me another armful of wood while I got you."

"Yessum," he said. He passed her on the steps and went to the woodpile. When he blundered again at the door a moment later, again invisible and blind within and beyond his wooden avatar, Dilsey opened the door and guided him across the kitchen with a firm hand.

"Jes throw hit at dat box again," she said, "Jes thow hit."

"I got to," Luster said, panting, "I cant put hit down no other way."

"Den you stand dar en hold hit a while," Dilsey said. She unloaded him a stick at a time. "Whut got into you dis mawnin? Here I sont you fer wood en you aint never brought mo'n six sticks at a time to save yo life twell today. Whut you fixin to ax me kin you do now? Aint dat show lef town yit?"

"Yessum. Hit done gone."

She put the last stick into the box. "Now you go on up dar wid Benjy, like I tole you befo," she said. "And I dont want nobody else yellin down dem stairs at me twell I rings de bell. You hear me."

"Yessum," Luster said. He vanished through the swing door. Dilsey put some more wood in the stove and returned to the bread board. Presently she began to sing again.

The room grew warmer. Soon Dilsey's skin had taken on a rich, lustrous quality as compared with that as of a faint dusting of wood ashes which both it and Luster's had worn, as she moved about the kitchen, gathering about her the raw materials of food, coordinating the meal. On the wall above a cupboard, invisible save at night, by lamp light and even then evincing an enigmatic profundity because it had but one hand, a cabinet clock ticked, then with a preliminary sound as if it had cleared its throat, struck five times.

"Eight oclock," Dilsey said. She ceased and tilted her head upward, listening. But there was no sound save the clock and the fire She opened the oven and looked at the pan of bread, then stooping she paused while someone descended the stairs. She heard the feet across the dining-room, then the swing door opened and Luster entered, followed by a big man who appeared to have been shaped of some substance whose particles would not or did not cohere to one another or to the frame which supported it. His skin was dead looking and hairless; dropsical too, he moved with a shambling gait like a trained bear. His hair was pale and fine. It had been brushed smoothly down upon his brow like that of children in daguerrotypes. His eyes were clear, of the pale sweet blue of cornflowers, his thick mouth hung open, drooling a little.

"Is he cold?" Dilsey said. She wiped her hands on her apron and touched his hand.

"Ef he aint, I is," Luster said. "Always cold Easter. Aint never seen hit fail. Miss Cahline say ef you aint got time to fix her hot water bottle to never mind about hit."

"Oh, 'lawd," Dilsey said. She drew a chair into the corner between the woodbox and the stove. The man went obediently and sat in it. "Look in de dinin room and see whar I laid dat bottle down," Dilsey said. Luster fetched the bottle from the dining-room and Dilsey filled it and gave it to him. "Hurry up, now," she said. "See ef Jason wake now. Tell em hit's all ready."

Luster went out. Ben sat beside the stove. He sat loosely, utterly motionless save for his head, which made a continual bobbing sort of movement as he watched Dilsey with his sweet vague gaze as she moved about. Luster returned.

"He up," he said, "Miss Cahline say put hit on de table." He came to the stove and spread his hands palm down above the firebox. "He up, too," he said, "Gwine hit wid bofe feet dis mawnin."

"Whut's de matter now?" Dilsey said. "Git away fum dar. How kin I do anything wid you standin over de stove?"

"I cold," Luster said.

"You ought to thought about dat whiles you wus down dar in dat cellar," Dilsey said. "Whut de matter wid Jason?"

"Sayin me en Benjy broke dat winder in his room."

"Is dey one broke?" Dilsey said.

"Dat's whut he sayin," Luster said. "Say I broke hit."

"How could you, when he keep hit locked all day en night?"

"Say I broke hit chunkin rocks at hit," Luster said.

"En did you?"

"Nome," Luster said.

"Dont lie to me, boy," Dilsey said.

"I never done hit," Luster said. "Ask Benjy ef I did. I aint stud'in dat winder."

"Who could a broke hit, den?" Dilsey said. "He jes tryin hisself, to wake Quentin up," she said, taking the pan of biscuits out of the stove.

"Reckin so," Luster said. "Dese is funny folks. Glad I aint none of em."

"Aint none of who?" Dilsey said. "Lemme tell you somethin, nigger boy, you got jes es much Compson devilment in you es any of em. Is you right sho you never broke dat window?"

"Whut I want to break hit fur?"

"Whut you do any of you devilment fur?" Dilsey said. "Watch him now, so he cant burn his hand again twell I git de table set."

She went to the diningroom, where they heard her moving about, then she returned and set a plate at the kitchen table and set food there. Ben watched her, slobbering, making a faint, eager sound.

"All right, honey," she said, "Here yo breakfast. Bring his

chair, Luster." Luster moved the chair up and Ben sat down, whimpering and slobbering. Dilsey tied a cloth about his neck and wiped his mouth with the end of it. "And see kin you kep fum messin up his clothes one time," she said, handing Luster a spoon.

Ben ceased whimpering. He watched the spoon as it rose to his mouth. It was as if even eagerness were muscle-bound in him too, and hunger itself inarticulate, not knowing it is hunger. Luster fed him with skill and detachment. Now and then his attention would return long enough to enable him to feint the spoon and cause Ben to close his mouth upon the empty air, but it was apparent that Luster's mind was elsewhere. His other hand lay on the back of the chair and upon that dead surface it moved tentatively, delicately, as if he were picking an inaudible tune out of the dead void, and once he even forgot to tease Ben with the spoon while his fingers teased out of the slain wood a soundless and involved arpeggio until Ben recalled him by whimpering again.

In the diningroom Dilsey moved back and forth. Presently she rang a small clear bell, then in the kitchen Luster heard Mrs Compson and Jason descending, and Jason's voice, and he rolled his eyes whitely with listening.

"Sure, I know they didn't break it," Jason said. "Sure, I know that. Maybe the change of weather broke it."

"I dont see how it could have," Mrs Compson said. "Your room stays locked all day long, just as you leave it when you go to town. None of us ever go in there except Sunday, to clean it. I dont want you to think that I would go where I'm not wanted, or that I would permit anyone else to."

"I never said you broke it, did I?" Jason said.

"I dont want to go in your room," Mrs Compson said. "I respect anybody's private affairs, I wouldn't put my foot over the threshold, even if I had a key."

"Yes," Jason said, "I know your keys wont fit. That's why I had the lock changed. What I want to know is, how that window got broken."

"Luster say he didn't do hit," Dilsey said.

"I knew that without asking him," Jason said. "Where's Quentin?" he said.

"Where she is ev'y Sunday mawnin," Dilsey said. "Whut got into you de last few days, anyhow?"

"Well, we're going to change all that," Jason said. "Go up and tell her breakfast is ready."

"You leave her alone now, Jason," Dilsey said. "She gits up fer breakfast ev'y week mawnin, en Cahline lets her stay in bed ev'y Sunday. You knows dat."

"I cant keep a kitchen full of niggers to wait on her pleasure, much as I'd like to," Jason said. "Go and tell her to come down to breakfast."

"Aint nobody have to wait on her," Dilsey said. "I puts her breakfast in de warmer en she—"

"Did you hear me?" Jason said.

"I hears you," Dilsey said. "All I been hearin, when you in de house. Ef hit aint Quentin er yo maw, hit's Luster en Benjy. Whut you let him go on dat way fer, Miss Cahline?"

"You'd better do as he says," Mrs Compson said, "He's head of the house now. It's his right to require us to respect his wishes. I try to do it, and if I can, you can too."

"Taint no sense in him bein so bad tempered he got to make Quentin git up jes to suit him," Dilsey said. "Maybe you think she broke dat window."

"She would, if she happened to think of it," Jason said. "You go and do what I told you."

"En I wouldn't blame her none ef she did," Dilsey said, going toward the stairs. "Wid you naggin at her all de blessed time yo in de house."

"Hush, Dilsey," Mrs Compson said, "It's neither your place nor mine to tell Jason what to do. Sometimes I think he is wrong, but I try to obey his wishes for you alls' sakes. If I'm strong enough to come to the table, Quentin can too."

Dilsey went out. They heard her mounting the stairs. They heard her a long while on the stairs.

"You've got a prize set of servants," Jason said. He helped his mother and himself to food. "Did you ever have one that was worth killing? You must have had some before I was big enough to remember."

"I have to humour them," Mrs Compson said. "I have to depend on them so completely. It's not as if I were strong. I wish I were. I wish I could do all the house work myself. I could at least take that much off your shoulders."

"And a fine pigsty we'd live in, too," Jason said. "Hurry up, Dilsey," he shouted.

"I know you blame me," Mrs Compson said, "for letting them off to go to church today."

"Go where?" Jason said. "Hasn't that damn show left yet?"

"To church," Mrs Compson said. "The darkies are having a special Easter service. I promised Dilsey two weeks ago that they could get off."

"Which means we'll eat cold dinner," Jason said, "or none at all."

"I know it's my fault," Mrs Compson said. "I know you blame me."

"For what?" Jason said. "You never resurrected Christ, did you?"

They heard Dilsey mount the final stair, then her slow feet overhead.

"Quentin," she said. When she called the first time Jason laid his knife and fork down and he and his mother appeared to wait across the table from one another, in identical attitudes; the one cold and shrewd, with close-thatched brown hair curled into two stubborn hooks, one on either side of his forehead like a bartender in caricature, and hazel eyes with black-ringed irises like marbles, the other cold and querulous, with perfectly white hair and eyes pouched and baffled and so dark as to appear to be all pupil or all iris.

"Quentin," Dilsey said, "Git up, honey. Dey waitin breakfast on you."

"I cant understand how that window got broken," Mrs Compson said. "Are you sure it was done yesterday? It could have been like that a long time, with the warm weather. The upper sash, behind the shade like that."

"I've told you for the last time that it happened yesterday," Jason said. "Dont you reckon I know the room I live in? Do you reckon I could have lived in it a week with a hole in the window you could stick your hand—" his voice ceased, ebbed, left him staring at his mother with eyes that for an instant were quite empty of anything. It was as though his eyes were holding their breath, while his mother looked at him, her face flaccid and querulous, interminable, clairvoyant yet obtuse. As they sat so Dilsey said,

"Quentin. Dont play wid me, honey. Come on to breakfast, honey. Dey waitin fer you."

"I cant understand it," Mrs Compson said, "It's just as if somebody had tried to break into the house—" Jason sprang up. His chair crashed over backward. "What—" Mrs Compson said, staring at him as he ran past her and went jumping up the stairs, where he met Dilsey. His face was now in shadow, and Dilsey said,

"She sullin. Yo ma aint unlocked—" But Jason ran on past her and along the corridor to a door. He didn't call. He grasped the knob and tried it, then he stood with the knob in his hand and his head bent a little, as if he were listening to something much further away than the dimensioned room beyond the door, and which he already heard. His attitude was that of one who goes through the motions of listening in order to deceive himself as to what he already hears. Behind him Mrs Compson mounted the stairs, calling his name. Then she saw Dilsey and she quit calling him and began to call Dilsey instead.

"I told you she aint unlocked dat do' yit," Dilsey said.

When she spoke he turned and ran toward her, but his voice was quiet, matter of fact. "She carry the key with her?" he said. "Has she got it now, I mean, or will she have—"

"Dilsey," Mrs Compson said on the stairs.

"Is which?" Dilsey said. "Whyn't you let—"

"The key," Jason said. "To that room. Does she carry it with her all the time. Mother." Then he saw Mrs Compson and he went down the stairs and met her. "Give me the key," he said. He fell to pawing at the pockets of the rusty black dressing sacque she wore. She resisted.

"Jason," she said, "Jason! Are you and Dilsey trying to put me to bed again?" she said, trying to fend him off, "Cant you even let me have Sunday in peace?"

"The key," Jason said, pawing at her, "Give it here." He looked back at the door, as if he expected it to fly open before he could get back to it with the key he did not have.

"You, Dilsey!" Mrs Compson said, clutching her sacque about her.

"Give me the key, you old fool!" Jason cried suddenly. From her pocket he tugged a huge bunch of rusted keys on an iron ring like a mediaeval jailer's and ran back up the hall with the two women behind him.

"You, Jason!" Mrs Compson said. "He will never find the right one," she said, "You know I never let anyone take my keys, Dilsey," she said. She began to wail.

"Hush," Dilsey said, "He aint gwine do nothin to her. I aint gwine let him."

"But on Sunday morning, in my own house," Mrs Compson

said, "When I've tried so hard to raise them Christians. Let me find the right key, Jason," she said. She put her hand on his arm. Then she began to struggle with him, but he flung her aside with a motion of his elbow and looked around at her for a moment, his eyes cold and harried, then he turned to the door again and the unwieldy keys.

"Hush," Dilsey said, "You, Jason!"

"Something terrible has happened," Mrs Compson said, wailing again, "I know it has. You, Jason," she said, grasping at him again. "He wont even let me find the key to a room in my own house!"

"Now, now," Dilsey said, "Whut kin happen? I right here. I aint gwine let him hurt her. Quentin," she said, raising her voice, "Dont you be skeered, honey, I'se right here."

The door opened, swung inward. He stood in it for a moment, hiding the room, then he stepped aside. "Go in," he said in a thick, light voice. They went in. It was not a girl's room. It was not anybody's room, and the faint scent of cheap cosmetics and the few feminine objects and other evidences of crude and hopeless efforts to feminize it but added to its anonymity, giving it that dead and stereotyped transience of rooms in assignation houses. The bed had not been disturbed. On the floor lay a soiled undergarment of cheap silk a little too pink; from a half open bureau drawer dangled a single stocking. The window was open. A pear tree grew there, close against the house. It was in bloom and the branches scraped and rasped against the house and the myriad air, driving in the window, brought into the room the forlorn scent of the blossoms.

"Dar now," Dilsey said, "Didn't I told you she all right?"

"All right?" Mrs Compson said. Dilsey followed her into the room and touched her.

"You come on and lay down, now," she said. "I find her in ten minutes."

Mrs Compson shook her off. "Find the note," she said. "Quentin left a note when he did it."

"All right," Dilsey said, "I'll find hit. You come on to yo room, now."

"I knew the minute they named her Quentin this would happen," Mrs Compson said. She went to the bureau and began to turn over the scattered objects there—scent bottles, a box of powder, a chewed pencil, a pair of scissors with one broken blade lying upon a darned scarf dusted with powder and stained with rouge. "Find the note," she said.

"I is," Dilsey said. "You come on, now. Me and Jason'll find hit. You come on to yo room."

"Jason," Mrs Compson said, "Where is he?" She went to the door. Dilsey followed her on down the hall, to another door. It was closed. "Jason," she called through the door. There was no answer. She tried the knob, then she called him again. But there was still no answer, for he was hurling things backward out of the closet: garments, shoes, a suitcase. Then he emerged carrying a sawn section of tongue-and-groove planking and laid it down and entered the closet again and emerged with a metal box. He set it on the bed and stood looking at the broken lock while he dug a key ring from his pocket and selected a key, and for a time longer he stood with the selected key in his hand, looking at the broken lock, then he put the keys back in his pocket and carefully tilted the contents of the box out upon the bed. Still carefully he sorted the papers, taking them up one at a time and shaking them. Then he upended the box and shook it too and slowly replaced the papers and stood again, looking at the broken lock, with the box in his hands and his head bent. Outside the window he heard some jaybirds swirl shrieking past, and away, their cries whipping away along the wind, and an automobile passed somewhere and died away also. His mother spoke his name again beyond the door, but he didn't move. He heard Dilsey lead her away up the hall, and then a door closed. Then he replaced the box in the closet and flung the garments back into it and went down stairs to the telephone. While he stood there with the receiver to his ear, waiting, Dilsey came down the stairs. She looked at him, without stopping, and went on.

The wire opened. "This is Jason Compson," he said, his voice so harsh and thick that he had to repeat himself. "Jason Compson," he said, controlling his voice. "Have a car ready, with a deputy, if you cant go, in ten minutes. I'll be there—What?—Robbery. My house. I know who it—Robbery, I say. Have a car ready—What? Aren't you a paid law enforcement—Yes, I'll be there in five minutes. Have that car ready to leave at once. If you dont, I'll report it to the governor."

He clapped the receiver back and crossed the diningroom, where the scarce-broken meal now lay cold on the table, and entered the kitchen. Dilsey was filling the hot water bottle. Ben sat, tranquil and empty. Beside him Luster looked like a fice dog, brightly watchful. He was eating something. Jason went on across the kitchen.

"Aint you going to eat no breakfast?" Dilsey said. He paid her no attention. "Go and eat yo breakfast, Jason." He went on. The outer door banged behind him. Luster rose and went to the window and looked out.

"Whoo," he said, "Whut happenin up dar? He been beatin' Miss Quentin?"

"You hush yo mouf," Dilsey said. "You git Benjy started now en I beat yo head off. You keep him quiet es you kin twell I get back, now." She screwed the cap on the bottle and went out. They heard her go up the stairs, then they heard Jason pass the house in his car. Then there was no sound in the kitchen save the simmering murmur of the kettle and the clock.

"You know whut I bet?" Luster said. "I bet he beat her. I bet he knock her in de head en now he gone fer de doctor. Dat's whut I bet." The clock tick-tocked, solemn and profound. It might have been the dry pulse of the decaying house itself; after a while it whirred and cleared its throat and struck six times. Ben looked up at it, then he looked at the bullet-like silhouette of Luster's head in the window and he begun to bob his head again, drooling. He whimpered.

"Hush up, loony," Luster said without turning. "Look like we aint gwine git to go to no church today." But Ben sat in the chair, his big soft hands dangling between his knees, moaning faintly. Suddenly he wept, a slow bellowing sound, meaningless and sustained. "Hush," Luster said. He turned and lifted his hand. "You want me to whup you?" But Ben looked at him, bellowing slowly with each expiration. Luster came and shook him. "You hush dis minute!" he shouted. "Here," he said. He hauled Ben out of the chair and dragged the chair around facing the stove and opened the door to the firebox and shoved Ben into the chair. They looked like a tug nudging at a clumsy tanker in a narrow dock. Ben sat down again facing the rosy door. He hushed. Then they heard the clock again, and Dilsey slow on the stairs. When she entered he began to whimper again. Then he lifted his voice.

"Whut you done to him?" Dilsey said. "Why cant you let him lone dis mawnin, of all times?"

"I aint doin nothin to him," Luster said. "Mr Jason skeered him, dat's whut hit is. He aint kilt Miss Quentin, is he?"

"Hush, Benjy," Dilsey said. He hushed. She went to the window and looked out. "Is it quit rainin?" she said.

"Yessum," Luster said. "Quit long time ago."

"Den ya'll go out do's a while," she said. "I jes got Miss Cahline quiet now."

"Is we gwine to church?" Luster said.

"I let you know bout dat when de time come. You keep him away fum de house twell I calls you."

"Kin we go to de pastuh?" Luster said.

"All right. Only you keep him away fum de house. I done stood all I kin."

"Yessum," Luster said. "Whar Mr Jason gone, mammy?"

"Dat's some mo of yo business, aint it?" Dilsey said. She began to clear the table. "Hush, Benjy. Luster gwine take you out to play."

"Whut he done to Miss Quentin, mammy?" Luster said.

"Aint done nothin to her. You all git on outen here."

"I bet she aint here," Luster said.

Dilsey looked at him. "How you know she aint here?"

"Me and Benjy seed her clamb out de window last night. Didn't us, Benjy?"

"You did?" Dilsey said, looking at him.

"We sees her doin hit ev'y night," Luster said, "Clamb right down dat pear tree."

"Dont you lie to me, nigger boy," Dilsey said.

"I aint lyin. Ask Benjy ef I is."

"Whyn't you say somethin about it, den?"

" 'Twarn't none o my business," Luster said. "I aint gwine git mixed up in white folks' business. Come on here, Benjy, les go out do's."

They went out. Dilsey stood for awhile at the table, then she went and cleared the breakfast things from the diningroom and ate her breakfast and cleaned up the kitchen. Then she removed her apron and hung it up and went to the foot of the stairs and listened for a moment. There was no sound. She donned the overcoat and the hat and went across to her cabin.

The rain had stopped. The air now drove out of the southeast, broken overhead into blue patches. Upon the crest of a hill beyond the trees and roofs and spires of town sunlight lay like a pale scrap of cloth, was blotted away. Upon the air a bell came, then as if at a signal, other bells took up the sound and repeated it.

The cabin door opened and Dilsey emerged, again in the maroon cape and the purple gown, and wearing soiled white elbow-length gloves and minus her headcloth now. She came into the yard and called Luster. She waited awhile, then she went to the house and around it to the cellar door, moving close to the wall, and looked into the door. Ben sat on the steps. Before him Luster squatted on the damp floor. He held a saw in his left hand, the blade sprung a little by pressure of his hand, and he was in the act of striking the blade with the worn wooden mallet with which she had been making beaten biscuit for more than thirty years. The saw gave forth a single sluggish twang that ceased with lifeless alacrity, leaving the blade in a thin clean curve between Luster's hand and the floor. Still, inscrutable, it bellied.

"Dat's de way he done hit," Luster said. "I jes aint foun de right thing to hit it wid."

"Dat's whut you doin, is it?" Dilsey said. "Bring me dat mallet," she said.

"I aint hurt hit," Luster said.

"Bring hit here," Dilsey said. "Put dat saw whar you got hit first."

He put the saw away and brought the mallet to her. Then Ben wailed again, hopeless and prolonged. It was nothing. Just sound. It might have been all time and injustice and sorrow become vocal for an instant by a conjunction of planets.

"Listen at him," Luster said, "He been gwine on dat way ev'y since you sont us outen de house. I dont know whut got in to him dis mawnin."

"Bring him here," Dilsey said.

"Come on, Benjy," Luster said. He went back down the steps and took Ben's arm. He came obediently, wailing, that slow hoarse sound that ships make, that seems to begin before the sound itself has started, seems to cease before the sound itself has stopped.

"Run and git his cap," Dilsey said. "Dont make no noise Miss Cahline kin hear. Hurry, now. We already late."

"She gwine hear him anyhow, ef you dont stop him." Luster said.

"He stop when we git off de place," Dilsey said. "He smellin hit. Dat's whut hit is."

"Smell whut, mammy?" Luster said.

"You go git dat cap," Dilsey said. Luster went on. They stood in the cellar door, Ben one step below her. The sky was broken now into scudding patches that dragged their swift shadows up out of the shabby garden, over the broken fence and across the yard. Dilsey stroked Ben's head, slowly and steadily, smoothing the bang upon his brow. He wailed quietly, unhurriedly. "Hush," Dilsey said, "Hush, now. We be gone in a minute. Hush, now." He wailed quietly and steadily.

Luster returned, wearing a stiff new straw hat with a coloured band and carrying a cloth cap. The hat seemed to isolate Luster's skull, in the beholder's eye as a spotlight would, in all its individual planes and angles. So peculiarly individual was its shape that at first glance the hat appeared to be on the head of someone standing immediately behind Luster. Dilsey looked at the hat.

"Whyn't you wear yo old hat?" she said.

"Couldn't find hit," Luster said.

"I bet you couldn't. I bet you fixed hit last night so you couldn't find hit. You fixin to ruin dat un."

"Aw, mammy," Luster said, "Hit aint gwine rain."

"How you know? You go git dat old hat en put dat new un away."

"Aw, mammy."

"Den you go git de umbreller."

"Aw, mammy."

"Take yo choice," Dilsey said. "Git yo old hat, er de umbreller. I dont keer which."

Luster went to the cabin. Ben wailed quietly.

"Come on," Dilsey said, "Dey kin ketch up wid us. We gwine to hear de singin." They went around the house, toward the gate. "Hush," Dilsey said from time to time as they went down the drive. They reached the gate. Dilsey opened it. Luster was coming down the drive behind them, carrying the umbrella. A woman was with him. "Here dey come," Dilsey said. They passed out the gate. "Now, den," she said. Ben ceased. Luster and his mother overtook them. Frony wore a dress of bright blue silk and a flowered hat. She was a thin woman, with a flat pleasant face.

"You got six weeks' work right dar on yo back," Dilsey said. "Whut you gwine do ef hit rain?"

"Git wet, I reckon," Frony said. "I aint never stopped no rain yit."

"Mammy always talkin bout hit gwine rain," Luster said.

"Ef I dont worry bout y'all, I dont know who is," Dilsey said. "Come on, we already late."

"Rev'un Shegog gwine preach today," Frony said.

"Is?" Dilsey said. "Who him?"

"He fum Saint Looey," Frony said. "Dat big preacher."

"Huh," Dilsey said, "Whut dey needs is a man kin put de fear of God into dese here triflin young niggers."

"Rev'un Shegog gwine preach today," Frony said. "So dey tells."

They went on along the street. Along its quiet length white people in bright clumps moved churchward, under the windy bells, walking now and then in the random and tentative sun. The wind was gusty, out of the southeast, chill and raw after the warm days.

"I wish you wouldn't keep on bringin him to church, mammy," Frony said. "Folks talkin."

"Whut folks?" Dilsey said.

"I hears em," Frony said.

"And I knows whut kind of folks," Dilsey said, "Trash white folks. Dat's who it is. Thinks he aint good enough fer white church, but nigger church aint good enough fer him."

"Dey talks, jes de same," Frony said.

"Den you send um to me," Dilsey said. "Tell um de good Lawd dont keer whether he smart er not. Dont nobody but white trash keer dat."

A street turned off at right angles, descending, and became a dirt road. On either hand the land dropped more sharply; a broad flat dotted with small cabins whose weathered roofs were on a level with the crown of the road. They were set in small grassless plots littered with broken things, bricks, planks, crockery, things of a once utilitarian value. What growth there was consisted of rank weeds and the trees were mulberries and locusts and syca-mores—trees that partook also of the foul desiccation which sur-rounded the houses; trees whose very burgeoning seemed to be the sad and stubborn remnant of September, as if even spring had passed them by, leaving them to feed upon the rich and unmis-takable smell of Negroes in which they grew.

From the doors Negroes spoke to them as they passed, to Dil-sey usually:

"Sis' Gibson! How you dis mawnin?"

"I'm well. Is you well?"

"I'm right well, I thank you."

They emerged from the cabins and struggled up the shading levee to the road—men in staid, hard brown or black, with gold watch chains and now and then a stick; young men in cheap violent blues or stripes and swaggering hats; women a little stiffly sibilant, and children in garments bought second hand of white people, who looked at Ben with the covertness of nocturnal animals:

"I bet you wont go up en tech him."

"How come I wont?"

"I bet you wont. I bet you skeered to."

"He wont hurt folks. He des a loony."

"How come a loony wont hurt folks?"

"Dat un wont. I teched him."

"I bet you wont now."

"Case Miss Dilsey lookin."

"You wont no ways."

"He dont hurt folks. He des a loony."

And steadily the older people speaking to Dilsey, though, unless they were quite old, Dilsey permitted Frony to respond.

"Mammy aint feelin well dis mawnin."

"Dat's too bad. But Rev'un Shegog'll cure dat. He'll give her de comfort en de unburdenin."

The road rose again, to a scene like a painted backdrop. Notched into a cut of red clay crowned with oaks the road appeared to stop short off, like a cut ribbon. Beside it a weathered church lifted its crazy steeple like a painted church, and the whole scene was as flat and without perspective as a painted cardboard set upon the ultimate edge of the flat earth, against the windy sunlight of space and April and a midmorning filled with bells. Toward the church they thronged with slow sabbath deliberation. The women and children went on in, the men stopped outside and talked in quiet groups until the bell ceased ringing. Then they too entered.

The church had been decorated, with sparse flowers from kitchen gardens and hedgerows, and with streamers of coloured crepe paper. Above the pulpit hung a battered Christmas bell, the accordion sort that collapses. The pulpit was empty, though the choir was already in place, fanning themselves although it was not warm.

Most of the women were gathered on one side of the room. They were talking. Then the bell struck one time and they dispersed to their seats and the congregation sat for an instant, expectant. The bell struck again one time. The choir rose and began to sing and the congregation turned its head as one, as six small children—four girls with tight pigtails bound with small scraps of cloth like butterflies, and two boys with close napped heads,—entered and marched up the aisle, strung together in a harness of white ribbons and flowers, and followed by two men in single file. The second man was huge, of a light coffee colour, imposing in a frock coat and white tie. His head was magisterial and profound, his neck rolled above his collar in rich folds. But he was familiar to them, and so the heads were still reverted when he had passed, and it was not until the choir ceased singing that they realised that the visiting clergyman had already entered, and when they saw the man who had preceded their minister enter the pulpit still ahead of him an indescribable sound went up, a sigh, a sound of astonishment and disappointment.

The visitor was undersized, in a shabby alpaca coat. He had a wizened black face like a small, aged monkey. And all the while that the choir sang again and while the six children rose and sang in thin, frightened, tuneless whispers, they watched the insignificant looking man sitting dwarfed and countrified by the minister's imposing bulk, with something like consternation. They were still looking at him with consternation and unbelief when the minister rose and introduced him in rich, rolling tones whose very unction served to increase the visitor's insignificance.

"En dey brung dat all de way fum Saint Looey," Frony whispered.

"I've knowed de Lawd to use cuiser tools dan dat," Dilsey said. "Hush, now," she said to Ben, "Dey fixin to sing again in a minute."

When the visitor rose to speak he sounded like a white man. His voice was level and cold. It sounded too big to have come from him and they listened at first through curiosity, as they would have to a monkey talking. They began to watch him as they would a man on a tight rope. They even forgot his insignificant appearance in the virtuosity with which he ran and poised and swooped upon the cold inflectionless wire of his voice, so that at last, when with a sort of swooping glide he came to rest again beside the reading desk with one arm resting upon it at shoulder height and his monkey body as reft of all motion as a mummy or an emptied vessel, the congregation sighed as if it waked from a collective dream and moved a little in its seats. Behind the pulpit the choir fanned steadily. Dilsey whispered, "Hush, now. Dey fixin to sing in a minute."

Then a voice said, "Brethren."

The preacher had not moved. His arm lay yet across the desk, and he still held that pose while the voice died in sonorous echoes between the walls. It was as different as day and dark from his former tone, with a sad, timbrous quality like an alto horn, sinking into their hearts and speaking there again when it had ceased in fading and cumulate echoes.

"Brethren and sisteren," it said again. The preacher removed his arm and he began to walk back and forth before the desk, his hands clasped behind him, a meagre figure, hunched over upon itself like that of one long immured in striving with the implacable earth, "I got the recollection and the blood of the Lamb!" He tramped steadily back and forth beneath the twisted paper and the Christmas bell, hunched, his hands clasped behind him. He was like a worn small rock whelmed by the successive waves of his voice. With his body he seemed to feed the voice that, succubus like, had fleshed its teeth in him. And the congregation seemed to watch with its own eyes while the voice consumed him, until he was nothing and they were nothing and there was not even a voice but instead their hearts were speaking to one another in chanting measures beyond the need for words, so that when he came to rest against the reading desk, his monkey face lifted and his whole attitude that of a serene, tortured crucifix that transcended its shabbiness and insignificance and made it of no moment, a long moaning expulsion of breath rose from them, and a woman's single soprano: "Yes, Jesus!"

As the scudding day passed overhead the dingy windows glowed and faded in ghostly retrograde. A car passed along the road outside, labouring in the sand, died away. Dilsey sat bolt upright, her hand on Ben's knee. Two tears slid down her fallen cheeks, in and out of the myriad coruscations of immolation and abnegation and time.

"Brethren," the minister said in a harsh whisper, without moving.

"Yes, Jesus!" The woman's voice said, hushed yet.

"Breddren en sistuhn!" His voice rang again, with the horns. He removed his arm and stood erect and raised his hands. "I got de ricklickshun en de blood of de Lamb!" They did not mark just when his intonation, his pronunciation, became negroid, they just sat swaying a little in their seats as the voice took them into itself.

"When de long, cold—Oh, I tells you, breddren, when de long, cold—I sees de light en I sees de word, po sinner! Dey passed away in Egypt, de swingin chariots; de generations passed away. Wus a rich man: whar he now, O breddren? Was a po man: whar he now, O sistuhn? Oh I tells you, ef you aint got de milk en de dew of de old salvation when de long, cold years rolls away!"

"Yes, Jesus!"

"I tells you, breddren, en I tells you, sistuhn, dey'll come a time. Po sinner saying Let me lay down wid de Lawd, lemme lay down my load. Den whut Jesus gwine say, O breddren? O sistuhn? Is you got de ricklickshun en de Blood of de Lamb? Case I aint gwine load down heaven!"

He fumbled in his coat and took out a handkerchief and mopped his face. A low concerted sound rose from the congregation: "Mmmmmmmmmmmmm!" The woman's voice said, "Yes, Jesus! Jesus!"

"Breddren! Look at dem like chillen settin dar. Jesus wus like dat once. He mammy suffered de glory en de pangs. Sometime maybe she helt him at de nightfall, whilst de angels singin him to sleep; maybe she look out de do' en see de Roman po-lice passin." He tramped back and forth, mopping his face. "Listen, breddren! I sees de day. Ma'y settin in de do' wid Jesus on her lap, de little Jesus. Like dem chillen dar, de little Jesus. I hears de angels singin de peaceful songs en de glory; I sees de closin eyes; sees Mary jump up, sees de sojer face: We gwine to kill! We gwine to kill! We gwine to kill yo little Jesus! I hears de weepin en de lamentation of de po mammy widout de salvation en de word of God!"

"Mmmmmmmmmmmmmmmmm! Jesus! Little Jesus!" and another voice, rising:

"I sees, O Jesus! Oh I sees!" and still another, without words, like bubbles rising in water.

"I sees hit, breddren! I sees hit! Sees de blastin, blindin sight! I sees Calvary, wid de sacred trees, sees de thief en de murderer en de least of dese; I hears de boasting en de braggin: Ef you be Jesus, lif up you tree en walk! I hears de wailin of women en de evenin lamentations; I hear de weeping en de crying en de turnt-away face of God: dey done kilt Jesus; dey done kilt my son!"

"Mmmmmmmmmmmmmmmm. Jesus! I sees, O Jesus!"

"O blind sinner! Breddren, I tells you; sistuhn, I says to you, when de Lawd did turn His mighty face, say, Aint gwine overload heaven! I can see de widowed God shet His do'; I sees de whelmin flood roll between; I sees de darkness en de death everlastin upon de generations. Den, lo! Breddren! Yes, breddren! whut I see? Whut I see, O sinner? I sees de resurrection en de light; sees de meek Jesus sayin Dey kilt Me dat ye shall live again; I died dat dem whut sees en believes shall never die. Breddren, O breddren! I sees de doom crack en hears de golden horns shoutin down de glory, en de arisen dead whut got de blood en de ricklickshun of de Lamb!"

In the midst of the voices and the hands Ben sat, rapt in his sweet blue gaze. Dilsey sat bolt upright beside, crying rigidly and quietly in the annealment and the blood of the remembered Lamb.

As they walked through the bright noon, up the sandy road with the dispersing congregation talking easily again group to group, she continued to weep, unmindful of the talk.

"He sho a preacher, mon! He didn't look like much at first, but hush!"

"He seed de power en de glory."

"Yes, suh. He seed hit. Face to face he seed hit."

Dilsey made no sound, her face did not quiver as the tears took their sunken and devious courses, walking with her head up, making no effort to dry them away even.

"Whyn't you quit dat, mammy?" Frony said. "Wid all dese people lookin. We be passin white folks soon."

"I've seed de first en de last," Dilsey said. "Never you mind me."

"First en last whut?" Frony said.

"Never you mind," Dilsey said. "I seed de beginnin, en now I sees de endin."

Before they reached the street, though, she stopped and lifted her skirt and dried her eyes on the hem of her topmost underskirt. Then they went on. Ben shambled along beside Dilsey, watching Luster who anticked along ahead, the umbrella in his hand and his new straw hat slanted viciously in the sunlight, like a big foolish dog watching a small clever one. They reached the gate and entered. Immediately Ben began to whimper again, and for a while all of them looked up the drive at the square, paintless house with its rotting portico.

"Whut's gwine on up dar today?" Frony said. "Something is."

"Nothin," Dilsey said. "You tend to yo business en let de white folks tend to deir'n."

"Somethin is," Frony said. "I heard him first thing dis mawnin. 'Taint none of my business, dough."

"En I knows whut, too," Luster said.

"You knows mo dan you got any use fer," Dilsey said. "Aint you jes heard Frony say hit aint none of yo business? You take Benjy on to de back and keep him quiet twell I put dinner on."

"I knows whar Miss Quentin is," Luster said.

"Den jes keep hit," Dilsey said. "Soon es Quentin need any of yo egvice, I'll let you know. Y'all g'awn en play in de back, now."

"You know whut gwine happen soon es dey start playin that ball over yonder," Luster said.

"Dey wont start fer awhile yit. By dat time T. P. be here to take him ridin. Here, you gimme dat new hat."

Luster gave her the hat and he and Ben went on across the back yard. Ben was still whimpering, though not loud. Dilsey and Frony went to the cabin. After a while Dilsey emerged, again in the faded calico dress, and went to the kitchen. The fire had died down. There was no sound in the house. She put on the apron and went up stairs. There was no sound anywhere. Quentin's room was as they had left it. She entered and picked up the undergarment and put the stocking back in the drawer and closed it. Mrs Compson's door was closed. Dilsey stood beside it for a moment, listening. Then she opened it and entered, entered a pervading reek of camphor. The shades were drawn, the room in halflight, and the bed, so that at first she thought Mrs Compson was asleep and was about to close the door when the other spoke.

"Well?" she said, "What is it?"

"Hit's me," Dilsey said. "You want anything?"

Mrs Compson didn't answer. After awhile, without moving her head at all, she said: "Where's Jason?"

"He aint come back yit," Dilsey said. "Whut you want?"

Mrs Compson said nothing. Like so many cold, weak people, when faced at last by the incontrovertible disaster she exhumed from somewhere a sort of fortitude, strength. In her case it was an unshakable conviction regarding the yet unplumbed event. "Well," she said presently, "Did you find it?"

"Find whut? Whut you talkin about?"

"The note. At least she would have enough consideration to leave a note. Even Quentin did that."

"Whut you talkin about?" Dilsey said, "Dont you know she all right? I bet she be walkin right in dis do' befo dark."

"Fiddlesticks," Mrs Compson said, "It's in the blood. Like uncle, like niece. Or mother. I dont know which would be worse. I dont seem to care."

"Whut you keep on talkin that way fur?" Dilsey said. "Whut she want to do anything like that fur?"

"I dont know. What reason did Quentin have? Under God's heaven what reason did he have? It cant be simply to flout and hurt me. Whoever God is, He would not permit that. I'm a lady. You might not believe that from my offspring, but I am."

"You des wait en see," Dilsey said. "She be here by night, right dar in her bed." Mrs Compson said nothing. The camphor-soaked cloth lay upon her brow. The black robe lay across the foot of the bed. Dilsey stood with her hand on the door knob.

"Well," Mrs Compson said. "What do you want? Are you going to fix some dinner for Jason and Benjamin, or not?"

"Jason aint come yit," Dilsey said. "I gwine fix somethin. You sho you dont want nothin? Yo bottle still hot enough?"

"You might hand me my Bible."

"I give hit to you dis mawnin, befo I left."

"You laid it on the edge of the bed. How long did you expect it to stay there?"

Dilsey crossed to the bed and groped among the shadows beneath the edge of it and found the Bible, face down. She smoothed the bent pages and laid the book on the bed again. Mrs Compson didn't open her eyes. Her hair and the pillow were the same color, beneath the wimple of the medicated cloth she looked like an old nun praying. "Dont put it there again," she said, without opening her eyes. "That's where you put it before. Do you want me to have to get out of bed to pick it up?"

Dilsey reached the book across her and laid it on the broad side of the bed. "You cant see to read, noways," she said. "You want me to raise de shade a little?"

"No. Let them alone. Go on and fix Jason something to eat."

Dilsey went out. She closed the door and returned to the kitchen. The stove was almost cold. While she stood there the clock above the cupboard struck ten times. "One oclock," she said aloud, "Jason aint comin home. Ise seed de first en de last," she said, looking at the cold stove, "I seed de first en de last."

AFTERWORD

We can better understand the function of this passage in *The Sound and the Fury* after reading Faulkner's account of how the novel was written. "It began with a mental picture," he says in the interview that he gave to Jean Stein for *Paris Review* (and one might add that some of his other novels began in the same fashion).

> I didn't realize at the time it was symbolical. The picture was of the muddy seat of a little girl's drawers in a pear-tree, where she could see through a window where her grandmother's funeral was taking place and report what was happening to her brothers on the ground below. By the time I explained who they were and what they were doing and how her pants got muddy, I realized it would be impossible to get all of it into a short story and that it would have to be a book. And then I realized the symbolism of the soiled pants. . . .

The original image seems to have pointed toward a family (the girl and her three brothers, with the dead grandmother in the background to represent the past) destroyed by a moral stain, that is, by the girl's promiscuity. But *The Sound and the Fury* was not one of the novels that carry out an original design. It grew and changed in the writing, as Faulkner makes clear in what follows.

> I had already begun to tell the story [he says] through the eyes of the idiot child, since I felt it would be more effective as told by someone capable only of knowing what happened, but not why. I saw that I had not told the story that time. I tried to tell it again, the same story through the eyes of another brother. That was still not it. I told it for the third time through the eyes of the third brother. That was still not it. I tried to gather the pieces together and fill in the gaps by making myself the spokesman.

That fourth part of the novel, in which Faulkner himself is the spokesman (but in the third person), is the one we have just been reading. What sort of spokesman is he? And what are the principal gaps he is filling in?

For the most part he is an objective rather than an omniscient narrator.

That is, he tells us how the characters looked, what they did, what they said, but he penetrates hardly at all into their minds. His attention is focused on Dilsey, who remains completely a person to be observed. Thus, he does not say, "Dilsey felt sad but uplifted." He says, as if looking at her, "Dilsey made no sound, her face did not quiver as the tears took their sunken and devious courses, walking with her head up, making no effort to dry them away even." As for the gaps that the objective narrator is filling in, the biggest of them result from the method followed in the three earlier parts of the novel.

It was the stream-of-consciousness method in all three.[1] They differ from one another to such an extent that they mark effective limits of the method in three directions, but the fact remains that each of them records the flow of impressions and memories in a single mind. One characteristic of the method is that the flow is associational rather than sequential, so that the author finds it difficult to establish a temporal pattern of events. Here the difficulty is greatest in the first part, since Benjy the idiot cannot distinguish cause from effect or past from present; but Quentin, in the second part, also passes confusingly from sensations to memories and back again, and even Jason, too foxy for his own good, sometimes leaves us uncertain about time. In the fourth part, however, the objective narrator gives us events in their strict temporal order, so that the *situation* Faulkner has been presenting now becomes a *story*, that is, a structure existing in time.

(The structure is tightly built. This passage from *The Sound and the Fury* is the longest in the present volume, and we should have liked to shorten it. We found, however, that not one incident, not even a paragraph, could be omitted without weakening the effect of the whole.)

Besides temporal sequence, the other big gap filled in is the *look* of the characters. It is something hard to convey by the stream-of-consciousness method. We cannot *see* Benjy or Quentin or Jason as long as we are inside their minds. We do not even see the other characters in the aspect they might present to strangers. In this fourth part, however, Faulkner as an objective narrator can use his talent for intense visualization. We now see all the members of the household except Quentin, dead for nearly eighteen years, and the girl Quentin, who in vanishing has left behind one stocking that dangles from a drawer and "a darned scarf dusted with powder and stained with rouge" as visible tokens of her personality.

---

[1] With the proviso that Part Three, about Jason, is simply an inner monologue. Jason doesn't descend into his subconscious mind, and there is some question whether he has one.

DILSEY: She had been a big woman once but now her skeleton rose, draped loosely in unpadded skin that tightened again upon a paunch almost dropsical, as though muscle and tissue had been courage or fortitude which the days or the years had consumed until only the indomitable skeleton was left rising like a ruin or a landmark above the somnolent and impervious guts. [There is more about Dilsey's appearance all through the passage, which centers on her.]

BENJY: ... a big man who appeared to have been shaped of some substance whose particles would not or did not cohere to one another or to the frame which supported it. His skin was dead looking and hairless; dropsical too, he moved with a shambling gait like a trained bear.

JASON and MRS. COMPSON: ... the one cold and shrewd, with close-thatched brown hair curled into two stubborn hooks, one on either side of his forehead like a bartender in caricature, and hazel eyes with black-ringed irises like marbles, the other cold and querulous, with perfectly white hair and eyes pouched and baffled and so dark as to appear to be all pupil or all iris.

BENJY and LUSTER: Ben shambled along beside Dilsey, watching Luster who anticked along ahead, the umbrella in his hand and his new straw hat slanted viciously in the sunlight, like a big foolish dog watching a small clever one.

In the writing of the novel, Faulkner's judgment of the Compsons has changed. They are no longer a family destroyed by the daughter's moral stain, and in fact Caddy herself has receded from view, leaving the girl Quentin as a surrogate. Now the girl vanishes in her turn, and Mrs. Compson takes Caddy's place as the spoiler. Reading the present passage, one comes to feel that the mother's inability to love was responsible for everything: for the father's drinking himself to death, for Quentin's suicide, for Caddy's promiscuity, for Jason's spitefulness, and of course not for Benjy's feeble mind, but for the neglect of him by others. Dilsey, mistreated as she is by Mrs. Compson, has become the only mother figure in the household.

That suggests another change in the author's attitude toward the Compsons. Where at first they were one particular family destroyed by the guilt of one member, they here—and even more in Faulkner's "Appendix," written many years later—come to stand for a whole social order. A crucial point is their relation with the Negroes of the household. "You've got a prize set of servants," Jason says to his mother. "I have to humour them," Mrs. Compson says. "I have to depend on them so completely. It's not as if I were strong." Indeed she is weak except in selfishness, and it is only because there are three Negroes living in the cabin behind the mansion that she can maintain her pride of family.

The Negroes are better than the Compsons by Faulkner's standards, and their superiority is shown in two essential ways. The first is in their treatment of Benjy—always a touchstone for characters in this novel—and the second is in their religious faith. The Compsons don't go to church on Easter morning and don't want to let the Negroes go, for fear they will let the fire die out in the kitchen stove. Jason is godless, as is the girl Quentin; and Mrs. Compson, who lets the Bible slip to the floor, regards God as a convenient protector of Southern gentlefolk. "It can't be simply to flout and hurt me," she says of Quentin's suicide and the girl Quentin's disappearance. "Whoever God is, He would not permit that. I'm a lady." Dilsey is not a lady, but after Reverend Shegog's sermon, she weeps "quietly in the annealment and the blood of the remembered Lamb."

The sermon is a masterly piece of writing. We have seen the skill with which Zola—in his account of the miners' mass meeting in the forest—solved the problem of reporting speeches and their effect on an audience. Faulkner does even better. He does not summarize what the preacher said; instead he shows him in the pulpit and directly quotes part of the sermon, so that the reader is under the illusion of having heard it all. After each group of phrases he gives us the response of the congregation in separate voices rising above a low concerted hum: "Mmmmmmm . . . Yes, Jesus! Jesus!" We are there in the weathered church, forgetting the hard seats. For us the real burden of the sermon is not the repeated phrase "I got de ricklickshun en de blood of de Lamb!" but rather another of Reverend Shegog's pronouncements: "Dey passed away in Egypt, de swingin chariots; de generations passed away. Wus a rich man, whar he now, O breddren?" There were Compsons once, but the generations have passed away. Now we know what Dilsey means when she murmurs over the almost cold stove, "I seed de first en de last."

As for Dilsey and her descendants, Faulkner tells us in his "Appendix": "They endured."

For Whom the Bell Tolls (1940)

ERNEST MILLER HEMINGWAY (1899-1961), the second in a family of six children, was born in the Chicago suburb of Oak Park, later to be called "the middle-class capital of the world." His father was a respected but not wealthy physician whose two passions in life were hunting and fishing. His mother was devoted to music and directed the choir at the Third Congregational Church. Both parents tried to model the son in their respective images. The father gave him a fishing rod when he was three years old and a shotgun when he was ten; the mother bought him a cello. Ernest preferred his father's gifts, as he also preferred his wilderness summers in northern Michigan to being a schoolboy in Oak Park.

He had a rage to excel in boyhood sports and was fond of telling adventure stories in which he was the hero. At the high school in Oak Park, then one of the best in the country, he contributed stories to the literary magazine and wrote a breezy column for the weekly *Trapeze*. He also played on the football team in his senior year, but without gaining distinction. Disheartened, as he later said, by the prospect of playing football in college, he decided to go straight into newspaper work. At the age of eighteen, he was hired as a cub reporter by the *Kansas City Star*, then admired as a newspaperman's newspaper.

The United States had entered the Great War and Hemingway said—as did many other teen-age boys of his generation, in almost the same words—"I can't let a show like this go on without getting into it." Certain of being rejected by the American Army because of defective vision in his left eye, he volunteered to drive an ambulance on the

Italian front for the American Red Cross. He was in a forward listening post on the night of July 8, 1918, when an Austrian mortar shell hit the post and killed most of its occupants. Hemingway, gravely wounded, hoisted another wounded man on his back and staggered up the road toward a dressing station. On the road he was hit again by two slugs from a heavy machine gun. The experience was to color most of his future writing.

Except for a brief return to the front, he spent the remaining months of the war in and around the American Red Cross Hospital in Milan, where more than two hundred mortar fragments were removed from his legs and where he fell in love with a nurse. In January 1919 he returned to Oak Park as a decorated war hero and, for the first time, a celebrity. The cheers died away, however, and after two summers in Michigan and a winter in Toronto, Hemingway found a job as editor of a consumers' magazine owned by a dishonest publisher. In September 1921 he married Hadley Richardson of St. Louis. In December they sailed for France, with a rather vague commission for Hemingway to write articles for the *Toronto Star* and with letters of introduction from his older friend Sherwood Anderson.

Paris was to be his base for the next seven years. They were busy years, at first interrupted by roving commissions for the *Star*, then occupied with trout fishing, betting on the horses, managing prize-fighters, skiing in the Austrian Tyrol, trips to Spain for the bullfights, especially those at Pamplona, and of course writing. Almost all his early manuscripts were in a suitcase stolen from Hadley in a Paris station, but he set to work replacing them with others in a new style. He came to be regarded as a disciple by Gertrude Stein and Ezra Pound, no friends of each other, and as a hero by Scott Fitzgerald and others of the new generation. His books began to appear in New York: first *In Our Times* (1925), a collection of stories; then *The Torrents of Spring* (1926), a cruel parody of Sherwood Anderson, and *The Sun Also Rises* (1926), which, without having a wide sale, earned him an international reputation.

Hemingway published a second collection of stories, *Men Without Women* (1927). Before it appeared he had been divorced by Hadley and had married Pauline Pfeiffer, also with St. Louis connections, though her family lived in Arkansas. His life soon assumed a new pattern: winters in Key West, late summers and autumns on a ranch in Wyoming. *A Farewell to Arms* (1929), written mostly in Wyoming, was his first novel to reach a very wide audience. It was followed by *Death in the Afternoon* (1932), a treatise on bullfighting that would have been more admired if it had not appeared in the trough of the Great Depression, and *Winner Take Nothing* (1933), a third collection of stories. In the winter of 1934-1935, Hemingway and Pauline were in East Africa on safari. He tried the experiment of writing a true account of the expedition—*The Green Hills of Africa* (1935)—by the use of fictional techniques.

His next novel, *To Have and Have Not* (1937), is about Key West and Havana. Brutal and episodic, though with passages of his best writing, it was not properly revised for publication, since Hemingway was eager to get back to the fighting in Spain. He was deeply committed to the Loyalist side of the Spanish Civil War and, through his friendship with military commanders, became a student of strategy. In Madrid he wrote a melodrama, *The Fifth Column*, which had a New York production in 1939; then in Havana he started work on a novel, *For Whom the Bell Tolls*, based on everything he had learned about Spain before and during the war.

The war had estranged him from Pauline. In 1940, the year when the novel was published—and enthusiastically received, though with rumbles from the Communists and the Fascists—he married the novelist Martha Gellhorn, another St. Louis girl. They flew out to write reports from the battlefront in China. After an autumn in Sun Valley, Idaho, they were driving back to Cuba—where Hemingway now had a country house, Finca Vigía—on the day when the Japanese attacked Pearl Harbor. Hemingway was eager to serve his country. First he organized a counter-espionage service in Havana, then he made over his fishing boat, the *Pilar*, as a decoy for submarines, and then in the spring of 1944 he became a correspondent again and flew to London.

The next few months were the most adventurous of his career. An accident in the London blackout gave him a head wound that required fifty-seven stitches. Still with blinding headaches, he was flown on missions for the Royal Air Force; he entered Paris with the vanguard of the French Army, and later he survived the grim battle of Hürtgen Forest in the command post of his close friend Colonel Lanham. "You can't keep that big bastard out of a fight," Lanham said.

Once again in his career, a war had shattered a marriage: Hemingway and Martha were divorced in 1945. He went back to Finca Vigía with his new and last wife Mary Walsh, this time from Minnesota, and tried to write the novel for which everyone was waiting. But the novel refused to be written, or rather, it refused to take shape even after he had amassed a thousand pages of manuscript. He changed his subject and wrote two thousand pages, mostly about adventures at sea. This time the writing went better, and he was especially proud of a long last section that he called, tentatively, "The Sea Chase," but he had some questions about the shape of the novel as a whole and did not live to submit a finally revised version to his publisher. The novel was *Islands in the Stream,* which did not appear until the fall of 1970. Still another novel, this time of average length, was *Across the River and into the Trees* (1950), which disappointed most of his readers. Among his later works it was a novella, *The Old Man and the Sea* (1952), that was most widely admired.

The safari he undertook in 1953-1954 came near having a fatal ending when two planes in which the Hemingways were passengers cracked up in succession. The novelist suffered another concussion, as well as internal injuries from which he never recovered. When he was awarded the Nobel Prize in 1954, he was unable to make the trip to Stockholm. "In going where you have to go, and doing what you have to do, and seeing what you have to see," he had written in the introduction to *The Fifth Column and the First Forty-Nine Stories* (1938), "you dull and blunt the instrument you write with. But I would rather have it bent and dulled and know that I had to put it on the grindstone again and hammer it into shape, and know that I had something to write about, than to have it bright and shining and nothing to say." He had many things to write about, more adventures than any other novelist since Cervantes, but "the instrument you write with"— if Hemingway meant his head—had been battered and scarred in a dozen serious accidents, and writing had become for him an appalling task. In his last book, *A Moveable Feast* (1964), he recovered much of his early evocative power, but he was still struggling with some of the episodes at the time of his suicide.

THE STORY

Robert Jordan, once an instructor at the University of Montana, is lying on the pine-needle floor of a Spanish forest and surveying the approaches to a bridge that he plans to destroy. A sturdy old peasant, Anselmo, has guided him through Franco's lines. Because of the requirement that charges be exploded at a given moment, this is the most dangerous mission that Jordan has undertaken for the Loyalists. Their troops under General Golz, a capable Russian, are about to open an offensive here in the mountains south of Segovia. In three days when their bombing planes come over the lines—but not a moment before—Jordan must close the only road by which Franco's men can bring up reinforcements.

The bridge is well guarded, and Jordan will need the help of guerillas from the bands that are scattered through the mountains. One band, led by wily Pablo and his woman Pilar, is established in a cave near the bridge. After a year of fighting bravely, Pablo has become a drunkard and a coward, as Jordan learns during his first evening in the cave. Pilar is earthy, brave, and dependable, as are the six men under their command. There is also a girl, Maria, whom they have rescued from the Fascists during an attack on a train. Jordan falls in love with her. He spreads his sleeping bag under the pine trees, and Maria comes to join him there.

On the second day in the morning, scores of Fascist planes pass overhead on their way to bomb Loyalist airfields. With Pilar and Maria, Jordan goes to see another guerilla leader, El Sordo (the deaf man), who promises to join in the attack on the bridge, but first to steal horses for the escape of the two bands. Pilar tells about a massacre of middle-class citizens on the day of the uprising in her native town. She leaves Jordan and Maria alone in a mountain meadow, and for both of them "the earth moves." Snow is falling when they get back to the cave, a bad augury. Pablo says he will not take part in their enterprise, and Jordan comes near shooting him to prevent treachery. He spends another night with Maria in the sleeping bag, this time spread in the snow.

On the third day, he is awakened by a Fascist cavalryman riding toward the mouth of the cave. He aims from the sleeping bag and shoots him out of the saddle; then Pablo rides off on the captured horse to confuse pursuers. Jordan sets up a machine gun behind a screen of pine branches, but fortunately does not fire when other cavalrymen appear; these ride off after Pablo without discovering the cave. The snow is melting in the sun. While waiting in ambush, Jordan and the others hear distant firing. They know that El Sordo's band has been surrounded as a result of the tracks left by stolen horses in the snow, but there is no hope of saving their comrades. Having learned that the enemy is prepared for the Loyalist offensive, which now has no chance of success, Jordan sends one of the guerillas, Andrés, across the lines to warn General Golz. At two in the morning, Pilar wakens him with the news that Pablo has stolen his detonators and disappeared. He will have to set off the charges with hand grenades, and he has only six men left, including Anselmo, to deal with twice that number guarding the bridge—that is, if the Loyalists attack in spite of his warning.

They rise at three in the morning of the fourth day. Pablo returns, saying, "There is a loneliness that cannot be borne." He has brought with him five mounted men from neighboring bands, so that there are now twelve disciples (and Robert Jordan) riding out to the attack. Andrés, after being held for execution as a spy by the crazed Communist André Marty, finally gets his message to Golz, but by then it is too late; the Loyalist planes have already crossed the lines. Jordan blows up the bridge, though he loses most of his men in the operation. Just as he is about to escape into the hills with Maria and the others, his horse is wounded and falls on him breaking his leg. The novel ends as it began, with Jordan lying on the pine-needle floor of the forest. This time he is waiting to kill one last Fascist, perhaps an officer, before blowing out his own brains.

The passage that follows is the account of El Sordo's last stand on a hilltop. The text is that of the first edition.

[*El Sordo on the Hilltop*]

El Sordo was making his fight on a hilltop. He did not like this hill and when he saw it he thought it had the shape of a chancre. But he had had no choice except this hill and he had picked it as far away as he could see it and galloped for it, the automatic rifle heavy on his back, the horse laboring, barrel heaving between his thighs, the sack of grenades swinging against one side, the sack of automatic rifle pans banging against the other, and Joaquín and Ignacio halting and firing, halting and firing to give him time to get the gun in place.

There had still been snow then, the snow that had ruined them, and when his horse was hit so that he wheezed in a slow, jerking, climbing stagger up the last part of the crest, splattering the snow with a bright, pulsing jet, Sordo had hauled him along by the bridle, the reins over his shoulder as he climbed. He climbed as hard as he could with the bullets spatting on the rocks, with the two sacks heavy on his shoulders, then, holding the horse by the mane, had shot him quickly, expertly, and tenderly just where he had needed him, so that the horse pitched, head forward down to plug a gap between two rocks. He had gotten the gun to firing over the horse's back and he fired two pans, the gun clattering, the empty shells pitching into the snow, the smell of burnt hair from the burnt hide where the hot muzzle rested, him firing at what came up to the hill, forcing them to scatter for cover, while all the time there was a chill in his back from not knowing what was behind him.

Once the last of the five men had reached the hilltop the chill went out of his back and he had saved the pans he had left until he would need them.

There were two more horses dead along the slope and three more were dead here on the hilltop. He had only succeeded in stealing three horses last night and one had bolted when they tried to mount him bareback in the corral at the camp when the first shooting had started.

Of the five men who had reached the hilltop three were wounded. Sordo was wounded in the calf of his leg and in two places in his left arm. He was very thirsty, his wounds had stiffened, and one of the wounds in his left arm was very painful. He also had a bad headache and as he lay waiting for the planes to come he thought of a joke in Spanish. It was, *"Hay que tomar la muerte como si fuera aspirina,"* which means, "You will have to take death as an aspirin." But he did not make the joke aloud. He grinned somewhere inside the pain in his head and inside the nausea that came whenever he moved his arm and looked around at what there was left of his band.

The five men were spread out like the points of a five-pointed star. They had dug with their knees and hands and made mounds in front of their heads and shoulders with the dirt and piles of stones. Using this cover, they were linking the individual mounds up with stones and dirt. Joaquín, who was eighteen years old, had a steel helmet that he dug with and he passed dirt in it.

He had gotten this helmet at the blowing up of the train. It had a bullet hole through it and every one had always joked at him for keeping it. But he had hammered the jagged edges of the bullet hole smooth and driven a wooden plug into it and then cut the plug off and smoothed it even with the metal inside the helmet.

When the shooting started he had clapped this helmet on his head so hard it banged his head as though he had been hit with a casserole and, in the last lung-aching, leg-dead, mouth-dry, bullet-spatting, bullet-cracking, bullet-singing run up the final slope of the hill after his horse was killed, the helmet had seemed to weigh a great amount and to ring his bursting forehead with an iron band. But he had kept it. Now he dug with it in a steady, almost machinelike desperation. He had not yet been hit.

"It serves for something finally," Sordo said to him in his deep, throaty voice.

"*Resistir y fortificar es vencer,*" Joaquín said, his mouth stiff with the dryness of fear which surpassed the normal thirst of battle. It was one of the slogans of the Communist party and it meant, "Hold out and fortify, and you will win."

Sordo looked away and down the slope at where a cavalryman was sniping from behind a boulder. He was very fond of this boy and he was in no mood for slogans.

"What did you say?"

One of the men turned from the building that he was doing. This man was lying flat on his face, reaching carefully up with his hands to put a rock in place while keeping his chin flat against the ground.

Joaquín repeated the slogan in his dried-up boy's voice without checking his digging for a moment.

"What was the last word?" the man with his chin on the ground asked.

"*Vencer,*" the boy said. "Win."

"*Mierda,*" the man with his chin on the ground said.

"There is another that applies to here," Joaquín said, bringing them out as though they were talismans, "Pasionaria says it is better to die on your feet than to live on your knees."

"*Mierda* again," the man said and another man said, over his shoulder, "We're on our bellies, not our knees."

"Thou. Communist. Do you know your Pasionaria has a son thy age in Russia since the start of the movement?"

"It's a lie," Joaquín said.

"*Qué va,* it's a lie," the other said. "The dynamiter with the rare name told me. He was of thy party, too. Why should he lie?"

"It's a lie," Joaquín said. "She would not do such a thing as keep a son hidden in Russia out of the war."

"I wish I were in Russia," another of Sordo's men said. "Will not thy Pasionaria send me now from here to Russia, Communist?"

"If thou believest so much in thy Pasionaria, get her to get us off this hill," one of the men who had a bandaged thigh said.

"The fascists will do that," the man with his chin in the dirt said.

"Do not speak thus," Joaquín said to him.

"Wipe the pap of your mother's breasts off thy lips and give me a hatful of that dirt," the man with his chin on the ground said. "No one of us will see the sun go down this night."

El Sordo was thinking: It is shaped like a chancre. Or the breast of a young girl with no nipple. Or the top cone of a volcano. You have never seen a volcano, he thought. Nor will you ever see one. And this hill is like a chancre. Let the volcanos alone. It's late now for the volcanos.

He looked very carefully around the withers of the dead horse and there was a quick hammering of firing from behind a boulder well down the slope and he heard the bullets from the submachine gun thud into the horse. He crawled along behind the horse and looked out of the angle between the horse's hindquarters and the rock. There were three bodies on the slope just below him where they had fallen when the fascists had rushed the crest under cover of the automatic rifle and submachine gunfire and he and the others had broken down the attack by throwing and rolling down hand grenades. There were other bodies that he could not see on the other sides of the hill crest. There was no dead ground by which attackers could approach the summit and Sordo knew that as long as his ammunition and grenades held out and he had as many as four men they could not get him out of there unless they brought up a trench mortar. He did not know whether they had sent to La Granja for a trench mortar. Perhaps they had not, because surely, soon, the planes would come. It had been four hours since the observation plane had flown over them.

This hill is truly like a chancre, Sordo thought, and we are the very pus of it. But we killed many when they made that stupidness. How could they think that they would take us thus? They have such modern armament that they lose all their sense with overconfidence. He had killed the young officer who had led the assault with a grenade that had gone bouncing and rolling down the slope as they came up it, running, bent half over. In the yellow flash and gray roar of smoke he had seen the officer dive forward to where he lay now like a heavy, broken bundle of old clothing marking the farthest point that the assault had reached. Sordo looked at this body and then, down the hill, at the others.

They are brave but stupid people, he thought. But they have sense enough now not to attack us again until the planes come. Unless, of course, they have a mortar coming. It would be easy with a mortar. The mortar was the normal thing and he knew that they would die as soon as a mortar came up, but when he thought of the planes coming up he felt as naked on that hilltop as though all of his clothing and even his skin had been removed. There is no nakeder thing than I feel, he thought. A flayed rabbit is as well covered as a bear in comparison. But why should they bring planes? They could get us out of here with a trench mortar easily. They are proud of their planes, though, and they will probably bring them. Just as they were so proud of their automatic weapons that they made that stupidness. But undoubtedly they must have sent for a mortar, too.

One of the men fired. Then jerked the bolt and fired again, quickly.

"Save thy cartridges," Sordo said.

"One of the sons of the great whore tried to reach that boulder," the man pointed.

"Did you hit him?" Sordo asked, turning his head with difficulty.

"Nay," the man said. "The fornicator ducked back."

"Who is a whore of whores is Pilar," the man with his chin in the dirt said. "That whore knows we are dying here."

"She could do no good," Sordo said. The man had spoken on the side of his good ear and he had heard him without turning his head. "What could she do?"

"Take these sluts from the rear."

"*Qué va,*" Sordo said. "They are spread around a hillside. How would she come on them? There are a hundred and fifty of them. Maybe more now."

"But if we hold out until dark," Joaquín said.

"And if Christmas comes on Easter," the man with his chin on the ground said.

"And if thy aunt had *cojones* she would be thy uncle," another said to him. "Send for thy Pasionaria. She alone can help us."

"I do not believe that about the son," Joaquín said. "Or if he is there he is training to be an aviator or something of that sort."

"He is hidden there for safety," the man told him.

"He is studying dialectics. Thy Pasionaria has been there. So have Lister and Modesto and others. The one with the rare name told me."

"That they should go to study and return to aid us," Joaquín said.

"That they should aid us now," another man said. "That all the cruts of Russian sucking swindlers should aid us now." He fired and said, "*Me cago en tal;* I missed him again."

"Save thy cartridges and do not talk so much or thou wilt be very thirsty," Sordo said. "There is no water on this hill."

"Take this," the man said and rolling on his side he pulled a wineskin that he wore slung from his shoulder over his head and handed it to Sordo. "Wash thy mouth out, old one. Thou must have much thirst with thy wounds."

"Let all take it," Sordo said.

"Then I will have some first," the owner said and squirted a long stream into his mouth before he handed the leather bottle around.

"Sordo, when thinkest thou the planes will come?" the man with his chin in the dirt asked.

"Any time," said Sordo. "They should have come before."

"Do you think these sons of the great whore will attack again?"

"Only if the planes do not come."

He did not think there was any need to speak about the mortar. They would know it soon enough when the mortar came.

"God knows they've enough planes with what we saw yesterday."

"Too many," Sordo said.

His head hurt very much and his arm was stiffening so that the pain of moving it was almost unbearable. He looked up at the bright, high, blue early summer sky as he raised the leather wine bottle with his good arm. He was fifty-two years old and he was sure this was the last time he would see that sky.

He was not at all afraid of dying but he was angry at being trapped on this hill which was only utilizable as a place to die. If we could have gotten clear, he thought. If we could have made them come up the long valley or if we could have broken loose across the road it would have been all right. But this chancre of a hill. We must use it as well as we can and we have used it very well so far.

If he had known how many men in history have had to use a hill to die on it would not have cheered him any for, in the moment he was passing through, men are not impressed by what has happened to other men in similar circumstances any more than a widow of one day is helped by the knowledge that other loved husbands have died. Whether one has fear of it or not, one's death is difficult to accept. Sordo had accepted it but there was no sweetness in its acceptance even at fifty-two, with three wounds and him surrounded on a hill.

He joked about it to himself but he looked at the sky and at the far mountains and he swallowed the wine and he did not want it.

If one must die, he thought, and clearly one must, I can die. But I hate it.

Dying was nothing and he had no picture of it nor fear of it in his mind. But living was a field of grain blowing in the wind on the side of a hill. Living was a hawk in the sky. Living was an earthen jar of water in the dust of the threshing with the grain flailed out and the chaff blowing. Living was a horse between your legs and a carbine under one leg and a hill and a valley and a stream with trees along it and the far side of the valley and the hills beyond.

Sordo passed the wine bottle back and nodded his head in thanks. He leaned forward and patted the dead horse on the shoulder where the muzzle of the automatic rifle had burned the hide. He could still smell the burnt hair. He thought how he had held the horse there, trembling, with the fire around them, whispering and cracking, over and around them like a curtain, and had carefully shot him just at the intersection of the cross-lines between the two eyes and the ears. Then as the horse pitched down he had dropped down behind his warm, wet back to get the gun to going as they came up the hill.

"*Eras mucho caballo,*" he said, meaning, "Thou wert plenty of horse."

El Sordo lay now on his good side and looked up at the sky. He was lying on a heap of empty cartridge hulls but his head was protected by the rock and his body lay in the lee of the horse. His wounds had stiffened badly and he had much pain and he felt too tired to move.

"What passes with thee, old one?" the man next to him asked.

"Nothing. I am taking a little rest."

"Sleep," the other said. "*They* will wake us when they come."

Just then some one shouted from down the slope.

"Listen, bandits!" the voice came from behind the rocks where the closest automatic rifle was placed. "Surrender now before the planes blow you to pieces."

"What is it he says?" Sordo asked.

Joaquín told him. Sordo rolled to one side and pulled himself up so that he was crouched behind the gun again.

"Maybe the planes aren't coming," he said. "Don't answer them and do not fire. Maybe we can get them to attack again."

"If we should insult them a little?" the man who had spoken to Joaquín about La Pasionaria's son in Russia asked.

"No," Sordo said. "Give me thy big pistol. Who has a big pistol?"

"Here."

"Give it to me." Crouched on his knees he took the big 9 mm. Star and fired one shot into the ground beside the dead horse, waited, then fired again four times at irregular intervals. Then he waited while he counted sixty and then fired a final shot directly into the body of the dead horse. He grinned and handed back the pistol.

"Reload it," he whispered, "and that every one should keep his mouth shut and no one shoot."

"*Bandidos!*" the voice shouted from behind the rocks.

No one spoke on the hill.

"*Bandidos!* Surrender now before we blow thee to little pieces."

"They're biting," Sordo whispered happily.

As he watched, a man showed his head over the top of the rocks. There was no shot from the hilltop and the head went down again. El Sordo waited, watching, but nothing more happened. He turned his head and looked at the others who were all watching down their sectors of the slope. As he looked at them the others shook their heads.

"Let no one move," he whispered.

"Sons of the great whore," the voice came now from behind the rocks again.

"Red swine. Mother rapers. Eaters of the milk of thy fathers."

Sordo grinned. He could just hear the bellowed insults by turning his good ear. This is better than the aspirin, he thought. How many will we get? Can they be that foolish?

The voice had stopped again and for three minutes they heard nothing and saw no movement. Then the sniper behind the boulder a hundred yards down the slope exposed himself and fired. The bullet hit a rock and ricocheted with a sharp whine. Then Sordo saw a man, bent double, run from the shelter of the rocks where the automatic rifle was across the open ground to the big boulder behind which the sniper was hidden. He almost dove behind the boulder.

Sordo looked around. They signalled to him that there was no movement on the other slopes. El Sordo grinned happily and shook his head. This is ten times better than the aspirin, he thought, and he waited, as happy as only a hunter can be happy.

Below on the slope the man who had run from the pile of stones to the shelter of the boulder was speaking to the sniper.

"Do you believe it?"

"I don't know," the sniper said.

"It would be logical," the man, who was the officer in command, said. "They are surrounded. They have nothing to expect but to die."

The sniper said nothing.

"What do you think?" the officer asked.

"Nothing," the sniper said.

"Have you seen any movement since the shots?"

"None at all."

The officer looked at his wrist watch. It was ten minutes to three o'clock.

"The planes should have come an hour ago," he said. Just then another officer flopped in behind the boulder. The sniper moved over to make room for him.

"Thou, Paco," the first officer said. "How does it seem to thee?"

The second officer was breathing heavily from his sprint up and across the hillside from the automatic rifle position.

"For me it is a trick," he said.

"But if it is not? What a ridicule we make waiting here and laying siege to dead men."

"We have done something worse than ridiculous already," the second officer said. "Look at that slope."

He looked up the slope to where the dead were scattered close to the top. From where he looked the line of the hilltop showed the scattered rocks, the belly, projecting legs, shod hooves jutting out, of Sordo's horse, and the fresh dirt thrown up by the digging.

"What about the mortars?" asked the second officer.

"They should be here in an hour. If not before."

"Then wait for them. There has been enough stupidity already."

"*Bandidos!*" the first officer shouted suddenly, getting to his feet and putting his head well up above the boulder so that the crest of the hill looked much closer as he stood upright. "Red swine! Cowards!"

The second officer looked at the sniper and shook his head. The sniper looked away but his lips tightened.

The first officer stood there, his head all clear of the rock and with his hand on his pistol butt. He cursed and vilified the hilltop. Nothing happened. Then he stepped clear of the boulder and stood there looking up the hill.

"Fire, cowards, if you are alive," he shouted. "Fire on one who has no fear of any Red that ever came out of the belly of the great whore."

This last was quite a long sentence to shout and the officer's face was red and congested as he finished.

The second officer, who was a thin sunburned man with quiet eyes, a thin, long-lipped mouth and a stubble of beard over his hollow cheeks, shook his head again. It was this officer who was shouting who had ordered the first assault. The young lieutenant who was dead up the slope had been the best friend of this other lieutenant who was named Paco Berrendo and who was listening to the shouting of the captain, who was obviously in a state of exaltation.

"Those are the swine who shot my sister and my mother," the captain said. He had a red face and a blond, British-looking moustache and there was something wrong about his eyes. They were a light blue and the lashes were light, too. As you looked at them they seemed to focus slowly. Then "Reds," he shouted. "Cowards!" and commenced cursing again.

He stood absolutely clear now and, sighting carefully, fired his pistol at the only target that the hilltop presented: the dead horse that had belonged to Sordo. The bullet threw up a puff of dirt fifteen yards below the horse. The captain fired again. The bullet hit a rock and sung off.

The captain stood there looking at the hilltop. The Lieutenant Berrendo was looking at the body of the other lieutenant just below the summit. The sniper was looking at the ground under his eyes. Then he looked up at the captain.

"There is no one alive up there," the captain said. "Thou," he said to the sniper, "go up there and see."

The sniper looked down. He said nothing.

"Don't you hear me?" the captain shouted at him.

"Yes, my captain," the sniper said, not looking at him.

"Then get up and go." The captain still had his pistol out. "Do you hear me?"

"Yes, my captain."

"Why don't you go, then?"

"I don't want to, my captain."

"You don't *want* to?" The captain pushed the pistol against the small of the man's back. "You don't *want* to?"

"I am afraid, my captain," the soldier said with dignity.

Lieutenant Berrendo, watching the captain's face and his odd eyes, thought he was going to shoot the man then.

"Captain Mora," he said.

"Lieutenant Berrendo?"

"It is possible the soldier is right."

"That he is right to say he is afraid? That he is right to say he does not *want* to obey an order?"

"No. That he is right that it is a trick."

"They are all dead," the captain said. "Don't you hear me say they are all dead?"

"You mean our comrades on the slope?" Berrendo asked him. "I agree with you."

"Paco," the captain said, "don't be a fool. Do you think you are the only one who cared for Julián? I tell you the Reds are dead. Look!"

He stood up, then put both hands on top of the boulder and pulled himself up, kneeing-up awkwardly, then getting on his feet.

"Shoot," he shouted, standing on the gray granite boulder and waved both his arms. "Shoot me! Kill me!"

On the hilltop El Sordo lay behind the dead horse and grinned.

What a people, he thought. He laughed, trying to hold it in because the shaking hurt his arm.

"Reds," came the shout from below. "Red canaille. Shoot me! Kill me!"

Sordo, his chest shaking, barely peeped past the horse's crupper and saw the captain on top of the boulder waving his arms. Another officer stood by the boulder. The sniper was standing at the other side. Sordo kept his eye where it was and shook his head happily.

"Shoot me," he said softly to himself. "Kill me!" Then his shoulders shook again. The laughing hurt his arm and each time he laughed his head felt as though it would burst. But the laughter shook him again like a spasm.

Captain Mora got down from the boulder.

"Now do you believe me, Paco?" he questioned Lieutenant Berrendo.

"No," said Lieutenant Berrendo.

"*Cojones!*" the captain said. "Here there is nothing but idiots and cowards."

The sniper had gotten carefully behind the boulder again and Lieutenant Berrendo was squatting beside him.

The captain, standing in the open beside the boulder, commenced to shout filth at the hilltop. There is no language so filthy as Spanish. There are words for all the vile words in English and there are other words and expressions that are used only in countries where blasphemy keeps pace with the austerity of religion. Lieutenant Berrendo was a very devout Catholic. So was the sniper. They were Carlists from Navarra and while both of them cursed and blasphemed when they were angry they regarded it as a sin which they regularly confessed.

As they crouched now behind the boulder watching the captain and listening to what he was shouting, they both disassociated themselves from him and what he was saying. They did not want to have that sort of talk on their consciences on a day in which they might die. Talking thus will not bring luck, the sniper thought. Speaking thus of the *Virgen* is bad luck. This one speaks worse than the Reds.

Julián is dead, Lieutenant Berrendo was thinking. Dead there on the slope on such a day as this is. And this foul mouth stands there bringing more ill fortune with his blasphemies.

Now the captain stopped shouting and turned to Lieutenant Berrendo. His eyes looked stranger than ever.

"Paco," he said, happily, "you and I will go up there."

"Not me."

"What?" The captain had his pistol out again.

I hate these pistol brandishers, Berrendo was thinking. They cannot give an order without jerking a gun out. They probably pull out their pistols when they go to the toilet and order the move they will make.

"I will go if you order me to. But under protest," Lieutenant Berrendo told the captain.

"Then I will go alone," the captain said. "The smell of cowardice is too strong here."

Holding his pistol in his right hand, he strode steadily up the slope. Berrendo and the sniper watched him. He was making no attempt to take any cover and he was looking straight ahead of him at the rocks, the dead horse, and the fresh-dug dirt of the hilltop.

El Sordo lay behind the horse at the corner of the rock, watching the captain come striding up the hill.

Only one, he thought. We get only one. But from his manner of speaking he is *caza mayor*. Look at him walking. Look what an animal. Look at him stride forward. This one is for me. This one I take with me on the trip. This one coming now makes the same voyage I do. Come on, Comrade Voyager. Come striding. Come right along. Come along to meet it. Come on. Keep on walking. Don't slow up. Come right along. Come as thou art coming. Don't stop and look at those. That's right. Don't even look down. Keep on coming with your eyes forward. Look, he has a moustache. What do you think of that? He runs to a moustache, the Comrade Voyager. He is a captain. Look at his sleeves. I said he was *caza mayor*. He has the face of an *Inglés*. Look. With a red face and blond hair and blue eyes. With no cap on and his moustache is yellow. With blue eyes. With pale blue eyes. With pale blue eyes with something wrong with them. With pale blue eyes that don't focus. Close enough. Too close. Yes, Comrade Voyager. Take it, Comrade Voyager.

He squeezed the trigger of the automatic rifle gently and it pounded back three times against his shoulder with the slippery jolt the recoil of a tripoded automatic weapon gives.

The captain lay on his face on the hillside. His left arm was under him. His right arm that had held the pistol was stretched forward of his head. From all down the slope they were firing on the hill crest again.

Crouched behind the boulder, thinking that now he would have to sprint across that open space under fire, Lieutenant Berrendo heard the deep hoarse voice of Sordo from the hilltop.

"*Bandidos!*" the voice came. "*Bandidos!* Shoot me! Kill me!"

On the top of the hill El Sordo lay behind the automatic rifle laughing so that his chest ached, so that he thought the top of his head would burst.

"*Bandidos*," he shouted again happily. "Kill me, *bandidos!*" Then he shook his head happily. We have lots of company for the Voyage, he thought.

He was going to try for the other officer with the automatic rifle when he would leave the shelter of the boulder. Sooner or later he would have to leave it. Sordo knew that he could never command from there and he thought he had a very good chance to get him.

Just then the others on the hill heard the first sound of the coming of the planes.

El Sordo did not hear them. He was covering the down-slope edge of the boulder with his automatic rifle and he was thinking: when I see him he will be running already and I will miss him if I am not careful. I could shoot behind him all across that stretch. I should swing the gun with him and ahead of him. Or let him start and then get on him and ahead of him. I will try to pick him up there at the edge of the rock and swing just ahead of him. Then he felt a touch on his shoulder and he turned and saw the gray, fear-drained face of Joaquín and he looked where the boy was pointing and saw the three planes coming.

At this moment Lieutenant Berrendo broke from behind the boulder and, with his head bent and his legs plunging, ran down and across the slope to the shelter of the rocks where the automatic rifle was placed.

Watching the planes, Sordo never saw him go.

"Help me to pull this out," he said to Joaquín and the boy dragged the automatic rifle clear from between the horse and the rock.

The planes were coming on steadily. They were in echelon and each second they grew larger and their noise was greater.

"Lie on your backs to fire at them," Sordo said. "Fire ahead of them as they come."

He was watching them all the time. *"Cabrones! Hijos de puta!"* he said rapidly.

"Ignacio!" he said. "Put the gun on the shoulder of the boy. Thou!" to Joaquín, "Sit there and do not move. Crouch over. More. No. More."

He lay back and sighted with the automatic rifle as the planes came on steadily.

"Thou, Ignacio, hold me the three legs of that tripod." They were dangling down the boy's back and the muzzle of the gun was shaking from the jerking of his body that Joaquín could not control as he crouched with bent head hearing the droning roar of their coming.

Lying flat on his belly and looking up into the sky watching them come, Ignacio gathered the legs of the tripod into his two hands and steadied the gun.

"Keep thy head down," he said to Joaquín. "Keep thy head forward."

"Pasionaria says 'Better to die on thy—' " Joaquín was saying to himself as the drone came nearer them. Then he shifted suddenly into "Hail Mary, full of grace, the Lord is with thee; Blessed art thou among women and Blessed is the fruit of thy womb, Jesus. Holy Mary, Mother of God, pray for us sinners now and at the hour of our death. Amen. Holy Mary, Mother of God," he started, then he remembered quickly as the roar came now unbearably and started an act of contrition racing in it, "Oh my God, I am heartily sorry for having offended thee who art worthy of all my love——"

Then there were the hammering explosions past his ears and the gun barrel hot against his shoulder. It was hammering now again and his ears were deafened by the muzzle blast. Ignacio was pulling down hard on the tripod and the barrel was burning his back. It was hammering now in the roar and he could not remember the act of contrition.

All he could remember was at the hour of our death. Amen. At the hour of our death. Amen. At the hour. At the hour. Amen. The others all were firing. Now and at the hour of our death. Amen.

Then, through the hammering of the gun, there was the whistle of the air splitting apart and then in the red black roar the earth rolled under his knees and then waved up to hit him in the face and then dirt and bits of rock were falling all over and Ignacio was lying on him and the gun was lying on him. But he was not dead because the whistle came again and the earth rolled under him with the roar. Then it came again and the earth lurched under his belly and one side of the hilltop rose into the air and then fell slowly over them where they lay.

The planes came back three times and bombed the hilltop but no one on the hilltop knew it. Then the planes machine-gunned the hilltop and went away. As they dove on the hill for the last time with their machine guns hammering, the first plane pulled up and winged over and then each plane did the same and they moved from echelon to V-formation and went away into the sky in the direction of Segovia.

Keeping a heavy fire on the hilltop, Lieutenant Berrendo pushed a patrol up to one of the bomb craters from where they could throw grenades onto the crest. He was taking no chances of any one being alive and waiting for them in the mess that was up there and he threw four grenades into the confusion of dead horses, broken and split rocks, and torn yellow-stained explosive-stinking earth before he climbed out of the bomb crater and walked over to have a look.

No one was alive on the hilltop except the boy Joaquín, who was unconscious under the dead body of Ignacio. Joaquín was bleeding from the nose and from the ears. He had known nothing and had no feeling since he had suddenly been in the very heart of the thunder and the breath had been wrenched from his body when the one bomb struck so close and Lieutenant Berrendo made the sign of the cross and then shot him in the back of the head, as quickly and as gently, if such an abrupt movement can be gentle, as Sordo had shot the wounded horse.

Lieutenant Berrendo stood on the hilltop and looked down the slope at his own dead and then across the country seeing where they had galloped before Sordo had turned at bay here. He noticed all the dispositions that had been made of the troops and then he ordered the dead men's horses to be brought up and the bodies tied across the saddles so that they might be packed in to La Granja.

"Take that one, too," he said. "The one with his hands on the automatic rifle. That should be Sordo. He is the oldest and it was he with the gun. No. Cut the head off and wrap it in a poncho." He considered a minute. "You might as well take all the heads. And of the others below on the slope and where we first found them. Collect the rifles and pistols and pack that gun on a horse."

Then he walked down to where the lieutenant lay who had been killed in the first assault. He looked down at him but did not touch him.

"*Qué cosa más mala es la guerra,*" he said to himself, which meant, "What a bad thing war is."

Then he made the sign of the cross again and as he walked down the hill he said five Our Fathers and five Hail Marys for the repose of the soul of his dead comrade. He did not wish to stay to see his orders being carried out.

AFTERWORD

This book has tried to be, in some real sense, an anthology of the novel, not merely a collection of showy passages from novels, *pages choisies* that could stand by themselves. We have looked instead for passages that bear a functional relation to the scheme of each novel as a whole, whether they serve in it as introduction, complication, confrontation, peripety, restatement, recognition, or finale. When we have made happy choices, the passages also illustrate the style, personality, and method of each author, as well as his contribution to the changing art of fiction. That explains the necessary presence of introductory and explanatory text. It also explains the absence of passages that often figure in anthologies of a different type, as does, for example, Ivan Karamazov's legend of the Grand Inquisitor. The legend is superb, but it casts more light on the author's leading ideas than it does on his novel about the four Karamazov brothers.

This final passage from Hemingway might seem an exception to our rule. It is a self-contained episode that deals with minor figures in the novel, and it might well be printed—and admired—in a selected volume of Hemingway's stories. At the same time, however, it plays a substantial part in his scheme for this particular novel.

For Whom the Bell Tolls is a much more complicated novel than it is often given credit for being. In one of many aspects it is of course a simple adventure story about the blowing up of a bridge. It begins with Robert Jordan's first inspection of the bridge, it proceeds in a rigorous sequence of hours, and it ends at the moment when Jordan, his mission completed, is waiting to kill a Fascist officer as his own dying service to the Loyalists. The mission, however, merely provides a framework for the novel, and we must look beyond it for underlying themes.

In another aspect, *For Whom the Bell Tolls* is concerned with one man's relation to the future of society. Robert Jordan is identical in spirit—one might say even in the flesh—with Hemingway's earlier heroes. As Frederic Henry he had made his farewell not really to arms, but to armies and, in a sense, to every type of social institution. As Jake Barnes, the maimed hero, he had existed in a social wasteland. Now, having committed himself to a dream of the social future, he recovers his ability to love, and he goes to his death as a willing victim. In so doing he becomes one of the many Christ figures in modern fiction and, as in the Gospels, he has exactly twelve disciples. Pablo is Judas, of course, and there are other analogies. Pilar stands in a way for Christ's mother. Maria is presented with overtones of Mary Magdalene.

In still another aspect, the novel is concerned with a victory over time. Jordan when facing death finds himself capable of living as full a life in seventy hours—sixty-eight by actual count—as he might have lived in seventy years. When he is with the woman he loves, time is transformed into an eternal present. Hemingway's working title for the novel, before he found an epigraph from John Donne, had been "The Undiscovered Country." The country to which that title refers is obviously not Spain; it is the timeless region, the "Now and forever now," that Jordan enters with Maria.

But Hemingway is also trying to present a wartime picture of Spain itself: the landscape, the weather, the military campaigns, the people, and the issues in their struggle. He is committed to the side of the Loyalists, but, to make the picture accurate, he wants to present their criminal follies as well as their virtues, and the virtues of the Fascists as well as their crimes. In other words, his book contains a great deal of information and opinion, elements condemned by some critics as impurities in fiction. But the novel as a genre, at its best as at its worst, has always been an impure medium; perhaps that explains its lasting appeal. Formalist critics like to discuss its imagery, its tempo, and its internal lines of force, but readers have always been more interested in learning "how it was" at a given moment, how everything worked in reality, and how people much like themselves have acted under stress.

The episode of El Sordo's stand on the hilltop is full of those informative details that Hemingway is eager to record. Here is the stoicism of Spanish peasants, as displayed at the moment of death with a mixture of jeering obscenity and brutal humor. Here is the innocence of a young Communist nourished on slogans, but abandoning them for prayers as the planes come over. Here is what many Spanish Republicans felt about La Pasionaria—and what Hemingway felt, though she was a saint for the Communists. Here are the Fascists in their superior numbers, screaming out their contempt for the Loyalists ("Red swine! *Bandidos!*"), and here are men killed like horses, with the same delicate gesture: it is all part of Hemingway's broad picture.

But the episode has other functions than merely filling in blank spaces in a panorama. It is true that the hero is not even mentioned, but, in the three preceding chapters, he has heard the firing from a distance and has decided that he must not go to El Sordo's help. Now we directly see what he merely conjectured. It is true that El Sordo and Joaquín are minor characters, but we have met them both in a still earlier chapter and they have gained our sympathy. Now we learn what each of them did in his last hour. Now too we are introduced to Lieutenant Berrendo, the good soldier and pious Catholic who will reappear at the end of the novel. The end is foreshadowed here, and though the hero is absent, El Sordo acts as his surrogate. Like Jordan he is a victim of the mission against the bridge; like Jordan he is betrayed by the snow (which serves throughout the novel as an omen of disaster); and like Jordan he kills a Fascist officer before he dies.

As for narrative point of view, the novel had started by using Jordan as a center of consciousness. Hemingway had so many events to record, however, and such a broad territory to cover that he became impatient with the limitations of the Jamesian method. After Chapter 13, he begins to use other characters as observers: first Pilar, then Anselmo, and then toward the end of the novel, Karkov and especially Andrés, whose adventures occupy too many chapters. In the present episode there is no central consciousness. Hemingway has become the omniscient narrator, moving from one character to another—even from the defenders of the hill to the attackers—and reading such of their thoughts as advance the story. It is Lieutenant Berrendo who has the last word and points the moral of the episode. "What a bad thing war is," he says— *Qué cosa más mala es la guerra.*